McGRAW-HILL PUBLICATIONS IN THE
ZOOLOGICAL SCIENCES

E. J. Boell, CONSULTING EDITOR

THE INVERTEBRATES:

Acanthocephala, Aschelminthes, and Entoprocta

THE INVERTEBRATES:

Acanthocephala, Aschelminthes, and Entoprocta

The pseudocoelomate Bilateria

VOLUME III

BY

LIBBIE HENRIETTA HYMAN

American Museum of Natural History
New York

FIRST EDITION

NEW YORK   TORONTO   LONDON

McGRAW-HILL BOOK COMPANY, INC.

1951

THE INVERTEBRATES: ACANTHOCEPHALA, ASCHELMINTHES,

AND ENTOPROCTA

THE MAPLE PRESS COMPANY, YORK, PA.

PREFACE

This volume completes the consideration of the noncoelomate invertebrates. The remaining volumes will deal with the coelomate groups, beginning with those having an enterocoelous mode of coelom formation (Chaetognatha, Echinodermata, Hemichordata). The remaining coelomates will be taken up in somewhat the following order: Sipunculoidea, Ectoprocta, Brachiopoda, Phoronidea, Annelida (including Echiuroidea), Mollusca, and Arthropoda. As it has proved impossible to determine in advance just how much can practically be included in a single volume, it appears inadvisable at present to attempt to divide these groups into volumes, but presumably they will occupy at least three volumes.

It is hoped the work will now go forward more rapidly than in the past, but it is not expected that volumes of this sort can be produced in less than five years. Not only does the writing of the text proceed very slowly because of the extensive documentation necessary, but the preparation of the illustrations is exceedingly time-consuming.

The present volume, like its predecessors, consists of a fusion of a small amount of original knowledge with a large amount of compilation from the literature. I particularly regret the almost complete absence of original work on the nematodes. I had hoped to be able to devote some months to a firsthand study of free-living nematodes, but to have done so would still further have delayed the publication of the volume, and hence the plan was abandoned. The illustrations are my own handiwork, except for those reproduced by photography.

The attention of those interested in invertebrate zoology is directed to the new French *Traité de zoologie,* now appearing, of which the first eleven volumes will be devoted to the invertebrates. No definite information has been received as to whether we may hope for a continuation of the great German treatises, the Kükenthal-Krumbach *Handbuch der Zoologie* and the Bronn *Klassen und Ordnungen des Tierreichs,* discontinued at the onset of the war.

Dr. Harley Van Cleave kindly read the chapter on the Acanthocephala and lent some of his best slides for study. The scheme of classification here presented differs slightly from any published arrangement and was worked out after intensive study of the groups involved. It presumably will not meet with the complete approval of all zoologists, but I believe

v

it represents an improvement over existing schemes. My scheme was advanced for the use of Brown's *Selected Invertebrate Types*.

I am pleased to have come this far on my self-appointed task and hope to be able to complete it to the finish.

LIBBIE HENRIETTA HYMAN

NEW YORK, N. Y.
March, 1951

CONTENTS

CHAPTER XII

THE PSEUDOCOELOMATE BILATERIA—PHYLUM ACANTHOCEPHALA

I. HISTORICAL

The acanthocephalan worms were noticed about the beginning of the eighteenth century but were not clearly distinguished from other intestinal worms until 1771 when Koelreuther proposed the name *Acanthocephalus* for one from a fish. In 1776, Zoega and O. F. Müller without knowledge of Koelruther's work gave the name *Echinorhynchus* to a similar fish parasite. All these authors realized that they were dealing with a distinct type of organization. Later Müller described a number of species under the name *Echinorhynchus*, and this name came into general use for the type of worm in question. Zeder in 1803 gave these worms a common name "Hakenwürmer" (hooked worms), and Rudolphi (1809) transcribed this into the form Acanthocephala (Greek, *akantho*, spiny, *kephalo*, pertaining to the head), by which the group has since been known. During the nineteenth century many species were described under the one generic name *Echinorhynchus*, and it was not until after 1890 that discriminating taxonomic work began to be done on the group, resulting in the definition of numerous genera and families.

The position of the Acanthocephala among the animal phyla has been very uncertain. Cuvier included the acanthocephalan worms with the flatworms in his group of parasitic worms termed Intestinaux parenchymatoux. Vogt in 1851 first clearly distinguished the flatworms from the roundworms under the names Platyelmia and Nematelmia, respectively. Whereas Vogt was fortunate in his conception of the Platyelmia, he was less happy with regard to the Nematelmia, in which he included the gregarines, nematodes, acanthocephalans, and gordiaceans. Vogt's name was altered to the more correct form Nemathelminthes by Gegenbaur (1859), who included under this term the three groups Nematoda, Acanthocephala, and Gordiacea, and this association of the three groups of parasitic worms of cylindroid shape has remained extant in textbooks to the present day. The association appears to be a matter of convenience rather than of any profound conviction of actual relationship among the three groups. In 1866, Schneider on the basis of similarity of musculature added to the assemblage the Chaetognatha (as well as several other groups), and this unfortunate combination with Chaetognatha persisted in some texts until recent times, although now generally abandoned. In the Kükenthal-Krumbach *Handbuch der Zoologie* the phylum Nemathelminthes is conceived as consisting of six groups: Rotifera, Gastrotricha, Kinorhyncha (Echinodera), Acanthocephala, Nematoda, and Nematomorpha (Gordiacea), and this arrangement was adopted by the author in the first volume of this treatise (P–C, pages 33, 35) except that the phylum name was altered to Aschelminthes following Grobben (1908). The name Nemathelminthes has been used to cover so many different groupings that it appears advisable to drop it altogether, in favor of the name Aschelminthes. The Acanthocephala are here removed from the Aschelminthes and made into a separate phylum, on grounds discussed at the end of this chapter.

1

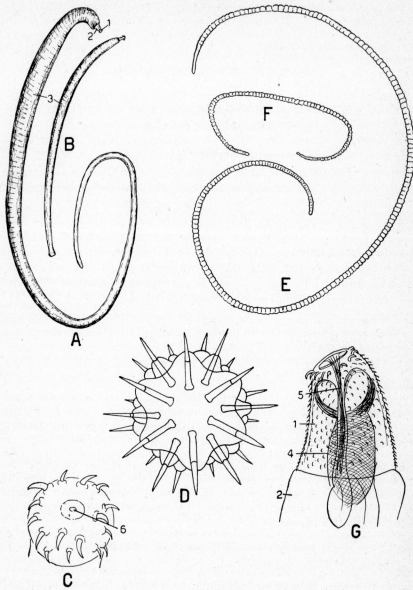

Fig. 1.—Types of Acanthocephala. *A. Macracanthorhynchus hirudinaceus*, female, original. *B. M. hirudinaceus*, male, original. *C.* Side view of proboscis of *M. hirudinaceus*, original. *D.* Scheme of the hook arrangement of *M. hirudinaceus*, end view, showing concentric circles. *E. Gigantorhynchus echinodiscus*, female. *F.* Same, male. *G.* Same, side view of proboscis, showing hooks. (*D–G, after Travassos, 1917.*)   1, proboscis; 2, neck; 3, trunk; 4, proboscis receptacle; 5, retractor muscle; 6, sense organ at summit.

The principal accounts of the Acanthocephala are those of Rauther (1930) in the *Handbuch der Zoologie* and Meyer (1933) in Bronn's *Klassen und Ordnungen des Tierreichs*. In the Americas, numerous articles on the group have been published by H. J. Van Cleave and L. Travassos.

II. CHARACTERS OF THE PHYLUM

1. Definition.—The Acanthocephala are entoparasitic pseudocoelomate vermiform Bilateria without a digestive tract and with the anterior end formed of an invaginable proboscis armed with hooks.

2. General Characters.—The Acanthocephala are entoparasitic worms of slender cylindroid or slightly flattened form and hollow construction. The diagnostic feature of the phylum is the organ of attachment consisting of an invaginable proboscis that forms the anterior end. This proboscis is armed with rows of recurved hooks, when the common name of spiny-headed worms applied to these parasites. The body wall consists of cuticle, syncytial epidermis permeated with spaces, and subepidermal musculature. In connection with the proboscis apparatus the epidermis forms two elongated bodies termed lemnisci that hang down into the trunk. The nervous system consists of a ganglion near the proboscis and two lateral cords proceeding posteriorly from this, plus various minor nerves. Mouth, anus, and digestive tube are completely wanting, and there is also no circulatory system. Excretory organs when present are of the nature of protonephridia and open into the terminal part of the reproductive system. The hollow interior is occupied by the reproductive system. The sexes are separate; the females are generally larger than the males. The males are provided with a copulatory apparatus, and the terminal part of the female apparatus is also somewhat complicated. The eggs develop within the maternal body into a larva that requires an intermediate invertebrate host for its further development. The invertebrate host is always an arthropod such as an insect, amphipod, or isopod. The adult parasites infest the digestive tract of various vertebrates, mainly fish, birds, and mammals, and occur throughout the world in marine, fresh-water, and terrestrial hosts. There are about 300 known species.

III. CLASSIFICATION OF THE PHYLUM

Following Meyer (1933) and Van Cleave (1936), the Acanthocephala are divided into three orders. Later Van Cleave (1948) arranged the phylum into two classes each with two orders. The author is unable to accept this arrangement, for the differences among the Acanthocephala are not sufficient to warrant the erection of classes and the sole difference between two of the orders is the presence or absence of body spines.

Order 1. Archiacanthocephala. Main lacunar channels median; proboscis spines arranged concentrically; with protonephridia; females

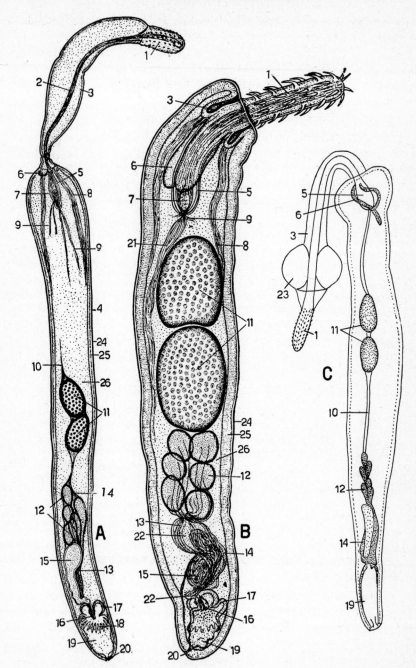

FIG. 2.—Types of Acanthocephala (continued). *A. Longicollum*, with especially long neck. *B. Acanthocephalus*, normal shape and proportions. (*A, B, after Yamaguti*, 1935.) *C. Pomphorhynchus bulbocolli (after Van Cleave*, 1919a), with long neck having a bulbous

with two persistent ligament sacs; males with eight cement glands; in terrestrial hosts.

Order 2. Palaeacanthocephala. Main lacunar channels lateral; proboscis hooks arranged in alternating radial rows; without protonephridia; ligament sacs ephemeral in females; males with mostly six cement glands; mostly in aquatic hosts.

Order 3. Eocanthocephala. Main lacunar channels median; proboscis hooks arranged radially; without protonephridia; ligament sacs persistent in females; cement gland syncytial with a reservoir; in aquatic hosts.

IV. MORPHOLOGY AND PHYSIOLOGY

1. External Characters.—The Acanthocephala are worms of elongated shape ranging from 1.5 mm. to over ½ m. in length. The majority of species fall under 25 mm.; the largest species are *Macracanthorhynchus hirudinaceus*, the common spiny-headed worm of pigs, to 65 cm. in length, and *Gigantorhynchus echinodiscus* from South American anteaters, to 45 cm (Fig. 1). In general the smaller forms inhabit fishes and the larger worms are found in avian and mammalian hosts. The females are nearly always larger than the males of the same species, and this size difference is naturally more striking in the larger species. The shape varies from short plump types, cylindroid, fusiform, or clavate, to long slender forms, cylindroid or laterally flattened. Many forms are slightly curved, and in *Hamanniella microcephala* (Fig. 3B) the body is spirally coiled. The surface may be smooth, wrinkled, or regularly ringed, and areas armed with spines occur in many genera. External criteria for distinguishing dorsal and ventral surfaces are limited; when the body is curved, the concave surface is ventral and, in case of unequal sizes of proboscis hooks, the larger hooks are ventrally located; but in most cases recourse must be had to internal structure for determining dorsoventrality, especially the position of the cerebral ganglion which is located in contact with what is thereby considered to be the ventral wall of the proboscis receptacle. The gonopore occurs at or near the posterior extremity. The Acanthocephala lack intrinsic coloration but frequently show red, orange, yellow, or brown colors resulting from absorption of food, especially fatty substances, from the host.

In many Acanthocephala, the body is ringed or constricted at regular intervals and so presents a more or less segmented appearance. Such segmentation reaches its height in certain species of *Moniliformis* (Fig.

enlargement. 1, proboscis; 2, retractor muscle; 3, neck; 4, trunk; 5, proboscis receptacle; 6, lemnisci; 7, ganglion; 8, neck retractors; 9, retinacula; 10, ligament; 11, testes; 12, cement glands; 13, cement ducts; 14, genital sheath; 15, Saefftigen's pouch; 16, penis; 17, muscular pockets of bursa; 18, muscle rays of bursa; 19, bursa; 20, gonopore; 21, receptacle retractor; 22, sperm duct; 23, neck bulb; 24, cuticle; 25, epidermis; 26, pseudocoel.

3C) and *Mediorhynchus* (Fig. 23B).   In the more extreme cases, the constrictions involve the entire body wall and the longitudinal muscle layers are directly attached to the epidermis at the constrictions, so that the circular musculature is thereby broken up into rings (Fig. 23D).   The segmentation of the Acanthocephala is similar to that of rotifers, kinorhynchs, and nematodes and may be termed *superficial* segmentation as it involves only surface structures.

The body is divisible into the short slender forebody or *presoma* and the much longer stouter *trunk* (Fig. 2); the boundary between these two regions consists of a cuticular fold extending the width of the epidermis (Fig. 5B).   The presoma is composed externally of the *proboscis* that bears the hooks and a *neck* region without hooks; internally it includes the *receptacle* or *sheath* into which the proboscis invaginates or withdraws, the *lemnisci*, and the main ganglion of the nervous system (Fig. 7).   The neck is generally short but sometimes much elongated as in *Longicollum* (Fig. 2A) and *Pomphorhynchus* (Fig. 2C) and in the latter bears a bulbous enlargement.   The trunk may be cylindroid, flattened, curved, or coiled with a smooth, wrinkled, or segmented surface.   In several genera the trunk is more or less noticeably differentiated into a broader foretrunk and a slender hindtrunk in varying proportions in different species.   Such regionation of the trunk reaches a climax in *Bolbosoma* (Fig. 3D), in which a swollen bulbous region immediately behind the neck is followed by a short very slender region and then a long hindtrunk of normal proportions.

Spines occur on the trunk in a number of genera of the orders Palae- and Eoacanthocephala.   Most commonly they are limited to a relatively short, thickly beset zone immediately behind the neck (Fig. 4C) but may also extend along the rest of the trunk in restricted areas.   Thus in *Acanthogyrus* (Fig. 4A) a spiny strip extends along each side from the anterior spiny region to the posterior end.   In *Pallisentis* (= *Farzandia*) *ophiocephali* the trunk spination consists of a short anterior girdle followed by single circlets at regular intervals along the remainder of the trunk (Fig. 5A).   In other *Pallisentis* species there are two anterior zones of spines separated by a short nonspiny area.   *Serrasentis* (Fig. 21A) has regularly spaced ventral transverse rows of spines in addition to the spiny girdle behind the neck.   Spines are somewhat sparsely strewn over the foretrunk in *Rhadinorhynchus*, and in *R. horridus* these are much larger than the proboscis spines (Fig. 4B).   The trunk spines often tend to extend farther posteriorly ventrally than dorsally as in *Corynosoma* (Fig. 3A).   Sometimes a girdle of genital spines surrounds the gonopore (Fig. 4D).   The trunk spination may be limited to or better developed in males than in females.

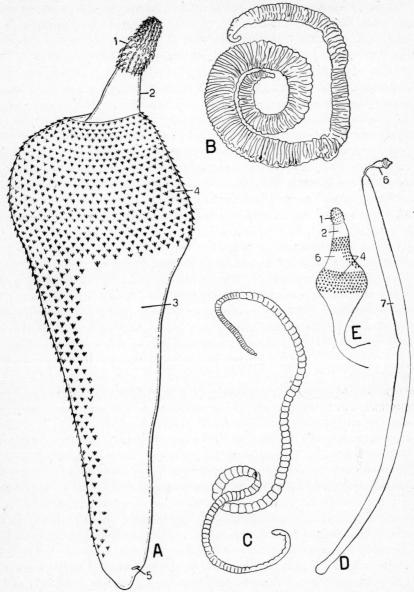

Fig. 3.—Types of Acanthocephala (continued). *A. Corynosoma*, showing arrangement of trunk spines (*after Yamaguti*, 1939). *B. Hamanniella microcephala*, with coiled body (*after Travassos*, 1917). *C. Moniliformis* with segmented cuticle (*after Meyer*, 1931b). *D. Bolbosoma*, with fore and hindtrunk. *E.* Anterior end of same, enlarged. (*D, E, after Porta*, 1909.) 1, proboscis; 2, neck; 3, trunk; 4, trunk spines; 5, gonopore; 6, foretrunk; 7, hindtrunk.

2. Body Wall.—Although the body wall has the usual layers—cuticle, epidermis, dermis, and muscle stratum—the epidermis is of peculiar and unique construction. The body is clothed with a thin cuticle (about 1 micron thick or less) of homogeneous structure. Beneath the cuticle lies the remarkable epidermis (usually called hypodermis in works on Acanthocephala), a thick layer of fibrous syncytial construction, that presumably corresponds to a one-layered epithelium. It comprises three fibrous strata: an outer layer, only slightly thicker than the cuticle, of parallel radial fibers, a middle somewhat thicker feltwork of layers of fibers running in different directions, and an inner layer of radial fibers (Fig. 5B). This inner layer is much the thickest of the three and by many authors is regarded as the epidermis proper while the outer radial and the felt layers are assigned to the cuticle. However, as these various strata are formed by the larval epidermis it seems proper to consider them part of the adult epidermis. The fibers of the epidermis do not appear to be of the nature of connective tissue but rather seem to be protoplasmic strands. There are no indications of cell walls, and the entire epidermis forms a syncytium. The nuclei and the lacunar system are situated in the inner radial layer.

In the Acanthocephala the number of nuclei is approximately constant for each species, at least in early stages, and in many families throughout life (Van Cleave, 1914). In the latter families the nuclei of the epidermis are few in number and more or less fixed in position, being regularly associated with the main channels of the lacunar system. Thus in the family Neoechinorhynchidae there are nearly always six nuclei in the epidermis, five dorsally along the main dorsal lacuna and one ventrally along the anterior part of the ventral lacuna (Van Cleave, 1914, 1928). In other families that retain the larval condition of the nuclei, there are up to 20 nuclei in the epidermis. These nuclei range in shape from globose or oval to rosette, amoeboid, or highly branched forms and are of relatively large size, up to 2 mm. or more in length (Fig. 23F). In some families of Acanthocephala as the Polymorphidae and Echinorhynchidae, the larval nuclei fragment during later development into numerous small nuclei so that in such case the epidermis is also provided with a considerable number of small nuclei.

The inner radial layer of the epidermis contains the lacunar system, a set of channels without definite walls but having a more or less definite pattern. Although in some Acanthocephala the system consists simply of a network (Fig. 6D), in most members there are a pair of main longitudinal channels with regularly spaced transverse connections (Fig. 6C). In the orders Archi- and Eoacanthocephala, the main channels are median, that is, dorsal and ventral, although the ventral vessel may be wanting; in the Palaeacanthocephala, the main channels are lateral (Fig.

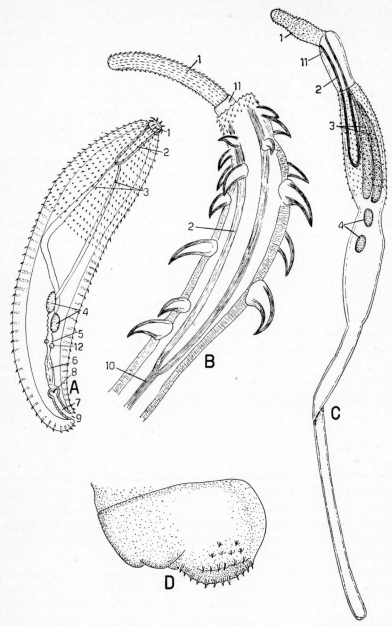

Fig. 4.—Trunk spination. *A. Acanthogyrus (after Thapar,* 1927), showing trunk spination. *B. Rhadinorhynchus horridus (after Lühe,* 1912), showing very large trunk spines. *C. Arhythmorhynchus* with spiny foretrunk and slender hindtrunk *(after Lühe,* 1912). *D.* Rear end of *Corynosoma,* showing genital spines *(after Van Cleave,* 1918). 1, proboscis; 2, proboscis receptacle; 3, lemnisci; 4, testes; 5, sperm ducts; 6, genital sheath; 7, bursa; 8, penis; 9, gonopore; 10, receptacle retractor; 11, neck; 12, spermiducal vesicles.

6*A*, *B*). Subsidiary longitudinal channels may also occur. The lacunar system does not communicate with the outside or with any other body structure, being confined strictly to the epidermis. It contains a nutritive fluid presumably obtained by absorption from the host and therefore serves as a food-distributing system in the absence of any other. The fluid in the system moves only with body movements.

Beneath the epidermis there is a thin layer of material that also permeates the underlying musculature. This material presumably represents a *dermis*, although called by various other names (basement layer, binding layer) in the literature. The muscle layer forming the innermost coat of the body wall is relatively thin, consisting of outer circular and inner longitudinal fibers (Fig. 5*E*). These muscle layers are also syncytial, forming a fibrous network (Fig. 5*D*), and probably contain a more or less definite number of nuclei. The muscle fibers consist of a cytoplasmic and a fibrillar portion; the fibrils may run along one side of the cytoplasmic part or may encircle the latter (Fig. 5*C*). No definite lining membrane bounds the body wall from the pseudocoel.

3. Proboscis Apparatus.—The everted proboscis varies from a short cylindrical to globose shape to a long cylinder; it usually equals but a fraction of the body length (Fig. 2). It is armed with recurved hooks that are similar in shape but varied in size and arrangement (Van Cleave, 1941a). They are most commonly arranged in alternating radial rows (*quincunxial* pattern, Fig. 9*A*) but may be concentric or irregular; they may be of even size over the proboscis (Fig. 2*B*), and this is presumably the original condition, but more commonly present size gradations. The hooks may be largest at the summit and decrease gradually toward the base (Fig. 8*A*) or often are largest in the middle region, decreasing toward the ends (Fig. 8*B*); they may also be larger ventrally than dorsally as in *Aspersentis* and *Rhadinorhynchus* (Fig. 8*D*, *E*) or certain especially large ventral hooks may occur (*Arythmorhynchus*, Fig. 8*B*). The number of rows, the number per row, and the size pattern of the hooks are fairly constant for each species, and in fact the proboscis armature constitutes one of the most important taxonomic characters of the phylum. The larger hooks have *roots* sunk into the proboscis wall (Fig. 6*E*), and some authors reserve the term hooks for these, calling the smaller, rootless members of the armature *spines*. The hooks and spines are of unknown chemical nature but apparently consist of the same material as the dermis from which they seem to originate (Fig. 6*E*). They are covered with cuticle.

The proboscis is invaginable and withdrawable into a muscular sac, the *proboscis receptacle*, that is fastened in a circle to the inner surface of the proboscis wall and hangs into the pseudocoel. It is composed in some groups of a single muscle layer, in others of two layers (Fig. 7), and in the

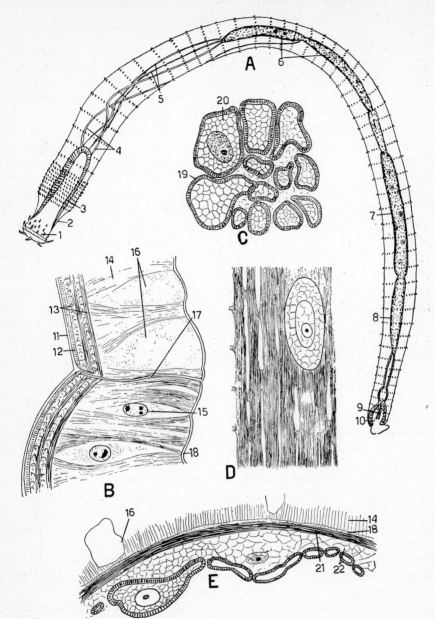

Fig. 5.—Trunk spination, histological structure. *A. Pallisentis ophiocephali* with girdles of trunk spines (*after Thapar*, 1930). *B.* Longitudinal section through the epidermis at the neck-trunk junction (*after Kaiser*, 1893). *C.* Section through the proboscis retractor. *D.* Surface view of body-wall musculature, showing its syncytial net-like nature. *E.* Cross section through the muscle layer of the body wall. (*C–E, after Hamann,* 1891.) 1, proboscis; 2, neck; 3, proboscis receptacle; 4, lemnisci; 5, receptacle retractors; 6, testes; 7, syncytial cement gland; 8, genital sheath; 9, penis; 10, bursa; 11, cuticle; 12, outer radial layer of epidermis; 13, felt layer; 14, inner radial layer; 15, nucleus; 16, channels of lacunar system; 17, cuticular partition between neck and trunk; 18, dermis; 19, fibrillar part of muscle fiber; 20, cytoplasmic part; 21, circular muscle layer; 22, longitudinal muscle layer.

Oligacanthorhynchidae is very thick dorsally, very thin ventrally, or completed ventrally by nonmuscular tissue (Fig. 9*C*). Proboscis and receptacle are operated by special muscle bands which are most complicated in the Oligacanthorhynchidae. From the proboscis summit there extends posteriorly along the proboscis interior a muscle or group of muscles termed the *retractor, invaginator,* or *invertor* muscle. This inserts on the receptacle wall and also passes through this wall to continue as the *dorsal* and *ventral receptacle retractors* that terminate on the trunk wall. In the more complicated types there are also a number of *dorsal, ventral,* and *lateral receptacle protrusors* that originate in a circle from the neck wall and insert on the rear part of the receptacle (Fig. 9*B, C*). In sections these protrusors form a circle around the receptacle with the lateral protrusors to the inner side of the dorsal and ventral ones (Fig. 9*B, C*). In the Oligacanthorhynchidae there is in line with the lateral protrusors attached to the mid-ventral wall of the receptacle a longitudinal muscle that acts to curve the receptacle ventrally. Finally generally distributed in the Acanthocephala there are the *retractors of the neck* that originate near the posterior boundary of the neck and insert on the trunk; they encircle all the other proboscis muscles and embrace the lemnisci as *compressors of the lemnisci* (Fig. 9*B, C*).

The body wall of the presoma is histologically similar to that of the trunk except that it is much thinner; it contains an abundance of lacunar channels but lacks main longitudinal lacunae. From the rear part of the neck region there extend posteriorly into the trunk pseudocoel a pair of projections of the inner radial layer of the epidermis known as *lemnisci* (Fig. 7). The lemnisci are generally long slender bodies; they are supplied by vessels of the lacunar system and contain either a limited and definite number of giant nuclei (six in *Macracanthorhynchus,* fewer in many species) or a large number of fragmented nuclei. They are clothed externally by the dermis; and, as noted above, at certain levels are enclosed in the neck retractors some fibers of which may in certain species continue beyond the free ends of the lemnisci, attaching them to the trunk wall; but usually they hang free. The accepted explanation of the function of the lemnisci is that they act as reservoirs for the fluid of the lacunar system of the presoma when the proboscis is invaginated.

4. Nervous System.—The nervous system has been studied chiefly in *Polymorphus* (Greeff, 1864), *Macracanthorhynchus* (Kaiser, 1893; Brandes, 1899), *Hamanniella* (Kilian, 1932), and *Bolbosoma* (Harada, 1931). It consists of the cerebral ganglion, the branches from this, and, in the male, a pair of genital ganglia with branches. The cerebral ganglion, often called simply the ganglion, is a large cellular mass enclosed in the proboscis receptacle in contact with its ventral wall (Fig. 7). It consists of a central fibrous mass embraced by ganglion cells, 86 in *Macracantho-*

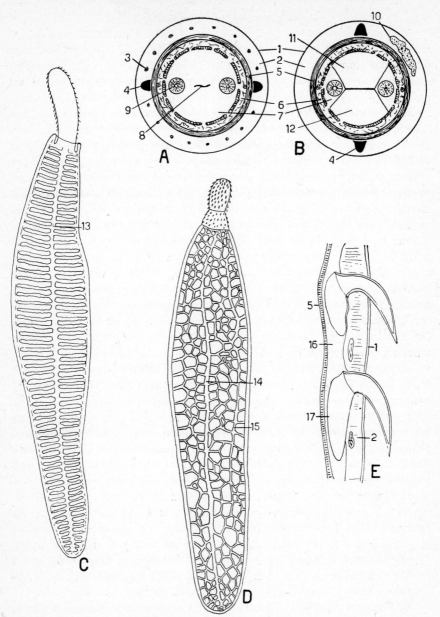

Fig. 6.—Epidermal structure, lacunar system. *A*. Scheme of a cross section through a palaeacanthocephalan. *B*. Same for an archiacanthocephalan. (*A, B, after Meyer*, 1931b). *C*. Lacunar system of *Moniliformis*, dorsal view, showing regular circular branches (*after Meyer*, 1931b). *D*. Lacunar system of *Centrorhynchus*, lateral view, showing net-like branching system (*after Yamaguti*, 1939). *E*. Longitudinal section through the proboscis wall, showing hook relations (*after Hamann*, 1891). 1, cuticle; 2, epidermis; 3, fragmented epidermal nuclei; 4, main lacunar channels; 5, circular muscle layer; 6, longitudinal muscle layer; 7, pseudocoel; 8, remnant of the ligament; 9, lemnisci; 10, giant epidermal nucleus; 11, dorsal ligament sac; 12, ventral ligament sac; 13, main dorsal channel; 14, main lateral channel; 15, subsidiary longitudinal channel; 16, dermis; 17, root of hook.

13

rhynchus, 80 in *Hamanniella*, and 73 in *Bolbosoma*. In the first two genera, the ganglion gives off two single and three pairs of nerves, in *Bolbosoma*, one single and five pairs of nerves. The former comprise: an anterior median and a ventral anterior nerve to the musculature and sensory papillae of the proboscis, a pair of lateral anterior nerves to the lateral protrusors, a pair of lateral medial nerves to the receptacle wall, and the pair of main lateral posterior nerves that proceed to the posterior end of the animal (Fig. 10*A*). In *Bolbosoma* there are similarly a number of nerves to the musculature and sense organs of the proboscis apparatus (a dorsomedial nerve, and paired dorsolateral anterior, ventrolateral anterior, supradorsal, and medial posterior) and the main lateral posterior nerves. The lateral posterior nerves pierce the receptacle wall, proceed laterally (enclosed in peculiar muscle sheaths termed *retinacula*) to the body wall of the trunk into which they give branches, and then run posteriorly in the lateral body wall in the longitudinal muscle layer to the posterior end, giving off genital branches in females. In males, however, branches from these nerves enter a pair of genital ganglia situated in the penis base and connected with each other by a ring commissure. From the genital ganglia branches proceed anteriorly along the male genital tract and posteriorly into the bursa where some terminate in bulbous sense organs (Fig. 10*C*, *E*, *F*).

5. Sense Organs.—As usual in entoparasites, the Acanthocephala are deficient in sense organs. The known sense organs comprise three in the proboscis and several in the male bursa and penis. In the proboscis there is a sensory organ in the center of the tip and in some genera one on each side in the neck. The terminal sense organ consists of a small pit beneath which there is a fusiform nerve ending of a nerve fiber that makes a coil just below its termination (Fig. 10*D*). The pair of lateral proboscis sense organs is similar except that several coiled nerve fibers are involved. These proboscis sense organs are supplied by certain of the anterior nerves coming from the cerebral ganglion (Fig. 10*A*). In males fibers from the genital ganglia terminate in bulbous or spherical sense organs of which there are seven or eight around the rim of the bursa (Fig. 10*E*) and a number in the penis (Fig. 10*E*, *F*). It is usually supposed that all the acanthocephalan sense organs are of a tactile nature.

6. Excretory System.—Protonephridia occur only in the order Archiacanthocephala where they consist of a pair of small bodies to either side of and closely adherent to the reproductive system. In most genera each organ consists of a branching mass of flame bulbs attached to a common stem (Fig. 11*A*, *B*). In certain genera (*Oligacanthorhynchus*, *Nephridiorhynchus*), the flame bulbs open directly into a sac from which the nephridial canal leads (Meyer, 1931b, 1931d, Figs. 11*D*, 12). In any case the two canals unite to a single canal or to a bladder and this joins the com-

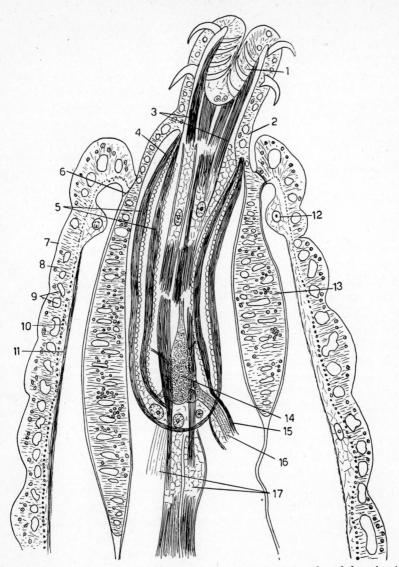

Fig. 7.—Longitudinal section through the anterior end of *Acanthocephalus*, showing details of structure (*after Hamann*, 1891). 1, proboscis, partly invaginated; 2, neck; 3, proboscis retractor; 4, proboscis receptacle; 5, double muscular wall of receptacle; 6, cuticular partition between neck and trunk; 7, cuticle; 8, epidermis; 9, lacunar system; 10, circular muscle layer of body wall; 11, longitudinal muscle layer; 12, nucleus of same; 13, lemniscus; 14, ganglion; 15, retinaculum; 16, lateral posterior nerve; 17, receptacle retractors.

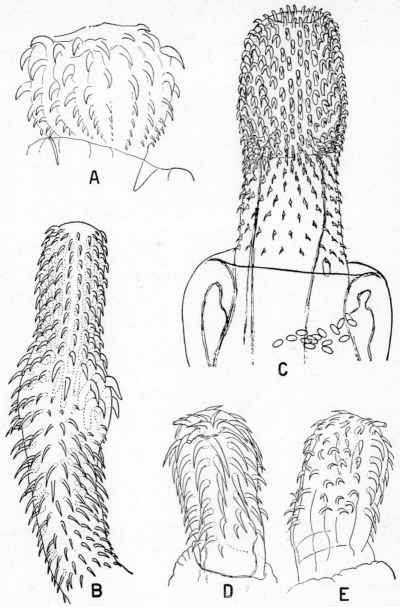

Fig. 8.—Proboscis armature. A. Proboscis of *Sphaerechinorhynchus* (after *Johnston and Deland*, 1929), showing hooks grading from summit to base. B. *Arythmorhynchus*, middle hooks largest, some especially large ones mid-ventrally. C. *Centrorhynchus*, anterior half of proboscis above attachment of proboscis receptacle armed with hooks, posterior half with much smaller spines. D. *Aspersentis*, ventral surface, with large hooks. E. *Aspersentis*, dorsal surface, with much smaller hooks. (*B–E, after Van Cleave*, 1941a.)

mon sperm duct in the male (Fig. 13*A*) and the uterus in the female (Fig. 11*D*).   The terminal canals of the reproductive system are then urogenital canals in the Archiacanthocephala.

The number of flame bulbs in each protonephridium ranges from about 250 to 700.   The flame bulbs are devoid of nuclei and are therefore not cells; usually three nuclei occur in the main branches or in the wall of the chamber.   The flame consists of a linear row of cilia (Fig. 11*C*).

7. The Ligament Sacs and the Ligament Strand.—These are structures peculiar to the Acanthocephala.   The *ligament sacs* (formerly called ligaments) are hollow tubes of connective tissue with or without accompanying muscle fibers that run the length of the body interior and enclose the reproductive organs.   Anteriorly they are attached to the posterior end of the proboscis receptacle or the adjacent body wall and posteriorly they terminate on or in some part of the reproductive system.   In the Archi- and Eoacanthocephala there are in the female two ligament sacs, a dorsal and a ventral, whose medial walls make contact in the frontal plane (Fig. 6*B*) and which communicate anteriorly by an opening.   The dorsal ligament sac attaches posteriorly to the anterior rim of the uterine bell; the ventral sac extends to the posterior end of the body, opening en route into the ventral aperture of the bell (Fig. 11*D*).   In males the ventral sac is wanting and the dorsal sac encloses the testes and the cement glands and posteriorly becomes continuous with the genital sheath (Fig. 13*D*).   In both sexes of the Palaeacanthocephala there is a single ligament sac that occupies the center of the pseudocoel, being attached anteriorly to the proboscis receptacle and posteriorly to the uterine bell in females, the genital sheath in males.   In females, however, it often ruptures with the onset of sexual maturity and becomes reduced to a band so that the developing eggs float free in the pseudocoel (Fig. 14*A*).

In a careful study of the urogenital system and ligament sacs of the Archiacanthocephala, Haffner (1942) has called attention to the *ligament strand*, a nucleated strand found between the two ligament sacs when present or situated along the ventral face of the single ligament sac.   The gonads in both sexes are attached to this strand.   According to Haffner's analysis, the ligament strand represents the entoderm or midgut and the terminal parts of the genital system of both sexes were probably originally the cloaca.   The ligament sacs are regarded by this author as separated parts of the pseudocoel, something that also occurs in gastrotrichs.

8. Pseudocoel.—Between the body wall and the ligaments there occurs a cavity not provided with any lining membrane.   It is of small extent in forms with two ligament sacs but attains considerable size in those with one sac; it also extends into the presoma between the muscle

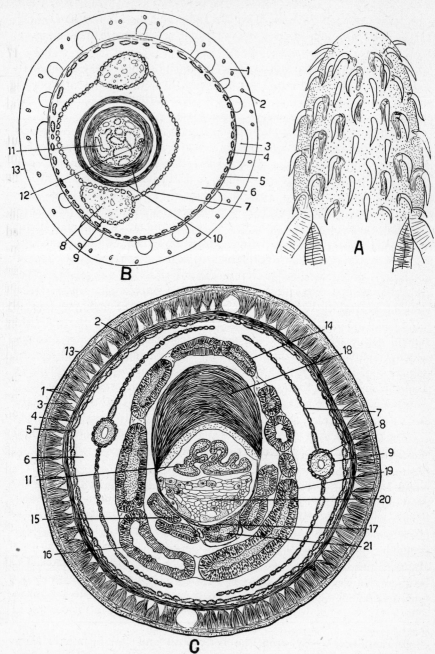

Fig. 9.—Proboscis armature, musculature. *A.* Proboscis of *Acanthocephalus* (*after Lühe*, 1912), with equally sized hooks in quincunxial arrangement. *B.* Section through the neck region of *Acanthocephalus* (*after Hamann*, 1891), showing proboscis and neck muscles. *C.* Section through the proboscis receptacle of *Hamanniella* (*slightly altered after*

bands.   As the cavity lacks a lining membrane, it is obviously not a coelom.   Early larval stages of Acanthocephala are of solid construction; the body cavity arises later by the simple withdrawal of the central mass (destined to become the ligament sacs, ligament strand, and reproductive system) from the body wall.   As the ligament strand apparently represents the entoderm, the body cavity is a space between the entoderm and the body wall and hence classifies as a pseudocoel.

9. Reproductive System.—The reproductive system of the Acanthocephala presents many peculiarities.   In males there are two oval, rounded, or elongated testes enclosed in tandem in the ligament sac and attached to the ligament strand.   From each testis a sperm duct proceeds posteriorly inside the ligament sac (Fig. 13*A*).   Small enlargements representing spermiducal vesicles may occur along the sperm ducts (Fig. 4*A*).   Shortly behind the more posterior testis in Archi- and Palaeacanthocephala occurs a cluster of unicellular gland cells known as *cement glands*, usually six or eight in number and of variable shape—rounded, pyriform, clavate, or tubular.   The ducts of these cement glands, either separately or after union into one or two main ducts, enter the common sperm duct (Fig. 13*A*).   In the Eoacanthocephala, the cement glands are fused to a syncytial mass containing 8, 12, or 16 giant nuclei (Fig. 13*D*) and the duct from this enters a *cement reservoir* from which a pair of ducts leads to the common sperm duct (Fig. 13*D*).   The sperm ducts, the cement ducts, and the protonephridial canals (when present) are all enclosed in a muscular tube, the *genital sheath* (Fig. 13*B*), continuous with the ligament sac (Fig. 13*A*) and formed by the application of muscle fibers from the body-wall musculature to the outer surface of the ligament sac (Bieler, 1913, 1914).   The genital sheath terminates on the muscle cap of the bursa.   Inside the genital sheath, the two sperm ducts unite to a common sperm duct, which may present a saccular enlargement, the seminal vesicle, the cement ducts enter the common sperm duct, and the common protonephridial canal, when present, also unites with the common sperm duct.   The urogenital canal so formed penetrates the center of the penis, a short conical protrusion (Fig. 13*A*, *D*).   In many acanthocephalans, there is also found inside the genital sheath, in addition to the above-named ducts, a conspicuous elongated pouch, formerly believed to be a seminal vesicle, but known since the work of Saefftigen (1885) to be a muscular pouch continuous with the spaces of the bursal cap and acting

Kilian, 1932), showing muscles.   1, epidermis; 2, epidermal nuclei; 3, lacunar spaces; 4, circular muscle layer of body wall; 5, longitudinal muscle layer of body wall; 6, pseudocoel; 7, neck retractors; 8, lemnisci; 9, compressors of lemnisci; 10, proboscis receptacle; 11, proboscis retractor; 12, nerve trunk; 13, cuticle; 14, dorsal receptacle protrusors; 15, lateral receptacle protrusors; 16, ventral receptacle protrusors; 17, thin ventral wall of receptacle; 18, thick dorsal receptacle wall; 19, fibrillar part of muscle; 20, cerebral ganglion; 21, midventral receptacle muscle.

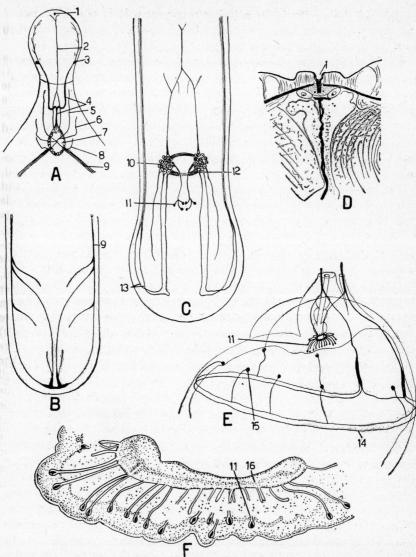

Fig. 10.—Nervous system and sense organs. *A.* Nervous system of anterior end of *Macr. hirudinaceus.* *B.* Posterior end of female of the same. *C.* Posterior end of the male. (*A–C, after Brandes,* 1899.) *D.* Sense organ of the proboscis summit (*after Kilian,* 1932). *E.* Sense bulbs of the penis and bursa of *Bolbosoma.* *F.* Section through ring of sense organs around the penis. (*E, F, after Harada,* 1931.) 1, apical sense organ; 2, anterior median nerve; 3, lateral sensory bulb; 4, ventral anterior nerve; 5, lateral anterior nerve; 6, lateral medial nerves; 7, cerebral ganglion; 8, retinacula; 9, lateral posterior nerves; 10, genital ganglia; 11, sensory bulbs of penis; 12, nerve ring in genital sheath; 13, bursal nerves; 14, nerve ring in bursa; 15, sensory bulbs of bursa; 16, nerve ring in penis.

to inject fluid into those spaces to assist eversion of the bursa (Fig. 13*D*). Following Yamaguti (1935), this pouch will be termed *Saefftigen's pouch* (*Markbeutel* of German authors).

The penis projects into a hemispherical or elongated cavity, the *bursa*, that is eversible to the exterior (Fig. 13*C*), and grasps the rear end of the female in copulation (Fig. 14*E*). The bursa is composed of inturned body wall of which the muscular layer is greatly thickened in the proximal part of the bursa, forming the *muscular cap* (Fig. 13*A*, *D*). This muscular cap may bulge anteriorly as a pair of muscular pockets (Fig. 2*B*) and from it in many species there radiate muscular rays along the bursal wall (Fig. 2*A*).

The process of spermatogenesis is similar to that of other animals and is cellular throughout. The sperm are long filaments with out definite heads (Fig. 14*D*).

The female reproductive system departs from the usual in many ways. The original single or double ovary breaks up into fragments termed ovarian balls that float free in the dorsal ligament sac in the Archi- and Eoacanthocephla and in the single sac in the Palaeacanthocephala; but as the latter sac soon ruptures the balls occupy the pseudocoel. The ligament sacs lead to the first part of the female canal, termed the *uterine bell*, a muscular funnel-shaped or tubular organ that by peristaltic contractions engulfs the developing eggs and passes them onward. In the Archi- and Eoacanthocephala, the uterine bell is continuous with the dorsal ligament sac, that is, this sac attaches in a circle to the anterior rim of the bell (Fig. 11*D*). In the Palaeacanthocephala, the single ligament sac terminates inside the bell on its wall (Fig. 14*B*) so that the beginning of the bell is widely open to the pseudocoel. The bell also has a posterior ventral opening, into the ventral ligament sac when this is present (Fig. 11*D*), otherwise into the pseudocoel. At its posterior end the bell narrows to a *uterine tube* composed of several large cells with conspicuous nuclei (Fig. 11*D*), and bearing two *bell pouches* that extend anteriorly. The uterine tube enters the *uterus*, a muscular tube of some length, and this is followed by the short nonmuscular *vagina* opening to the exterior (Fig. 11*D*). In females, the nephridia (when present) lie alongside the uterine bell, the two protonephridial ducts run in the dorsal wall of the bell, and the common canal formed by their union opens into the beginning of the uterine tube (Fig. 11*D*).

The ovarian balls consist of a central syncytium from which ovogonia separate, passing to the periphery for further development.

10. Copulation and Egg Production.—In copulation the everted male bursa grasps the posterior end of the female (Fig. 14*E*) and the penis enters the vagina and discharges sperm into the uterus. This is followed by the discharge of the cement secretion which sets as a plug in the gono-

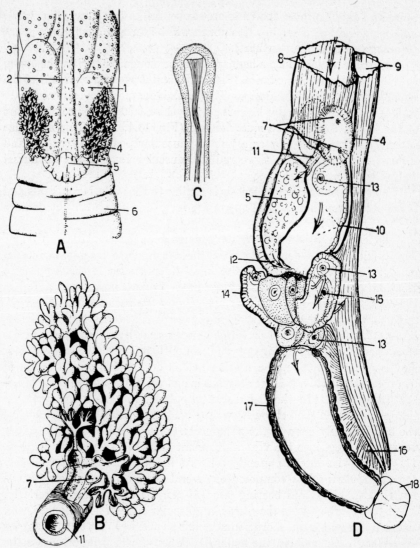

FIG. 11.—Urogenital system. *A.* Part of male system of *Hamanniella*, showing location of the two protonephridia. *B.* Enlarged view of one protonephridium of the same. (*A, B, after Kilian,* 1932.) *C.* An acanthocephalan flame bulb. *D.* Side view of female system of *Oligacanthorhynchus*, showing also location of the two sacciform protonephridia. (*C, D, after Meyer,* 1931d.) 1, cement glands; 2, sperm duct; 3, ligament sac; 4, protonephridium; 5, bladder; 6, genital sheath; 7, nephridial nuclei; 8, dorsal ligament sac; 9, ventral ligament sac; 10, uterine bell; 11, nephridial canal; 12, exit of bladder into bell; 13, nuclei of bell apparatus; 14, bell pockets; 15, exit into ventral ligament sac; 16, membrane, part of ventral ligament sac; 17, uterus; 18, vagina.

pore and as a cap over the whole posterior tip, preventing escape of the sperm. The ripe ovocytes, of elliptical form and surrounded by a membrane, break through the surface of the ovarian ball and are then entered by a sperm. A fertilization membrane arises inside the original egg membrane and maturation ensues. The eggs in the meantime have escaped from the ovarian balls and continue development in the pseudocoel or inside the dorsal ligament sac until a larval stage provided with a rostellum armed with hooks is reached. Meanwhile, a third membrane,

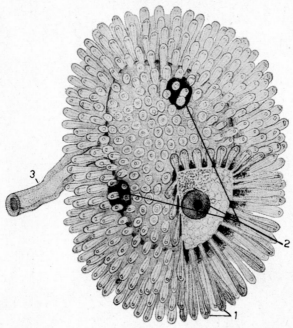

Fig. 12.—Nephridium of *Oligacanthorhynchus* (*after Meyer*, 1931d), sac type with attached flame bulbs; a part of the wall is reflected to show one of the three nuclei. 1, flame bulbs; 2, the three nuclei; 3, canal.

usually termed shell, has formed between the two membranes already present around the embryo. This shell is hard in forms that use terrestrial intermediate hosts, softer in those with aquatic life histories (Fig. 19C, D). These ovic larvae are engulfed by the uterine bell and passed toward the uterine tube; those not sufficiently mature may be returned through the ventral bell aperture into the pseudocoel or ventral ligament sac. The ripe ones proceed into the bell pockets and then along the uterus and vagina to the exterior. These elliptical ovic larvae must be ingested by the proper invertebrate hosts before they can develop further.

11. Embryology.—The embryonic development has been investigated chiefly for the common acanthocephalan of the pig, *Macracanthorhynchus*

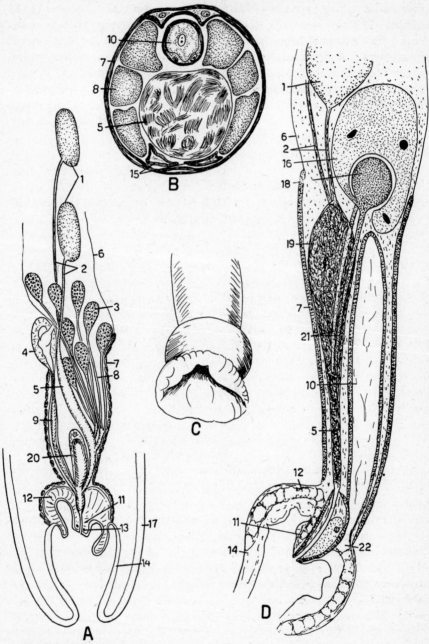

Fig. 13.—Male reproductive system. *A.* Male system of *Hamanniella,* seen from the side, somewhat schematic (*altered after Kilian,* 1932). *B.* Section through the genital sheath (*after Kaiser,* 1893). *C.* Everted bursa (*after Johnston and Deland,* 1929). *D.* Male system of *Neoechinorhynchus,* seen from the side, showing syncytial cement gland,

hirudinaceus, because of its ready obtainability (Schneider, 1871; Hamann, 1891; Kaiser, 1893, 1913; Meyer, 1928, 1936, 1937, 1938). The account of Meyer is here followed. The egg, as already noted, is of marked elliptical form and enclosed within four membranes (Fig. 18*A*), that prevent any alteration of shape or expansion of volume. These factors strongly affect the development, the study of which is a matter of great technical difficulty. According to Meyer, the cleavage is of the spiral determinate type but the elliptical shape greatly displaces the blastomeres. The egg cleaves into four blastomeres which, however, are very oblique to each other (Fig. 15*A*) instead of taking the usual parallel position. The cleavages are not very synchronous; they occur according to a bilateral pattern similar to that of rotifers (Figs. 15*C*, 17*D*). There are given off two quartets of micromeres toward the end that is shown by subsequent development to be the posterior end of the larva (Fig. 15*E*). By comparison with other examples of spiral cleavage it would appear that this end represents the animal pole and is so called by Meyer; however, the polar bodies arise at the opposite pole considered by Meyer to be the vegetal pole and destined to become the anterior end of the larva. The polar relations therefore seem to be the opposite of those usually found, but it appears less confusing to use the terms animal and vegetal with reference to the cleavage pattern rather than in relation to the egg polarity. The third quartet of micromeres is given off at the vegetal pole (future anterior end of the larva, site of the polar bodies). The macromeres thus lie between the third quartet on the one hand and the other two quartets on the other hand (Fig. 15*E*). Because, however, of the extreme displacements resulting from the elliptical shape, the resulting cleavage pattern is widely dissimilar from that typical of spiral cleavage. Micromeres and macromeres cleave with a marked lack of synchronism until a 34-cell stage is attained (Fig. 15*E*) in which there are in each quadrant four animal micromeres, two macromeres, and two vegetal micromeres, except that the *D*-quadrant has two additional animal micromeres. This stage is regarded as a stereoblastula, and following it cell walls begin to disappear starting at the animal pole (Fig. 15*F*). The further development thus takes place in a syncytium, in which nuclear divisions continue to the eventual number of about 200 (Fig. 16*A*, *B*). At the time when there are about 42 nuclei, a group of four nuclei that appear to originate from the third, or vegetal, quartet wanders into the

cement reservoir, and relations of Saefftigen's pouch (*based on Bieler*, 1913, 1914). 1, testes; 2, sperm ducts; 3, cement glands; 4, urinary bladder; 5, common sperm duct; 6, ligament sac; 7, genital sheath; 8, ducts of cement glands; 9, common nephridial canal; 10, Saefftigen's pouch; 11, penis papilla; 12, muscular cap of bursa; 13, nerve ring in penis papilla; 14, bursa; 15, muscles; 16, syncytial cement gland; 17, body wall; 18, cement reservoir; 19, seminal vesicle; 20, pouch of urogenital canal; 21, ducts from cement reservoir; 22, entrance of Saefftigen's pouch into bursa cap.

interior and becomes the primordium of the gonads and the ligaments (Fig. 15F). This inwandering seems to represent a kind of gastrulation, and the ligaments and gonads are interpretable as formed from entoderm and entomesoderm, respectively. As nuclear division continues, additional nuclei wander into the interior from the vegetal region of the embryo. One group comes from a circular region involving nuclei of all four quadrants; this group becomes the primordium of the cerebral ganglion. Another group coming from the future ventral surface, mainly from nuclei of the D-quadrant, is the source of the musculature. In the meantime all these inner nuclei undergo a condensation process in which they become much smaller and by elimination of nonchromatic material come to consist almost wholly of chromatin. Meyer explains this nuclear condensation process as an adaptation to lack of space for the continually increasing number of nuclei. The inner nuclei continue to divide, and there eventuates at a stage of around 150 nuclei the characteristic acanthocephalan embryo, consisting of a central elongated mass of densely staining nuclei and a peripheral region containing ordinary vesicular nuclei (Fig. 16B). The condensed nuclei are arranged in three illy defined groups: the primordia of the ganglion, the musculature, and the ligaments and gonads, respectively (Fig. 16A–D). The surface layer, containing the vesicular nuclei (eventually numbering about 50) is the definitive epidermis of the trunk region. There next occurs at the vegetal pole (future anterior end) an ingrowth of a mass of nuclei and cytoplasm that places itself anterior to the ganglion primordium and constitutes the primordium of the proboscis. A similar ingrowth at the animal pole (future posterior end) is the primordium of the urogenital tract, and takes up a position directly behind the gonad-ligament primordium; the epidermis closes together after these ingrowths (Fig. 16C, D). About this time, the embryonic shell, consisting of two valves (Fig. 18A) begins to form between the fertilization membrane and the original egg membrane. Three pairs of larval hooks, strikingly like those of the cestode hexacanth, appear on the embryo's anterior end, which thus becomes a rostellum, and spines develop over the entire surface (Fig. 18A). Circular fibers and a pair of retractor muscles differentiate in connection with the rostellum, and a subepidermal musculature in the form of a thin network of fibers appears. The embryo, now termed the *acanthor* larva, develops no further until ingested by the proper intermediate host, which in the case of *Macr. hirudinaceus* is the grub of the June beetle, or of other scarabaeid beetles.

The only other detailed account of the embryology is that of Meyer (1931c) for *Neoechinorhynchus rutili*, a parasite of many fresh-water fishes. The four-cell stage of this worm is similar to that of the foregoing species (Fig. 16E). The A, B, and C blastomeres give off two sets of

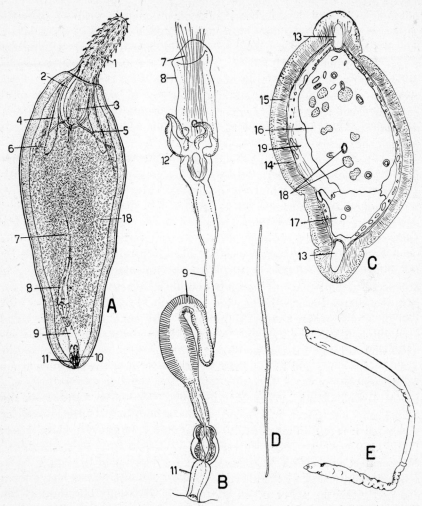

FIG. 14.—Reproduction (continued). *A.* Ripe palaeacanthocephalan female (*Acanthocephalus, after Yamaguti*, 1935), showing interior filled with shelled embryos. *B.* Female reproductive system of a palaeacanthocephalan (*Bolbosoma, after Yamaguti*, 1939), showing single ligament attached inside the uterine bell. *C.* Section through a female archiacanthocephalan (*after Meyer*, 1931b), showing the two ligament sacs. *D.* Acanthocephalan sperm (*after Kaiser*, 1893). *E.* Acanthocephalans in copulation (*after Johnson and Deland*, 1929). 1, proboscis retractor; 2, proboscis receptacle; 3, ganglion; 4, lemnisci; 5, retinacula; 6, neck retractor; 7, ligament sac; 8, uterine bell; 9, uterus; 10, sphincter; 11, vagina; 12, bell pockets; 13, main lacunar channels; 14, epidermis; 15, muscle layer of body wall; 16, dorsal ligament sac; 17, ventral ligament sac; 18, embryos; 19, pseudocoel.

micromeres toward the pole bearing the polar bodies (here also apparently the vegetal pole), but the *D* blastomere which is larger and with denser cytoplasm than the others gives off two micromeres toward the opposite pole. Following this 12-cell stage cell walls disappear except in the *D*-quadrant which, however, becomes syncytial later (Fig. 17*A–C*). The *D*-quadrant then by a sort of epiboly grows over the other quadrants and encloses them, thus revealing itself to be the source of the entire epidermis (Fig. 17*C*). The end result is the same as in *Macr. hirudinaceus* in that the embryo comes to consist of a central syncytial core of condensed nuclei enclosed in a syncytial epidermis containing vesicular nuclei (Fig. 17*C*). The pole opposite the original location of the *D*-quadrant becomes the anterior end of the acanthor.

Although the cleavage in the Acanthocephala seems to be of the spiral determinate type, thus linking the group to the other Protostomia, the embryology presents many peculiarities, such as the occurrence of the polar bodies at the apparent vegetal pole, the displacements caused by the elliptical form of the egg, the early disappearance of cell walls, the absence of definite gastrulation and entoderm and mesoderm formation, and the sharp demarcation of the primordium of the epidermis with vesicular nuclei from the other primordia with condensed nuclei. The early differentiation of the epidermis would seem to possess some physiological importance for the well-being of the embryo. The peculiarities of the embryology add to the difficulty of determining the affinities of the Acanthocephala.

12. Development in the Intermediate Host.—The history of the acanthocephalan larva in the intermediate host has been followed for several species and takes a similar course in all of them (Hamann, 1891; Kaiser, 1893; Meyer, 1938; Kates, 1943; Moore, 1946). As noted above, the so-called eggs of the Acanthocephala are really acanthors enclosed in a heavy elliptical shell (Fig. 18*A*). These pass out in the host's feces dropped either in water or on the earth. The acanthor develops no further until ingested by the proper invertebrate host, usually a larval insect, amphipod, or isopod. Upon reaching the midgut of the intermediate host, the shell splits, along the preformed raphe when this is present, and the released acanthor perforates the host gut wall by means of its rostellum aided by body contortions. During the passage through the gut wall, which may require up to several weeks, the acanthor loses its torpedo shape, becoming oval and eventually nearly spherical, and the larval structures, such as the rostellar hooks, the body spines, and the rostellar muscles, begin to degenerate and sooner or later disappear (Fig. 18). Having passed through the gut wall, the larva falls into the host haemocoel where it begins to elongate again and to differentiate, being now termed *acanthella* (Van Cleave, 1947).

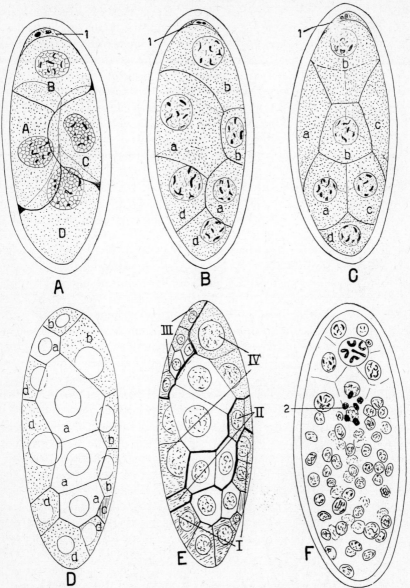

Fig. 15.—Development of *Macr. hirudinaceus*. *A*. Four-cell stage. *B*. Eight-cell stage. *C*. Another view of eight-cell stage, showing bilateral arrangement. *D*. 17-cell stage. *E*. 34-cell stage. *F*. Embryo becoming syncytial, first group of condensed nuclei passing into the interior. (*All after Meyer*, 1928.) In *D*, the descendants of *A* form a central strip, not stippled with *D* descendants to the left; and *B* to the right, both stippled, with one *C* descendant at the lower right, vertically hatched. Similarly in *E*, *A* descendants are blank; *B*, quadrant stippled, *D* quadrant transversely hatched; further, the three quartets are marked off from the macromeres by heavy boundaries. 1, polar bodies; 2, condensed nuclei; I, II, III, the three micromere quartets; IV, macromeres.

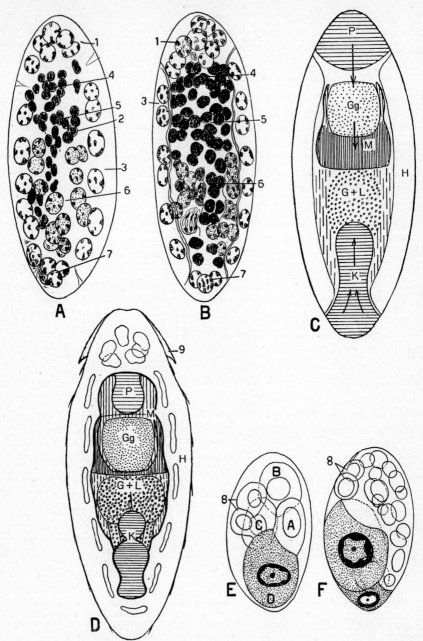

FIG. 16.—Development (continued). *A–D, Macr. hirudinaceus (after Mayer, 1936).*
A. Stage of 163 nuclei, many condensed nuclei, definitive epidermis separating. *B.* Stage
of 179 nuclei, definitive epidermis separated off, various primordia indicated. *C.* Scheme
of the primordia, primordia of the proboscis and urogenital system preparing to invaginate.
D. Proboscis and urogenital primordia have passed into the interior, epidermis has closed

As already explained, the central core of condensed nuclei, or *inner nuclear mass,* consists in linear order of the primordia of the proboscis, the ganglion, the musculature, the gonads and ligament sacs, and the urogenital system (Fig. 16*B–D*).   These primordia are usually indistinguishable in the acanthor but they now begin to differentiate and become recognizable.   The nuclei enlarge, develop nuclear membranes, and gradually return to a vesicular condition.   At the anterior end of the inner nuclear mass brain and proboscis primordia become identifiable. The brain forms a small rounded mass in which the nuclei proliferate (Fig. 18*C–E*).   Anterior to this the proboscis primordium separates from the epidermis except anteriorly and the beginnings of hooks are soon noticeable upon it (Fig. 18*E*).   Between the brain and the proboscis, the proboscis receptacle differentiates and eventually extends posterior to the brain, enclosing the latter.   The nuclei of the muscle primordium migrate to the inner surface of the epidermis, forming in *Macracanthorhynchus* two lateral strands (Fig. 17*E*).   The ligament primordium hollows out to form the ligament sac or sacs and separates from the body wall to make the pseudocoel (Fig. 18*D*).   The gonads early become evident in the gonad primordium and the other parts of the urogenital system become recognizable in the most posterior primordium.   The nephridia in *Macr. hirudinaceus* grow out from this primordium in the region of the uterine bell in females or the genital sheath in males as two projecting cytoplasmic masses each containing three nuclei.   The periphery of these masses differentiates into flame bulbs and the nuclei remain in the main duct. According to Meyer (1938) the primordia of the protonephridia come from the second quartet or thereabouts.   In the meantime a number of epidermal nuclei have migrated to form a ring, the *lemniscal ring,* around the base of the proboscis (Fig. 18*E*).   The number of nuclei in the ring is definite for each species.   The lemnisci arise as solid cytoplasmic buds from the inner surface of the epidermis; as they grow into the pseudocoel, the lemniscal nuclei move into them.   The lacunar system develops by the formation of spaces, a process beginning with the appearance of the two main channels and spreading from these.   Eventually the proboscis breaks through the thinned epidermis covering its summit and already has the structure and armature characteristic of the adult worm.   The above changes take place during the acanthella stage and the resulting worm, which may be considered a juvenile, has all the adult structures

over them, acanthor now complete.   *E, F.* Early stages of the development of *Neoechinorhynchus (after Meyer,* 1931c).   *E.* Four-cell stage.   *F.* 16 nuclei, all but the *D*-quadrant syncytial.   1, proboscis primordium; 2, condensed nuclei; 3, definitive epidermis; 4, brain primordium; 5, primordium of the musculature; 6, primordium of the gonads and ligaments; 7, primordium of the urogenital system except gonads; 8, polar bodies; 9, hooks; *P,* proboscis; *Gg,* ganglion; *M,* musculature; *G+L,* gonads plus ligaments; *H,* epidermis; *K,* urogenital system.

except that the reproductive system is immature, although the sexes can be distinguished.

The development in the intermediate host from its penetration by the acanthor through the acanthella stages to the finished juvenile worm requires some 6 weeks to 3 months in the different species investigated. The juvenile worm is enclosed in a membrane, that may appear during acanthella stages, and passes into a quiescent state in which the proboscis is invaginated into the interior (Fig. 19A). It undergoes no further change until ingested by the definitive vertebrate host. In many cases, however, encysted juveniles are regularly found in vertebrates other than the definitive host, as fish, frogs, lizards, snakes, etc. Such vertebrates are regarded as second intermediate hosts by some but are preferably designated transport hosts. As far as known, the juveniles undergo no development in such hosts and are directly infective to the definitive host without passing through the transport host but the transport host may be a necessary part of the life cycle because it is a more acceptable food item to the definitive host than the primary invertebrate host would be. The juveniles when ingested by transport hosts simply migrate through the intestine into various tissues where they reencyst. Development to the adult stage may also occur in hosts other than the regular definitive hosts, and the former are then known as reservoir hosts that thus serve to maintain the parasite.

As already intimated, the Acanthocephala have in common with the Aschelminthes the property of nuclear constancy or eutely. Except in the gonads, the number of nuclei in the various tissues and organs attained during larval development remains fixed throughout life, so that size increase results entirely from cytoplasmic augmentation without nuclear division. The nuclei of the epidermis eventually lose their vesicular character, becoming more condensed, and in some families fragment into many small nuclei. Those that remain intact are generally called "giant" nuclei (Fig. 23F). During the larval development certain organs become cellular, namely, the brain ganglion, gonads, muscles, and parts of the urogenital system but this cellularity is later lost again except in the brain.

13. Order Archiacanthocephala.—In this order the proboscis hooks are arranged in concentric circles (Fig. 1D), trunk spination is wanting, the epidermal nuclei are of the unfragmented giant type, the main lacunar channels are medially located, the two ligament sacs are persistent in females, the males have eight separate cement glands, and nephridia are generally present. The members of the order parasitize terrestrial birds and mammals and pass their larval stages in terrestrial intermediate hosts. The main families are the Gigantorhynchidae, Oligacantho- rhynchidae, Moniliformidae, and Pachysentidae. The first is character-

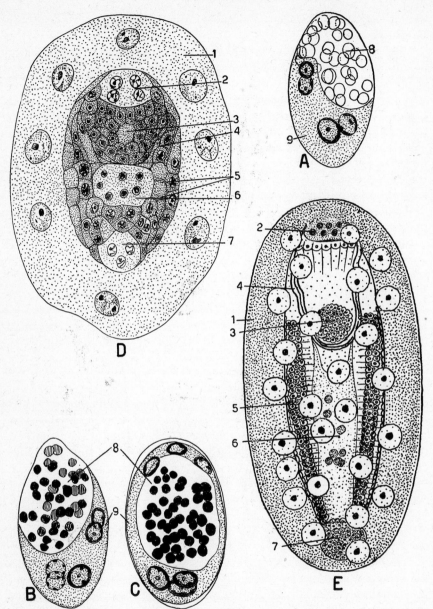

FIG. 17.—Development (continued). *A–C.* Further stages of *Neoechinorhynchus* (*after Meyer*, 1931c), showing *D*-quadrant closing over the condensed nuclei to become the epidermis. *D.* Late embryo of *Macr. hirudinaceus* (*after Kaiser*, 1893) showing bilateral arrangement. *E.* Acanthella of *Macr. hirudinaceus* (*after Meyer*, 1938), showing beginning differentiation of the primordia and muscle strands separating from the ligament. 1, epidermis; 2, proboscis; 3, ganglion; 4, proboscis sheath; 5, body-wall musculature; 6, ligament ; 7, urogenital primordium; 8, condensed nuclei; 9, *D*-quadrant; 10, pseudocoel.

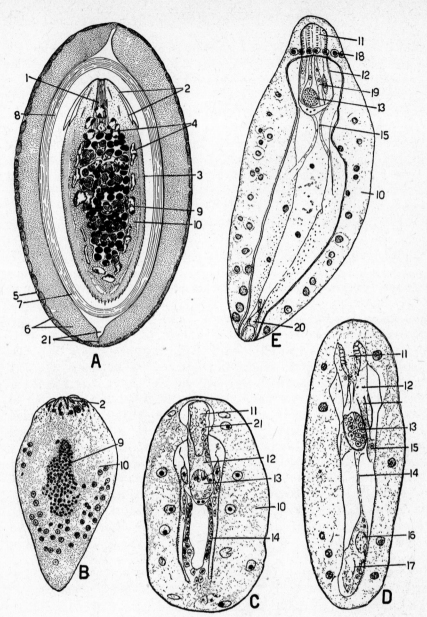

Fig. 18.—Acanthor and acanthella stages. *A.* Acanthor of *Macr. hirudinaceus* within its membranes (*after Meyer*, 1936). *D–E*, Development of *Moniliformis dubius* in the invertebrate host (*after Moore*, 1946a). *B.* Acanthor after hatching. *C.* Young acanthella, proboscis differentiating. *D.* Further differentiation of the primordia. *E.* Proboscis hooks visible, lemniscal ring formed. 1, larval retractor; 2, larval hooks; 3, larval spines; 4, epidermal nuclei; 5, outermost membrane (original egg membrane); 6, shell; 7, fertilization membrane; 8, innermost membrane; 9, core of condensed nuclei; 10, definitive epidermis; 11, proboscis; 12, proboscis receptacle; 13, brain; 14, ligament; 15, receptacle retractors; 16, testis; 17, urogenital primordium; 18, lemniscal ring; 19, proboscis retractors; 20, uterine bell; 21, raphe.

ized by the proboscis armature, consisting anteriorly of hooks, posteriorly of small spines, and by the lack of nephridia. *Mediorhynchus* (includes *Empodius*) with a number of species in birds has the proboscis armature about equally divided between hooks and spines; some species are superficially segmented and this feature is especially marked in *M. taeniatus* (Fig. 23B). *Gigantorhynchus* with one species *echinodiscus* in Central and South American anteaters is very long and slender (Fig. 1E, F) with slightly ringed trunk and short proboscis covered with spines except for a circlet of hooks at the summit (Fig. 1G). In a study of the urogenital system of this worm, Haffner (1942) discovered the presence of rudimentary nephridia.

The Oligacanthorhynchidae are worms of considerable length with long, slender, often slightly ringed bodies that are frequently curved or coiled. The short ovoid or globular proboscis is armed with a few circles of hooks that decrease in size basally. Protonephridia are generally present. Some genera are *Oligacanthorhynchus* in South American birds, *Hamanniella* with spirally rolled body (Fig. 3B) in neotropical marsupials, *Prosthenorchis* with anterior testes in South American monkeys, and *Macracanthorhynchus* in various mammals. *Macracanthorhynchus hirudinaceus* (= *Echinorhynchus gigas, Gigantorhynchus gigas*), the best known acanthocephalan, is found throughout the world in pigs, less often in dogs and other mammals (Fig. 1A–C). Its embryology was extensively studied by Meyer (see above) and its life cycle, discovered by Schneider in 1871, has been the subject of several studies (Wolffhügel, 1924; Glasgow, 1926; Kates, 1943); another species, *M. ingens*, a parasite of raccoons, was studied by Moore (1946b). In both species, larvae of scarabaeid beetles serve as intermediate hosts; these grubs live in cultivated soil from which they are presumably rooted out by the definitive hosts. The acanthellas and juveniles remain viable and infective through the transformation of the grubs into adult beetles and the latter may also serve as food for the definitive hosts. The cycles of other oligacanthorhynchids have not been worked out except that snakes were found by Travassos (1917) to act as transport hosts for *Oligacanthorhynchus*.

The Moniliformidae comprise a single genus *Moniliformis*, a parasite of terrestrial mammals, chiefly rodents. This worm has a long, slender, ringed body and a cylindrical proboscis armed with small hooks decreasing basally, and lacks protonephridia (Fig. 3C). The species are somewhat confused (Chandler, 1941) but the principal ones appear to be *M. moniliformis*, a variable form inhabiting many small mammals, and *M. dubius*, cosmopolitan in rats. Insects, especially beetles and cockroaches, serve as intermediate hosts. As the hosts of *M. dubius*, cockroaches and rats, are easily reared in laboratories, this species is favorable for experimental studies (Moore, 1946a; Burlingame and Chandler, 1941).

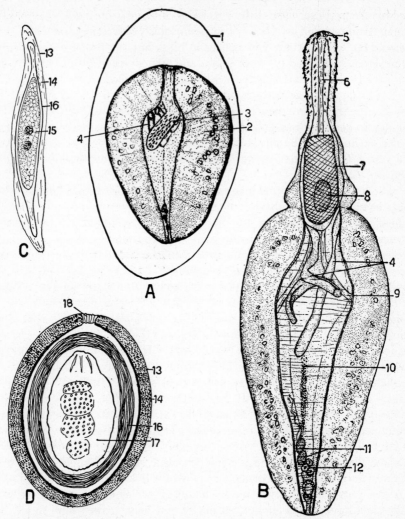

Fig. 19.—Juvenile stages, types of embryonic shell. *A.* Encysted infective juvenile of *Moniliformis dubius.* *B.* Same, with proboscis everted. (*A, B, after Moore,* 1946a.) *C.* Aquatic type of shelled embryo (*Echinorhynchus, after Van Cleave,* 1919a). *D.* Terrestrial type of shelled embryo (*Pachysentis, after Meyer,* 1931b). 1, cyst wall; 2, epidermis; 3, proboscis; 4, lemnisci; 5, apical nuclei; 6, proboscis retractor; 7, proboscis receptacle; 8, ganglion; 9, receptacle retractors; 10, ligament; 11, testes; 12, cement glands; 13, outer membrane; 14, shell; 15, embryo; 16, fertilization membrane; 17, acanthor; 18, raphe.

The Pachysentidae are worms of short plump form with a short ovoid or globular proboscis armed with several circles of hooks, and are provided with protonephridia. They are parasites of carnivores, occurring chiefly in the dog and cat families. The chief genera are *Pachysentis* with more than 36 proboscis hooks and *Oncicola* with 36 or fewer hooks.

Oncicola canis (Van Cleave, 1920c) is the chief acanthocephalan found in North American dogs (Fig. 24*A*). The principal record comes from Texas, where more than 300 specimens were taken from one dog (Kaupp, 1909; Parker, 1909). In this region, the armadillo appears to serve as transport and reservoir host.

14. Order Palaeacanthocephala.—In this order the proboscis hooks have a quincunxial arrangement, the main lacunar channels are lateral, the single ligament sac ruptures in females, the males usually have six cement glands, and nephridia are wanting. The principal families are the Rhadinorhynchidae, Gorgorhynchidae, Polymorphidae, and Echinorhynchidae. The first family, as limited by Van Cleave and Lincicome (1939), comprises fish parasites of elongated form with a very long clavate proboscis (Fig. 20*A*), showing dorsoventral hook differentiation. In the genus *Rhadinorhynchus*, with a number of species in marine and fresh-water fish, there are irregular spines on the foretrunk (Fig. 20*D*) and these are very large in *R. horridus* (Fig. 4*B*). Some other genera of this family, as *Telosentis* and *Illiosentis*, possess genital spines (Fig. 21*C*), as well as anterior trunk spines. *Leptorhynchoides* lacks trunk spination altogether; *L. thecatus*, common in fishes of the eastern United States (Van Cleave, 1919a, 1919b) and the Atlantic Coast (Linton, 1891), appears to be the only member of the family of which the life cycle is known (Van Cleave, 1920a). The larval stages are passed in the amphipod *Hyalella knickerbockeri* and various fishes may also serve as transport hosts (Fig. 20*B*, *C*).

The Gorgorhynchidae, also fish parasites, differ from the foregoing family primarily in the shorter proboscis. *Serrasentis* is notable for the short, comb-like, regularly repeated rows of spines along the ventral trunk surface (Fig. 21*A*, *B*). *Gorgorhynchus* with proboscis spines all alike and with very long tubular cement glands and *Aspersentis* with markedly longer ventral proboscis spines (Fig. 8*D*, *E*) and pyriform cement glands, both possess a girdle of small spines around the foretrunk.

The Polymorphidae parasitize aquatic birds and marine mammals; they have fragmented epidermal nuclei and long cement glands. *Polymorphus* with a number of species in aquatic birds is relatively short with a short proboscis, plump spiny foretrunk, and narrower spineless hindtrunk (Fig. 22*A*). *P. minutus* occurs in ducks and other birds and uses crayfish and amphipods as intermediate hosts (Greeff, 1864; Scheer, 1934a, Fig. 22*C*) and fishes as transport hosts. Greeff's account is the second description of an acanthocephalan life cycle; he fed amphipods containing the orange juveniles to young ducks and 17 days later recovered the sexually mature worms attached to the intestinal wall. Another species of *Polymorphus* uses hermit crabs as intermediate hosts (Reinhard, 1944). In *Filicollis*, the female neck is differentiated into a bulb, that bears the small proboscis, and a slender stalk (Figs. 21*E*, 22*B*); in this genus also

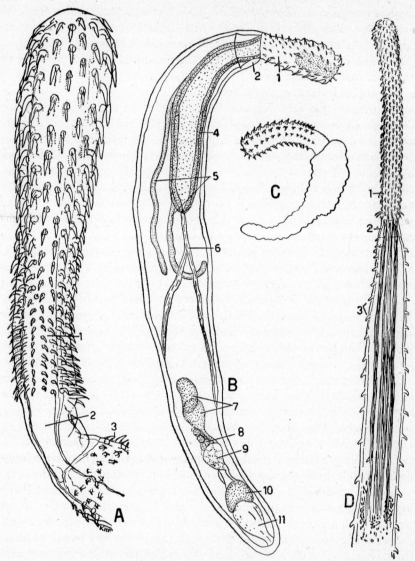

Fig. 20.—Rhadinorhynchidae. *A*. Rhadinorhynchid proboscis (*Illiosentis, after Van Cleave*, 1945e). *B. Leptorhynchoides thecatus (after Van Cleave*, 1919a). *C*. Juvenile of *Lept. thecatus* from an amphipod (*after Van Cleave*, 1920a). *D. Rhadinorhynchus pristis* (*from slide, courtesy H. J. Van Cleave*). 1, proboscis; 2, neck; 3, trunk spines; 4, receptacle; 5, lemnisci; 6, receptacle retractors; 7, testes; 8, cement glands; 9, Saefftigen's pouch; 10, muscular cap of bursa; 11, bursa.

the male proboscis and spination (Fig. 21*F*) differ markedly from those of the female. The best known species is *F. anatis*, common in ducks and other birds, with fresh-water isopods as intermediate hosts (Szidat, 1931). *Corynosoma* (Van Cleave, 1945c) in water birds and seals and other marine mammals is characterized by: anterior hooks and posterior spines on the proboscis, swollen spiny foretrunk with posterior extension of the ventral spines (Fig. 3*A*), genital spines (Fig. 4*D*), and introversible posterior end (genital vestibule, Van Cleave, 1945d). The best known species are *C. strumosum* (Fig. 22*D*) and *C. semerne* in seals and marine birds with amphipods as primary and fishes as transport and reservoir hosts, and *C. constrictum* in aquatic birds. *Bolbosoma* in marine mammals is notable for the bulbous spiny foretrunk (Fig. 3*D*). *Arhythmorhynchus* (Van Cleave, 1916b) is characterized by the fusiform proboscis usually with enlarged mid-ventral hooks (Fig. 8*B*), the spiny foretrunk with nucleated epidermis, and the slender spineless hindtrunk devoid of epidermal nuclei (Fig. 4*C*). Encysted juveniles of *A. roseus* have been found in fresh-water shrimp (*Palaemon squilla*, Porta, 1905) with fish as transport hosts.

The remaining genera of the Polymorphidae lack trunk spination and therefore are usually separated into other subfamilies. In *Centrorhynchus* with many species in birds, especially birds of prey, the proboscis armature is divided by the attachment of the receptacle into an anterior hooked region and a posterior spiny one (Fig. 8*C*). The primary intermediate host for this genus appears to be unknown but frogs, lizards, and snakes act as transport hosts. In *Prosthorhynchus*, also in birds, the receptacle attaches to the proboscis base and the proboscis armature gradually diminishes in size from tip to base.

The Echinorhynchidae, parasitic in fishes, are characterized by the lack of trunk spination, moderately long proboscis armed with rooted hooks decreasing in size basally, double-walled proboscis receptacle, and fragmented epidermal nuclei. The principal genera, *Acanthocephalus* (Figs. 2*B*, 7, 9*A*) and *Echinorhynchus*, include some of the most common acanthocephalans of fishes. The two genera differ only in the longer proboscis and more anterior position of the brain in *Echinorhynchus*. *Acanthocephalus lucii* and *anguillae* are common in European fishes, especially fresh-water ones; both pass their larval stages in isopods of the genus *Asellus* (Leuckart, 1876; Nybelin, 1923). Several species of *Acanthocephalus* occur in toads, frogs, and salamanders; of these, *A. ranae* (Fig. 23*A*), also employing *Asellus* as intermediate host (Kaiser, 1893), is the most common (Van Cleave, 1915). *Echinorhynchus* species common in fishes are *clavula, gadi, salmonis, coregoni,* and *truttae*. Several species of marine amphipods act as intermediate hosts for *E. gadi* (Nybelin, 1923); *Gammarus* serves for *E. clavula* and *truttae* (Nybelin, 1923; Scheer,

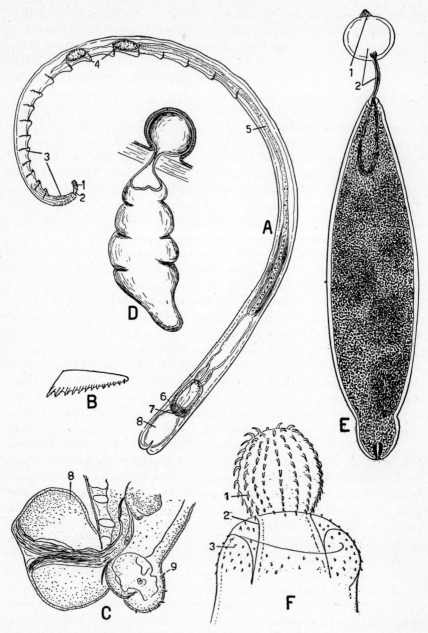

FIG. 21.—Rhadinorhynchidae, Gorgorhynchidae, Polymorphidae. *A. Serrasentis sagittifer* (*from slide, courtesy H. J. Van Cleave*). *B.* Spine row of the same, enlarged. *C.* Rear end of *Telosentis* with everted bursa, showing also genital spines (*after Van Cleave, 1923*). *D. Filicollis anatis* attached in duck intestine (*after de Marvel, 1905*). *E. Filicollis anatis*, ripe female (*from slide, courtesy H. J. Van Cleave*). *F. Filicollis anatis*, anterior end of male (*after Lühe, 1911*). 1, proboscis; 2, neck; 3, trunk spines; 4, testes; 5, cement glands; 6, sphincter; 7, penis; 8, bursa; 9, genital spines.

1934b), and the amphipod *Pontoporea hoyi* is the primary host of *E. coregoni* (Van Cleave, 1920a). Another echinorhynchid genus widely distributed in fresh-water fishes is *Pomphorhynchus*, notable for the bulbous neck swelling. *P. bulbocolli* (Fig. 2*C*) has been repeatedly found in the United States (Van Cleave, 1919; Van Cleave and Mueller, 1934). A European species, *P. proteus*, was the subject of the first elucidation of an acanthocephalan life cycle, by Leuckart (1862), who followed the ingestion of the acanthors and development of the acanthellas in the amphipod *Gammarus*. Various fishes preyed on by larger fishes appear to serve as transport hosts for *Pomphorhynchus* (Hamann, 1891; Linstow, 1892).

15. Order Eoacanthocephala.—This order was proposed by Van Cleave (1936) for certain families that had been included in the two preceding orders by Meyer (1933). The order differs from the Archiacanthocephala in that the proboscis hooks have the quincunxial arrangement, nephridia are wanting, the cement glands are syncytial masses containing giant nuclei and discharging into a cement reservoir, and the hosts are aquatic, nearly always fishes. The families are the Pallisentidae and Quadrigyridae with trunk spines and the Neoechinorhynchidae and Hebesomidae without them. *Pallisentis* (includes *Farzandia*) has circles of spines along part or all of the trunk (Fig. 5*A*), plus a spiny girdle just behind the neck; *Quadrigyrus* lacks the girdle but also has circles of trunk spines (Fig. 23*E, F*).

The Neoechinorhynchidae are an important family of fish parasites, of rather small size, with giant epidermal nuclei. The principal genus *Neoechinorhynchus* is easily recognized by the short globular proboscis with a few circlets of hooks of which the anteriormost hooks are much the largest (Fig. 24*B*). Species of this genus are common in marine and fresh-water fishes and *Neo. emydis* is found in turtles in North America. The life cycle is known for *Neo. rutili*, of which the intermediate host is the aquatic larva of the neuropteroid insect *Sialis* (Villot, 1885), and for *Neo. cylindratus* with ostracods as intermediate and small fish as transport hosts (Ward, 1940). Another genus *Octospinifer*, with the species *macilentus* common in suckers (Van Cleave and Mueller, 1934), is distinguished by the three circles of hooks of eight each (Fig. 23*C*).

16. Ecology and Physiology.—Very little information is available upon these topics. The so-called eggs of the Acanthocephala consist of the acanthor enclosed in two shells and an outer membrane; there may also be an inner membrane surrounding the acanthor. The inner shell is the thickened fertilization membrane; the outer shell arises during embryonic development; and the outer membrane is the original egg membrane. The inner shell appears to be equally developed in the three orders but the outer shell is thick and conspicuous only in forms with terrestrial cycles, i.e., in the order Archiacanthocephala (Figs. 18*A*, 19*D*).

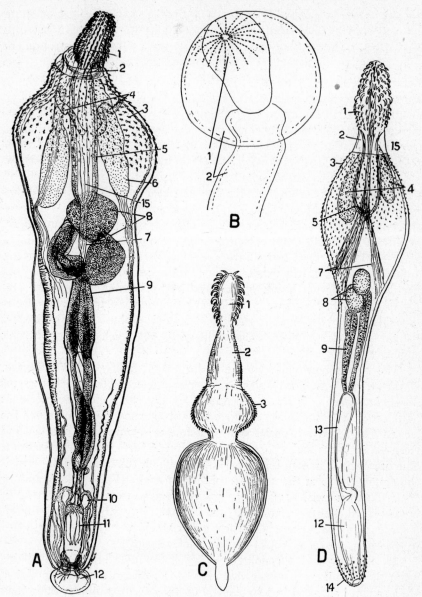

Fig. 22.—Polymorphidae. *A. Polymorphus trochus*, from the coot (*after Van Cleave*, 1945b). *B. Filicollis anatis*, anterior end of female (*after Lühe*, 1911). *C.* Juvenile of *Polymorphus minutus* from *Gammarus* (*after Greeff*, 1864). *D. Corynosoma strumosum* (*from slide, courtesy H. J. Van Cleave*). 1, proboscis; 2, neck; 3, trunk spines; 4, lemnisci; 5, receptacle; 6, neck retractor; 7, receptacle retractor; 8, testes; 9, cement glands; 10, pockets of bursal cap; 11, muscle rays on bursa; 12, bursa; 13, Saefftigen's pouch; 14, genital spines; 15, proboscis retractor.

In the orders with aquatic cycles it is poorly developed and then the inner shell is the most conspicuous of the embryonic envelopes. In forms with aquatic cycles, the "egg" is further of long elliptical shape and the inner shell has a characteristic form, something like a rolling pin (Fig. 19C). The elongated shape is regarded by Meyer (1933) as an adaptation for ingestion by aquatic arthropods. In Acanthocephala with terrestrial intermediate hosts, both embryonic shells are oval and the outer shell is thick, often brown, and granular or striated (Fig. 18A). In *Macr. hirudinaceus*, the membrane that directly encloses the acanthor (making a total of four embryonic coverings in this species) is about as thick as the fertilization membrane and consists of chitin (Brand, 1940). This author also found that the inner shell (fertilization membrane) dissolves in strong alkali, swells in weak alkali, and gives indications of a carbohydrate nature; apparently its swelling properties are responsible for the cracking open of the outer shell. The chemical nature of the latter was not ascertained.

Nothing is known of the precise conditions that bring about the hatching of the acanthors. Although Manter (1928) found that hatching of *Macr. hirudinaceus* and *Mediorhynchus* sp. occurred readily on drying followed by rewetting, this was true only for "eggs" removed from the female worms and did not succeed with those taken from the host's feces. The shells appear to be very resistant to external conditions. Spindler and Kates (1940) planted out "eggs" of *Macr. hirudinaceus* in various soil mixtures with or without pig feces and with varying exposures to sun and shade and found no difference in viability (as tested by feeding to beetle grubs) in the various lots; in some cases viability was retained for $3\frac{1}{2}$ years. Later Kates (1942) reported that the viability of the shelled acanthors (also taken from females) was not affected by temperatures up to 45°C., by continuous freezing either dry or in water at −10 to −16°C. for periods as long as 140 days, or by drying at either low or warm (to 39°C.) temperatures for periods up to 265 days. Alternate wetting and drying on soil proved fatal to the acanthors in about a year at temperatures of 37 to 39°C. but probably would not have damaged naturally laid material.

The number of worms per host is often very large. In experimental infections of beetle grubs with acanthors of *Macr. hirudinaceus*, Kates (1942) recovered as many as 2852 acanthors in one grub but not more than about 400 have been found in natural infections. The number of adult worms in the intestine of the definitive host may also be very large in the case of small species. Thus various authors have published photographs of opened intestines literally covered with acanthocephalans (Fig. 25). Wolffhügel (1900) records up to 1000 *Polymorphus minutus* in the intestine of ducks, Ball (1930) reported 1154 *Corynosoma strumosum* in a

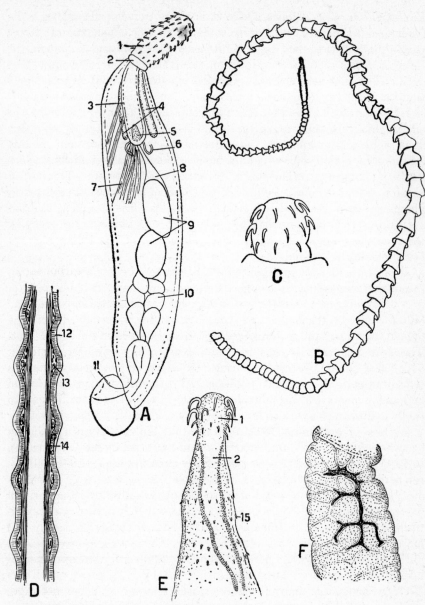

Fig. 23.—Echinorhynchidae, Gigantorhynchidae, Moniliformidae, Quadrigyridae, Neoechinorhynchidae. *A. Acanthocephalus ranae (after Van Cleave,* 1915). *B. Mediorhynchus taeniatus (after Meyer,* 1933). *C. Octospinifer (after Van Cleave,* 1919a). *D.* Part of *Moniliformis,* showing relation of longitudinal muscle layer to the superficial segmentation *(from slide, courtesy H. J. Van Cleave). E. Quadrigyrus. F.* Giant epidermal nucleus of *Quadrigyrus,* showing size relative to the body width; it occupies channels of the lacunar system. *(E, F,* after Van Cleave, 1920b). 1, proboscis; 2, neck; 3, receptacle; 4, lemnisci; 5, ganglion; 6, retinaculum; 7, retractor muscles; 8, ligament sac; 9, testes; 10, cement glands; 11, bursa; 12, epidermis; 13, circular muscles; 14, longitudinal muscles; 15, body spines.

seal, and Perry (1942) found 1482 *Polymorphus altmani* in a marine bird. Larger species naturally occur in smaller numbers; thus Meyer (1933) gives 70 as about the maximum number of *Macr. hirudinaceus* found in pigs.

As in other parasites, the reproductive capacity is high. Kates (1944) reported that gravid females of *Macr. hirudinaceus* contain up to 10,000,-000 shelled acanthors at one time without exhausting their egg-producing potentiality. In this species emission of shelled acanthors begins about 60 to 80 days after infection and continues at an average rate of 260,000 per day for a period of about 10 months. The life of this species therefore seems to last for about a year. Smaller species probably live several months, and may have seasonal cycles. Van Cleave (1916a) reported in the case of two acanthocephalans of fresh-water fish an incidence from October to April in one species, and from May to December in another, whereas *Neoechinorhynchus emydis* in turtles could be found in this host at all times of the year.

Acanthocephalans are undoubtedly among the most injurious of helminth parasites. The proboscis hooks embedded in the intestinal wall are damaging to tissues, especially in mammals, where nodules that persist after elimination of the worm result and where infections may follow the mechanical damage. Whereas massive infections with acanthocephalans have often been reported without apparent detriment to the host, in other cases the presence of the worms is correlated with an unhealthy state of the host. Schwartz (1921) found the pseudocoel fluid of *Macr.* to contain a substance haemolytic to the red blood corpuscles of cattle and pigs.

In regard to immune reactions only the study of Burlingame and Chandler (1941) on *Moniliformis dubius* in rats is available. This worm evokes no immune reactions as rats were as susceptible to the second as to the first infection. Worms developed from a second feeding of acanthors are unable to obtain a foothold in the most favorable site, the anterior part of the intestine, as this is already occupied by worms from the first feeding. Consequently they are forced to attach lower down where the less favorable conditions are evidenced by the slower growth, smaller size, and poorer survival. Starvation of the host for 2 days caused expulsion of many worms.

Experiments on survival in artificial media have been made by Gettier (1942) and Van Cleave and Ross (1944), using *Neoech. emydis*. Survival up to 20 days was obtained in 0.5 per cent NaCl plus a little $CaCl_2$ but in this medium the worms are swollen and turgid, an indication of hypotonicity of the medium. The latter authors found the normal flattened form of this species to be well retained in 0.85 per cent NaCl, a concentration that seems to be isotonic with the body fluids of the worm. The worm is evidently highly permeable to water as the body shape could be readily altered by changes in the osmotic concentration of the medium.

Very little is known of the metabolism of the Acanthocephala. The lacunar system of the epidermis is believed to be related to the necessity in these worms of absorbing food through the surface. The pseudocoel fluid and water extracts of the body of *Macr.* were found to have no lipolytic action, a slow proteolytic action in alkaline medium, and a rapid amylolytic effect (Schwartz, 1921). This last fact is indicative of the

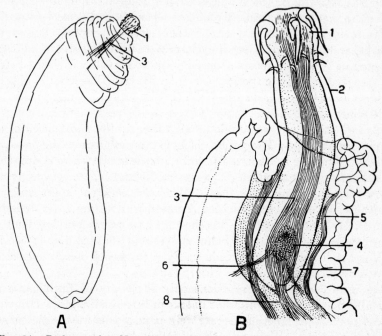

Fig. 24.—Pachysentidae, Neoechinorhynchidae. *A. Oncicola canis (from slide, courtesy H. J. Van Cleave). B. Neoechinorhynchus (after Yamaguti, 1939).* 1, proboscis; 2, neck; 3, proboscis retractor; 4, ganglion; 5, neck retractors; 6, retinaculum; 7, proboscis receptacle; 8, proboscis retractor.

importance of glycogen in the metabolism of these worms. The metabolism appears to be primarily anaerobic since the consumption of glycogen is about the same in the presence or absence of air (Brand, 1940).

Data on the chemical composition have been presented by Mueller (1929), Brand (1939, 1940, 1942), Brand and Saurwein (1942), and Sister Miller (1943); all used *Macr. hirudinaceus.* This worm consists on the average of 88.5 per cent water, 8 per cent protein, 1.13 per cent glycogen, 0.95 per cent lipoid substances, and 0.58 per cent inorganic salts, all reckoned on the basis of fresh weight. In addition to glycogen another polysaccharide that yields galactose on hydrolysis is present. The lipoid substances include phosphatides, lecithin, cholesterol or some other sterol, and saturated and unsaturated fatty acids. The inorganic substances are salts of sodium, potassium, calcium, magnesium, manganese, aluminum, iron, and copper, in the form of phosphates, sulphates, carbonates, and chlorides. The cuticle consists chiefly of a sulphur-containing protein. The glycogen and lipoid content are higher in males than in females. Glycogen is abundant in the inner nuclear mass of acanthors but disappears rapidly after the acanthors hatch, reappearing later. In juveniles and adults, the glycogen is localized mainly in the epidermis, including the lacunar fluid, and in the musculature, not only of the body wall but also of the proboscis apparatus and the reproductive system. The fatty substances are deposited primarily in the epidermis and in the female reproductive system, especially the ovary.

V. PHYLOGENY

Because of the many peculiarities of structure of the Acanthocephala and the parasitic degeneration or alteration of some of their systems, determination of their affinities poses a difficult problem. The various attempts to associate them with other groups for classificatory purposes have already been briefly reviewed at the beginning of this chapter. At the present time there are only two views that need be seriously considered, those associating the Acanthocephala with the Platyhelminthes or with the Aschelminthes. The best way to decide between these two possibilities is to discuss, system by system, the similarities and dissimilarities between the three groups, something that has also been done by Chitwood (1940) and Van Cleave (1941b).

In their general structural plan, that of the pseudocoelomate grade, the acanthocephalans certainly more nearly resemble the aschelminths than they do the platyhelminths. The division of the body into presoma and trunk is not found in the flatworms but is a noticeable feature of certain aschelminths, namely, the priapulids and the gordiacean larva. The structural features of the latter (see page 466) cannot, in the author's opinion, be dismissed as mere larval adaptations. An armed proboscis invaginable or withdrawable into the interior occurs in cestodes and there is certainly considerable resemblance to the proboscides of the Trypanorhyncha as to shape and arrangement of the hooks, method of operation, and associated sheath and muscles. On the other hand, a similar armed proboscis is found among the Aschelminthes in the echinoderids, priapulids, and gordiacean larva. Superficial segmentation is wanting in flatworms but is common in aschelminths, being a conspicuous feature of rotifers, echinoderids, priapulids, and nematodes, and may involve the musculature in some of these groups as in some acanthocephalans. The clothing of the body with cuticle is a common feature of trematodes, cestodes, and aschelminths. According to Mueller (1929), the cuticle of acanthocephalans is practically identical chemically with that of nematodes; but it is probable that the cuticle of all the protostomial Bilateria is chemically similar. In the possession of a syncytial nucleated epidermis the acanthocephalans resemble both the turbellarians and the aschelminths and the epidermis with its numerous spaces and striated appear-

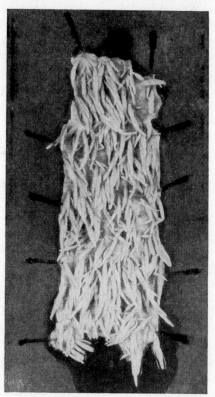

Fig. 25.—Opened intestine of a marine bird showing infestation with *Polymorphus altamani* (*photograph, courtesy Dr. Mary Louise Perry*).

ance suggests the former rather than the latter group. The body-wall musculature of circular and longitudinal layers is distinctly platyhelminthic and differs from conditions in the aschelminths, except the priapulids where the same muscular arrangement obtains. The pseudocoel is a definite feature of the aschelminths, but its manner of formation in the Acanthocephala is peculiar and leaves some doubt as to its comparability with the aschelminth pseudocoel. However, the division of the pseudocoel by partitions and tissues resembling mesenteries is distinctly aschelminthic. As pointed out by Haffner (1942), the ligament sacs resemble the partitions of some gastrotrichs, which divide the body cavity into central and lateral compartments (page 158). The nervous system presents no particular resemblances to that of other phyla but is built on the general protostome pattern of cerebral center and pair of main cords. As noted above, Haffner (1942) considers that the ligament strand represents the greatly reduced digestive tract and he points out that similar reduction of the gut to a strand is seen in male rotifers. Flame-bulb protonephridia occur in both Platyhelminthes and Aschelminthes. The reproductive system seems more suggestive of flatworms than of aschelminths. If the cement glands be taken to correspond to prostatic glands, then the general picture in the male of paired testes and sperm ducts, penis papilla, and muscular antrum (bursa) recalls conditions found in many flatworms. The female system presents less similarity to that of flatworms. A close relationship of nephridial and reproductive systems, such as occurs in Acanthocephala, is wanting in flatworms but is exemplified among the aschelminths in priapulids; in rotifers also both systems enter a common cloaca which according to Haffner's views is represented in the Acanthocephala by the bursa. In the phenomenon of eutely or nuclear constancy, the acanthocephalans are ranged with the aschelminths as no such condition is known among the flatworms.

The embryology is strongly suggestive of that of cestodes. Much was made by Meyer of the resemblance of certain cleavage stages of *Macr. hirudinaceus* to those of rotifers, particularly in the bilateral arrangement of the blastomeres, but a comparison of Figs. 17*D* and 50*D* indicates that the resemblance is rather superficial; further the cleavage of *Neoechinorhynchus* lacks such bilateral patterns, and in the enclosure of a central mass by surface cells resembles the development of cestodes. Other resemblances between acanthocephalan and cestode development are the early separation of the epidermis from the interior mass, the formation of shells, and the eventual production of a larva showing little differentiation except for the six hooks at one end. The main difference between the cestode hexacanth and the acanthor seems to be that the latter retains its epidermis whereas in the former the epidermis becomes one of the larval envelopes. The resemblance of the hooked rostellum of the acanthella stages to that of cestodes is also notable, but it must be recalled that a similar hooked invaginable anterior end is seen in the larval stages of aschelminths, notably the gordioid larva.

The serological tests of Eisenbrandt (1938) indicate a relationship of the Acanthocephala with cestodes rather than with nematodes. However, the technique used cannot be depended upon to yield reliable results. Further the above analysis indicates affinity with echinoderids, priapulids, and gordioids rather than with nematodes.

The foregoing comparisons do not furnish a decisive answer to the question whether the Acanthocephala are allied to the platyhelminths or to the aschelminths.   The general structure is rather on the aschel-minthic side, whereas the embryology presents more points of resemblance with the platyhelminths.   Chitwood (1940) and Van Cleave (1941b) favor a platyhelminth affinity, and on this basis the former has proposed a superphylum Parenchymata to embrace the flatworms, nemertines, and acanthocephalans.   Leaving apart the fact that the Acanthocephala are not parenchymatous animals, one doubts the utility of the superphylum concept.   On present evidence, raising the Acanthocephala to the rank of an independent phylum appears the best disposition of the group.

Bibliography

Ball, G. H.   1930.   Corynosoma strumosum from the harbor seal.   Univ. California Publ. Zool. 33.   **Bieler, W.**   1913.   Kittapparat von Neoechinorhynchus. Zool. Anz. 31.   Zur Kenntnis des männlichen Geschlechtsapparats einiger Acanthocephalen von Fischen.   Zool. Jahrb. Abt. Anat. 36.   1914.   Zur Kenntnis des männlichen Geschlechtsapparats von Corynosoma und Arhythmorhynchus.   Zool. Anz. 43.   **Brand, T. von.**   1939.   Chemical and morphological observations upon the composition of Macr. hirudinaceus.   Jour. Parasitol. 25.   1940.   Further observations upon the composition of Acanthocephala.   Jour. Parasitol. 26.   **Brand, T. von,** and **J. Saurwein.**   1942.   Further studies upon the chemistry of Macr. hirudinaceus.   Jour. Parasitol. 28.   **Brandes, G.**   1899.   Das Nervensystem der als Nemathelminthen zusammengefassten Wurmtypen.   Abhandl. Naturforsch. Gesell. Halle 21.   **Burlingame, P. L.,** and **A. C. Chandler.**   1941.   Host-parasite relations of Moniliformis.   Amer. Jour. Hygiene 33, Sect. D.   **Chandler, A. C.**   1934.   Revision of Rhadinorhynchus.   Parasitology 26.   1941.   Review of the species of Moniliformis in the western hemisphere.   Jour. Parasitol. 27.   **Chitwood, B. G.**   1940. Nemic relationships.   Chap. XIII, *An introduction to nematology*, Sect. I, Pt. 3. **Eisenbrandt, L.**   1938.   Serological relationships of some helminths.   Amer. Jour. Hygiene 27.   **Gettier, D.**   1942.   Saline requirements of Neoechin. emydis.   Proc. Helminthol. Soc. Washington 9.   **Glasgow, R.**   1926.   New intermediary insect host records for the giant thorny-headed worm of swine.   Ann. Entomol. Soc. America 19, 20.   **Graybill, H.**   1902.   Points in the structure of the Acanthocephala.   Trans. Amer. Micro. Soc. 23.   **Greeff, R.**   1864.   Bau und Naturgeschichte von [Polymorphus minutus].   Arch. Naturgesch. 30, Abt. 1.   **Haffner, K. v.**   1942.   Untersuchungen über das Urogenitalsystem der Acanthocephalen.   Teil I–III.   Ztschr. Morphol. Ökol. Tiere 38.   **Hamann, O.**   1891.   Monographie der Acanthocephalen. Jena. Ztschr. Naturwiss. 25.   **Harada, I.**   1931.   Nervensystem von Bolbosoma. Jap. Jour. Zool. 3.   **Johnston, T. H.,** and **E. W. Deland.**   1929.   Australian Acanthocephala, No. 2.   Trans. Roy. Soc. South Australia 53.   **Kaiser, J. E.**   1893.   Die Acanthocephalen und ihre Entwickelung.   Bibliotheca Zoologica 2, Heft 7.   1913. *Die Acanthocephala und ihre Entwickelung.*   **Kates, K. C.**   1942.   Viability of eggs of Macr. hirudinaceous.   Jour. Agricult. Research 64.   1943.   Development of Macr. hirudinaceous in its intermediate host.   Amer. Jour. Veterinary Research 4.   1944. Observations on experimental infections of pigs with Macr.   Amer. Jour. Veterinary Research 5.   **Kaupp, B. F.**   1909.   Echinorhynchus canis.   Amer. Veterinary Rev. 35.   **Kilian, R.**   1932.   Zur Morphologie und Systematik der Gigantorhynchidae. Ztschr. Wiss. Zool. 141.   **Leuckart, R.**   1862.   Helminthologische Experimentaluntersuchungen III.   Nachrichten August. Univ. Gesell. Wiss. Göttingen, No. 22. 1876. *Die menschlichen Parasiten,* Bd. II.   **Linstow, O. von.**   1892.   Beobach-

tungen an Helminthenlarven. Arch. Mikro. Anat. 39. **Linton, E.** 1890, 1891.
Notes on Entozoa of marine fishes. Rept. U.S. Comm. Fisheries for 1888, 1889.
Lühe, M. 1911. Acanthocephalen. *Die Süsswasserfauna Deutschlands*, Heft 16.
1912. Zur kenntnis der Acanthocephalen. Zool. Jahrb. Suppl. 15. **Luther, A.** 1904.
Larva of Polymorphus minutus in Gammarus. Meddel. Soc. Fauna Flora Fennica 31.
Manter, H. W. 1928. Notes on the eggs and larvae of the thorny-headed worm of
hogs. Trans. Amer. Micro. Soc. 47. **Marvel, L. de.** 1905. Monographie des
Acanthocyphales d'oiseuax. Rev. Suisse Zool. 13. **Meyer, A.** 1928. Die Furchung
nebst Eibildung, Reifung, und Befruchtung des Marc. Zool. Jahrb. Abt. Anat. 50.
1931a. Das Hautgefcssystem von Neoechinorhynchus. Arch. Zellforsch. Mikro.
Anat. 14. 1931b. Neue Acanthocephalen aus dem Berliner Museum. Zool.
Jahrb. Abt. System. 62. 1931c. Urhautzelle, Hautbahn, und plasmodiale Entwick-
lung der Larve von Neoechinorhynchus. Zool. Jahrb. Abt. Anat. 53. 1931d. Das
Urogenitale Organ von Oligacanthorhynchus. Ztschr. Wiss. Zool. 138. 1933.
Acanthocephala. In **H. G. Bronn** (ed.), *Klassen und Ordnungen des Tierreichs*, Bd. 4,
Abt. 2, Buch 2. 1936–1938. Die plasmodiale Entwicklung und Formbildung des
Riesenkratzers. Zool. Jahrb. Abt. Anat. 62, 63, 64. **Miller, Sister Mary.** 1943.
Developmental stages and glycogen metabolism of Macr. in the Japanese beetle larva.
Jour. Morphol. 73. **Moore, D. V.** 1946a. Life history and development of Monili-
formis. Jour. Parasitol. 32. 1946b. Life history and development of Macr. ingens.
Jour. Parasitol. 32. **Mueller, J. F.** 1929. Cuticle of Macr. hirudinaceus. Ztschr.
Zellforsch. Mikro. Anat. 8. **Nybelin, O.** 1923. Zur postembryonalen Entwick-
lungsgeschichte der Acanthocephalen. Zool. Anz. 58. **Parker, J. W.** 1909. Oncicola
canis. Amer. Veterinary Rev. 35. **Parona, C.** 1893. Sopra una straordinaria
polielmintiasi da echinorinco. Atti. Soc. Ligustica Sci. Natur. Genova 4, vol. 4.
Perry, Mary. 1942. New species of Filicollis. Jour. Parasitol. 28. **Porta, A.**
1905. Gli echinorhynchi dei pesci. Arch. Zool. Ital. 2. 1909. Gli Acantocefali dei
Mammiferi. Arch. Zool. Ital. 4. **Reinhard, E. G.** 1944. Hermit crab as intermediate host of Polymorphus. Jour. Parasitol. 30. **Saefftigen. A.** 1885. Zur Organisation der Echinorhynchen. Morph. Jahrb. 10. **Scheer, D.** 1934a. Gammarus
und Caricogammarus als Zwischenwert von Polymorphus minutes. Ztschr.
Parasitenk. 7. 1934b. Die Jugendform des Echinorhynchus truttae. Ztschr.
Parasitenk. 7. **Schneider, A.** 1871. Entwicklung von Echinorhynchus gigas. Sitzungsber. Oberhess. Gesell. Natur. und Heilk. **Schwartz, B.** 1921. Active sub-
stances in Macr. Jour. Parasitol. 7. **Spindler, C. A.,** and **K. C. Kates.** 1940.
Survival on soil of eggs of Macr. Jour. Parasitol. 26, Suppl. **Stiles, C. W.,** and
A. Hassall. 1920. Index-catalogue of medical and veterinary zoology. U.S. Public
Health Service, Hygienic Lab. Bull. 114. **Szidat, L.** 1931. Entwicklungsgeschichte
und Biologie von Filicollis anatis. Arch. Geflügelk. 5. **Thapar, G. S.** 1927. On
Acanthogyrus. Jour. Helminthol. 5. 1930. Farzandia ophiocephali. Ann. Mag.
Natur. Hist. ser. 10, vol. 6. **Travassos, L.** 1917. Fam. Gigantorhynchidae. Mem.
Inst. Oswaldo Cruz 9. **Van Cleave, H. J.** 1914. Studies on cell constancy. Jour.
Morphol. 25. 1915. Acanthocephali in North American Amphibia. Jour. Parasi-
tol. 1. 1916a. Seasonal distribution of some Acanthocephala. Jour. Parasitol. 2.
1916b. Revision of the genus Arhythmorhynchus. Jour. Parasitol. 2. 1918.
Acanthocephala of North American birds. Trans. Amer. Micro. Soc. 37. 1919a.
Acanthocephala from the Illinois River. Bull. Illinois State Lab. Natur. Hist. 13,
art. 8. 1919b. Acanthocephala from fishes of Douglas Lake, Michigan. Occasion.
Papers Mus. Zool. Univ. Michigan No. 72. 1920a. Notes on the life cycle of two
Acanthocephala. Jour. Parasitol. 6. 1920b. Acanthocephalan worms from Vene-
zuelan fishes. Proc. U.S. Nation. Mus. 58. 1920c. Acanthocephala parasitic in the

dog. Jour. Parasitol. 7. 1923. Telosentis. Jour. Parasitol. 9. 1925. Acanthocephala described by Joseph Leidy. Proc. Acad. Natur. Sci. Philadelphia 76. 1928.
Nuclei of the subcuticula in the Acanthocephala. Ztschr. Zellforsch. Mikro. Anat. 7.
1935. Larval stages of Acanthocephala. Jour. Parasitol. 21. 1936. Recognition of
a new order in the Acanthocephala. Jour. Parasitol. 22. 1914a. Hook patterns in
the Acanthocephala. Quart. Rev. Biol. 16. 1941b. Relationships of the Acanthocephala. Amer. Natural. 75. 1945a. Status of the genus Arhythmorhynchus.
Trans. Amer. Micro. Soc. 64. 1945b. New species of Polymorphus from the American coot. Jour. Parasitol. 31. 1945c. Genus Corynosoma. Jour. Parasitol. 31.
1945d. Genital vestibule and its significance in the morphology and taxonomy of the
Acanthocephala. Jour. Morphol. 77. 1945e. New species of Illiosentis. Jour.
Parasitol. 31. 1947. Critical review of terminolgoy for immature stages in acanthocephalan life histories. Jour. Parasitol. 33. 1948. Expanding horizons in the recognition of a phylum. Jour. Parasitol. 34. **Van Cleave, H. J.,** and **D. Lincicome.**
1939. New genus of Rhadinorhynchidae. Parasitology 37. **Van Cleave, H. J.,** and
J. F. Mueller. 1934. Parasites of Oneida Lake fishes. Pt. III. Roosevelt Wild
Life Annals 3, Nos. 3 and 4. **Van Cleave, H. J.,** and **Elizabeth Ross.** 1944. Physiological responses of Neoechinorhynchus emydis to various solutions. Jour. Parasitol.
30. **Van Cleave, H. J.,** and **W. C. Starrett.** 1940. Acanthocephala of wild ducks in
central Illinois. Trans. Amer. Micro. Soc. 59. **Villot, A.** 1885. Sur l'état larvaire
et l'hôte intermediaire de Neoechinorhynchus rutili. Zool. Anz. 8. **Ward, Helen.**
1940. Studies on the life history of Neoechinorhynchus cylindratus. Trans. Amer.
Micro. Soc. 59. 1943. Redescription of Polymorphos obtusus. Jour. Parasitol. 29.
Wolffhügel, K. 1900. Beitrag zur Kenntnis der Vogelhelminthen. Thesis, Basel.
Yamaguti, S. 1935, 1939. Studies on the helminth fauna of Japan. Pt. 8. Acanthocephala I. Pt. 29. Acanthocephala II. Jap. Jour. Zool. 6, 8.

CHAPTER XIII

THE PSEUDOCOELOMATE BILATERIA—PHYLUM ASCHELMINTHES

I. HISTORICAL

The groups that comprise this phylum have had the usual varied history. In general they fell under the categories Intestina and Infusoria in Linnaeus's class Vermes and Intestinaux or Entozoa and Infusoires in Cuvier's Radiata or Zoophyta. Cuvier made a step in the right direction when he divided the Intestinaux into the hollow roundworms (Intestinaux cavitaires) and the solid flatworms (Intestinaux parenchymatoux) although he had no precise idea of the limitations of these groups. Rudolphi (1808) with remarkable perspicacity, distinguished clearly the various types of parasitic worms or Entozoa, which he recognized as an artificial assemblage, and correctly delimited the groups Nematoidea, Acanthocephala, Trematoda, and Cestoidea, creating these names. It was not until 1851, however, that progress was made toward a more natural grouping of the parasitic worms. At that time, Carl Vogt united the flatworms and nemertines under the name Platyelmia, and the gregarines, acanthocephalans, nematodes, and gordiaceans under the name Nematelmia. Gegenbaur in 1859 altered the latter to Nemathelminthes and improved it by removing the gregarines. Although he later also removed the Acanthocephala, making them a separate group under Vermes, the association of nematodes, acanthocephalans, and gordiaceans under the phylum Nemathelminthes has continued extant in textbooks to the present time. Schneider in 1864 added the Chaetognatha to the Nemathelminthes, on the basis of resemblances in the muscular system, and also included most annelids. Haeckel (1868) limited the Nemathelminthes to the chaetognaths, nematodes, and acanthocephalans, and this arrangement is not infrequently seen in textbooks, although there is not the least justification for uniting chaetognaths with nematodes, and as early as 1875 T. H. Huxley understood that the chaetognaths are coelomate animals allied to echinoderms. The dissimilarities between *Gordius* and nematodes were recognized by von Siebold in 1843, and the former made the basis of the order Gordiacea that unfortunately also included the nematode *Mermis*. It remained for Vejdovsky (1866) to delimit adequately the gordiaceans from the nematodes and hence his name, Nematomorpha, for the former group is preferred. The Nematomorpha are usually placed under the phylum Nemathelminthes.

The rotifers were classified as Infusoria even long after they had been recognized as a more or less distinct group. Ehrenberg (1838) is usually credited with having separated the rotifers from the Protozoa under the name Rotatoria, but in fact the rotifers under the name Rotifera had been considered a natural group of animals years before this time, especially by Dutrochet (1812), and hence we prefer the name Rotifera. After Ehrenberg's classical work, the rotifers were variously placed taxonomically, often as a group under the phylum Vermes, at times allied to bryozoans, annelids, and arthropods. The Gastrotricha were considered to be rotifers until separated from the latter by Metschnikoff (1864) under the name Gastrotricha, and Zelinka in 1889 then suggested that the two groups be included under the phylum Trochelminthes, an arrangement now generally in use. The animal *Echinoderes*, discovered in 1851, at first considered allied to arthropods or annelids, later to nematodes, was placed in the separate class Kinorhyncha by Reinhard in 1887.

The taxonomic disposition of the groups here under consideration—Rotifera, Gastrotricha, Kinorhyncha, Nematoda, and Nematomorpha—has always been troublesome to zoologists. The usual method of dividing these groups between the phyla Trochelminthes and Nemathelminthes does not commend itself because of the difficulty of deciding on available evidence which of these groups belong together and which do not. Thus the gastrotrichs appear more closely allied to nematodes than they do to rotifers. The alternatives in regard to these groups would seem to be to elevate each to the rank of a separate phylum, or to associate them loosely as classes under one phylum. Those who prefer the first alternative should not hesitate to adopt it. The second alternative is here accepted because there are evidences, which will be presented in due course, of relationships between the five groups. The phylum name Nemathelminthes will probably be preferred by many zoologists for these five classes simply because it is a familiar name; but this name has been used in the past to cover so many and so varied assemblages that the author prefers the name Aschelminthes (Greek, *ascos*, cavity, *helminth*, worm) proposed by Grobben in 1910. Grobben had previously suggested the name Coelhelminthes, meaning hollow worms, but dropped this on finding it had been used before in other senses.

We thus adopt the conception of a phylum Aschelminthes (or Nemathelminthes for those who wish to retain the old name) comprising the classes Rotifera, Gastrotricha, Kinorhyncha, Nematoda, and Nematomorpha; and grounds have become evident for the inclusion of the Priapulida, another problematical group, between the Kinorhyncha and Nematoda. It is frankly admitted that the relationship between these six groups is looser than is the case with the classes of most other phyla. But the evidences of relationship are so concrete and so specific that in the author's opinion they cannot be disregarded.

II. CHARACTERS OF THE PHYLUM

1. Definition.—The Aschelminthes are pseudocoelomate, mostly vermiform Bilateria with an unsegmented or superficially segmented body clothed with a cuticle and with a straight or sometimes curved digestive tube lacking a definite muscular wall (except Priapulida) and terminating in an anus located at or near the posterior end or at least well posterior to the mouth.

2. General Characters.—The Aschelminthes are mostly of minute to small size although some reach considerable to great lengths. The body is usually vermiform, often markedly so, cylindroid or flattened, without definitely delimited head, and is clothed in a tough resistant cuticle, not infrequently ringed, and often developed into spines, scales, plates, bristles, etc. The cuticle is subject to molt in nematodes and kinorhynchs during growth and in priapulids throughout life. Beneath the cuticle is found a syncytial or cellular epidermis underlain by muscle fibers not arranged in regular circular and longitudinal layers except in priapulids. The nervous system consists of an anterior brain mass or of a circumenteric nerve ring and from these nerves extend, including main ventral or lateral ones. Between the body wall and the digestive tract lies a cavity, known to be a pseudocoel except in priapulids where its nature is unknown. The digestive tract is a straight, sometimes curved, epithelial tube that may be covered with a net of muscle fibers but lacks a definite muscle layer except in Priapulida; its two ends are of stomodaeal and proctodaeal nature. There is commonly present a highly differentiated pharynx. Respiratory and circulatory systems are absent but typical protonephridia occur in rotifers, gastrotrichs, kinorhynchs, and priapulids. Excretory canals and also gonoducts may open into the rear part of the digestive tube that then constitutes a cloaca. The sexes are nearly always separate, and the reproductive system is relatively simple. The cleavage is generally of the determinate type, and the life cycle may be simple or complicated. Cell or nuclear constancy prevails throughout the phylum. The Aschelminthes are predominantly aquatic animals, inhabiting both fresh and salt waters but many nematodes occupy terrestrial habitats. The phylum includes free-living, epizoic, and parasitic members.

III. CLASSIFICATION OF THE PHYLUM

Class I. Rotifera. Aquatic microscopic Aschelminthes with the anterior end modified into a ciliary organ, the corona; pharynx provided with internal jaws; with a pair of flame-bulb protonephridia. About 1500 known species.

Order 1. Seisonacea or Seisonidea. Epizoic marine rotifers of very elongated form with long neck region; corona slightly developed; mastax fulcrate; sexes of similar size and morphology; gonads paired; ovaries without vitellaria.

Order 2. Bdelloidea. Swimming or creeping rotifers with retractile anterior end; corona with two trochal disks or reduced from this condition; mastax ramate; with two germovitellaria; males wanting; with more than two pedal glands, foot often with spurs and more than two toes.

Order 3. Monogononta. Swimming or sessile rotifers with one germovitellarium; males more or less reduced with one testis; mastax not ramate.

Suborder 1. Ploima. Swimming rotifers with normal corona; foot when present with two toes and two pedal glands.

Superfamily 1. Notommatoidea. Trophi virgate, cardate, or forcipate.

Superfamily 2. Brachionoidea. Trophi malleate; usually broad, flattened, heavily loricate forms.

Superfamily 3. Asplanchnoidea. Sacciform pelagic forms with incudate trophi; foot absent or ventrally displaced.

Suborder 2. Flosculariacea. Sessile or swimming rotifers; corona often circular or lobed, provided with trochal and cingular circlets; trophi malleoramate; foot without toes; males greatly reduced.

Suborder 3. Collothecacea. Sessile rotifers with anterior end in the form of an expanded simple or lobed funnel, devoid of definite ciliary circlets but often provided with motionless bristles; trophi mostly uncinate; males greatly reduced; foot without toes.

Class II. Gastrotricha. Aquatic microscopic Aschelminthes without corona; cilia present on limited areas; cuticle unsegmented, often with spines, scales, plates, etc.; with two to many adhesive tubes; pharynx of the nematode type, without trophi. About 1500 known species.

Order 1. Macrodasyoidea. Marine, with a number of adhesive tubes along the body; without protonephridia; hermaphroditic.

Order 2. Chaetonotoidea. Mostly fresh-water, a few marine species; adhesive tubes limited to the posterior end, two or four in number; with a pair of one-bulbed protonephridia; occur only as parthenogenetic females.

Class III. Kinorhyncha or Echinodera. Microscopic marine Aschelminthes, devoid of cilia, more or less spiny; superficially segmented into 13, sometimes 14, segments; spiny anterior end invaginable into the following segments that form a lid of two or more plates over it; with a pair of protonephridia; dioecious. About 100 known species.

Class IV. Priapulida. Marine animals of moderate size and warty appearance; body divisible into anterior proboscis introversible into the interior and ringed trunk; anus terminal separated in both sexes from the two urogenital pores; dioecious; with solenocytic protonephridia sharing a common duct with the gonads. Three species.

Class V. Nematoda. Aquatic, terrestrial, or parasitic vermiform Aschelminthes; body generally cylindrical, circular in cross section; cuticle smooth or ringed, often with bristles, devoid of cilia; epidermis with four or more longitudinal chords; subepidermal musculature of longitudinal fibers only, arranged in longitudinal fields between the epidermal chords; brain in the form of a circumenteric ring with attached ganglia; pharynx long, of triradiate structure; excretory system not protonephridial, composed of one or two gland cells or of canals or of both; mostly dioecious, also parthenogenetic or hermaphroditic; gonads single or double, tubular; male duct enters the rectum, female duct has own external opening (one exception).

The classification is difficult but considerable agreement and stability have been reached in recent years, chiefly through studies on free-living nematodes. Students of parasitic nematodes had little or no knowledge of or interest in free-living members and their taxonomic schemes therefore lacked general applicability. Homage is due to the great Russian nematodologist, Filipjev, for leading the way toward a satisfactory classification of the nematodes. Present differences of opinion concern chiefly the rank assigned the various groups. What are here called orders are often regarded as superfamilies; and when they are raised to ordinal rank, the ending *oidea* is often altered to *ida* or *ata*.

In 1934 Filipjev reported that by 1930, 4601 species of nematodes had been described, about equally divided between the free-living and parasitic forms. Some counts made by the author in the *Zoological Record* indicate about 200 descriptions of new species of nematodes annually since Filipjev's count, so that by 1950 some 9000 nematode species will have been named. But clearly this is only a minute fraction of the existing species. It was long ago pointed out by Cobb that every vertebrate is infested with at least one and usually with more than one kind of nematode and as there are some 45,000 species of vertebrates, it is clear that at least 100,000 nematode parasites of vertebrates must exist. To these must be added the phytoparasitic forms and those parasitizing invertebrates, chiefly mollusks, crustaceans, insects, centipedes, and millipedes. Formidable as is this array of parasitic nematodes, the figures become still more incredible when it is considered that the free-living nematodes far outnumber in species the parasitic ones, according to the opinion of students of the former. It therefore seems reasonable to suppose that there are at least 500,000 species of nematodes in the world.

The first seven orders given below are mostly free-living and have the following common characteristics: relatively small size, except mermithids; conspicuous sensory bristles or papillae or both on the anterior end in definite circlets; relatively large amphids; and caudal adhesive glands. Orders 2 and 3 are often placed under order 1.

Order 1. Enoploidea. Cuticle not ringed, often with bristles; anterior end with six labial papillae, 10 or 12 bristles in one or two circlets, a pair of cephalic slits, and cyathiform amphids.

Order 2. Dorylaimoidea. Cuticle smooth, without bristles; anterior end with two circlets of papillae of 6 and 10 each; buccal cavity armed with a protrusible spear; amphids cyathiform; rear part of pharynx enlarged.

Order 3. Mermithoidea. Smooth filiform nematodes parasitic in invertebrates, chiefly insects, in juvenile stages, usually free-living in soil or water as adults; head sense organs reduced to papillae, usually 16; amphids cyathiform or reduced; pharynx long and tenuous accompanied by stichocytes, blind; intestine also blind, altered into a food-storing organ.

Order 4. Chromadoroidea. Aquatic nematodes with smooth or ringed cuticle, usually heavily ornamented with bristles, knobs, punctations, etc.; pharynx with a posterior bulb; amphids spiral or derivable from a spiral.

Order 5. Araeolaimoidea. Cuticle smooth, sometimes with bristles; with labial papillae; anterior end usually with four cephalic bristles; amphids spiral or loop-like.

Order 6. Monhysteroidea. Cuticle smooth or slightly ringed, often bristly; anterior end with four, six, or eight bristles, or multiples thereof; amphids circular.

Order 7. Desmoscolecoidea. Cuticle heavily ringed, with prominent bristles throughout or in restricted areas; anterior end with four bristles; amphids crescentic; marine.

Order 8.   Rhabditoidea or Anguilluloidea.   Free-living or parasitic nematodes with ringed or smooth cuticle; pharynx with posterior bulb and also usually with swelling anterior to the nerve ring; amphids small pockets; caudal glands absent.

Order 9.   Rhabdiasoidea.   Smooth nematodes without definite pharyngeal bulb; parasitic stage in animals hermaphroditic or partheno-genetic; free-living stages may develop into males and females.

The remaining eight orders are parasites of animals in the adult stage; they are generally of larger size than the free-living nematodes and usually lack sensory bristles and caudal glands; the amphids are present but very reduced and inconspicuous.

Order 10.   Oxyuroidea.   Pharynx with a posterior bulb, usually valvulated; females with a long pointed tail; terminal parts of female system often heavily muscularized; males with one spicule or two equal spicules; usually with caudal alae forming a cuticular bursa.

Order 11.   Ascaroidea.   Mouth surrounded by three prominent lips; pharynx without a posterior bulb or if this is present it is not valvu-lated; pharynx or intestine or both often with caeca; buccal capsule wanting; tail of female blunt; males usually without caudal alae and with two equal or nearly equal spicules.

Order 12.   Strongyloidea.   Mouth without conspicuous lips but often with leaf crowns; pharynx without bulb; females usually with ovejectors; males with a copulatory bursa supported by muscular rays, typically 13 in number.

Order 13.   Spiruroidea.   Mouth usually with two lateral lips, sometimes four or six small ones; often with interlabia acting as shields; pharynx without bulb, anteriorly muscular, posteriorly glandular; males without a bursa; spicules unequal and dissimilar.

Order 14.   Dracunculoidea.   Without definite lips or cuticularized buccal capsule; pharynx as in Spiruroidea; vulva near or behind the body middle, usually not functional; males with equal filiform spicules; bursa wanting.

Order 15.   Filarioidea.   Filiform worms without lips; buccal cap-sule small or rudimentary; no pharyngeal bulb; pharynx as in Spiruroidea; vulva anterior; bursa wanting; spicules as in Spiruroidea.

Order 16.   Trichuroidea or Trichinelloidea.   Body filiform ante-riorly; mouth without lips; pharynx slender, provided with a stichosome; males without copulatory apparatus or with a cirrus, provided or not with one spicule.

Order 17.   Dioctophymoidea.   Moderate to very long nematodes; mouth without lips surrounded by 6, 12, or 18 papillae; pharynx elon-gated, without bulb; males with a muscular bursa without rays.

Class VI. Nematomorpha or Gordiacea. Very long, slender, cylindrical worms without cuticular ringing; lateral epidermal chords wanting; nervous system, closely related to the epidermis, consists of brain and a mid-ventral cord; without differentiated pharynx; ends of digestive tube tend to degenerate in adults; dioecious; gonoducts in both sexes enter the intestine; parasitic as juveniles, adults free-living.

Order 1. Gordioidea. Fresh-water forms, with parasitic stage in terrestrial or aquatic arthropods; cuticle without natatory bristles; subcuticular muscle sheath interrupted only ventrally; pseudocoel much reduced by mesenchymal tissue.

Order 2. Nectonematoidea. Marine, with parasitic stage in Crustacea; with a double row of natatory bristles; muscle sheath interrupted both dorsally and ventrally; pseudocoel not reduced.

IV. CLASS ROTIFERA

1. Historical.—Following the invention of the microscope, rotifers were seen, described, and figured by the early microscopists, notably Leeuwenhoek, but were not distinguished from Protozoa. In those days all microscopic animals were called Infusoria. Leeuwenhoek thought the mastax was a heart and that the trochal disks of the Bdelloidea were actually rotating wheels. Linnaeus listed a few rotifers under zoophytes in the 10th edition of his *Systema Naturae* (1758) and Pallas (1776) was familiar with a number of rotifers. In his classical works, *Vermium terrestrium et fluviatilium* (1773) and *Animalculia Infusoria fluviatilia et marina* (1786), O. F. Müller described and figured a number of rotifers but still called them Infusoria, applying this name to a mixture of microscopic animals. Although the common name wheel animal was already in use at the time, its Latin equivalent *Rotifer* appears to have been created by Cuvier in 1798; in the same publication he used the group name Rotifères, placing this under his division Zoophytes. Lamarck (1801) placed the rotifers under the group Polypes as Polypes rotifères and, although he confused them with peritrichous ciliates, he considered them to be structurally intermediate between Protozoa (Polypes amorphes) and coelenterates (Polypes à rayons). Dutrochet (1812, 1813) recognized the Rotifères as a group of animals higher in structure than zoophytes (coelenterates); he was familiar with a number of forms and gave the correct explanation of the apparent "rotating wheels." At about this time Cuvier also distinguished rotifers from protozoans and recognized their higher grade of structure but in his great work *Le Regne animal* (1817) he continued the practice of placing the rotifers under Infusoires. Ehrenberg in his classical work *Die Infusorientierchen als volkommene Organismen* (1838) is usually credited with having achieved the separation of the rotifers from the protozoans under the name Rotatoria, although as just seen this separation had been more or less recognized during the prior 25 years. Ehrenberg still regarded the rotifers as Infusoria but did consider them a distinct class of Infusoria; he, however, had very incorrect ideas as to their anatomy. Dujardin (1841) corrected many of Ehrenberg's erroneous ideas concerning rotifer morphology and Huxley in 1853 and later propounded the idea of some relationship between the vermiform groups provided with protonephridia. He was the first to recognize the phylogenetic importance of protonephridia with flame bulbs. In 1878, the brilliant zoologist Hatschek promulgated his trochophore theory which assigns great phylogenetic significance to the rotifers.   As already remarked, Hatschek was correct in recognizing the trochophore larva and the rotifers as standing at the same grade of structure.

About 1886, a new era in the study of the rotifers was inaugurated by the superior anatomical studies of Zelinka and by the appearance of Hudson and Gosse's *The*

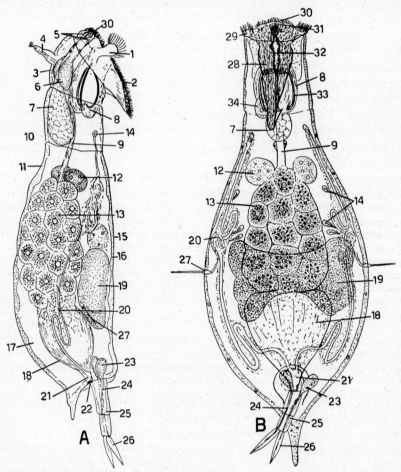

Fig. 26.—*Notommata copeus*, showing general rotifer structure, from life. *A*. Lateral view. *B*. Ventral view. 1, auricle expanded; 2, corona; 3, head joint; 4, dorsal antenna; 5, exits of retrocerebral organ; 6, subcerebral glands; 7, retrocerebral sac; 8, mastax; 9, esophagus; 10, neck joint; 11, trunk; 12, gastric glands; 13, stomach; 14, flame bulb; 15, cuticle; 16, epidermis; 17, pseudocoel; 18, intestine; 19, germovitellarium; 20, protonephridium; 21, junction of protonephridium with intestine; 22, anus; 23, pedal glands; 24, ducts of pedal glands; 25, foot; 26, toes; 27, lateral antennae; 28, buccal field of corona; 29, auricle retracted; 30, circumapical band of corona; 31, apical field; 32, mouth; 33, trophi; 34, salivary gland cell.

Rotifera or Wheel Animalcules, a two-volume work that is essentially a manual of identification. During the next 20 years a number of excellent anatomical and taxonomic studies were published but new ground was first broken by de Beauchamp with his brilliant analysis of the corona (1909), in which he showed that what was regarded as the primitive form of the corona is in fact highly derived. De Beauchamp's exposition of the true form of the primitive corona has been accepted by students of the rotifers but has failed to find its way into the textbooks.

The classification proposed by Hudson and Gosse was widely adopted and has been promulgated in textbooks to the present time. These authors created four orders: Rhizota for the sessile forms, Bdelloidea and Ploima in practically the present sense, and Scirtopoda for *Pedalia;* no provision was made for *Seison.* In 1899, Wesenberg-Lund created the order Seisonacea for *Seison* and united this order with Bdelloidea to form the subclass Digononta with two gonads; the other rotifers with one gonad were placed under the subclass Monogononta with three orders: Notommatida, Brachionida, and Melicertida. Through de Beauchamp's work (1909) on the corona, a better understanding was obtained of the natural relationships within the Monogononta, but a greater improvement was achieved by Harring (1913) who recognized five orders: Ploima, Flosculariacea, Collothecacea, Bdelloida, and Seisonacea. Wesenberg-Lund in the *Handbuch der Zoologie* (1929) took a backward step in splitting the Ploima into three orders and once more refusing a proper place to *Seison.* The system of Harring, however, prevails at present among students of the rotifers and was accepted by Remane (1933) in Bronn, except that the three groups Ploima, Flosculariacea, and Collothecacea were reduced to suborders under the order Monogononta. As there can be little doubt of the correctness of Remane's view, his system is followed in the present work.

The outstanding modern account of the rotifers is that of Remane (1933) in Bronn's *Klassen und Ordnungen des Tierreichs.* Other valuable articles are those of Wesenberg-Lund (1929) in the *Handbuch der Zoologie* and of Lucks (1929) in the *Biologie der Tiere Deutschlands.* Worthy of mention also are the taxonomic studies of Jennings, Harring, and Myers, the experiments of Whitney and Shull on life cycles and male production, and the work of Wesenberg-Lund on male morphology and general ecology.

2. Definition.—The rotifers, or wheel animalcules, are microscopic, mostly free-living Aschelminthes with the anterior end formed into a ciliary apparatus, the corona, or a funnel derivable therefrom, with a differentiated pharynx containing movable pieces acting as jaws, and with typical flame-bulb protonephridia.

3. External Characters.—The rotifers are noteworthy among Metazoa for their minute size; they range from 0.04 to 2 mm. in length and most do not exceed 0.5 mm. They are usually no larger than Protozoa, with which animals they were naturally confused by early microscopists, and yet within these minute limits they possess several complete organ-systems.

The rotifer body is generally of elongated form and is divisible into the broad or narrowed or lobed anterior end, usually provided with a ciliary apparatus, an elongated *trunk,* often enlarged, and a slender terminal region, the *tail* or *foot* (Fig. 26). Variations from the typical elongated form are short stout types, leading to sacciform (*Asplanchna,* Fig. 29D) or even spherical (*Trochosphaera,* Fig. 62C) shapes through reduction or loss of the foot; broad types with wide flattened trunk (*Brachionus,* Fig. 56A, *Euchlanis,* Fig. 57B); and long slender types,

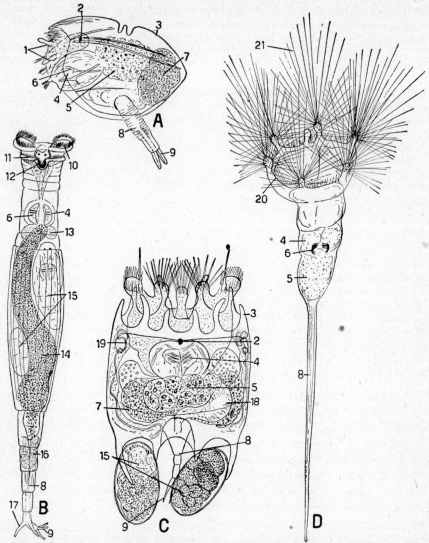

FIG. 27.—Some types of rotifers. *A. Ploesoma truncatum*, a ploimate pelagic rotifer with lorica, palps, and ventrally displaced foot. *B.* A bdelloid rotifer, *Rotaria*, viviparous, with trochal disks, two spurs, and three toes. *C.* A brachionoid rotifer, *Platyias patulus*, with two attached embryos, illustrating flattened shape and spiny lorica. *D.* A sessile rotifer, *Collotheca*, with seven-lobed corona and foot altered into a long stalk. (*All from life.*) 1, palps; 2, eye; 3, lorica; 4, mastax; 5, stomach; 6, trophi; 7, germovitellarium; 8, foot; 9, toes; 10, trochal disks; 11, cingulum; 12, mouth; 13, gastric glands; 14, stomach-intestine; 15, embryos; 16, pedal glands; 17, spurs; 18, intestine; 19, protonephridium; 20, corona; 21, coronal bristles.

through lengthening of the foot (*Rotaria*, Fig. 30*E*), or in the Seisonacea through the interpolation of a longer slender "neck" between head and trunk (Fig. 51*A*). The body is often cylindrical, circular in cross section, but dorsal or ventral or lateral surfaces may be flattened or even concave. Bilateral symmetry obtains throughout the class but asymmetries may occur in some external features, particularly in the toes, and in the family Trichocercidae (= Rattulidae), the body is spirally twisted to the left with consequent reduction or displacement of many structures of the right side (Fig. 29*E*). In many forms the body, although bilateral, is ventrally curved (Fig. 30*A*).

The body is covered with an evident yellowish cuticle that is often ringed throughout or in certain regions, simulating segmentation. The cuticle may be thickened, chiefly on the trunk, to form a hard encasement, the *lorica*, of one to several plates, that may be variously ornamented (Fig. 34).

The anterior end bearing the mouth, corona, and various projections is not definitely delimited as a head but may be called so for convenience. It is typically broad and truncate or slightly convex, presenting an unciliated central region, the *apical field*, encircled by a ciliated zone, the *corona*, the presence of which distinguishes the rotifers from all other metazoans. The apical field may be bare but commonly is provided with several projections, some of which serve as outlets for the ducts of the retrocerebral organ, while others are sensory and bear stiff hairs, bristles, etc. The appearance of the head may be greatly modified by the lobulation of the corona. Especially in sessile types of the orders Flosculariacea and Collothecacea, the corona is scalloped into broad or slender lobes, that may exhibit a radial arrangement (Fig. 27*D*). On the other hand in the bdelloid rotifers, the corona is partially subdivided into retractile *trochal disks* (Fig. 27*B*). The head may also bear a pair of prominent lateral ciliated projections, termed *auricles*, as in *Notommata* (Fig. 26) and *Synchaeta* (Fig. 29*B*); these can be retracted. Characteristic of the bdelloids and many notommatids is a middorsal projection of the head, the *rostrum*, whose tip is provided with cilia and sensory bristles and may be protected by two thin cuticular plates, the *rostral lamellae* (Fig. 29*A*). In bdelloids the rostrum is used as if it were the anterior end, in locomotion by the looping method, with the trochal disks retracted. Eyes (pigment-spot ocelli), appearing as red flecks, occur singly or paired in the brain, as lateral paired eyes in or near the corona, and as paired frontal eyes on the apical field or on the rostrum. The eyes may be elevated on papillae or sunk into depressions. The mouth is located in the corona in the mid-ventral line of the head and often a coronal protrusion serves as lower lip. In the Collothecacea the mouth is at the bottom of the funnel-shaped anterior end resulting from the expansion of the corona.

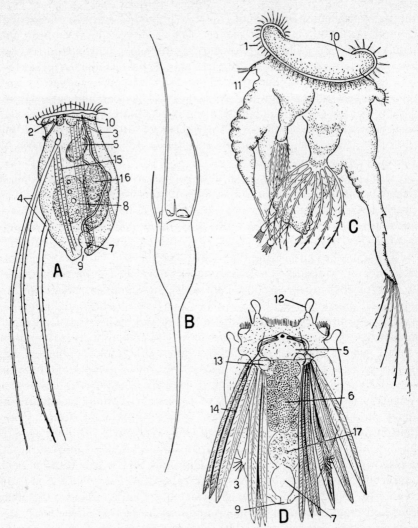

Fig. 28.—Types of rotifers with trunk projections. *A. Filinia longiseta (after Weber, 1898)*, common pelagic rotifer without foot and with three skipping spines. *B. Notholca longispina*, pelagic rotifer with long-spined lorica, from life. *C. Pedalia mira (after Hudson and Gosse, 1886)*, with movable arms tipped with setose bristles. *D. Polyarthra trigla*, from life, footless pelagic rotifer with six pairs of skipping blades. 1, corona; 2, coronal matrix; 3, lateral antenna; 4, skipping spines; 5, mastax; 6, stomach; 7, cloaca; 8, germovitellarium; 9, anus; 10, eye; 11, dorsal antenna; 12, palps; 13, gastric glands; 14, skipping blades; 15, retractor muscles; 16, stomach-intestine; 17, intestine.

The trunk may be cylindrical or variously flattened and broadened and is frequently enclosed in a lorica, often ornamented or spiny. Non-movable lorical spines are characteristic of the genera *Brachionus, Keratella,* and *Notholca* (Figs. 27*C*, 34*C*) of the family Brachionidae and reach great length in *Notholca longispina* (Fig. 28*B*), a common pelagic rotifer. Long movable spines used in producing a skipping motion (Fig. 28*A*) occur in the Filiniidae; and in *Polyarthra,* belonging to the Synchaetidae, there are six skipping blades on each side (Fig. 28*D*). Such movable projections reach a climax in the curious genus *Pedalia* (Fig. 28*C*) where they are body extensions tipped with setose bristles. Cuticular tubercles and spines also occur in bdelloids, especially those of mosses and of polar regions that are subject to desiccation and freezing (Fig. 52*A, B*).

Characteristic trunk structures of rotifers are the *dorsal* and *lateral antennae* or *palps.* The dorsal antenna, usually single, sometimes and probably originally paired, is commonly situated in the middorsal line of the anterior end of the trunk (Fig. 26*A*) and when well developed is a finger-like projection tipped with sensory hairs. From this condition it varies to a bristly tuft or single bristle. The similar lateral antennae, lacking in the Bdelloidea and Seisonacea, are situated on either side of the posterior part of the trunk (Fig. 26*B*), more anteriorly in many sessile types (Fig. 33*C*).

The anus is found in the middorsal line at or near the boundary of trunk and foot, is elevated on a papilla in the Flosculariacea, and in the Notommatidae is often overhung by a caudal projection (Fig. 26*A*).

The body may taper gradually into the foot or the foot may be sharply set off from the stout trunk as a short or long cylindrical tail-like region. Its cuticle is commonly ringed into a few to many joints (Fig. 56*A*). It serves for clinging to objects in creeping types and is then in line with the general body axis; or acts as a rudder in swimming types in which it is often displaced ventrally as a short appendage to the stout trunk (Fig. 27*A*). In sessile forms, the foot is modified to a long stalk (Fig. 64). The foot is reduced or absent in a number of forms, especially those that have adopted a wholly pelagic life (Fig. 28*A, D*). The foot may terminate in an adhesive disk as in the Seisonacea or form a simple flat surface for attachment as in sessile types but commonly is provided at or near its end with one to four movable projections known as toes, used in holding to the substratum while creeping. The toes may be short and conical as in bdelloids or slender and spine-like. The single toe results from the fusion of two original toes or from the loss of one toe. Commonly one pair of toes is present; other arrangements are a single dorsal toe and a pair of ventral ones or a smaller dorsal and a larger ventral pair. In the Trichocercidae, because of the spiral asymmetry already mentioned, the right toe is often reduced or lost (Fig. 29*E*). The pedal glands (see

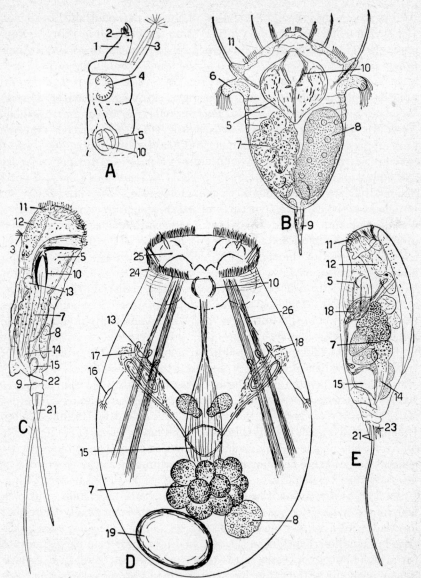

FIG. 29.—Additional types of rotifers. *A.* Anterior end of a bdelloid rotifer, with retracted trochal disks, showing rostrum and dorsal antenna. *B.* Pelagic ploimate rotifer, *Synchaeta*, with auricles, tufts of sensory bristles, and reduced foot. *C.* Notommatoid rotifer *Monommata* with very long unequal toes. *D.* Sacciform pelagic rotifer, *Asplanchna*, without intestine or foot. *E.* Notommatoid pelagic rotifer, *Trichocerca*, with spiral asymmetry, and very unequal toes accompanied by styles. (*All from life.*) 1, rostrum; 2, rostral lamella; 3, dorsal antenna; 4, trochal disk; 5, mastax; 6, auricles; 7, stomach; 8, germovitellarium; 9, foot; 10, trophi; 11, corona; 12, retrocerebral organ; 13, gastric gland; 14, intestine; 15, bladder; 16, lateral antennae; 17, flame bulb; 18, protonephridium; 19, egg; 20, esophagus; 21, toes; 22, anus; 23, styles; 24, circumapical band; 25, apical field; 26, retractor muscles.

below) commonly open at the tips of the toes. In addition to the toes, the foot may bear other similar projections, termed *styles, spurs,* etc.; the spurs occur chiefly in the bdelloids as a pair of projections similar to and dorsal to the toes (Fig. 27*B*).

The rotifers are dioecious but only in the Seisonacea and some Ploima are the males similar in size and morphology to the females. In the majority of rotifers the males are greatly reduced in size and morphology. Males are altogether wanting in the order Bdelloidea which therefore consists of parthenogenetic females. The rotifers ordinarily seen are all females as the males usually appear only at certain seasons for brief intervals.

The rotifers are commonly transparent and colorless or slightly yellowish from the enclosing cuticle, but brown, red, and orange colors, usually localized in the digestive tract, also occur, especially in rotifers inhabiting alpine and polar regions.

The rotifers are among the most common inhabitants of fresh waters everywhere; some also live in brackish water and a few in the ocean or on land in damp sites. They have adopted a variety of habitats and ways of life; and this is strongly reflected in their body form, coronal pattern, and type of mastax. Thus there are creeping, swimming, pelagic, and sessile types, as well as carnivores and bacteria feeders. Sessile types and also some pelagic forms are commonly enclosed in a gelatinous or cuticular tube or envelope in which foreign bodies may be incorporated (Fig. 33*C*). The class also includes epizoic and parasitic members, which also show adaptive structural features. Although the rotifers are generally solitary, some of the sessile species form spherical swimming colonies (Fig. 63*B*) in which, however, the individuals have no organic continuity. Because of their varied and often beautiful forms and interesting habits, the rotifers have always been among the most admired and most studied of microscopical objects.

4. The Corona.—The corona, or "wheel organ," is the most striking feature of the rotifers; the metachronous beating of its cilia, especially in the Bdelloidea, produces the illusion of a rotating wheel, whence the name Rotifera (Latin, *rota,* a wheel, *fero,* to bear), or wheel bearers. The corona was long and mistakenly interpreted in terms of the trochophore theory and only through the outstanding work of de Beauchamp (1907, 1908, 1909) has an understanding of this organ been achieved. It is probable that the rotifers derive from creeping, ventrally ciliated animals, and that the corona originally consisted simply of a ventral ciliated field around the mouth, used primarily for creeping. According to de Beauchamp, the ground plan of the corona comprises a large oval ventral field, the *buccal field,* evenly ciliated with short cilia and surrounding the mouth, and a *circumapical band* extending from this to encircle the margin

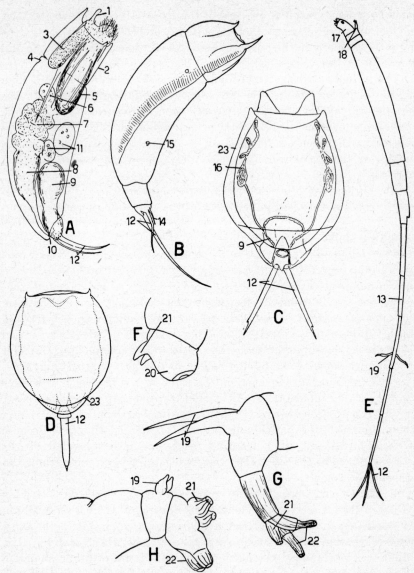

Fig. 30.—Types of rotifer feet.   *A.* Trichocercid genus *Diurella*, from life, with slightly unequal toes.   *B.* Another species of *Diurella* with very unequal toes (*courtesy F. J. Myers*).   *C. Lecane*, from life, with very short foot and long equal toes.   *D. Monostyla* with one toe derived by fusion of condition in *Lecane* (*courtesy Dr. F. J. Myers*).   *E–H.* Types of bdelloid feet.   *E. Rotaria neptunia* (*after Weber*, 1898), with very long foot, two spurs, and three toes.   *F. Habrotrocha*, foot terminating in a disk with two dorsal toes. *G. Macrotrachela*, with three toes and two long spurs.   *H. Philodinavus* with two spurs, two dorsal and two ventral toes.   (*F–H, after Murray*, 1905.)   1, palp-like outlet of retrocerebral organ; 2, head joint; 3, retrocerebral organ; 4, neck joint; 5, mastax; 6, gastric glands; 7, stomach; 8, intestine; 9, urinary bladder; 10, anus; 11, germovitellarium; 12, toes; 13, foot; 14, styles; 15, lateral antenna; 16, protonephridium; 17, rostrum; 18, dorsal antenna; 19, spurs; 20, terminal disk; 21, dorsal toes; 22, ventral toes; 23, lorica.

of the head (Fig. 31*A–C*). The center of the anterior surface is thus left as an unciliated area, the *apical field* already mentioned. This condition of the corona occurs in many notommatids and is associated with a creeping mode of life. The creeping *Dicranophorus* (Fig. 31*D*) has a fully developed buccal field but no circumapical band; whether this condition is primitive or the result of the loss of the circumapical band is not certain. The various modifications from the ground plan are correlated with the assumption of free-swimming or sessile habits and altered modes of food getting.

In the change from the creeping to the swimming life, there usually occurs a reduction in the buccal field. In some forms its posterior part has been lost except for cilia immediately beneath the mouth while the anterior or supraoral half remains as a broad transverse or triangular area leading into the mouth as in *Adineta* (Fig. 31*E*). Often the marginal cilia of this supraoral remnant of the buccal field enlarge to stiff cirri as in *Euchlanis* (Fig. 32*A–C*) and through loss or reduction of the interior cilia such arcs of cirri, called the *pseudotroch*, may constitute the chief part of the buccal field as in *Epiphanes* and *Brachionus* (Fig. 32*D, E*). The dorsal part of the pseudotroch may break up into one or more arcs or tufts of cirri. Three such tufts occur in *Epiphanes* and *Brachionus* (Fig. 27*C*). Apparently these large stiff cirri or styles no longer serve in locomotion but are probably sensory. In many cases, the buccal field becomes reduced to a small ciliated zone around the mouth as in *Asplanchna* and *Synchaeta*. On the other hand, a special development of the buccal field is seen in the Collothecacea where the corona is extended into one, three, five, or seven, rarely two or four, blunt or elongated lobes (Fig. 27*D*) so that the anterior ends forms a funnel with the mouth at the center of the bottom. The coronal lobes in such case are edged with setae or with tufts of setae or the setae are limited to long bundles at the tips of the lobes (Fig. 64). It is believed that in these forms the circumapical band has been completely lost and the coronal funnel consists of the enlarged and lobed buccal field; this interpretation also explains the central position of the mouth. The coronal funnel of the Collothecacea acts as a trap to catch small organisms.

The circumapical band, originally a broad band of uniform short cilia, alters mostly in the direction of enlargement of its marginal cilia with loss of the interior cilia. This tendency is first seen in rotifers with an otherwise primitive corona, as many notammatids, in the formation of the auricles, a pair of lateral coronal projections provided with long cilia. They assist in swimming and are retracted during creeping (Fig. 26). Further change in this direction leads in some groups of rotifers to the enlargement of the cilia along both margins of the apical band, so that there result two circles of cilia, or, rather, membranelles, an inner or anterior circlet, the *trochus*, and an outer or posterior one, the *cingulum*. The reduced buccal field becomes incorporated into these circlets, and hence the corona comes to consist essentially of two circlets of membranelles, with the mouth between them ventrally (Fig. 33*C*). This type

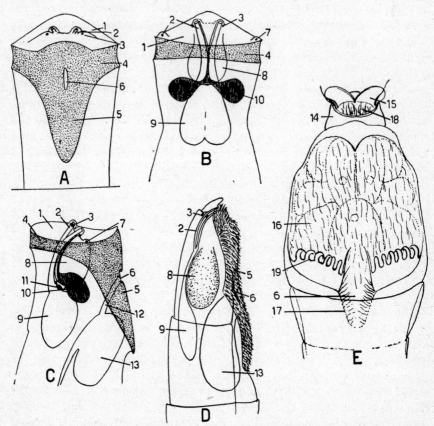

Fig. 31.—Corona. *A–C.* Scheme of the primitive corona (*after Beauchamp*, 1907, 1909). *A.* Ventral view. *B.* Dorsal view. *C.* Lateral view. *D. Dicranophorus*, showing corona (*after Beauchamp*, 1907). *E.* Corona of *Adineta* (*after Murray*, 1910), with large supraoral and reduced infraoral parts of the buccal field. 1, apical field; 2, outlets of retrocerebral organ; 3, apical eyes; 4, circumapical band; 5, buccal field; 6, mouth; 7, lateral eyes; 8, brain; 9, retrocerebral sac; 10, subcerebral glands; 11, cerebral eye; 12, buccal tube; 13, mastax; 14, rostrum; 15, rostral lamellae; 16, supraoral part of buccal field; 17, infraoral part of buccal field; 18, cilia of rostrum; 19, food rakes.

of corona was formerly regarded as primitive and as directly referable to the trochophore larva. The trochus was considered to represent the preoral ciliary band of the trochophore, the cingulum its postoral band. The whole comparison fails when we realize that such a corona is not primitive but highly modified. This kind of corona may retain its original form as a band encircling the head margin as in *Pedalia* (Fig. 33*A, B*) and *Tes-*

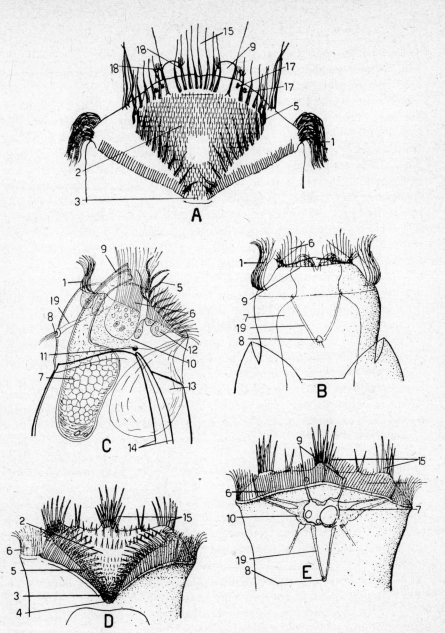

Fig. 32.—Corona (continued). *A.* Corona of *Euchlanis*, ventral view, large supraoral buccal field, pseudotroch indicated (*after Stoszberg*, 1932). *B.* Corona of *Euchlanis*, dorsal view. *C. Euchlanis*, laterial view. *D.* Corona of *Epiphanes*, pseudotroch differentiated, three tufts of cirri. *E. Epiphanes*, dorsal view. (*B–E, after Beauchamp* 1907, 1909.) 1, auricle; 2, supraoral part of buccal field; 3, mouth; 4, infraoral part of buccal field; 5, pseudotroch; 6, circumapical band; 7, retrocerebral organ; 8, dorsal antenna; 9, outlets of retrocerebral organ; 10, brain; 11, cerebral eye; 12, coronal matrix; 13, mastax; 14, plates of lorica; 15, tufts of cirri; 16, apical field; 17, ciliated pits; 18, sense organs; 19, nerves to dorsal antenna.

tudinella (Fig. 61*D*), but more often heads with such coronas expand into conspicuous circular, oval, or lobed disks employed wholly or partly in food getting and a groove appears between trochus and cingulum along which microscopic food is carried to the mouth (Fig. 33*C*). Coronas of this sort evolve along two main lines. In the sessile Flosculariacea, the broadly expanded apical field forms a round, oval, or lobed disk edged by the two circlets of which the trochus has the larger membranelles (Fig. 33*C*). This apparatus is employed wholly in producing currents for bringing microscopic particles into the mouth and has no locomotory function. In the other line of development, seen in the Bdelloidea, the apical field enclosed by the trochus gradually subdivides into two trochal disks, raised on pedicels, while the cingulum encircles the base of both pedicels and passes below the mouth (Fig. 27*B*). The trochal disks are used in swimming and in producing food currents but are folded up and retracted when the animal creeps. In both these types the mouth lies outside the disk, a further proof that the funnel of the Collothecacea is not homologous with the disks of the Bdelloidea and Flosculariacea.

In rotifers that lead an exclusively swimming life, as *Asplanchna* and *Synchaeta*, the circumapical band is reduced to a single girdle of membranelles, often incomplete and broken up into arcs and tufts, situated around the margin of the broad anterior end (Fig. 29*B*). In these genera the buccal field is also greatly reduced. However, reduced and broken circumapical bands may also occur in conjunction with fairly developed buccal fields as the pseudotroch of *Brachionus* and *Epiphanes*.

As already indicated, the coronal cilia are frequently not simple cilia but are often compounded into cirri, membranelles, styles, etc. The nature of the exceedingly long stiff immotile hairs on the tips of the coronal lobes of some Collothecacea (Fig. 27*D*) is uncertain.

A corona is absent in the adult females of the genera *Atrochus*, *Cupelopagis*, and *Acyclus* (Fig. 65) but is present in normal form in the males and young females of these genera. The corona of male rotifers often differs from that of females of the same species, being usually less modified.

5. Body Wall and Associated Glands.—The body wall consists of cuticle, epidermis, and subepidermal muscles (Fig. 33*D*). The cuticle, secreted by the epidermis, is not chitinous and presumably consists of scleroproteins. It is frequently, especially in forms that move by creeping or looping, divided into rings or segments that lend flexibility and usually can be telescoped into each other, permitting a variety of body movements. These joints are often referred to by the name of the body region they cover, as head joint, neck or cervical joint, etc. In strictly swimming types, the cuticle is usually undivided. The cuticle may be marked with a polygonal pattern (Fig. 34*B*) or with longitudinal or trans-

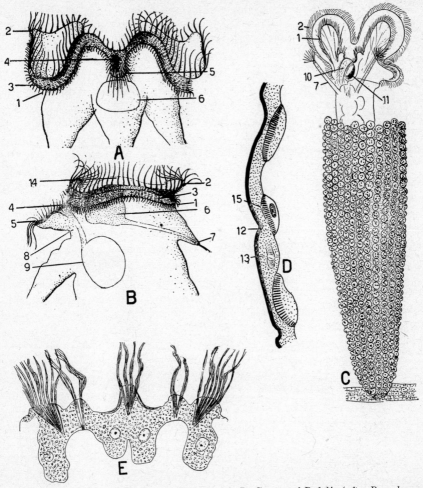

Fig. 33.—Corona (concluded), epidermis. *A, B.* Corona of *Pedalia* (*after Beauchamp,* 1907), with reduced buccal field and complete circumapical band with beginning trochus and cingulum. *A.* Ventral view. *B.* Lateral view. *C. Floscularia ringens,* from life, with four-lobed corona edged with the trochus and the cingulum and case made of pellets. *D.* Longitudinal section of the body wall of a bdelloid (*Mniobia, after Brakenhoff,* 1937). *E.* Coronal matrix of *Epiphanes* (*after Martini,* 1912). 1, cingulum; 2, trochus; 3, circumapical band; 4, mouth; 5, remains of buccal field; 6, brain; 7, dorsal antenna; 8, buccal tube; 9, mastax; 10, lip; 11, pouch for making pellets; 12, cuticle; 13, epidermis; 14, apical field; 15, ring muscle.

verse striations, grooves, or ridges, or may bear spines, tubercles, or other projections (Fig. 34*C*). In many rotifers the trunk cuticle is thickened and hardened into a lorica that, however, is slightly flexible. The formation of a lorica appears to have occurred independently in various families and genera of rotifers so that its possession does not indicate relationship. The lorica usually encases the entire trunk but in some genera as *Dicrano-*

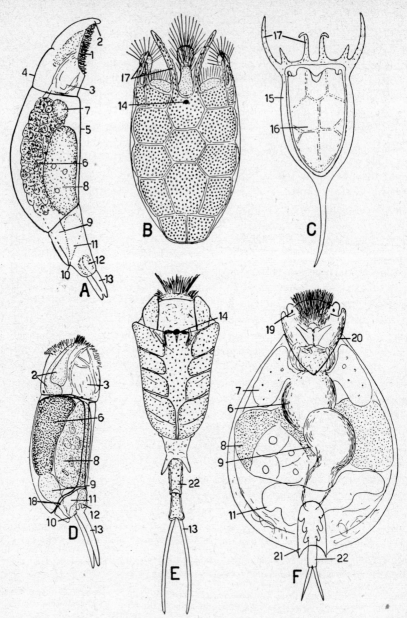

Fig. 34.—Lorica. *A. Dicranophorus*, with slightly developed lorica partly enclosing the trunk. *B. Keratella cochlearis*, with spiny sculptured two-piece lorica, dorsal view. *C. Keratella cochlearis*, variety with terminal spine, ventral view, showing ventral plate of lorica. *D. Cephalodella mucronata*, with special piece covering the rear part of the trunk. *E. Trichotria pocillum*, completely encased in a lorica. *F. Lepadella*, with hood-like head shield. (*All from life.*) 1, buccal field; 2, retrocerebral organ; 3, mastax; 4, neck joint; 5, lorica; 6, stomach; 7, gastric glands; 8, germovitellarium; 9, intestine; 10, anus; 11, bladder; 12, pedal glands; 13, toes; 14, cerebral eye; 15, dorsal plate of lorica; 16, ventral plate of lorica; 17, lorical spines; 18, piece of lorica over rear part of trunk; 19, lateral eyes; 20, head shield; 21, aperture of lorica for emission of foot; 22, foot.

phorus (Fig. 34*A*) and *Cephalodella* the anterior and posterior parts of the trunk are left free; but in *Cephalodella mucronata*, a special piece of lorica covers the latter (Fig. 34*D*). The lorica may consist of several pieces or of two dorsal and two ventral plates or two dorsal and one ventral or of single dorsal and ventral plates or of one piece with or without a longitudinal suture (Fig. 34). Loricate forms are often dorsoventrally or laterally flattened; the margins of the lorica may project as teeth or spines (Fig. 34*B*, *C*) and these are subject to much variation within a single species. The part of the lorica covering the neck region may be marked off from the general trunk lorica by a groove and is then termed *head shield;* this may form a sort of hood covering the dorsal surface of the entire head as in *Lepadella* (Fig. 34*F*). In a few rotifers the entire body except the toes is enclosed in a lorica as *Trichotria pocillum* (Fig. 34*E*).

The epidermis is a thin syncytium containing scattered nuclei (Fig. 33*E*) bilaterally arranged and constant in position and number for each species. Around each nucleus or group of nuclei the cytoplasm is heaped up into an elevation projecting into the pseudocoel. Such epidermal cushions containing one to several nuclei are particularly conspicuous beneath the corona where their arrangement and size are correlated with the distribution of the coronal cilia (Fig. 33*E*). They contain the basal bodies and roots of the cilia and constitute the epidermal part of the corona, sometimes termed the *coronal matrix*. In some species, the epidermis at the foot end bears cilia, in a circle or tuft.

Some pelagic rotifers are enclosed in a loose gelatinous envelope and the sessile Flosculariacea and Collothecacea are generally provided with a tube into which they can withdraw (Fig. 64). These secretions appear to come from the foot epidermis or possibly only from the pedal glands. They may harden into a cuticular-like material. Foreign particles may be added to the tube in irregular manner by the general action of the corona or definite pellets may be formed by concentrating particles in a special ciliated pit under the pouch-like lower lip. These pellets are then stuck to the tube in regular rows producing a beautifully built case as in some species of *Floscularia* (= *Melicerta*, Fig. 33*C*). Other floscularians use fecal balls or sand grains in a similar manner.

The principal glands attached to the epidermis are the *retrocerebral organ* and the *pedal glands*. The former, situated above and behind the brain, consists typically of a median *retrocerebral sac* and a pair of lateral *subcerebral glands* (Fig. 35 *A–D*). The duct of the sac forks and the forks accompanied by the outlets of the glands open on the apical field, often on a single or paired papilla. Sac and glands vary much in relative and absolute size in different rotifers; there may be a single subcerebral gland or the sac may occur without glands or the glands without the sac (Fig.

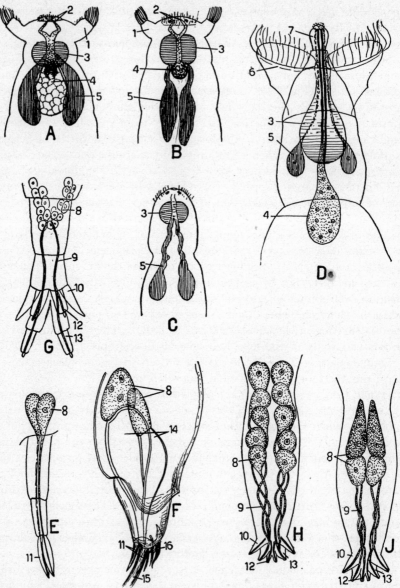

FIG. 35.—Glands. *A–D*. Retrocerebral organs of various rotifers (*after Beauchamp*, 1909). *A. Notommata*, organ well-developed. *B. Dicranophorus*, retrocerebral sac reduced. *C. Encentrum*, sac vanished. *D*. Callidinid bdelloid, sac and glands well-developed. *E–J*. Types of pedal glands. *E*. Usual ploimate type, *Notommata*, from life. *F. Trichocerca* with large reservoirs (*after Beauchamp*, 1909). *G. Philodina* (*after Janson*, 1893), with numerous gland cells. *H, J. Embata parasitica* (*after Brakenhoff*, 1937). *H*. Dorsal view. *J*. Ventral view. 1, auricle; 2, outlets of retrocerebral organ; 3, brain; 4, retrocerebral sac; 5, subcerebral glands; 6, trochal disks; 7, rostrum; 8, pedal glands; 9, outlets of pedal glands; 10, spurs; 11, toes; 12, dorsal toes; 13, ventral toes; 14, reservoirs; 15, base of long toe; 16, styles.

35*C*). The organ is most typically developed in the Ploima, especially the notommatids (Fig. 26), occurs in some Bdelloidea, is reduced or absent in the Flosculariacea and Collothecacea, and in the Seisonacea is apparently represented by large gland cells (Fig. 51*A*). Sac and glands consist of a syncytium and secrete droplets that give them a vacuolated appearance. The sac and sometimes also the glands contain strongly diffractive granules formerly mistakenly thought to be of calcareous nature; red pigment grains may be present. The function of the retro-cerebral organ is uncertain; probably it corresponds to the frontal organ of Turbellaria and therefore originally produced an adhesive secretion but is now in process of degeneration.

The pedal glands are unicellular glands or multinucleate syncytia located in the foot (Fig. 35*E–J*). They are numerous (up to 30) and of several different kinds in the Seisonacea, less numerous (1 to 15 pairs) and alike in the Bdelloidea, reduced to a single pair, sometimes accompanied by smaller accessory glands, in most Ploima, and often rudimentary or absent in adults of the sessile orders. They open by ducts on the tips of the toes, less often at the sides or base of the toes or on the spurs or at the foot end; a swelling, the reservoir, sometimes very large, may occur in the course of the ducts (Fig. 35*F*). The pedal glands secrete an adhesive material used for permanent attachment or in creeping and also in the construction of tubes and cases.

Other epidermal glands are rare in rotifers, except in the Seisonacea where a number occur in the neck region. The pit in the Flosculariacea (Fig. 33*C*) where the pellets for the tube are shaped is provided with glands secreting a sticky material.

6. Muscular System.—Definite subepidermal muscle layers such as characterize the Platyhelminthes are lacking in rotifers and instead there is a bewildering array of single muscles. Most of these can be regarded as constituting subepidermal circular and longitudinal groups but it is improbable that they represent remnants of originally complete sub-epidermal layers. In addition to these body-wall muscles there are *cutaneovisceral* muscles that extend to the viscera, especially the digestive tract, from the body wall, and *visceral* muscles in the walls of the viscera themselves. These last two sorts of muscles will be considered in connection with the viscera. The musculature is best known in the order Ploima where it has been thoroughly studied in the genera *Asplanchna* (Nachtwey, 1925), *Lindia* (Dehl, 1934), *Epiphanes* (Martini, 1912), *Synchaeta* (Peters, 1931), and *Euchlanis*, *Brachionus*, and *Rhinoglena* (Stoszberg, 1932).

The circular musculature of the body wall, best developed in the illoricate Ploima, consists of single muscle bands, mostly three to seven, widely spaced, running close to the underside of the epidermis in a circular direction (Fig. 36*A*). These bands may form complete rings but are often very incomplete ventrally, frequently also dorsally, so that they may consist chiefly of short lateral arcs. They occur in the neck and trunk, frequently only the anterior part of the trunk, are generally absent from the foot, and reduced in forms with a well-developed lorica (Figs. 36–39). The circular bands contain no nuclei, hence are really part of the epidermal syncytium, and thus comparable with the epitheliomuscular fibers of the cnidarian epidermis. The contraction of the ring musculature serves to extend the body. In flattened loricate types like *Brachionus*, the circular muscles by loosening from their epidermal connections except at the ends become converted into dorsoventral bands that serve to bring the plates of the lorica closer together. Transverse bands acting on lateral lorica plates may arise in the same manner.

The circular musculature is especially developed in the head directly behind the corona where it forms the *coronal sphincter*, composed of one to several (up to seven) broad bands often united into a meshwork by cross connections and serving to close the neck over the retracted corona (Figs. 36*A*, 39*A*, *B*). A similar *pedal sphincter* may occur at the junction of trunk and foot. Muscles that operate external movable parts as the arms of *Pedalia* are also derived from the ring muscle system.

The longitudinal body-wall muscles consisted originally of bands running the body length directly under the circular bands and attached at frequent intervals to the epidermis. By loss of many of these insertions the longitudinal bands come to run more directly through the pseudocoel and to act primarily on the head and foot as *retractors* (Figs. 36–39). They frequently then break up into anterior and posterior portions and may also split lengthwise in whole or at their ends to form additional retractors. The principal head retractors are the *central, dorsal, lateral*, and *ventral* pairs; the lateral is commonly subdivided into three bands, *superior, median*, and *inferior*. The central retractors originate on the dorsal trunk wall, run forward between the brain and digestive tract, and insert on the apical or buccal field. The dorsal retractors may originate at the end of the foot and run the body length to the corona, or may be divided into head and foot retractors. When so divided, the dorsal head retractors originate on the dorsal trunk wall and extend forward near the dorsal surface to insert dorsally on either side on the circumapical band. The dorsal foot retractors begin on the posterior dorsal trunk wall and run to the distal end of the foot. The lateral retractors are usually present only as head retractors, originating on the sides of the trunk and inserting on the lateral regions of head and corona; but may extend into the posterior part of the trunk or into the foot. The ventral retractors are usually continuous bands between the distal end of the foot and the buccal field and ventral head. Head retractors usu-

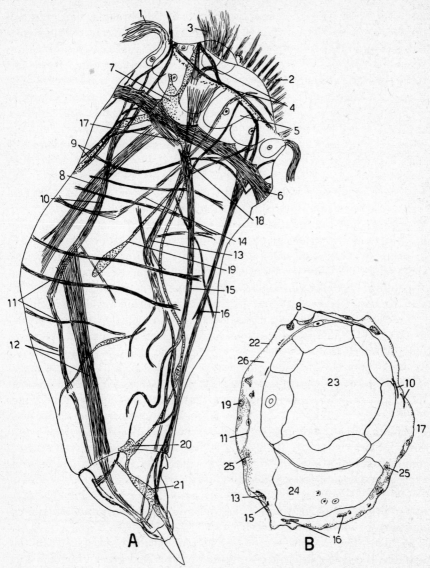

Fig. 36.—Musculature. *A. Epiphanes*, lateral view, showing muscles and nerves. *B.* Section through *Epiphanes* showing relation of muscle bands to epidermis. (*Both after Martini*, 1912.)   1, auricle; 2, pseudotroch; 3, tuft of cirri; 4, coronal muscles; 5, coronal matrix; 6, coronal sphincter; 7, brain; 8, central retractor; 9, retractors and nerve of the dorsal antenna; 10, dorsal retractor; 11, ring muscles; 12, rear parts of dorsal retractor; 13, medial part of lateral retractor; 14, superior part of lateral retractor; 15, inferior part of lateral retractor; 16, ventral retractor; 17, main ventral nerve; 18, geniculate ganglion; 19, nerve to lateral antenna; 20, vesicular ganglion; 21, pedal ganglion; 22, epidermis; 23, stomach; 24, germovitellarium; 25, protonephridium; 26, pseudocoel.

ally split up anteriorly to supply all parts of the corona.   Various small muscles such as the retractors of the auricles, retractors of the dorsal antenna and other sensory projections, and muscles of the apical field are probably offshoots of the main retractors.   The longitudinal retractors serve to retract the head and corona and foot into the trunk region; this is accomplished by the telescoping of the cuticular rings into each other or, when a lorica is present, by the spreading apart of its plates.   When the foot is reduced or absent, the foot retractors are correspondingly reduced or missing and in fact the degree of development of the whole musculature is correlated with the other anatomical features in a given species.

The musculature is less known for the other orders.   In a typical sessile rotifer, *Conochiloides*, studied by Hlava (1905), the ring musculature is reduced and limited to the anterior part of the body and there are three pairs of strong longitudinal retractors that run the body length or nearly so (Fig. 39*A*, *B*).   Obviously in sessile rotifers retraction into the tube is the chief function of the musculature.   The musculature is also known for the swimming flosculariaceans *Testudinella* (Seehaus, 1930) and *Pedalia* (Remane, 1932).   In the former the ring muscles are altered to dorsoventral bands, and in the latter they act chiefly as elevators and depressors of the appendages; both genera have a good development of longitudinal retractors anteriorly.   Among the Collothecacea details are available only for the aberrant *Atrochus* (Wierzejski, 1893); here as might be expected there is a full complement of retractors for the entire body but the ring musculature is unusual in that it forms a complete investiture of fine rings (Fig. 65*C*).   Bdelloid musculature was studied in *Mniobia* by Zelinka (1886) and in *Rotaria* and *Adineta* by Brakenhoff (1937).   In these genera there are 11, 7, and 8 ring muscles, respectively, and a number of longitudinal retractors, of which the coronal retractors are especially developed in *Rotaria* (Fig. 38*A*, *B*).

In a given rotifer, the muscles are smooth or cross-striated or both apparently without relation to other factors.   The longitudinal retractors have one or more nuclei.

7. The Pseudocoel.—A cavity, often spacious, exists in rotifers between the body wall and the digestive tract and other viscera.   This space has none of the characteristics of a coelom; it is not lined by a mesodermal epithelium or crossed by mesenteries supporting the viscera. Study of the embryology of rotifers shows that their viscera arise by the migration of blastomeres into the interior and that the cavity in question is the space formed between the interior cells and those left on the surface. The cavity therefore corresponds to a blastocoel and hence constitutes a pseudocoel according to the terminology adopted in this treatise.

The pseudocoel is filled with fluid and a loose network formed by the

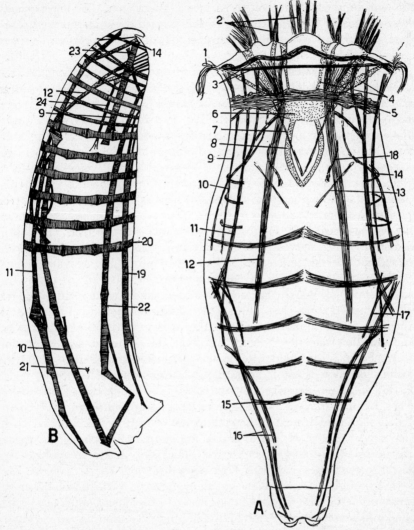

Fig. 37.—Musculature (continued).   *A. Epiphanes*, dorsal view (*after Martini*, 1912). *B. Lindia*, with numerous ring muscles; side view (*after Dehl*, 1934).   1, auricle; 2, tufts of cirri; 3, coronal muscles; 4, sensory nerves; 5, coronal sphincter; 6, brain; 7, retractor of the dorsal antenna; 8, nerves to dorsal antenna; 9, medial part of lateral retractor; 10, superior part of lateral retractor; 11, dorsal retractor; 12, central retractors; 13, cutaneogastric muscle; 14, first ring muscle; 15, eighth ring muscle; 16, rear parts of dorsal retractor; 17, cutaneointestinal muscle; 18, dorsopharyngeal muscle; 19, ventral retractor; 20, fourteenth ring muscle; 21, lateral antenna; 22, inferior part of lateral retractor; 23, ventrolateral retractor; 24, dorsolateral retractor.

union of branched amoeboid cells into a syncytium.   Embryologically these cells come from the same cells that furnish the epidermis and hence may be regarded as a kind of ectomesoderm.   They presumably have phagocytic and excretory functions.

8. Nervous System.—The nervous system somewhat resembles that of the turbellarian flatworms, consisting of a main bilobed mass, the brain or cerebral ganglia, sensory and motor nerves from this to adjacent parts, some additional ganglionic masses, and two main ventral nerve cords. The brain is a rounded, triangular, or quadrangular body (Fig. 39*C*) dorsal to the mastax and is composed of a central fibrous mass enclosed, especially dorsally and laterally, by a cortical layer of ganglion cells, in which four main types, differing in size and nuclear details, can be distinguished.   A number of paired sensory nerves extend to the brain from the various sensory organs of the head: the eyes, the sensory bristles and pits on the apical field, the rostrum, and the dorsal antenna.   The brain also sends motor nerves to the anterior parts of the various muscles, as the dorsal, lateral, and central retractors, and to the salivary glands.

From the brain a pair of pharyngeal nerves proceeds ventrally into the mastax wall where they form on each side a plexus supplying the mastax musculature (Fig. 40).   This plexus connects with the mastax ganglion, a loose unpaired mass in the mid-ventral wall of the mastax. This ganglion was once thought to correspond to the subenteric ganglion of annelids but the comparison is not now regarded as valid.   From the mastax ganglion there extends in most forms studied a *visceral* nerve passing into the digestive tract on each side.   A paired *epipharyngeal* nerve, arising from the brain or from the pharyngeal nerve, proceeds to the *epipharyngeal* ganglion, a small group of cells in the epipharynx on each side.   The main ventral nerves are ganglionated cords that spring from the sides of the brain and proceed backward in a lateroventral position into the foot.   Near the brain they bear an *anterior* ganglion and farther posteriorly a *geniculate* ganglion, from which there usually spring two main nerves, the *lateral sensory* nerve to the lateral antenna on each side, and the *scalar* nerve, a longitudinal nerve to the ring muscle bands of the trunk (Fig. 40*A*).   The scalar nerve has a ganglion cell for each muscle band.   Both these nerves may arise directly from the ventral cord.   A nerve to the coronal sphincter may spring from the geniculate ganglion or from more anterior levels of the ventral cords.   Branches to the main longitudinal retractor muscles may arise from the geniculate ganglion or from the ventral cords.   Posteriorly the ventral cords terminate in ganglia serving the urinary bladder (*vesicular* ganglion) and foot (*pedal* or *caudal* ganglion); these ganglia may be fused in one mass, the *caudovesicular* ganglion) (Figs. 40, 41*A*).   These ganglia may be more or less definite masses or may consist of cells or groups of cells connected by strands. In *Asplanchna* there occur two dorsal ganglionated cords not found in other rotifers that extend backward in close connection with the lateral retractors and have ganglion cells where they pass the coronal sphincter and the ring muscles of the trunk (Fig. 40*B*) so that they take the place of the scalar nerves.

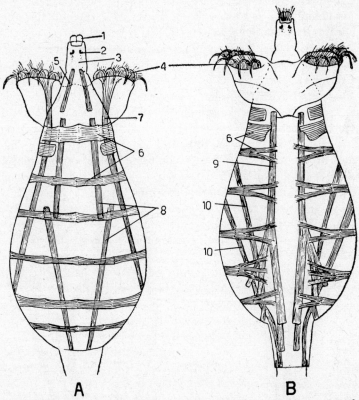

A   **B**

Fig. 38.—Musculature (continued). *A. Rotaria*, dorsal view, illustrating the Bdelloidea. *B. Rotaria*, ventral view. (*Both after Brakenhoff*, 1937.) 1, rostral lamellae; 2, eyes; 3, rostrum; 4, trochal disks; 5, rostral retractor; 6, ring muscles; 7, retractors of the trochal disks; 8, dorsal retractors; 9, ventral retractors; 10, lateral retractors.

9. Sensory Structures.—The rotifers are richly supplied with sensory cells and sense organs. These occur abundantly on the anterior end in the form of sensory membranelles and styles, ciliated pits, sensory papillae, etc. (Figs. 41*B*, *C*, 42*A*). These structures are probably specialized remnants of the original ciliation of the corona. The sensory membranelles or styles are single stiff bristles situated near the inner edge of the circumapical band and named from their position dorsolateral, lateral, and ventrolateral styles. Similar apical styles occur on the apical field and oral styles may be present near the mouth. These styles seem

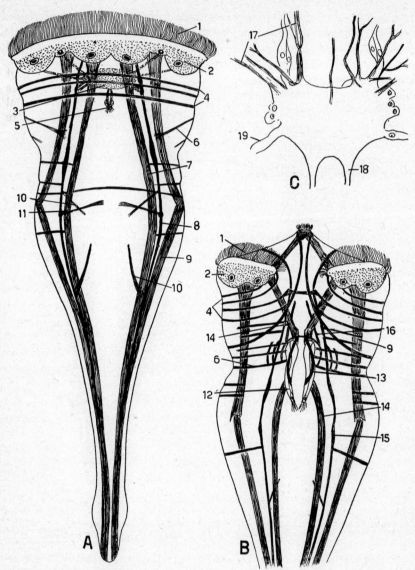

Fig. 39.—Musculature (concluded), nervous system. *A. Conochiloides*, illustrating the Flosculariacea, dorsal view. *B. Conochiloides*, ventral view. (*Both after Hlava*, 1905.) *C.* Brain of *Epiphanes* (*after Martini*, 1912). 1, circumapical band; 2, coronal matrix; 3, brain; 4, coronal sphincter; 5, dorsal antenna; 6, ring muscles; 7, central retractor; 8, dorsal retractor; 9, medial part of lateral retractor: 10, cutaneointestinal muscles; 11, cutaneocloacal muscle; 12, lateral antennae; 13, retractors of lateral antennae; 14, ventral retractors; 15, inferior part of lateral retractor; 16, cutaneopharyngeal muscle; 17, anterior sensory nerves; 18, dorsal sensory nerves; 19, main ventral nerves.

to be tactile organs and each is underlain by one or two sensory nerve cells from which fibers go to the brain. Paired ciliated pits, apparently chemoreceptors, also underlain by sensory nerve cells, may occur on the apical field (Fig. 41*B*). Conical or finger-like palps tipped with sensory hairs or without hairs may also be present on the apical field. The foregoing types of sensory structures are most common in the Ploima and vary greatly from genus to genus in presence and number. Some may be borne on the papillae that carry the exits of the retrocerebral organ.

Ocelli, visible as red pigment spots, are of common occurrence in the Ploima, Bdelloida, and free stages of the sessile orders. Usually there is a single, less often paired, cerebral eye, embedded in the dorsal or ventral surface of the brain (Fig. 42*B*). A few forms have one or two lateral eyes on each side in the corona and a number have a pair of apical eyes on the apical field, often on the rostrum in Bdelloidea. Cerebral and apical or cerebral and lateral eyes may be present simultaneously. The cerebral eye consists of a single cell resembling a brain cell (Fig. 42*B*) while the lateral and apical eyes are epidermal cushions with one or more nuclei (Fig. 41*C, D*). The red pigment is located inside the optic cell or the epidermal cushion. A lens-like body, not formed of cuticle, may also be present.

A sensory organ constantly present in rotifers is the dorsal antenna or tentacle already mentioned. This is typically a movable papilla or finger-like projection provided at its tip with one or more tufts of sensory hairs (Fig. 42*F*). It may, however, consist simply of a tuft of sensory hairs, or of one or two styles, or of styles encircled by sensory hairs, and such types usually project through an opening in the cuticle or lorica (Fig. 42*D*). In a few cases the organ is reduced to an unciliated pit. The dorsal antenna is underlain by a small cluster of sensory nerve cells. The paired lateral antennae occur in all rotifers except the Seisonacea and Bdelloidea. They vary in location from near the mouth to the end of the trunk and while usually lateral may be shifted dorsally or ventrally. They show the same range of structure as the dorsal antenna but are provided with only one sensory nerve cell. A *caudal* antenna (Fig. 42*H*) is found among the Ploima above the base of the toes as a hairless papilla or a tuft of bristles or a pit and a *supra-anal* sense organ sometimes occurs (Fig. 42*G, H*). The *pharyngeal* sense organ of the Collothecacea is a tuft of stiff sensory hairs on the diaphragm (Fig. 46*D*).

10. Digestive Tract.—The mouth is commonly situated ventrally on the head and may be rounded, slit-like, or triangular. Beneath the mouth the cingulum may form a definite lower lip that in some rotifers is a conspicuous spout-like eminence (Fig. 33*C*). In forms with a large buccal field, the posterior end of the field may project as the so-called chin (Fig. 26*A*). In the Collothecacea, the funnel formed by the coronal

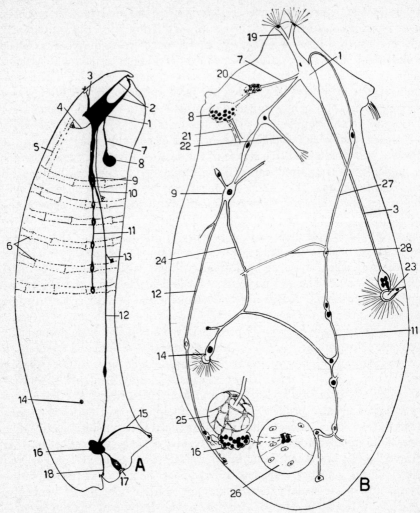

Fig. 40.—Nervous system. *A.* Nervous system of *Lindia (after Dehl,* 1934). *B.* Nervous system of *Asplanchna (after Nachtwey,* 1925). 1, brain; 2, sensory nerves to anterior end; 3, sensory nerve to dorsal antenna; 4, motor nerve to dorsal retractor; 5, dorsal retractor; 6, ring muscles; 7, pharyngeal nerve; 8, mastax ganglion; 9, geniculate ganglion; 10, nerve to gastric gland; 11, scalar nerve; 12, main ventral nerve cord; 13, branch to nephridium; 14, lateral antenna; 15, nerve to sphincter of ducts of pedal glands; 16, caudovesicular ganglion; 17, caudal antenna; 18, nerve to anal sphincter; 19, apical sense organs; 20, epipharyngeal ganglion; 21, visceral nerve; 22, nerve to coronal sphincter; 23, dorsal antenna; 24, nerve to lateral antenna; 25, urinary bladder; 26, germovitellarium; 27, dorsal ganglionated cord; 28, nerve to lateral retractor.

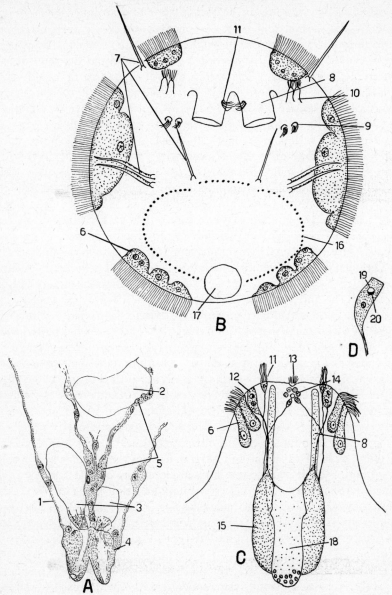

FIG. 41.—Nervous system, sense organs. *A*. Caudovesicular complex of *Epiphanes* (*after Martini*, 1912). *B*. Corona of *Euchlanis*, showing sense organs. *C*. Rostrum of *Rhinoglena* with frontal eyes. *D*. Frontal eye enlarged. (*B–D, after Stoszberg,* 1932.) 1, foot; 2, urinary bladder; 3, pedal glands; 4, toes; 5, caudovesicular complex; 6, coronal matrix; 7, tactile styles; 8, exits of retrocerebral organ; 9, ciliated pits; 10, tactile papillae; 11, apical sense organs; 12, frontal eye; 13, rostral sense organ; 14, neurosensory cells of same; 15, brain; 16, pseudotroch; 17, mouth; 18, retrocerebral sac; 19, lens; 20, pigment.

lobes is divisible into an outer *infundibulum* and an inner *vestibule* by a ridge, the *diaphragm*, that bears the pharyngeal sensory tufts mentioned above (Fig. 46D). Prey can be trapped in the vestibule by the contraction of the diaphragm. In this order the mouth lies in the center of the bottom of the vestibule. The mouth of rotifers may be provided with a sphincter muscle for closure and with one or two pairs of dilator muscles that run close beneath the head epidermis and fasten to the underside of the corona. The dilator muscles seem to be particularly characteristic of raptorial rotifers, that must open the mouth quickly to grasp prey.

The mouth may open directly into the pharynx or may lead to the latter by way of a ciliated tube, the *buccal tube*, that resembles histologically the buccal field, being underlain by syncytial epidermal cushions, and probably represents an invaginated part of this field. The buccal tube is particularly characteristic of forms that gather microscopic food by coronal currents, as the Bdelloidea and Flosculariacea, whereas in raptorial forms, the mouth generally opens directly into the pharynx.

The pharynx or mastax[1] is characteristic of and peculiar to rotifers. It is a highly muscular, rounded, trilobed, or elongated organ of complicated form and structure, whose inner wall bears the masticatory apparatus, composed of hard cuticularized pieces, the *trophi*. The trophi consist of seven main pieces, the unpaired *fulcrum*, and the paired *rami*, *unci*, and *manubria*. Fulcrum and rami together are often termed the *incus*, unci and manubria, the *malleus*. The fulcrum, the median, usually posterior piece, is commonly a thin plate lying in the sagittal plane of the body. The rami extend forward from the fulcrum and are usually thicker triangular pieces with the point directed anteriorly. The unci are pieces along the anterior parts of the rami, with their long axis mostly transverse to the rami. The manubria are elongated pieces attached anteriorly to the outer ends of the unci and extending backward somewhat parallel to the rami. Their pointed rear ends are known as *caudae*. Small pieces termed *subunci* may occur between unci and rami, and other accessory pieces may be present in particular species. Right and left pieces often differ in shape and size since they are constructed to interlock when used. The trophi occur in several different types that are correlated with different modes of feeding.

a. Malleate Type.—In this, the most primitive type, all the pieces are relatively stout and strong, the rami are untoothed, and the unci are curved plates bearing on their medial sides several prong-like teeth (Fig. 43A, B). This type serves primarily for chewing, through the interplay of the uncal teeth, but may also assist in grasping prey. It is common among rotifers, occurring in *Brachionus*, *Epiphanes*, and their relatives, and in a slightly modified form, called *submalleate*, in *Euchlanis*.

[1] The term mastax is used as synonymous with trophi by many authors.

b. Virgate Type.—Fulcrum and manubria are elongated and rod-like, the rami are broad triangular plates, serving chiefly to support the piston, and the unci bear only one or two teeth (Fig. 43*C–F*). In this type the prey is grasped by the unci and its contents are sucked in by the action of

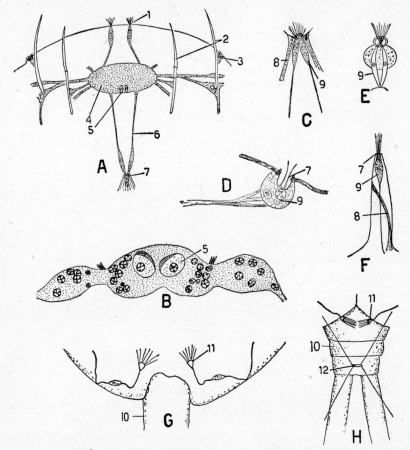

Fig. 42.—Sense organs. *A.* Coronal sense organs of *Synchaeta*. *B.* Section through the brain of *Synchaeta* showing cerebral eyes. *C.* Lateral antenna of *Synchaeta*. (*A–C, after Peters,* 1931.) *D.* Dorsal antenna of *Eosphora* (*after Hirschfelder,* 1910). *E.* Lateral antenna of *Conochiloides*. *F.* Dorsal antenna of *Conochiloides*. (*E, F, after Hlava,* 1905.) *G.* Supra-anal sense organ of *Brachionus*. *H.* Supra-anal sense organ and caudal antenna of *Euchlanis*. (*G, H, after Stoszberg,* 1932.) 1, apical sense organs; 2, tactile styles; 3, ciliated pits; 4, brain; 5, cerebral eyes; 6, nerves to dorsal antenna; 7, dorsal antenna; 8, retractor muscle of antenna; 9, sensory nerve cell of antenna; 10, foot; 11, supra-anal sense organ; 12, caudal antenna.

the *piston* or *hypopharynx*, a muscular mass in the center of the mastax operated by strong muscles attached to the posterior end of the fulcrum. In addition, the anterior dorsal wall of the mastax is stiffened by one or more cuticular plates, the *epipharynx*. The virgate type is characteristic

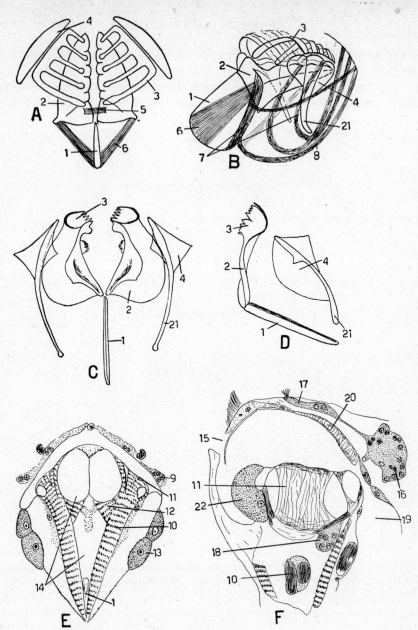

Fig. 43.—Mastax. *A.* Scheme of the malleate type of trophi. *B.* Malleate trophi, seen from the side. (*A, B, after Beauchamp,* 1909.) *C.* Virgate type of trophi, *Synchaeta.* *D.* Virgate trophi, seen from the side. *E.* Frontal section through the mastax of *Synchaeta,* showing piston. *F.* Sagittal section through the mastax of *Synchaeta.* (*E–F, after Peters,* 1931.) 1, fulcrum; 2, ramus; 3, uncus; 4, manubrium; 5, adductor rami muscle; 6, abductor rami; 7, abductors mallei; 8, general adductors; 9, epipharyngeal ganglion; 10, depressors of the piston; 11, piston; 12, dilators esophagi; 13, salivary glands; 14, cavities in the mastax; 15, mouth; 16, brain; 17, apical sense organ; 18, mastax ganglion; 19, esophagus; 20, epipharynx; 21, cauda of the manubrium; 22, piston gland.

of pelagic raptorial rotifers, comprising many notommatids, Trichocercidae, Gastropodidae, and Synchaetidae.

c. Cardate Type.—This type, found chiefly in the notommatid genus *Lindia* is also employed in sucking but the suction is produced mainly by movements of the unci as a piston is lacking. An epipharynx of several pieces is present and the manubria are forked (Fig. 44*B*).

d. Forcipate Type.—All the pieces are slender and elongated. The curved rami form with the fulcrum a forceps-like structure, and their sharp tips are closely approximated to the rod-shaped pointed unci. This type, characteristic of *Dicranophorus* (Fig. 44*A*), is protruded from the mouth to grasp prey.

e. Incudate Type.—This is similar to the forcipate type, having a general forceps-like shape though stouter with rudimentary manubria (Fig. 44*D, E*). It occurs among asplanchnids where it is employed to grasp food organisms. Its orientation in the mastax is such that protrusion through the mouth entails a rotation of 90 to 180 degrees.

f. Ramate Type.—The ramate mastax, characteristic of the Bdelloidea, is stout with reduced fulcrum and manubria, and large plate-like unci whose surface is provided with several parallel ridges (Fig. 44*C*). The grinding of the ridges of the unci upon each other produces an effective masticatory mill. A slight variant of the ramate type, termed *malleoramate*, occurs in the Flosculariacea.

g. Uncinate Type.—Here also fulcrum and manubria are greatly reduced, the unci bear a few teeth, the rami are stout, and large subunci are present (Fig. 44*F*). This type occurs in the Collothecacea that ingest large prey and hence have a voluminous sacciform mastax in which the trophi seem to play a minor role.

h. Fulcrate Type.—The trophi of the Seisonacea differ markedly from those of other rotifers, consisting of a median elongated piece, presumably the fulcrum, to whose anterior end are attached a pair of leaf-like manubria (Fig. 44*G*), and of several additional small pieces.

The lumen of the mastax is lined by cuticle and is ciliated only in current-feeding forms with a ramate mastax. The wall consists of an epithelium that is wholly syncytial or partly cellular and partly syncytial. This epithelium secretes the trophi and the numerous muscles of the mastax appear to be fibrillar extensions of its cytoplasm. The highly complicated musculature of the mastax has been thoroughly studied in a few Ploima as *Epiphanes* (Martini, 1912), *Brachionus*, and *Euchlanis* (Stoszberg, 1932) but can be only briefly summarized here (Fig. 45*A*). The muscles extend between pieces of the trophi and from the trophi to adjacent soft parts. The former include the *abductor rami* or *fulcroscapalis*, acting to open the rami; the *adductor rami* (Fig. 44*D*) running between the rami and closing them; *fulcro-manubricus*, from fulcrum to manubrium; *ramo-manubricus* from ramus to the cauda of the manubrium; *flexor mallei* from cauda to unci, causing the unci to strike against the rami; *uncicus*, attached to uncus and both ends of the manubrium, acting in cooperation with the preceding to rub the uncal teeth on the ramus; *adductor mallei*, a continuous band in the pharynx wall between the caudae of the two manubria, the chief muscle producing the chewing movements of the unci; *lateralis manubrii*, similar in relations to the preceding and assisting its action; and the *abductors* and *adductors of the cauda.* Muscle bands extending from the trophi to the mastax walls or to regions outside the mastax include: the *fulcro-oralis* from the fulcrum to the buccal field and adjacent portions of the head; the *fulcro-mucosus* from the fulcrum to the pharynx wall between the rami and acting as piston muscle in the virgate mastax; the *fulcro-esophagus* from fulcrum to esophagus; and the *scapalis*, of one or more bands from fulcrum to pharynx walls. All the muscles mentioned are of course paired; they are cross-striated and mostly devoid of nuclei.

Cutaneo-pharyngeal muscles between the mastax and the body wall are of general occurrence in rotifers. In addition to those already noted, there occur the *dorsopharyngeus* between mastax and dorsal body wall and the *retractor pharyngeus* between pharynx and ventral body wall with an extension to the corona in *Euchlanis.*

Salivary glands, two to seven in number, occur in the mastax wall in many rotifers as uninucleate or syncytial masses with granular or vacuolated cytoplasm (Fig. 45C). Usually there is a ventral pair of such glands. The ducts, which may be provided with a reservoir, open anterior to the trophi or even in the buccal tube or near the mouth. The function of the salivary glands is uncertain but presumably concerns ingestion or digestion.

The mastax is followed by a short or long tube, the esophagus, that may be lined with cuticle or ciliated throughout or at the posterior end only. The wall is syncytial and provided with muscle fibers that may form a sphincter at the entrance to the stomach. The esophagus is devoid of glands.

The next part of the digestive tract, the stomach, is an enlarged thick-walled sac or tube (U-shaped in the Synchaetidae), the wall of which is composed of a definite number (30 to 45) of large, granular, usually ciliated cells (Fig. 46C), filled with inclusions; except in the Bdelloidea where the stomach wall is syncytial (Fig. 46A). In the latter case, the lumen forms a broad or narrow ciliated tube that may bend or coil inside the syncytium. The stomach is provided with a muscular layer consisting of muscle cells whose circular and longitudinal fibers form a mesh (Fig. 45B) over its external surface; or if the stomach wall is syncytial, there are syncytial muscle fibers. At the junction of esophagus and stomach occurs a pair of gastric glands, seldom more, composed of a syncytium having a constant number of nuclei, and opening into the stomach by a simple pore on each side, seldom by a tube. The secretion consists of droplets or granules aggregated around the pore and presum-

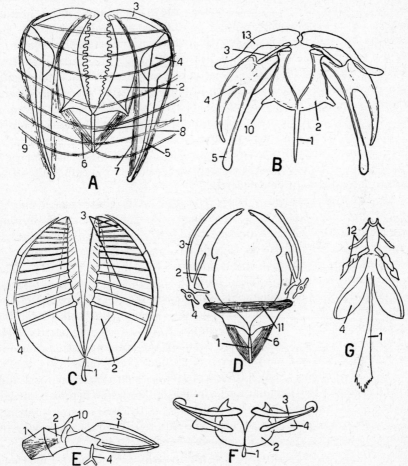

Fig. 44.—Trophi (continued). A. Forcipate trophi, schematic. B. Cardate trophi of Lindia. C. Ramate trophi. D. Incudate trophi. E. Incudate trophi, seen from the side. F. Uncinate trophi. G. Fulcrate trophi of Seison. (B, after Harring and Myers, 1921; others after Beauchamp, 1909.) 1, fulcrum; 2, ramus; 3, uncus; 4, manubrium; 5, cauda of the manubrium; 6, abductors rami; 7, ramo-manubricus; 8, flexor mallei; 9, general adductors; 10, alula of the ramus; 11, adductors rami; 12, accessory pieces; 13, epipharynx.

ably enzymatic. Sacculations of the stomach wall may occur (Fig. 58E) and in some Collothecacea the gastric glands are situated at the posterior end of the stomach.

The stomach may grade imperceptibly into the intestine, whence both are often spoken of together as stomach-intestine, or the intestine may be sharply constricted from the stomach by a pyloric sphincter. In the one case, the intestine is tubular, in the other, bladder-like. It consists of a thin syncytium, ciliated or not, and is provided with continuations of the muscle fibers of the stomach. The end of the intestine receives the protonephridial tubules and also usually the oviducts and hence is termed cloaca. It is histologically similar to and usually continuous with the intestine but may be constricted off as a sacciform chamber, especially when it assumes the function of a urinary bladder.

The stomach and intestine are attached to the body wall by the usual cutaneo-visceral muscles, including one or more pairs of *cutaneo-gastric* muscles from the lateral body wall to the stomach, similar *cutaneo-intestinal* muscles to the intestine, and often *dilator* muscles of the cloaca.

The position of the anus was already noted. An anus and cloaca are absent in certain strictly pelagic forms, such as *Asplanchna*, *Ascomorpha*, and *Chromogaster*, that suck their prey and therefore have no indigestible remnants requiring to be defecated.

11. Excretory System.—The excretory system consists of a pair of typical protonephridial tubules provided with flame bulbs and opening posteriorly into a common urinary bladder. The main tubules extend lengthwise the animal, one on each side, commonly in coils and loops and often fork into an anterior and a posterior branch (Fig. 47*B*, *D*). The flame bulbs, usually two to eight on each side, but up to 50 in asplanchnids (Fig. 47*D*), open into a ciliated capillary that enters the end of the main tubule or its branches and may run alongside the main tubule for some distance (Fig. 47*C*, *D*). A similar capillary, known as *Huxley's anastomosis*, may run transversely between the anterior terminations of the main tubules and may receive additional flame bulbs (Fig. 47*C*). The flame bulbs vary from a tubular to a flattened triangular form and contain a slender to triangular membranelle of fused cilia, kept in constant motion. The thickened cap-like end frequently bears one to several protoplasmic filaments that anchor the bulbs, mostly to the body wall; in asplanchnids there are instead external flagella that beat in the pseudocoel. The flame bulbs are not cells and usually contain no nucleus but are part of the general nephridial syncytium. Capillary and tubule are merely channels in a nephridial syncytium, often of some extent and with scattered nuclei; parts outside the syncytium have delicate syncytial walls. Driving cilia occur in the tubules in a few species.

Posteriorly the tubules open separately into a urinary bladder situated ventral to the cloaca into which it empties (Ploima); or they unite to a common stem that enters the ventral wall of the cloaca (Bdelloidea, Flosculariacea, some notommatids). In the former case, the bladder is a rounded sac with a syncytial wall covered externally by a muscle net

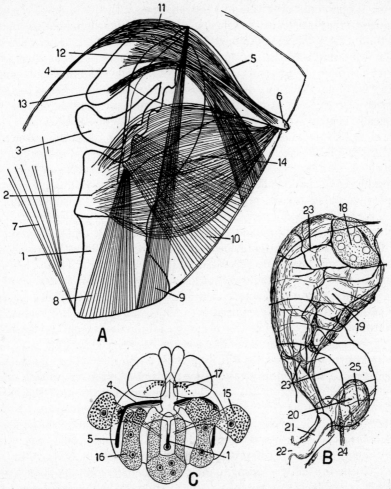

FIG. 45.—Mastax, digestive system. *A*. Scheme of the trophi of *Epiphanes*, showing some of the muscles, side view. *B*. Stomach and bladder of *Epiphanes*, showing muscle net on surface. (*A*, *B*, *after Martini*, 1912.) *C*. Frontal section through the mastax of *Epiphanes* (*after Beauchamp*, 1909), showing salivary glands. 1, fulcrum; 2, ramus; 3, subuncus; 4, uncus; 5, manubrium; 6, cauda of the manubrium; 7, fulcro-oralis; 8, fulcro-scapalis (= abductors rami); 9, fulcro-manubricus; 10, scapalis; 11, extensor mallei; 12, flexor mallei; 13, uncicus; 14, abductor caudae; 15, dorsal salivary glands; 16, ventral salivary glands; 17, secretory granules in buccal cells; 18, gastric glands; 19, stomach; 20, bladder; 21, cloaca; 22, anus; 23, muscle net; 24, caudovesicular ganglion; 25, main ventral nerve.

(Fig. 45*B*). In the latter, the cloaca serves as *cloacal bladder*, sharply marked off from the intestine as a rounded vesicle, well provided with dilator muscles (Fig. 46*A*).

12. Reproductive System and Sexual Dimorphism.—The rotifers are exclusively dioecious. As already mentioned, there exists in rotifers a

marked sexual dimorphism.   In the Seisonacea, the males have the same
grade of organization as the females, although somewhat smaller, and are
abundant at all times.   Among the Ploima, various degrees of reduction
of males occur, and the males appear only at certain seasons when great
numbers may be present.   They may resemble the female in general
external appearance but differ in their smaller size and in showing some
degree of reduction of the digestive tract, such as the loss of anus and
cloaca.   Generally, however, they are reduced to one-half to one-eighth
the size of the female and differ from her in shape, form of the lorica, form
of the corona, digestive tract, that is more or less degenerated, and lack of
a urinary bladder.   The greatest sexual dimorphism is seen in the orders
Flosculariacea and Collothecacea where the free-swimming males are
one-tenth or less the size of the females and have a simple ciliated anterior
end in place of the elaborate coronal lobes of the female (Fig. 48C).   The
reduction of the males is most pronounced in pelagic and sessile rotifers
and appears to be an adaptation to ensure fertilization under these conditions of life.   The minute size of the males results from the facts that they
come from smaller eggs and do not grow after hatching, often resembling
the juvenile phase of females; hence large numbers of them capable of
sexual activity can be produced in a short time.   The Bdelloidea lack
males and the members of this order are all parthenogenetic females.

The female reproductive system in the majority of rotifers consists of
a single syncytial ovary and a syncytial vitellarium (Fig. 47E) bound
together in a common membrane that continues to the cloaca as a simple
tubular oviduct (Fig. 46B).   In the Bdelloidea the germovitellaria and
oviducts are paired (Fig. 51D) and the Seisonacea have paired ovaries
without vitellaria.   The male system (Fig. 47F) usually consists of a
single large sacciform testis from which a ciliated sperm duct receiving a
pair, sometimes more, of prostatic glands, proceeds to the genital pore
(as a cloaca is usually wanting in males).   The posterior end of the sperm
duct is eversible as a cirrus (Fig. 48D, E) and may be lined with hardened
cuticle; or it may bear a cuticular tube protrusible as a penis (Fig. 48B);
or the body wall around the gonopore can assume a tubular form and so
act as copulatory organ.   It appears that only in a very few rotifers does
copulation occur by insertion of the copulatory apparatus into the cloaca
(Fig. 48A); in the majority hypodermic impregnation is the rule and the
sperm are injected through the body wall into the pseudocoel.   As the
early stages of spermatogenesis occur during embryonic development,
the testis of the mature male contains only spermatids and sperm.   The
sperm are of two kinds: typical sperm with large rounded or oval heads
and a tail provided with an undulating membrane (Fig. 49A); and
atypical sperm in the form of rod-shaped bodies.   The latter are believed
to assist in penetrating the cuticle during insemination.

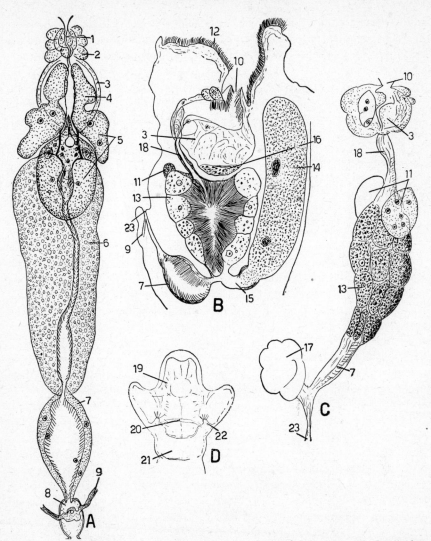

Fig. 46.—Digestive tract. *A.* Digestive tract of *Rotaria*, illustrating the Bdelloidea (*after Beauchamp*, 1909). *B.* Digestive tract of *Conochiloides*, illustrating the Floscu-lariacea. *C.* Digestive tract of *Epiphanes*, illustrating the Ploima (*after Beauchamp*, 1909). *D.* Coronal funnel of *Collotheca*, from life. 1, buccal tube; 2, buccal cells; 3, mastax; 4, reservoirs of the salivary glands; 5, ventral salivary glands; 6, syncytial stomach; 7, intes-tine; 8, cloacal bladder; 9, protonephridal tubules; 10, mouth; 11, gastric glands; 12, corona; 13, cellular stomach; 14, germovitellarium; 15, oviduct; 16, mastax ganglion; 17, urinary bladder; 18, esophagus; 19, infundibulum; 20, diaphragm; 21, vestibule; 22, pharyngeal sense organ; 23, anus.

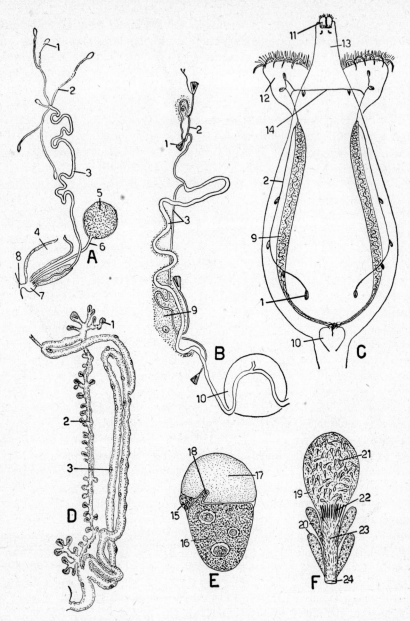

Fig. 47.—Excretory system, reproductive system. *A.* Excretory system of *Collotheca* (*after Montgomery*, 1903); capillaries spring from anterior end of tubule. *B.* Excretory system of *Euchlanis* (*after Stoszberg*, 1932); tubule forks, capillaries attached to the end of each fork. *C.* Excretory system of *Rotaria* (*after Brakenhoff*, 1937); capillary parallels tubule, Huxley's anastomosis present. *D.* Excretory system of *Asplanchna sieboldi* (*after Tannreuther*, 1920); capillary parallels tubule, opens into it at both ends. *E.* Germovitellarium of *Synchaeta* (*after Peters*, 1931). *F.* Male system (*Rhinoglena*, after *Wesenberg-*

The male system of the Seisonacea differs much from the foregoing account. The testes are paired, there is no copulatory apparatus, and the sperm duct enters a syncytial mass within which its coils are provided with ciliated enlargements (Fig. 51B). In the latter, the sperm, which are of ordinary flagellate type, are stuck together into bundles (spermatophores, Fig. 51C).

13. Histological Peculiarities of Rotifers.—It will have been noticed that practically all the structures of rotifers are syncytial. Definite cell walls occur chiefly in the stomach, although this, too, is syncytial in the Bdelloidea, and in the ganglia. The syncytial condition arises through the confluence of originally separate cells. Another notable characteristic of rotifers is their cell, or, rather, nuclear constancy. In any given species each organ and part contains a definite number of cells or nuclei, definitely located and bilaterally arranged. Thus for the common species *Epiphanes senta*, Martini (1912) records the following numbers of nuclei: coronal epidermis, 172; trunk and foot epidermis, 108; pedal glands, 19; circular muscles of the body wall, 22; retractor muscles, 40; brain, 183; peripheral nervous system, 63; mastax epithelium, 91; mastax musculature, 42; mastax nerve cells, 34; esophagus, 15; stomach, 39; each gastric gland, 6; intestine, 14; vitellarium, 8; oviduct, 3; each protonephridium, 14. The occurrence of six nuclei in each gastric gland and eight in the vitellarium is very common throughout rotifers (Van Cleave, 1922). The total number of nuclei in those rotifers that have been studied is 900 to 1000. The number is fixed during development and does not alter later.

14. Embryonic Development.—The maturing egg becomes constricted from the syncytial ovary by a delicate membrane that ruptures on the side of contact with the vitellarium. The edges turn back into the egg forming a canal along which yolk material passes from the vitellarium into the egg (Fig. 47E). The eggs are laid on the substratum or are stuck to the body of the female (Fig. 27C) or to other animals or are floating; some species are viviparous. Each female can lay only as many eggs as there are nuclei present in her ovary at birth. The number is limited, less than 50, often 10 to 20. The eggs are usually of oval form and enclosed in an evident shell within which there are often one or two thinner membranes closely adherent to the egg. Shell and membranes are formed by the egg itself. Outside the shell there may be an additional thin membrane or a gelatinous envelope acting as a float. A shell is lacking on eggs developing inside the mother's body.

In the Seisonacea, the eggs are all of one sort, require to be fertilized,

Lund, 1923). 1, flame bulb; 2, capillary; 3, tubule; 4, intestine; 5, germovitellarium; 6, oviduct; 7, cloacal bladder; 8, anus; 9, syncytium around tubule; 10, urinary bladder; 11, rostral lamellae; 12, trochal disk; 13, rostrum; 14, Huxley's anastomosis; 15, ovary; 16, vitellarium; 17, developing egg; 18, feeding tube from vitellarium into egg; 19, testis; 20, prostatic glands; 21, typical sperm; 22, rod sperm; 23, cirrus, 24, gonopore.

and hatch into either sex. The Bdelloidea lack males and their eggs develop parthenogenetically into females. In the Monogononta, three kinds of eggs occur: thin-shelled *amictic* eggs that cannot be fertilized and that develop parthenogenetically into females; smaller thin-shelled *mictic* eggs that if not fertilized develop into males; and thick-shelled dormant eggs that are simply fertilized mictic eggs and invariably hatch into amictic females (Fig. 48*F–H*). The amictic and mictic females do not differ anatomically except as to their ovocytes that present nuclear differences during their growth nor do they differ as to chromosomes (Shull, 1921). Any given female is either amictic or mictic and does not produce both kinds of eggs. The mictic eggs give off only one polar body at maturation and hence are diploid; the mictic eggs undergo normal maturation with two polar bodies and are haploid. The sperm penetrates the mictic egg while it is still immature. The egg then grows larger than it would if unfertilized, receives a larger supply of nutritive material from the vitellarium, which thereby alters much in appearance and color, and secretes a heavy shell, often spiny, warty, or ridged (Figs. 48*H*, 49*C*, 60*E*). Amictic eggs, although usually smooth, may also bear ornamentations. Dormant eggs and usually also amictic eggs are provided with a furrow where the shell springs open on hatching. Amictic and mictic eggs hatch in a day or less to a few days, depending on temperature, while the dormant eggs require days, weeks, or months, and can endure desiccation and low temperatures.

The best account of the embryology is that of Nachtwey (1925) for the amictic eggs of the viviparous *Asplanchna* and this account is here followed; Tannreuther (1920) also studied the development of *Asplanchna*. Unfortunately *Asplanchna* is a highly adapted pelagic form without intestine or anus, and its development may not be typical of the group. The egg cleaves totally into four blastomeres, *A*, *B*, *C*, and *D*, of which *D* is the largest and cleaves more rapidly (Fig. 49*D*). The next cleavages produce a 10-celled embryo, composed of two tiers of cells, except in the *D*-quadrant where there is a row of four cells (Fig. 49*E*, *F*). The lowermost cell of this row, at the vegetal pole, is again the largest cell of the embryo. It is the primordial sex cell; it passes into the interior (Fig. 49*G*) and becomes enclosed by the other blastomeres. This cell was formerly erroneously believed to be the entoderm cell but in *Asplanchna* there is no definite entoderm formation or process of gastrulation. The embryo at this time is therefore a stereoblastula (Fig. 49*H*) and furnishes a striking illustration of the early segregation of the germ cells from other body cells. The primordial germ cell is distinguished from the other blastomeres by the presence in its cytoplasm of a cloud of granules or *ectosomes*. After giving off two minute cells, the primordial germ cell divides into two equal cells. The posterior cell receives the ectosomes

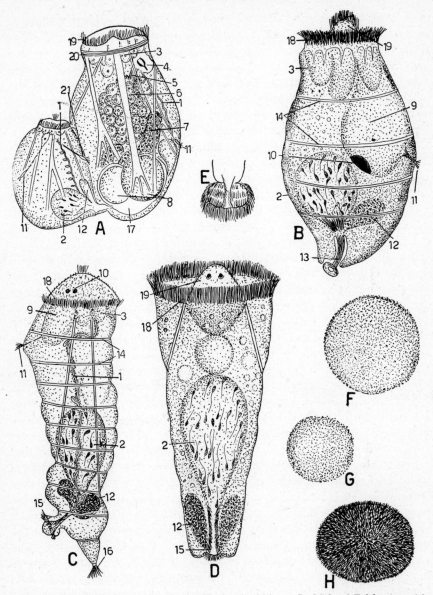

Fig. 48.—Reproduction. A. *Asplanchna* in copulation. B. Male of *Trichocerca* with penis (female in Fig. 29E). C. Male of *Collotheca* (females in Fig. 64). D. Male of *Conochilus*, with cirrus (female in Fig. 63D). E. Cirrus of D everted. F. Amictic egg of *Epiphanes*. G. Mictic egg of same. H. Fertilized dormant egg of same. (*All after Wesenberg-Lund*, 1920, 1923.) 1, protonephridium; 2, testis; 3, coronal matrix; 4, mastax; 5, esophagus; 6, stomach; 7, germovitellarium; 8, eggs; 9, brain; 10, eye; 11, dorsal antenna; 12, prostatic gland; 13, penis; 14, ring muscles; 15, cirrus; 16, caudal tufts; 17, oviduct; 18, corona; 19, rostrum; 20, coronal sphincter; 21, lateral antenna.

and its further offspring (32 cells) become the ovary. The anterior cell is the mother cell of the vitellarium; its divisions result in eight cells that soon fuse to a syncytium. All the other organs come from the surface layer of blastomeres that continues to proliferate without any definite formation of germ layers. The vegetal pole becomes the anterior end of the rotifer, the animal pole, marked by the polar body, is the posterior end, the *D*-quadrant cells are ventral, and the *A*-, *B*-, and *C*-quadrants constitute the dorsal and lateral regions.

At the anterior end (original vegetal pole) a mass of cells pushes into the interior; they are the primordium of the pharynx, whose formation may be regarded as a stomodaeal invagination (Fig. 50*A*–*C*). The cells of the mass arrange themselves into a blind tube whose connection with the surface is shoved ventrally by the later participation of *D*-quadrant cells in the invagination. The connection thus becomes located in the middle of the ventral surface and breaks through as the mouth (Fig. 50*C*). Through the shift mentioned, the pharyngeal tube comes to lie at right angles to the body axis so that its blind end touches the dorsal wall. In the floor of the tube an extensive proliferation of cells occurs; some of these cells become the mastax ganglion (Fig. 50*C*) while the others differentiate into the greater part of the mastax including the trophi. In the meantime, the dorsal wall of the embryo proliferates to form a double layer of cells, which by formation of a cavity between them, become the walls of the stomach (Fig. 50*C*). The stomach, thus at first part of the dorsal wall of the embryo, is displaced into the interior by overgrowth by future epidermal cells. To either side of the anterior end of the stomach a group of cells of the dorsal embryonic wall passes into the interior to become the gastric glands. Anterior to these, four pairs of large cells from the dorsal wall attach to the blind end of the pharynx tube and differentiate into the posterior part of the mastax and the salivary glands while two additional pairs of small cells give rise to the esophagus. Meanwhile the anterodorsal wall of the embryo has become a thick mass of small cells that takes up an interior position as the cerebral ganglia (Fig. 50*B*, *C*). A similar mass of small cells in the posterior part of the ventral surface becomes the caudal ganglion. A group of five small cells to either side directly behind the primordia of the gastric glands develops into a dorsal antenna (Fig. 50*D*). In this same region a group of cells passes into the interior on each side; most of these wander off into the pseudocoel as amoeboid cells while the remainder, seven in number on each side, become the protonephridia. Three of the seven cells unite to a syncytium in which the main canal appears as a coiled intrasyncytial channel (Fig. 50*E*). The other four become that part of the syncytium in which the capillary forms and from which four projections differentiate into the four flame bulbs. Those cells that remain on the surface after

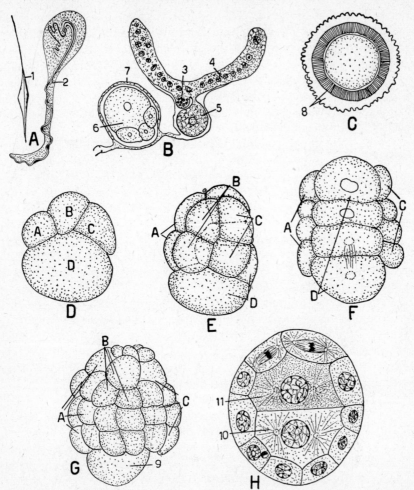

FIG. 49.—Reproduction, embryology. *A*. Sperm of *Sinantherina* (*after Hamburger*, 1907). *B*. Female system of *Asplanchna*. *C*. Fertilized dormant egg of *Asplanchna*. *D–H*. Development of *Asplanchna*. *D*. Four-cell stage. *E*. 10-cell stage, *D*-quadrant behind the others. *F*. 16-cell stage, *D*-quadrant in center, flanked by *A*- and *C*-quadrants. *G*. 35-cell stage, *D* macromere beginning to invaginate; note bilateral arrangement of blastomeres. (*B–G*, *after Tannreuther*, 1920.) *H*. Section through the embryo after invagination; *D* macromere has divided into the mother cells of the ovary and the vitellarium (*after Nachtwey*, 1925). 1, rod sperm; 2, normal sperm; 3, ovary; 4, yolk gland; 5, maturing egg; 6, embryo in the oviduct; 7, oviduct; 8, shells; 9, primordial germ cell; 10, mother cell of ovary; 11, mother cell of vitellarium.

all the organ primordia have sunk into the interior become the epidermis and certain large ones anterior to the mouth (which is shoved anteriorly again by growth in the ventral region) furnish the coronal matrix; others take a more interior position as the retractor muscles. The coronal and circular muscles are parts of the epidermal layer. After the primordia of

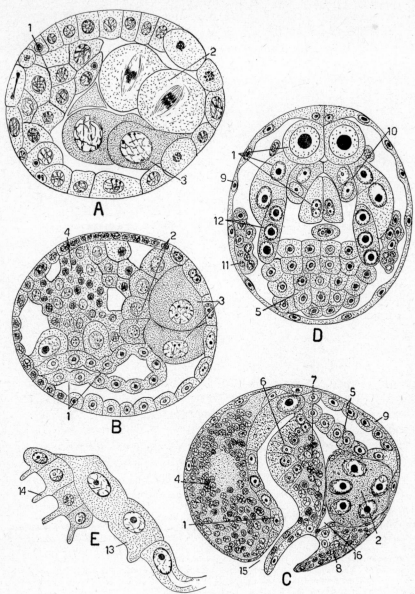

FIG. 50.—Embryology of *Asplanchna* (continued). *A.* Sagittal section through the embryo showing beginning formation of the pharynx. *B.* Sagittal section of a later stage, pharynx and brain indicated. *C.* Sagittal section still later, pharynx has reached stomach. *D.* Frontal section through the dorsal part of an embryo similar to *C*, showing bilateral arrangement of the primordia. *E.* Formation of nephridial tubule from three cells, and the four flame bulbs, each from a cell. (*All after Nachtwey*, 1925.) 1, primordium of the pharynx; 2, ovary; 3, vitellarium; 4, brain; 5, stomach; 6, mastax; 7, mastax ganglion; 8, caudovesicular ganglion; 9, definitive epidermis; 10, esophagus; 11, dorsal antenna; 12, primordium of the gastric glands; 13, protonephridium; 14, flame bulbs; 15, mouth; 16, oviduct.

all the organs have been laid down, cell multiplication ceases and there is no formation of additional cells or nuclei. Thus the number of cells or nuclei is fixed in early embryonic stages and consequently remains constant throughout the life of the rotifer. Soon after the organ primordia begin to differentiate, their cells unite to syncytia, except in the case of the stomach wall.

At hatching, female rotifers of free-swimming groups usually have the adult form and structure and grow to sexual maturity in a few days; males are commonly sexually mature at birth and do not grow. The lorica is generally a postnatal formation. In sessile rotifers, the females hatch as free-swimming juvenile forms, often termed larvae, that are of typical rotifer appearance, with short foot terminating in a tuft or circlet of cilia, and unlobed head bearing a simple circumapical band and two eyes (Fig. 64*C*). On attachment, the eyes degenerate, the foot end loses its ciliation, the foot elongates into a stalk, and the coronal lobes develop or in certain genera the corona is lost.

The embryonic development of rotifers, so far as known, presents many peculiarities and is difficult to compare with that of other low invertebrates. The early cleavage is suggestive of the determinate spiral type but the later stages differ from this type in their marked bilateral symmetry. Such a bilateral cleavage pattern is found among other invertebrates only in Acanthocephala and in fact Meyer has emphasized the general resemblance between acanthocephalan and rotiferan cleavage patterns (compare Figs. 50*D* and 17*D*). The formation of the pharynx seems to be a stomodaeal invagination and that of the longitudinal muscles and amoeboid cells of the pseudocoel could be regarded as ectomesodermal. The mode of origin of the posterior part of the pharynx, the esophagus, and the stomach from inwandered surface cells is peculiar and the origin of these parts in less specialized rotifers needs to be determined before conclusions can be reached. The primordial germ cell may represent all that remains of an entomesoderm cell and its enclosure may be a relic of epibolic gastrulation. In older studies on *Asplanchna* and other genera, this cell is stated to form the digestive tract (except pharynx) as well as the reproductive system and these accounts may not be as erroneous as Nachtwey believed. On the whole the embryology of rotifers considerably resembles that of the acoel Turbellaria but studies on less specialized genera than *Asplanchna* are needed before the embryology can be interpreted.

15. Order Seisonacea.—The Seisonacea are a small group of marine rotifers comprising one family Seisonidae, one genus *Seison* (= *Saccobdella, Paraseison*), and a few species, known only from European waters. *Seison* was discovered by Grube in 1859; other articles on the Seisonacea are those of Claus (1876, 1880), Plate (1887), and Illgen

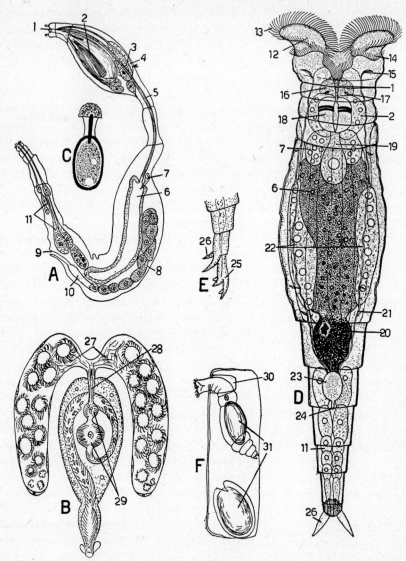

Fig. 51.—Seisonacea, Bdelloidea. *A. Seison (after Plate,* 1887). *B.* Scheme of the male system of *Seison (after Remane,* 1929). *C.* Spermatophore of *Seison (after Plate,* 1887). *D. Philodina roseola. E.* Foot of *Philodina.* *(D, E, after Hickernell,* 1917.) *F. Habrotrocha reclusa* inside a cell of *Sphagnum (after Budde,* 1925). 1, mouth; 2, mastax; 3, gland cells; 4, brain; 5, esophagus; 6, stomach; 7, gastric gland; 8, ovary; 9, female gonopore; 10, oviduct; 11, pedal glands; 12, trochal disk; 13, trochus; 14, cingulum; 15, flame bulb; 16, brain; 17, eyes; 18, trophi; 19, salivary glands; 20, intestine; 21, nephridium; 22, germovitellaria; 23, bladder; 24, anus; 25, toes; 26, spurs; 27, testes; 28, sperm duct; 29, spermatophoral vesicles; 30, aperture cut by rotifer in *Sphagnum* cell; 31, eggs.

(1916). *Seison* is epizoic or possibly ectoparasitic on the crustacean *Nebalia*, occurring chiefly on the gills. It is of peculiar external appearance (Fig. 51*A*). The body, up to 3 mm. in length, is covered with a jointed cuticle and is subdivided into a small oval head, a slender elongated neck, a stouter fusiform trunk, and a stalk-like foot terminating in an adhesive disk that receives the secretions of the numerous pedal glands. The corona is reduced to a few tufts of bristles. The head contains the mastax of fulcrate type (Fig. 44*G*), supplied by two large long-stalked salivary gland cells; the long esophagus extends the length of the neck to the stomach situated in the trunk and provided with numerous gastric glands. The very delicate intestine pursues a different course in the two sexes. In females there is a pair of ovaries without yolk glands; the oviducts unite to a short common oviduct that parallels and finally joins the intestine to form a cloaca (absent in the species figured). The intestine runs caudad to the anus situated in the anterior part of the foot stalk. The males, although a little smaller and less abundant than the females, are fully developed and similar to the latter in structure. There is a pair of testes from which the common sperm duct proceeds anteriorly in coils through a syncytial mass; in this it presents two ciliated enlargements or vesicles in which the sperm are formed into spermatophores (Fig. 51*B*, *C*). The intestine in males also turns forward and after receiving the sperm duct opens on the anterior part of the trunk. A cirrus or penis is lacking.

Seison moves about on the surface of the host in a leech-like manner by alternately attaching mouth and adhesive disk. These rotifers feed on minute particles, mostly detritus, and also suck out the contents of the host's eggs. They lay but one kind of egg, an ordinary fertilized egg, that is attached by a stalk to the host's gills.

Despite their aberrant appearance and adaptations for an epizoic existence, the Seisonacea are believed to be primitive rotifers as shown by their paired gonads, lack of a vitellarium and penis, presence of gland cells in place of the retrocerebral apparatus, general abundance of integumental glands, absence of sexual dimorphism, and production of only one kind of egg.

16. Order Bdelloidea.—The bdelloid rotifers are among the most familiar of fresh-water microscopic animals. Some of the more extensive articles about them are those of Zelinka (1886, 1888, 1892), Murray (1906), Bryce (1910), Dobers (1915), and Brakenhoff (1937). They are of very characteristic appearance and habits. The agile elongated body is made up of a number of cylindrical cuticular joints, typically 16, of which the shorter, smaller head, cervical, and foot segments are telescopically retractile into the larger, longer trunk joints. In typical Bdelloidea, as the Philodinidae, the corona is seen in its characteristic form, consisting of two trochal disks and the cingulum (Fig. 51*D*).   The circular trochal disks, raised on pedicels, may bear a central bristle or tuft of bristles mounted on a papilla, and are edged except medially by a single row of large trochal membranelles.   The cingulum, of small cilia, is borne to the the inner side of a collar-like ridge that encircles the pedicel bases, continues ventrally behind the mouth as a spout-like lower lip, and may project dorsally in front of the rostrum as a single or bilobed flap, the so-called upper lip.   The corona can be completely withdrawn by the action of retractor muscles and the true anterior end is then noticeable; it is formed of a finger-like, usually two-jointed rostrum, of which the tip, covered with cilia and often provided in addition with long stiff sensory bristles, is protected by the arched rostral lamella, usually more or less bifurcated (Fig. 29*A*).   The rostrum is also retractile and is not noticeable when the corona is unfurled.

In the less typical Bdelloidea, an entirely different type of corona, known as the *Adineta* type, is present.   This consists simply of a large ventral area covered uniformly with cilia (Fig. 31*E*) with the mouth toward its rear end.   According to the interpretation of Brakenhoff (1937) this ventral area represents the buccal field and the trochal disks and cingulum are reduced to a small group of cilia near the rostral lamellae.

There are typically in the Bdelloidea three head segments of which the corona and mouth occupy the third.   This is followed by three short cervical or neck segments of which the first bears the conspicuous palp-like dorsal antenna, located just behind the rostrum (Fig. 29*A*).   The eyes are cerebral or rostral.   Lateral antennae are lacking.   There are some large stout trunk segments of which the last bears the anus middorsally, followed by the more slender foot joints, varying from one to six, typically four in number.   The penultimate foot joint carries dorsally a pair of conspicuous spurs of obscure function; the final joint is provided with two, three, or four small toes or terminates in an adhesive disk (Fig. 30*E–H*).   The numerous pedal glands open on the spurs, toes, or adhesive disk.   The Bdelloidea are not loricate but the cuticle is often grooved or sculptured and is warty or spiny in a number of moss-dwelling callidinids (Fig. 52*A*, *B*).

From the large, often funnel-like mouth, a ciliated buccal tube leads to the mastax with ramate trophi kept in constant motion.   As already noted, it is the unci, not the rami, that form the important elements of this type of mastax.   The unci here are large plates provided with parallel ridges of which the middle ones are the most conspicuous (Fig. 44*C*).   The rolling of these ridges against each other produces a grinding action.   The syncytial intestine is usually brownish, often red in alpine and polar Bdelloidea; its terminal portion forms a contractile urinary bladder that

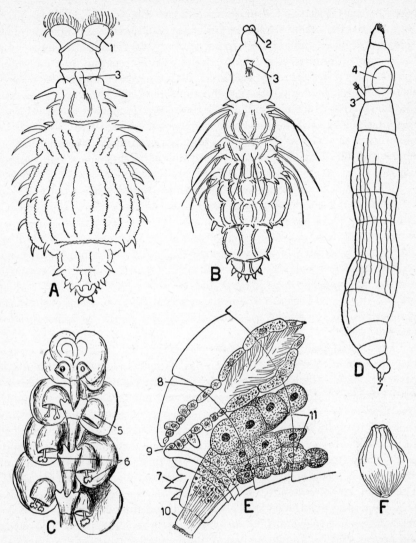

FIG. 52.—Bdelloidea. *A*, *B*. Variants of the very variable, spiny, moss-dwelling callidinid, *Macrotrachela multispinosus* (*after Murray*, 1911). *C*. Piece of the liverwort *Frullania*, with cups containing *Mniobia symbiotica*. *D*. *Mniobia symbiotica*, with corona retracted. *E*. Foot of *Mniobia symbiotica*, showing adhesive disk and large pedal glands. *F*. *Mniobia symbiotica*, contracted after drying. (*C–F, after Zelinka*, 1886.) 1, trochal disks; 2, rostral lamellae; 3, dorsal antenna; 4, retracted trochal disk; 5, cups; 6, rotifers; 7, spurs; 8, intestine; 9, anus; 10, adhesive disk; 11, pedal glands.

receives the common protonephridial canal (Fig. 46*A*).   Each nephridium consists of a syncytial strand that contains the sinuous main tubule and of a capillary that parallels the syncytium and bears several flame bulbs; there are also usually anterior capillaries that may be united by a Huxley's anastomosis (Fig. 47*C*).   The paired germovitellaria occur one to either side of the intestine and the common oviduct opens into the cloaca anterior to the nephridial entrance.   Several genera are viviparous and in these the oviducts may be degenerate or wanting.   Males have never been observed in the Bdelloidea and are presumably lacking so that only one kind of egg is laid and this develops parthenogenetically into a female.

The eggs are laid on the substratum or other objects, often fastened by pedal gland secretion, or may be enclosed in the case that harbors the adult as in *Habrotrocha*.   While usually thin-shelled the eggs may be thick-shelled and ornamented like the dormant eggs of the Ploima. They may hatch in 1 or 2 days as in *Philodina* but usually require a few days to a week or even 2 weeks.   The young on hatching are completely formed but undergo a growth period of a few to many days.   Most species live a few weeks to 3 months, not counting periods of desiccation through which the life of an individual rotifer might be prolonged for several years (see later).

The Bdelloidea consist of four families: the Habrotrochidae and Philodinidae with trochal disks, and the Adinetidae and Philodinavidae without them.   The Habrotrochidae are characterized by the broad solid stomach composed of a syncytium without lumen (Burger, 1948). The food is formed in pellets in the esophagus and these pellets become enclosed in vacuoles and are digested in the stomach syncytium (Fig. 53*A*).   The trochal disks of this family are somewhat reduced and may be partially fused.   The short plump body terminates in a short foot of three or four joints ending in three toes or two toes and a disk (Fig. 30*F*). The main genus *Habrotrocha*, with numerous species, usually inhabits a flask-shaped gelatinous case (Fig. 53*A*) within which the eggs are deposited.   Two species, *H. reclusa* (Fig. 51*F*) and *H. Roeperi*, live inside the hollow end cells of branches of the moss *Sphagnum* (Milne, 1888).

The Philodinidae have well-developed trochal disks, and as they do not form food pellets, their stomach is thick-walled with a narrow lumen. *Philodina*, perhaps the commonest microscopic metazoan, has a smooth surface, jointed elongated body, usually two eyes, four toes, and free-living oviparous habits (Fig. 51*D*, *E*).   *Macrotrachela* is a short form with a short foot provided with three toes; of the numerous species some are smooth-surfaced but in many the cuticle is ridged, papillate, or provided with long spines or other projections (Fig. 52*A*, *B*).   *Pleuretra* is of similar appearance with hard ridged cuticle and four toes.   *Mniobia* is

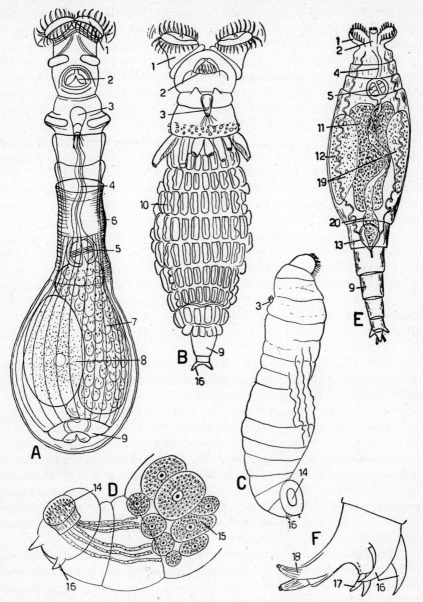

FIG. 53.—Bdelloidea (continued). *A. Habrotrocha*, in flask-shaped case. *B. Mniobia incrassata*, covered with secreted plates. (*A, B, after Murray*, 1905.) *C. Zelinkiella synaptae*, with corona retracted. *D.* Foot of *Zelinkiella*. (*C, D, after Zelinka*, 1888.) *E. Embata parasitica* (*after Giglioli*, 1863). *F.* Foot of *Embata* (*after Murray*, 1906). 1, trochal disks; 2, rostrum; 3, dorsal antenna; 4, buccal tube; 5, mastax; 6, case; 7, stomach with pellets; 8, egg; 9, foot; 10, plates; 11, syncytial stomach; 12, protonephridia; 13, bladder; 14, adhesive disk; 15, pedal glands; 16, spurs; 17, dorsal toes; 18, ventral toes; 19, germovitellaria; 20, intestine.

another short-footed form but the foot lacks toes and instead terminates in an adhesive disk although spurs are retained (Fig. 52*E*).   Certain species (*M. incrassata, M. mirabilis*) cover themselves with secretion that hardens into plates (Fig. 53*B*) and may be slipped off as a case for the eggs (Bartos, 1942).   *Mniobia symbiotica* (Fig. 52*C–F*) inhabits the pitcher-like leaves of the liverwort *Frullania* that fill with water during rains; other bdelloids may also occur in these pitchers (Zelinka, 1886). Members of the genus *Embata* are transparent thin-cuticled forms that lead an epizoic life on the gill plates of amphipods and isopods, in the gill chambers of crayfish, and on the surface of insect larvae, moving about in leech-like manner.   The oviparous *Embatas* attach their eggs to the host. The best known species, *Embata parasitica*, inhabits the gill plates and feet of amphipods and the gills of crayfish (Giglioli, 1863; Budde, 1925; Allen, 1933, Fig. 53*E, F*).   With the exception of some species of *Embata*, the foregoing bdelloids are all oviparous; the remaining genera are viviparous, incubating their young in the pseudocoel.   *Rotaria* (= *Rotifer*) has three toes and a pair of spurs (Fig. 27*B*) and in some species the entire foot region is greatly elongated (Fig. 30*E*).   *Zelinkiella* (= *Discopus*) is represented by one species, *Z. synaptae*, that lives in pits in the skin of sea cucumbers (Zelinka, 1888).   The foot lacks toes and is altered into an adhesive disk on which open the ducts of the 12 pedal glands (Fig. 53*C, D*).

In the Philodinavidae and Adinetidae there is progressive reduction of the trochal disks and loss of the cingulum, accompanied by greater prominence and diminished retractility of the rostrum, while the general body construction remains bdelloid.   Thus in *Abrochtha*, the disks are reduced to a pair of lobes to either side of the prominent rostrum (Fig. 54*A*); and in *Philodinavus* (= *Microdina*) they are fused to form a small bilobed ciliated area (Fig. 54*B*).   In these genera, members of the Philodinavidae, the mastax can be protruded to grasp food by means of especially developed uncal teeth.   *Adineta*, chief genus of the Adinetidae, appears to lack trochal disks altogether, but they are probably represented by a small ciliated area found near the rostral lamellae (Fig. 31*E*).

The Bdelloidea are typically bottom dwellers and crawl about on plants or the substratum in a leech-like manner by alternately attaching rostrum and toes, with the corona retracted.   The typical members can also swim by unfurling the trochal disks and telescoping the foot into the trunk but usually swim for only brief periods.   Upon finding a favorable situation, they obtain a firm hold with the toes aided by the adhesive secretion of the pedal glands, expand the trochal disks, and feed on minute organisms and particles brought in by the powerful rotary currents created by the trochal membranelles.   *Adineta* and related forms

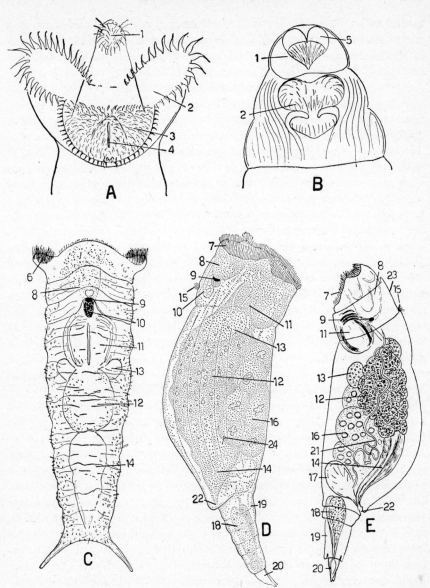

FIG. 54.—Bdelloidea (concluded), notommatoid Ploima. *A*. Corona of *Abrochtha* (*after Beauchamp*, 1909). *B*. Corona of *Philodinavus* (*after Murray* 1905). *C*. *Taphrocampa*, from life. *D*. *Eosphora* (*courtesy Dr. F. J. Myers*). *E*. *Pleurotrocha petromyzon* (*after Weber*, 1898). 1, rostrum; 2, trochal disks; 3, buccal field; 4, mouth; 5, rostral lamellae; 6, auricles; 7, corona; 8, brain; 9, cerebral eye; 10, retrocerebral sac; 11, mastax; 12, stomach; 13, gastric glands; 14, intestine; 15, dorsal antenna; 16, germovitellarium; 17, bladder; 18, pedal glands; 19, foot; 20, toes; 21, protonephridium; 22, anus; 23, cervical joint; 24, lateral antenna.

cannot swim but glide along the bottom gathering particles with their cilia.   At the rear border of the buccal field in *Adineta* is located a pair of transverse toothed bars resembling rakes that halt nutritive particles and direct them into the adjacent mouth (Fig. 31*E*).

The Bdelloidea are not only among the commonest inhabitants of standing fresh waters everywhere from the smallest pools to the littoral zone of large lakes but they also dwell in mosses, lichens, and liverworts, either such as are always wet or those that contain water only after rain. They inhabit moss growth on rocks, walls, and tree trunks; they occur in eave troughs, urns, and any other depressions that will hold water for a time after a rain; they are found on mountain heights either on moss or other cushion plants or in alpine lakes or in the muck of glaciers; and they have been recorded on mosses from Spitsbergen (78 degrees north latitude) and from antarctic lakes (77 degrees south latitude).   The bdelloids of habitats subject to desiccation are mostly members of the old genus *Callidina*, now broken up into several genera (*Habrotrocha*, *Macrotrachela*, *Pleuretra*, *Mniobia*, etc.), and may conveniently be referred to as callidinids; they are short, plump forms with short foot and no eyes. They can endure extreme desiccation lasting for months or years, and those of antarctic lakes remain frozen in ice for most of the year (see more later).   The life cycle of such rotifers consists of an alternation of a few days or weeks of activity after a rain or a thaw with days, weeks, or months spent in the desiccated or frozen state.   Bdelloid rotifers occur in hot springs at temperatures of 46°C. (Dobers, 1915) and a few fresh-water philodinids have occasionally been taken in brackish coastal waters but no members of the groups are characteristically marine.   In addition to the epizoic forms (*Embata* species), a philodinid has been recorded from the digestive tract of aquatic dipterous larvae (Marchaux, 1898).

17. Order Monogononta and Suborder Ploima.—This order embraces the remaining rotifers, characterized by the presence of not more than two toes, a single germovitellarium, and the greater or less reduction of the males which are provided with one testis and a cirrus or penis and do not form spermatophores.   Of the three suborders, Ploima, Flosculariacea, and Collothecacea, the first includes the majority of the rotifers and those of more normal body shape and coronal type.   The Ploima are ecologically divisible into benthic forms, inhabiting the bottom, vegetation, and littoral zones of fresh waters, and pelagic or limnetic types, characteristic of the open waters of lakes, ponds, and large rivers.   The former include the elongated vermiform Ploima with normal foot, that glide about or swim among plants or near the bottom, feeding on algae, diatoms, and detritus, whereas the pelagic Ploima are often sacciform with reduced or no foot and tend to carnivorous habits.   There are also a number of loricate Ploima of broad, dorsoventrally flattened shape.

The cuticle of the Ploima is usually less segmented than in the Bdelloidea; there is often a single, sometimes paired cerebral eye; lateral tentacles are present; the foot commonly terminates in two evident toes, supplied by a pair of pedal glands; and the corona does not consist of trochal and cingular circlets, being closer to the buccal-field–circumapical-band pattern.

Following Harring and Myers, the Ploima are here divided into the three groups Notommatoidea, Brachionoidea, and Asplanchnoidea, although Remane does not recognize this arrangement. The notommatoid Ploima are a large and complex assemblage of rotifers of normal elongate form, without a lorica, with mostly a virgate mastax, and corona referable to the buccal-field–circumapical-band pattern. The principal family, Notommatidae, has been taxonomically treated by Harring and Myers (1921, 1924) but there is no great certainty as to the genera to be included. Some common genera are *Proales* with definite neck segment, somewhat malleate trophi, and no auricles (Fig. 56*C*); *Notommata* with large buccal field, large retrocerebral organ, and protrusible auricles (Fig. 26*A*, *B*); *Taphrocampa* (Fig. 54*C*) with transversely wrinkled body, auricles, and degenerate foot; *Pleurotrocha* (Fig. 54*E*) with a foot, neck joint, and cerebral eye but no auricles or retrocerebral organ; *Cephalodella* (= *Diaschiza*, *Furcularia*), short, plump, with arched dorsal surface, fold separating neck from trunk, plates incompletely covering the trunk, and conspicuous elongated toes (Fig. 34*D*); *Eosphora* with broad plump trunk, fairly long foot, and well-developed retrocerebral organ (Fig. 54*D*); *Monommata* (Fig. 29*C*) with extremely long toes of which the right one is longer than the left; and *Drilophaga* and *Balatro* with parasitic habits (see later). *Cephalodella* is treated by Nuttall and Freeman (1903) and Wulfert (1938) and the anatomy of *Eosphora* by Hirschfelder (1910). Remane recommends the separation from the Notommatidae of *Lindia* (Fig. 55*D*) with cardate mastax (anatomical study by Dehl, 1934) as the Lindiidae and of *Dicranophorus* and related genera as the Dicranophoridae (monographed by Harring and Myers, 1927). The latter have a forcipate mastax and large buccal field without circumapical band (Fig. 31*D*). The principal genera are *Dicranophorus* (Fig. 34*A*) with distinct neck joint, conspicuous lobed rostrum, large retrocerebral sac, and two eye-spots; *Encentrum* (= *Diglena* in part), similar, without eyes or rostral lobes, and with short toes (Fig. 55*C*); and the parasitic *Albertia* (Fig. 55*B*) with a small head and minute rostrum, without neck, eyes, or retrocerebral organ, and with very minute toes or none at all.

From the Notommatidae are derivable three families with virgate mastax and pelagic carnivorous habits: Trichocercidae, Gastropodidae, and Synchaetidae. The Trichocercidae (= Rattulidae), monographed by Jennings (1903), common swimming rotifers of ponds, have cylindrical, spirally twisted bodies covered with a delicate lorica, and long spine-like toes with basal substyles; the chief genera are *Trichocerca* (= *Rattulus*) with right toe greatly reduced or absent (Fig. 29*E*) and *Diurella* with equal or somewhat unequal toes (Fig. 30*A, B*). The Gastropodidae are

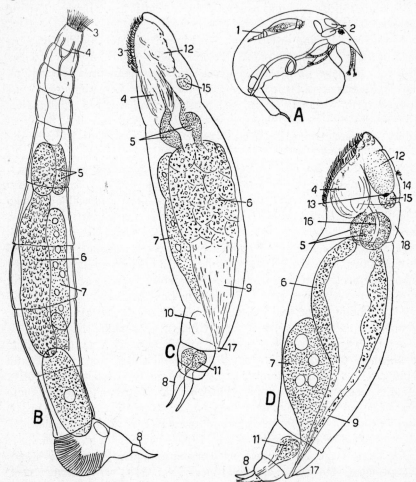

FIG. 55.—Notommatoid Ploima (continued). *A. Pleurotrocha petromyzon* inside dead cladoceran in which it has laid three eggs (*after Budde*, 1925). *B. Albertia* (*after Murray*, 1905). *C. Encentrum. D. Lindia.* (*C, D, from slides, courtesy Dr. F. J. Myers.*) 1, rotifer; 2, its eggs; 3, corona; 4, mastax; 5, gastric glands; 6, stomach; 7, germovitellarium; 8, toes; 9, intestine; 10, bladder; 11, pedal glands; 12, brain; 13, cerebral eye; 14, dorsal antenna; 15, retrocerebral sac; 16, esophagus; 17, anus; 18, cervical joint.

highly modified pelagic types with sacciform loricate bodies and syncytial lobulated stomach in which intracellular digestion occurs (Beauchamp, 1932); the genera are *Chromogaster* (= *Anapus*) and *Ascomorpha* (= *Sacculus*) without foot or anus, and *Gastropus* with anus and ventral foot (Figs. 58*C*, *E*, 67*A*). The Synchaetidae include *Synchaeta* (mono-graphed by Rousselet, 1902), of broad form tapering to the short foot, with prominent auricles, and four conspicuous sensory bristles on the apical field (Fig. 29*B*); *Ploesoma*, rounded with ringed foot projecting ventrally from the lorica (Fig. 27*A*); and *Polyarthra*, sacciform, footless, with six cuticular blades on each side of the trunk (Fig. 28*D*) used to produce a skipping motion.

Apparently allied to the Synchaetidae is the curious *Microcodon*, sole genus of the Microcodonidae. This (Fig. 58*G*) has a conical body taper-ing to the single toe, a virgate mastax, and a cordate corona edged with cilia and having a central pseudotrochus of long stiff membranelles.

The brachionoid Ploima are mostly stout forms, often dorsoventrally flattened, tending to the production of a heavy lorica, with malleate trophi, simple circumapical girdle, and persistent preoral portion of the buccal field. The Epiphanidae lack a lorica and have soft bodies of normal form tapering to the foot and a well-developed pseudotroch. In *Epiphanes* (= *Hydatina* and includes *Notops*), there are three tufts of membranelles above the pseudotroch (Fig. 37*A*) and eyes are wanting; *Rhinoglena* (= *Rhinops*) has a conspicuous rostrum bearing two eyes (Fig. 60); and *Cyrtonia* with one eye is strongly arched dorsally. In the Brachionidae, the broad flattened trunk is enclosed in a lorica of generally two pieces, dorsal and ventral, that are often provided with projections. *Brachionus* (including *Noteus*) has six such spines on the anterior edge of the dorsal plate, a slender wrinkled foot, and three conspicuous tufts of bristles on the corona (Fig. 56*A*); the similar *Platyias* differs in the foot of a few joints (Fig. 27*C*). *Brachionus* and *Platyias* have been mono-graphed by Ahlstrom (1940). Other brachionids are *Keratella* (= *Anu-raea*) and *Notholca*, pelagic rotifers without foot and with five tufts of bristles (Fig. 34*B*). *Euchlanis* and related forms lack lorical projections and have a simple preoral buccal field without special tufts (Fig. 57*A*, *B*). *Euchlanis* was monographed by Myers (1930) and its anatomy was treated by Lehmensick (1926). In the genera *Lepadella* (= *Metopidia*), *Colurella* (= *Colurus*), and *Squatinella* (= *Stephanops*) the one-piece lorica has a hood-like anterior extension over the dorsal surface of the head (Fig. 34*F*). In *Trichotria* (= *Dinocharis*) the tuberculate lorica completely encloses the head (Fig. 34*E*). The Lecanidae differ from the Brachionidae chiefly in the absence of a pseudotroch. The principal genera, *Lecane* with two toes (Fig. 30*C*) and *Monostyla* with one toe (Fig. 30*D*), have been monographed by Harring and Myers (1926).

The asplanchnoid Ploima comprise the single family Asplanchnidae, pelagic rotifers with delicate sacciform bodies, incudate trophi, and corona reduced to a simple circumapical circlet. The genera are *Harringia* (= *Notops*) with anus and small foot, *Asplanchnopus* with foot but no

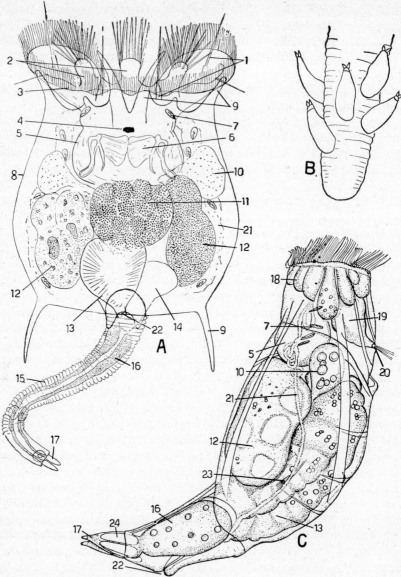

Fig. 56.—Ploima (continued). *A. Branchionus quadridentatus* (= *Noteus bakeri*), from life, dorsal view. *B. Proales daphnicola* attached to the tail of an oligochaete (*after Murray*, 1906). *C. Proales daphnicola* (*after Hollowday*, 1947). 1, sensory styles; 2, bunches of bristles; 3, circumapical band; 4, eye; 5, mastax; 6, trophi; 7, flame bulbs; 8, lorica; 9, spines of lorica; 10, gastric glands; 11, stomach; 12, germovitellarium; 13, intestine; 14, bladder; 15, foot; 16, pedal gland; 17, toes; 18, coronal matrix; 19, brain; 20, dorsal antenna; 21, nephridium; 22, anus; 23, lateral antenna; 24, reservoirs of pedal glands.

intestine or anus (Fig. 57C), and *Asplanchna* without intestine, foot, or anus (Fig. 29D). Some Asplanchnidae are notable for their possession of numerous flame bulbs, up to 50 on each side (Fig. 47D).

The Ploima not only furnish many of the most characteristic benthonic and pelagic rotifers but they also occupy various other habitats. The Epiphanidae appear to be characteristic of small pools full of decaying matter. A few Ploima can withstand desiccation in the same way as do the Bdelloidea and live with the latter in mosses and other sites subject to drying as well as in hot springs, polar lakes, etc. A considerable number of Ploima have been recorded from the ocean but many of these also occur in fresh or brackish waters; however, there are about 20 species of strictly marine pelagic Ploima. The Ploima, especially the genus *Proales*, also exhibit a variety of relations to other animals, varying from simple epizoic habits to endoparasitism. *Proales* (= *Furcularia*) *gammari* occurs on the legs and gills of amphipods along with *Embata* parasitica (Plate, 1886). *Proales daphnicola* (Fig. 56C) lives as an associate on the valves of *Daphnia* and other Cladocera to which it attaches its eggs (Thompson, 1892); it was also found once attached to an oligochaete (Murray, 1906, Fig. 56B). Some other notommatoids with epizoic habits are *Notommata paracyrtops* on Asellus (Beauchamp, 1932), *Pleurotrocha petromyzon* (Fig. 54E) on colonial vorticellids, also on *Daphnia*, *Cyclops*, and insect larvae (Thompson, 1892), on *Hydra* (Beauchamp, 1905), and inside the valves of dead and dying Cladocera (Budde, 1925), and *Cephalodella* (= *Pleurotrocha*) *parasitica* that temporarily fastens by the mastax on fresh-water oligochaetes (Jennings, 1900; Beauchamp, 1905).

The following forms are more definitely parasitic, inhabiting the interior of animals or plants, whose substance they devour. *Proales latrunculus* penetrates into the interior of the heliozoan *Acanthocystis* which it devours, laying about two eggs in the host; it then escapes, followed later by the young (Stokes, 1884; Pénard, 1905, 1909). *Proales gigantea* is a parasite of the eggs of pond snails (Glasscott, 1893; Stevens, 1912); it enters the snail egg by boring a hole through the tough membrane and feeds on the contents, causing the death of the snail embryo. Seven to thirteen eggs are laid inside the snail egg; these develop rapidly into young rotifers that devour any remaining egg contents and escape to infect new snail eggs. Probably the most famous parasitic rotifer is *Proales* (= *Notommata*) *werneckii* (Fig. 58A, B) that enters the tips of the filaments of the alga *Vaucheria*, causing the formation of a gall in the form of a variously shaped, often lobed excrescence (Fig. 57D) within which the rotifer lives, feeding on the contents and dying after depositing up to 50 eggs (Debray, 1890; Rothert, 1896; Budde, 1925). The eggs are of the usual sorts, subitaneous and dormant; the former hatch in a few days to either females or males; the latter develop only after several

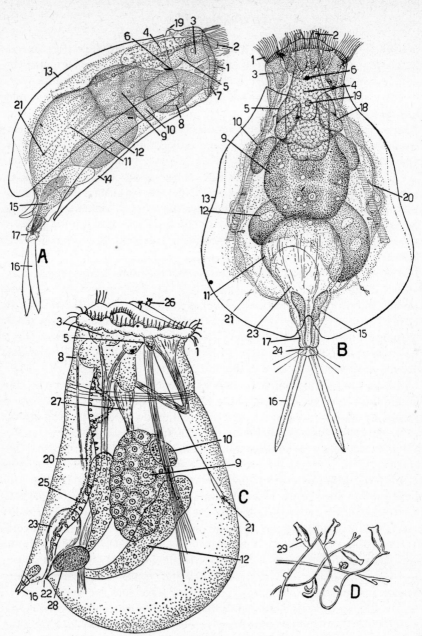

FIG. 57.—Ploima (continued). *A. Euchlanis*, from the side. *B. Euchlanis*, dorsal view. (*A, B, courtesy Dr. F. J. Myers.*) *C. Asplanchnopis* (*after Weber*, 1898). *D.* Galls formed by *Proales werneckii* in *Vaucheria* (*after Balbiani*, 1878). 1, corona; 2, duct of retrocerebral organ; 3, coronal matrix; 4, retrocerebral sac; 5, brain; 6, cerebral eye; 7, mouth; 8, mastax; 9, stomach; 10, gastric glands; 11, intestine; 12, germovitellarium; 13, dorsal plate of carapace; 14, ventral plate of carapace; 15, pedal glands; 16, toes; 17, foot; 18, subcerebral glands; 19, dorsal antenna; 20, nephridium; 21, lateral antenna; 22, anus; 23, bladder; 24, caudal sense organ; 25, flame bulbs; 26, apical sense organ; 27, esophagus; 28, embryo; 29, galls.

months. The young escape to the exterior and infect new *Vaucheria* filaments. *Proales werneckii* is one of the very few Ploima in which the male is almost as large as the female (Fig. 58*A, B*) and of similar morphology; although its salivary and gastric glands are reduced, its eye and dorsal antenna are better developed than in the female, and its digestive tract is complete. Several species of notommatoid Ploima, especially *Proales parasita* and *Ascomorpha volvocicola*, penetrate into the interior of *Volvox* colonies where they live and breed, feeding on the zooids. These two species have been greatly confused in the literature. *Proales parasita*, the less common species, has two toes (Rousselet, 1911; Searle, 1923). The more common *Ascomorpha volvocicola*, without toes (Fig. 58*C*), has been extensively treated by Plate (1886) and Budde (1925). The usual three kinds of eggs are laid (only one kind in a given *Volvox*) and these hatch into females or males; the males (Fig. 58*D*) are only half the size of the females and lack mouth, trophi, intestine, and anus. The mother rotifer and the young females escape and infect new *Volvox* colonies but the males remain where hatched so that a female can be fertilized only by happening to penetrate a *Volvox* colony already occupied by males. Still another parasitic *Proales* is *P. gonothyraeae* (Fig. 59*A*) that lives and lays eggs inside the hydrotheca of the hydroid *Gonothyraea*, feeding on the latter's tissues (Remane, 1929a).

An even more marked development of parasitic habits is seen in the notommatoid genera *Drilophaga*, *Albertia*, and *Balatro*, nearly all members of which are obligatory parasites. They are generally vermiform, with soft, colorless, transparent bodies, reduced anterior end and corona, and reduced or altered foot. All attach to the host by means of the mastax and are presumed to feed on the host fluids or tissues. *Drilophaga* (Vejdovsky, 1882; Beauchamp, 1904; Pawlowski, 1934, 1935) attaches to the surface of fresh-water oligochaetes and leeches (Fig. 59*C*). *Albertia*, discovered by Dujardin in 1838, lives in the intestine or coelom of earthworms and naid oligochaetes or in the intestine of slugs (Hlava, 1904b); it is a very sluggish form with a very small corona, a small conical toe, and reduced mastax (Fig. 55*B*). *Balatro*, described by Claparède (1867) and Issel (1904), is parasitic on the exterior or in the intestine of small oligochaetes. The species described by Issel is devoid of a corona.

The lorica of the brachionoid Ploima does not lend itself to epizoic or parasitic habits although some association with other animals may occur. Beauchamp (1932) mentions that brachionids may perch on *Daphnia* valves and *Lepadella* and *Lecane* may occur in the branchial cavities of decapod crustaceans.

The Ploima are sexually dimorphic and three sorts of eggs are laid, as already explained: mictic, amictic, and fertilized. The eggs are dropped on the substratum or fastened singly or in groups to objects. Pelagic

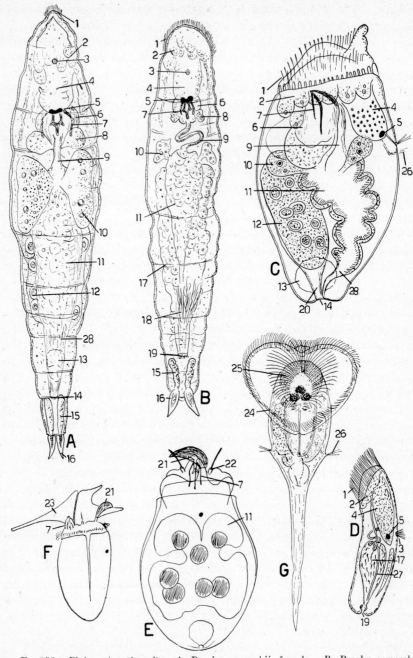

Fig. 58.—Ploima (continued). *A. Proales werneckii*, female. *B. Proales werneckii*,
male; note similarity of sexes in size and anatomy. (*A, B, after Rousselet*, 1897.) *C.
Ascomorpha volvocicola*, female. *D.* Same, male. (*C, D, after Plate*, 1886.) *E. Chromo-*

Ploima very often carry their eggs stuck to the posterior end of the body or may attach them to other plankton organisms, as algae, protozoans, other rotifers, or crustaceans, or the resting eggs may be provided with a floating device such as a jelly hull or long spines or air spaces. Some plankton Ploima, as *Asplanchna* (Fig. 48*A*) and *Rhinoglena* (Fig. 60*C*), are viviparous as regards the parthenogenetic eggs. The dormant eggs when carried by the mother either outside or inside are freed by her death and then usually sink, but later may form an air bubble and rise.

Males develop only from unfertilized mictic eggs (Fig. 60*D*). A valuable account of all the male rotifers known at that date was published by Wesenberg-Lund in 1923. Although males have been observed in only about 10 per cent of the Monogononta, it is to be presumed that they exist in all species of this order. In a very few Ploima, as *Proales werneckii* (Fig. 58*A, B*) and *Rhinoglena frontalis* (Fig. 60*A, B*), the males differ but little in size and anatomy from the females and have a fully developed digestive tract except that the anus is apparently wanting. Generally, however, the males are considerably smaller than the females and differ from them in structure, having no mouth or mastax and only a rudiment of the stomach-intestine (Figs. 48, 58*D*). The corona of males, being used solely for locomotion, is often simplified into a terminal disk of cilia, or a girdle encircling some bunches of cilia. The lorica is often less developed in the male or wanting when the female possesses one; but in some species only the male is loricate. The excretory system may be present but appears to be absent in the most reduced males. The greatest differences in size, shape, and anatomy between the sexes occur in the most strictly pelagic Ploima. The males commonly appear only at certain seasons of the year when they may occur in incredible numbers but live for only a few hours to a few days. Such a sexual period, recognizable not only by the presence of males but more readily by the production of the hard-shelled dormant eggs, is usually preceded by a great increase in the number of individuals. Some species are monocyclic, having only one such maximum and sexual period annually, generally in summer; others are dicyclic with two such periods per year, in spring and in autumn; others are polycyclic with several such maxima annually; while many species are acyclic without definite periodicity in male production. It is chiefly the pelagic rotifers that display one or two maxima annually with some regularity whereas those living in the vegetation zones of permanent ponds have less definite cycles and are often acyclic.

---

gaster with palp and lobulate stomach. *F. Chromogaster* attacking a dinoflagellate, holding it with the palp. (*E, F, after Kolisko,* 1938.) *G. Microcodon,* from life. 1, corona; 2, coronal matrix; 3, dorsal antenna; 4, brain; 5, cerebral eye; 6, mastax; 7, trophi; 8, salivary glands; 9, esophagus; 10, gastric glands; 11, stomach; 12, germovitellarium; 13, bladder; 14, anus; 15, pedal glands; 16, toes; 17, testis; 18, sperm; 19, gonopore; 20, oviduct; 21, palp; 22, sensory styles; 23, dinoflagellate; 24, circumapical band; 25, pseudotroch; 26, lateral antennae; 27, nephridium; 28, intestine.

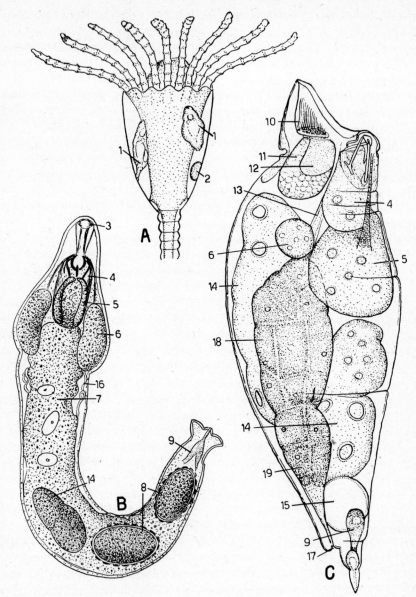

Fig. 59.—Ploima (continued). *A.* Hydranth of *Gonothyraea* with *Proales gonothyraeae* inside the hydrotheca (*after Remane*, 1929). *B. Balatro* (*after Issel*, 1906). *C. Drilophaga* (*after Pawlowski*, 1934). 1, rotifer; 2, its egg; 3, mouth; 4, mastax; 5, salivary glands; 6, gastric glands; 7, stomach-intestine; 8, eggs; 9, pedal glands; 10, corona; 11, retrocerebral organ; 12, brain; 13, esophagus; 14, germovitellarium; 15, bladder; 16, nephridium; 17, anus; 18, stomach; 19, intestine.

18. Suborder Flosculariacea.—Following recent workers, this suborder is taken to include not only the familiar sessile rotifers formerly known as melicertaceans but also a number of free-swimming genera, as *Testudinella* (= *Pterodina*), *Pompholyx*, *Filinia* (= *Triarthra*), *Pedalia* (= *Pedalion*), and *Trochosphaera*. The Flosculariacea have a malleoramate mastax, a corona in the form of a circumapical girdle generally differentiated into trochal and cingular circlets, no toes, and more than two pedal glands. The free-swimming forms, placed in the family Testudinellidae, lack a foot (except *Testudinella*), have apical eyes, and a corona in the form of a ciliary wreath. *Testudinella* (anatomy by Seehaus, 1930), found in ponds among vegetation, is flattened and turtle-shaped, with a lorica of dorsal and ventral plates, and a ventrally displaced foot terminating in a ciliated cup (Fig. 61*D*). The other genera of the family are pelagic with habits and reproductive cycles similar to those of the pelagic Ploima. *Pompholyx* (anatomy in Remane, 1933) is an oval loricate form with a posterior tube that seems to represent an invaginated foot and along which pass gelatinous threads for holding the eggs (Fig. 61*E*). *Filinia* has spine-like projections that in the ubiquitous *F. longiseta* (Fig. 28*A*) are very long and slender. The famous *Pedalia mira* (Hudson, 1872) is provided with six movable arms tipped with setose bristles (Fig. 28*C*) by the flapping of which it swims in a jumpy fashion. Originally supposed to be transitional to Crustacea and made the basis of a separate rotifer order, the Scirtopoda, in older taxonomic works, *Pedalia* is now regarded simply as a somewhat modified rotifer whose appendages are derivable from those of *Filinia*. Other species of *Pedalia* (Levander, 1894; Hauer, 1941) show a less development of the appendages and one species altogether lacks them. The male of *Pedalia mira* (Fig. 62*A*) has only three short elevations in place of the six "limbs" of the female. Even more noted is *Trochosphaera*, discovered in 1859 in the rice fields of the Philippines by Semper and since recorded from Australia, China, and the United States (Semper, 1872; Thorpe, 1893; Kofoid, 1896; Jennings, 1898; Valkanov, 1936). The female is spherical and transparent, encircled at or above the equator by a single row of cilia, in which on each side an eye is located (Fig. 62*C*). The mouth, below the ciliary girdle, leads to a curved digestive tract of normal construction, and protonephridia and sex organs present nothing special. At the time of its discovery and long afterward, *Trochosphaera* was hailed as a primitive ancestral type, having the construction of a trochophore larva, hence constituting a link between rotifers and annelids, and suggesting that rotifers are simply neotenous annelids. Students of rotifers now regard *Trochosphaera* simply as a highly specialized rotifer having no phylogenetic significance. The male, seen by Thorpe (1891), is quite different

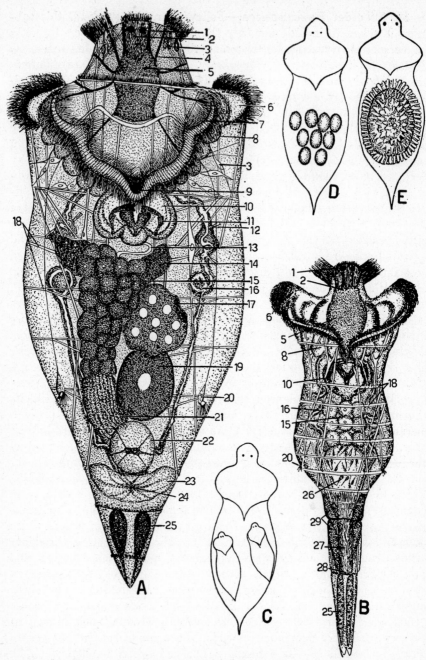

Fig. 60.—Ploima (concluded). A. *Rhinoglena*, female. B. *Rhinoglena*, male. C. Amictic female with parthenogenetic young. D. Mictic female containing male-producing eggs. E. Fertilized mictic female, containing fertilized dormant egg. (All after Wesenberg-

from the female and resembles the males of other flosculariaceans, being of oval form with an anterior ciliary wreath (Fig. 62*B*).

The sessile Flosculariacea, belonging to the family Flosculariidae (formerly Melicertidae) are (together with the Collothecacea) among the animals most admired by microscopists for their elegance of form. The family has been monographed by Joliet (1883) and Hlava (1908) and the sessile rotifers in general especially as regards their ecology have been treated by Edmondson (1940, 1944, 1945). The adult female has a trumpet-shaped body fastened by the elongated stalk-like foot and expanded at the anterior end into a circular, oval, cordate, or two-, four-, or eight-lobed disk, edged by the circumapical band, usually broken dorsally, and composed of prominent trochal and cingular circlets with a ciliated groove between them leading to the ventral mouth. These rotifers feed on minute particles and organisms directed into the coronal groove and so into the mouth by the currents created by the cilia of the disk. The conspicuous lateral tentacles are usually anterior in position, near the corona, and in some forms are also displaced ventrally. The anus, often elevated on a papilla, is also somewhat anterior because of a curve in the intestine. The foot stalk is enclosed in a gelatinous secretion that in many species is built up into a tube into which the animal can withdraw. The eggs are laid inside the jelly or tube or are stuck to the foot stalk or to the anal region. The excretory system, studied by Hlava (1904a, 1908), has the peculiarity that the capillary also opens into the cloaca; there is generally a Huxley's anastomosis but no urinary bladder. *Ptygura* (= *Oecistes*) has a more or less circular corona and a gelatinous envelope that may incorporate foreign bodies or fecal balls (Fig. 61*A*). *Limnias*, with bilobed corona (Fig. 61*C*), also inhabits a gelatinous tube. *Megalotrocha* and *Sinantherina* (= *Lacinularia*), with cordate coronal disk, exist as spherical free-swimming or attached colonies in which the individuals are fastened together at their foot ends by a gelatinous secretion (Huxley, 1853; Surface, 1906). The freshly hatched young are attached to the old colonies by gelatinous threads, that become entangled and so assist the young to aggregate into new colonies. These break loose and swim about or in the case of *Megalotrocha* (Surface, 1906) the balls come to rest on a suitable plant site. The individuals then leave the ball and crawl about on the plant while remaining attached to each other by gelatinous threads. Finally they settle on the plant and come together to a permanently attached ball, from which the individuals can no longer escape (Fig. 63*E*). *Beauchampia* (= *Cephalosiphon*) is charac-

---

Lund, 1903.) 1, eyes; 2, rostrum; 3, nerve cells; 4, nerves from brain; 5, brain; 6, auricles; 7, corona; 8, coronal matrix; 9, mouth; 10, mastax; 11, trophi; 12, flame bulb; 13, esophagus; 14, gastric gland; 15, stomach; 16, nephridium; 17, germovitellarium; 18, ring muscles; 19, egg; 20, lateral antenna; 21, intestine; 22, bladder; 23, cloaca (eversible); 24, anus; 25, pedal glands; 26, testis; 27, cirrus; 28, gonopore; 29, prostatic glands.

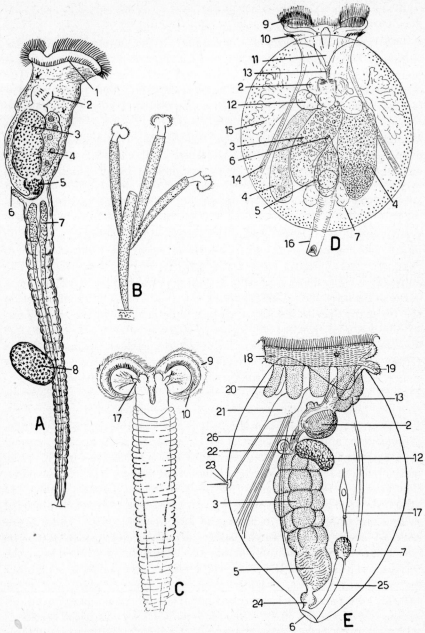

FIG. 61.—Flosculariacea. *A. Ptygura (after Weber, 1898). B.* Aggregation of *Limnias,* from life. *C. Limnias,* from life. *D. Testudinella,* from life. *E. Pompholyx (after Remane,* 1933). 1, corona; 2, mastax; 3, stomach; 4, germovitellarium; 5, intestine; 6, anus; 7, pedal glands; 8, egg; 9, trochus; 10, cingulum; 11, mouth; 12, gastric glands; 13, buccal tube; 14, lateral retractor; 15, nephridial complex; 16, foot; 17, lateral antenna; 18, circumapical band; 19, lip; 20, coronal matrix; 21, brain; 22, dorsal gastric gland; 23, dorsal antenna; 24, cloacal bladder; 25, tube representing invaginated foot; 26, esophagus.

terized by a very long conspicuous dorsal antenna. The beautiful *Floscularia* (= *Melicerta*) has a four-lobed disk (Fig. 33*C*) and inhabits a tubular case built up from a gelatinous basal ring by the deposition thereon, often in very regular rows, of fecal balls or of pellets formed in a special pit below the projecting lower lip (Fig. 33*C*). Particles directed into this pit from the mouth are whirled about and shaped into an oval form by the pit cilia aided by a sticky secretion from the pit glands. When the pellet is ready, the creature seems to feel with the dorsal antennae for a suitable spot on which to place it and then with its lip presses the pellet into the chosen site. Very perfect cases are built up in this way by the well-known species *F. ringens* (Fig. 33*C*). The cases may be attached to those of other individuals so that irregular colonies are formed (Fig. 61*B*). In the genus *Octotrocha*, reported from China, the coronal disk is eight-lobed. The Flosculariidae are bottom dwellers, attached to plants, stones, and other objects in fresh water.

The third and last flosculariacean family is the Conochilidae with the same sessile habit and general appearance as the Flosculariidae but differing in the horseshoe-shaped corona and dorsal mouth located in a bay of the inner ciliary circlet (Fig. 63*C*). The family comprises the two genera *Conochilus* (Rousselet, 1892), forming radial colonies (Fig. 63*B*), lacking a dorsal antenna and with lateral antennae situated on the coronal disk (Fig. 63*C, D*); and *Conochiloides* (Hlava, 1905), solitary or loosely aggregated into small colonies, with a dorsal antenna, and with lateral antennae below the disk. Colony formation in *Conochilus unicornis* (Fig. 63*B*) was described by Kolisko (1939); the young produced by a female adhere to her foot by their foot ends inside a delicate jelly hull and when the colony gets too large it breaks up into smaller colonies. *Conochilus* is viviparous or nearly so.

The Flosculariacea are sexually dimorphic, produce three kinds of eggs, and entirely resemble the Ploima in their sexual biology. They appear to be mostly monocyclic summer forms. In the sessile genera, the young females and the males are free-swimming and morphologically similar. They are of conical form, tapering from the ciliated anterior end bearing a pair of apical eyes to the concave foot provided with a circlet or tuft of cilia (Fig. 48*D*). The females usually lose the eyes later. The males are much smaller than the females, lack a digestive tract, and copulate by clinging to the female with the foot end and injecting sperm into the pseudocoel.

19. Suborder Collothecacea.—These are mostly sessile rotifers characterized by the expanded funnel-shaped anterior end, central mouth, uncinate mastax, and lack of toes. The digestive tract in correlation with the habit of ingesting large prey presents a voluminous mastax, often called crop or proventriculus, in which digestion takes place. The trophi

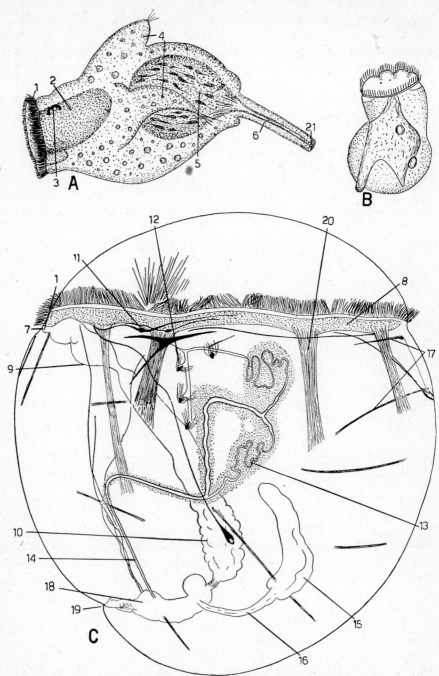

Fig. 62.—Flosculariacea (continued). *A.* Male of *Pedalia* (*after Wesenberg-Lund*, 1923). *B.* Male of *Trochosphaera* (*after Thorpe*, 1891). *C. Trochosphaera*, female (*after Valkanov*,

are found at the posterior end of the mastax and seem to play a minor role. The suborder comprises one family, the Collothecidae (= Flosculariidae) with five genera (morphology of the family by Montgomery, 1903). In *Collotheca* (= *Floscularia*), the coronal funnel may have a circular rim but is generally scalloped into broad or slender lobes tipped with long stiff bristles (Fig. 64*A, B*). In some species there is a single dorsal lobe; in others a single or divided ventral lobe is added; while in the most striking forms there are five or seven lobes. The body is of slender trumpet shape with a long foot stalk fastened to objects and is generally provided with a gelatinous envelope; a few species are pelagic, swimming about enclosed in a jelly case. *Stephanoceros* (anatomy by Jurcyzk, 1927) is similar to *Collotheca* but the five long narrow coronal lobes have whorls of stiff cilia (Fig. 63*A*). Both genera live mostly among water plants and feed by spreading the coronal funnel until some small animal happens to swim inside, whereupon the funnel suddenly contracts upon the prey while the bristles prevent escape. The eggs, containing a fully developed young in *Stephanoceros*, are laid inside the case.

To the Collothecidae also belong the three genera that lack a corona, namely, *Acyclus, Atrochus*, and *Cupelopagis* (= *Apsilus*). *Acyclus*, living attached in colonies of *Megalotrocha*, on whose young it feeds, has the same general shape as *Collotheca* but the anterior end consists of a hood-like expansion devoid of marginal cilia (Leidy, 1882; Beauchamp, 1912, Fig. 65*A*). In *Atrochus* and *Cupelopagis*, the funnel-shaped anterior part is marked off by a constriction from the stout oval posterior part. *Atrochus* (Fig. 65*C*) has a lobed coronal funnel bearing hollow tentacle-like projections; in the absence of a foot the animal moves slowly about on the bottom by muscular contractions and feeds on algae (Wierzejski, 1893). *Cupelopagis* is permanently fastened by the sucker-like foot that shifts during development to the ventral surface. It feeds by closing the funnel over small animals. The single species, *C. vorax* (Fig. 66), has been the object of studies by Metschnikoff (1866), Gast (1900), and Cori (1925). *Atrochus* and *Cupelopagis* are viviparous while *Acyclus* lays its eggs inside its gelatinous case.

The Collothecacea are sexually dimorphic with the same sexual biology as in the Ploima. The young females and the males are free-swimming and are much like those of the Flosculariacea. They are conical with a ciliary wreath, two apical eyes, and a ciliated foot end (Fig. 48*C*). A similar ciliary wreath occurs in the embryos or young females of those genera that lack a corona in the adult state. The young

---

1936). 1, corona; 2, brain; 3, eye; 4, body projections; 5, testis; 6, cirrus; 7, mouth; 8, coronal matrix; 9, mastax; 10, stomach; 11, nerve cells; 12, flame bulbs; 13, capillary; 14, nephridium; 15, germovitellarium; 16, oviduct; 17, ring muscles; 18, intestine; 19, anus; 20, retractor muscles; 21, gonopore.

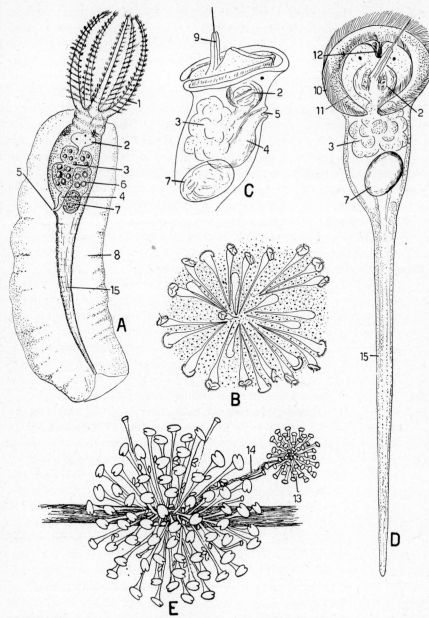

Fig. 63.—Flosculariacea, Collothecacea. *A. Stephanoceros (after Weber, 1898). B.* Colony of *Conochilus unicornis*, from life. *C. Conochilus*, side view, from life. *D. Conochilus unicornis*, dorsal view. *E.* Colony of *Megalotrocha (after Surface, 1906).* 1, arms of corona; 2, mastax; 3, stomach; 4, intestine; 5, anus; 6, germovitellarium; 7, egg; 8, case; 9, lateral antennae (fused to one); 10, trochus; 11, cingulum; 12, mouth; 13, young colony; 14, gelatinous strands between old and young colonies; 15, foot stalk.

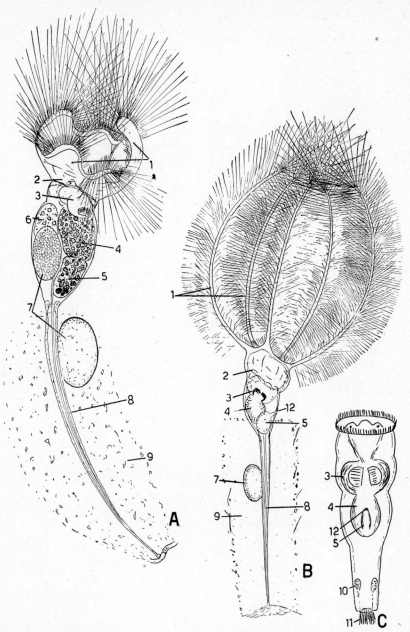

Fig. 64.—Collothecacea. *A, B*. Two species of *Collotheca*, from life. *C*. Young female of *Collotheca*, from life; for male see Fig. 48*C*. 1, lobes of corona; 2, vestibule; 3, mastax; 4, stomach; 5, intestine; 6, germovitellarium; 7, egg; 8, foot stalk; 9, case; 10, pedal glands; 11, caudal tuft of cilia; 12, anus.

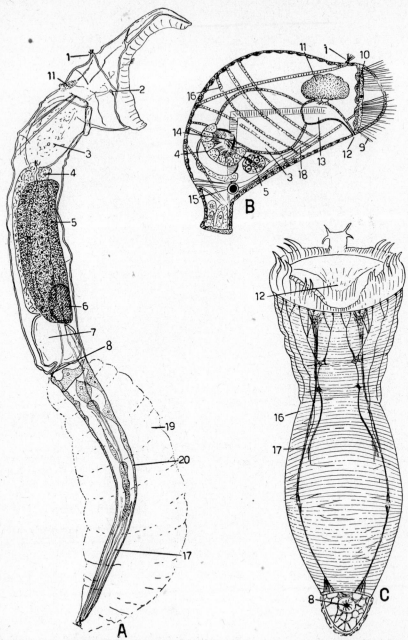

Fig. 65.—Collothecacea (continued). *A. Acyclus*, from the side (*after Beauchamp*, 1912). *B.* Young female of *Cupelopagis vorax* (*after Hünerhoff*, 1931). *C. Atrochus* (*after Wierzejski*, 1893), showing shape and muscles. 1, dorsal antenna; 2, lateral antenna; 3, mastax; 4, stomach; 5, germovitellarium; 6, egg; 7, intestine; 8, anus; 9, corona; 10, coronal matrix; 11, brain; 12, mouth; 13, buccal tube; 14, trophi; 15, statocyst; 16, ring muscles; 17, retractors; 18, nephridium; 19, tube; 20, foot stalk.

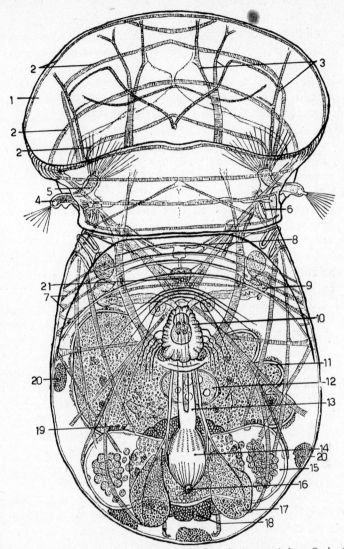

FIG. 66.—Collothecacea (concluded). *Cupelopagis vorax* (*after Cori,* 1925). 1, anterior funnel; 2, ring muscles of funnel; 3, longitudinal muscles; 4, lateral antenna; 5, pharyngeal sense organ; 6, flame bulb; 7, ring muscles of trunk; 8, mouth; 9, nephridium; 10, adhesive disk; 11, mastax; 12, embryo; 13, nephridial tubules; 14, intestine; 15, bladder; 16, anus; 17, gastric glands; 18, stomach; 19, cut ends of dorsoventral muscles; 20, pseudo-coelocyte; 21, ovary.

females (Fig. 64*C*) undergo a considerable transformation to the adult condition and hence are sometimes regarded as larvae. The eyes degenerate, the foot loses its ciliary tuft, attaches, and elongates into a stalk, the several pedal glands deteriorate, and the anterior end expands into a funnel with loss of the circumapical band or of the entire corona. The greatest changes are seen in the larva of *Cupelopagis* (Fig. 65*B*) in which a posterior curvature carries the foot end to the ventral surface of the trunk where it alters to a sucking disk. In this genus also, the larva possesses near the cloaca a structure resembling a statocyst (Fig. 65*B*) that soon disappears (Hünerhoff, 1931). The males of the Collothecacea are very minute and devoid of a digestive tract; copulation occurs as in the Flosculariacea.

20. Experimental Studies on Sex Determination in Rotifers.—As already explained, two sorts of females, amictic and mictic, occur in sexually dimorphic rotifers, and differ only in the type of egg they produce. Somewhere in the ontogeny of the females, it must be determined what kind of egg they are destined to lay. The determination occurs during the maturation of the egg from which the female comes, that is, during the last few hours before the egg is laid. The fate of an egg might be controlled during maturation by either external or internal factors. A number of zoologists have attempted to discover whether and what external conditions induce the appearance of mictic females. For this purpose various benthic rotifers, notably *Epiphanes* (= *Hydatina*) *senta*, have been bred in laboratory cultures and subjected to a variety of conditions. The main articles on this species are those of Shull (1910, 1911, 1912, 1915, 1918a, 1918b, 1923), Shull and Ladoff (1926), Whitney (1907, 1909, 1912, 1914, 1915, 1917), Hodgkinson (1918), Punnett (1906), and Hertel (1942). The status of the problem until 1929 was reviewed by Shull (1929). Experiments on other species were made by Tauson (1925, 1927), Luntz (1926, 1929), and Buchner (1936, 1941).

This work has shown that certain internal factors are involved. Some strains of a given species have an inherent tendency to produce a higher percentage of mictic females than do other strains. Further, under constant cultural conditions mictic females tend to recur in certain strains at more or less regular intervals. However, environmental factors are also operative in the production of mictic females. The early work claimed an increase in mictic females with high temperature (Maupas, 1891) or starvation (Nussbaum, 1897) but subsequent workers have failed to find any effect of temperature on percentage of mictic females and most deny any action of starvation, although Mitchell (1913) stated that in the humped form of *Asplanchna amphora* high feeding followed by brief starvation of newly hatched young results in male production while low feeding brings about return to the parthenogenetic saccate form. The experiments on *Epiphanes senta* by Whitney and Shull and on *Brachionus* and *Testudinella* by Luntz have shown that the percentage of mictic females can be decreased by concentrated manure culture, old culture water, urea, ammonia, and ammonium salts, beef extract, creatin, and other substances, and long continued culture under the same conditions; whereas an increase in mictic females results from change to fresh dilute culture medium, high oxygen content, change of carbonate content, change of acidity or alkalinity, and notably change of diet, particularly from colorless food organisms (e.g., *Polytoma*) to green food organisms, especially *Chlamydomonas*. The effectiveness of change from colorless to green food in greatly increasing male production was discovered by Whitney in 1914 and since repeatedly verified, most recently by Hertel (1942), although it now appears that in some cases any change of diet is operative. Tauson in a series of studies on *Asplanchna intermedia* transferred from one natural water to another concluded that any change of medium, especially change of hydrogen-ion concentration or carbonate content, in either direction, induces mictic females in a few days; they occur for about a week and then disappear as the rotifers acclimate to the medium. The conclusion from these numerous researches seems to be that, in addition to an inherent rhythm as regards male production, monotony of conditions suppresses mictic females, whereas any sudden change, especially of diet and of physicochemical composition of the water, induces the appearance of mictic females and consequently of males. In nature such changes of medium and available food might well happen at definite seasons of the year and so bring about a seasonal recurrence of males.

21. Regeneration.—The rotifers in general are incapable of regeneration and die shortly after amputations, often without even healing of the wound (Pai, 1934). Wound healing may occur in young animals and in *Asplanchna brightwelli* nonnucleated parts of the corona are replaced in young specimens (Pai, 1934). *Stephanoceros* when young can regenerate the coronal lobes as these contain no nuclei (Jurczyk, 1926, 1927; Ubisch, 1926) and simply grow out from the nucleated basal region. The regenerated arms are uniformly ciliated at first but later the cilia arrange into whorls. Regeneration of *Stephanoceros* takes place at the expense of growth and egg production. Similarly *Cupelopagis* will replace parts of the coronal funnel (Hünerhoff, 1931); and according to this author this occurs even when the removed parts contain nuclei although he was unable to state whether the regenerated areas are nucleated. Theoretically animals with constant cell or nuclear number should be incapable of replacing nucleated parts as their nuclei have ceased to divide.

22. Physiology.—The cuticle, lorica, trophi, and shells of the dormant eggs dissolve in potassium hydroxide and sodium hypochlorite with decreasing ease in the order named; the trophi are very soluble in concentrated hydrochloric acid, the other hard parts less acid-soluble (Beauchamp, 1909). These results indicate that these hard parts are scleroproteins, probably of several different kinds, as they are unequally soluble. Chitin is definitely absent. Kunike (1925) also verified the absence of chitin in rotifer trophi.

As regards feeding habits the rotifers fall into three categories: the current producers, the grasping carnivores, and the trapping carnivores. The less modified current producers, as many of the benthic Ploima, employ the corona both for locomotion and for wafting relatively large prey such as protozoans into the mouth. Specific adaptation for feeding by means of ciliary currents is seen in the bdelloids and the sessile flosculariaceans and is associated with sessile habits and loss of locomotory function of the corona. These forms have either two trochal disks or a large lobed corona; they maintain powerful water currents that bring to them the minute particles and organisms on which they feed. It was shown by Zelinka (1886) that the bdelloid trochal disks create two rotary water currents in opposite directions and that these currents direct two food streams into the groove between trochus and cingulum. The ciliary feeders have trophi of the chewing type, that is, ramate or malleoramate or malleate, with plate-like ridged or toothed unci that grind upon each other.

The carnivorous rotifers that feed by grasping relatively large prey, often other rotifers, are provided with trophi of the forceps type that can be protruded from the mouth. They include creeping rotifers such as the Dicranophoridae with forcipate mastax but are mostly pelagic forms as the Trichocercidae, Synchaetidae, and Gastropodidae with virgate mastax, and the Asplanchnidae with incudate mastax. They may chew the prey after catching it but those provided with a piston apparatus mostly suck out the contents, discarding the rest. Such food habits are generally accompanied by reduction or loss of the intestine and anus. The manner of feeding of a sucking rotifier has been well described by Kolisko (1938b) for *Chromogaster*, family Gastropodidae. The members of this family, highly adapted for a pelagic life, feed principally on dinoflagellates. Upon contacting the prey, the *Chromogaster* searches for a suitable hold by means of a sensory palp borne on the buccal field (Fig. 58*F*). It then grasps the dinoflagellate by the protruded trophi, bores a minute hole in the latter's armor, and then suddenly sucks in its contents in a stream. The same mechanism that operates the forceps action of the trophi simultaneously holds open the lumen of the pharynx.

A different carnivorous method of feeding is seen in the Collothecacea that wait for prey with widely spread coronal funnel. This lacks motile cilia and instead is provided with long motionless bristles (Fig. 64).

Whenever a small animal accidentally enters the funnel, the lobes or arms close over the prey, whose escape is prevented by the bristles. The latter probably also serve to keep out unsuitable organisms. The prey is taken into the voluminous pharynx where the trophi probably act principally to prevent too large particles from entering the stomach. *Atrochus* differs in feeding habits from other collothecaceans in that it creeps slowly about ingesting algae that are gathered in by the coronal tentacles (Wierzejski, 1893).

Very little definite information is available concerning digestion in rotifers. It is generally believed that digestion is extracellular in the majority of rotifers and takes place in the stomach through enzymes secreted by the gastric glands and operating in an alkaline medium. Beauchamp (1909) has given a very detailed account of the changes in the stomach wall during digestion in living, vitally stained *Epiphanes senta*. This rotifer feeds chiefly on flagellate protozoans. In the presence of ample food it rapidly stuffs its stomach with a pulp composed of chewed flagellates. Digestion is extremely rapid, for within 15 to 20 minutes the products of digestion begin to appear in the cells of the stomach wall which rapidly become packed with protein spherules and fat droplets (Fig. 67*B*). The stomach wall therefore appears to serve as a depot for the storage of food reserves. If the rotifer is starved, the protein spherules disappear from the stomach wall (Fig. 67*C*) within several hours, and the fat is also utilized. In a well-nourished animal, fine fat droplets are found throughout all the organs. Although the rotifers apparently cannot digest carbohydrates, glycogen is present in them, especially in the coronal matrix. They also appear unable to utilize chlorophyll for when *Epiphanes* feeds on green flagellates the greenish-brown material derived from chlorophyll that accumulates in the stomach wall is later ejected into the lumen.

Although extracellular digestion predominates in rotifers, intracellular digestion is practiced by the Gastropodidae (Remane, 1929; Beauchamp, 1932). As noted above, the members of this family suck the contents of their prey. They have large, lobulate stomachs devoid of cilia (Fig. 67*A*) and after feeding recognizable structures of the prey can be seen in the stomach wall in which digestion takes place. The gastric glands of the Gastropodidae appear to be in process of reduction.

The minute size of the rotifers precludes the necessity for any respiratory or circulatory mechanism. The function of the nephridial system is not definitely known. The bladder contracts one to four times per minute in different species and thus in a very short time discharges a volume of fluid equal to the body volume. Apparently water continually enters the rotifer body and is discharged through the protonephridia which thus act primarily as regulators of water content.

23. Ecology.—As already indicated the rotifers are adapted to a wide range of ecological conditions and include benthic, pelagic, terrestrial, epizoic, and parasitic members. The majority of the rotifers have benthic habits, frequenting the bottom and vegetation of small bodies of fresh water or the littoral zone of larger bodies. The free-swimming forms creep or swim about on the bottom or among vegetation, feeding on small organisms. The study of Ahlstrom (1933) indicates about 5000 such rotifers per liter in weedy ponds. The rotifers of such habitats endure wide ranges of temperature and pH. In general the number of species is greater but the number of individuals fewer in acid than in alkaline ponds, and some species are limited by the pH of the water or at least by the chemical conditions that determine acidity or alkalinity. Acid ponds are usually sphagnum bogs with dark water containing humus acids, with a pH of 7 to 4. The rotifer species characteristic of such situations have been listed by Wulfert (1940) who quotes Myers as reporting about 100 rotifer species in North America found only in acid waters.

The sandy shores of lakes just above the water's edge constitute a special kind of habitat in which the water film between the sand grains is occupied by a surprising number and variety of microscopic organisms. This habitat, termed the psammolittoral, is characterized by moderate temperatures, low oxygen, and high salt concentration. The psammolittoral habitat and its rotifers have been studied by Wiszniewski (1934), Myers (1936b), and Pennak (1940). The rotifer population consists in part of species characteristic of beaches and not found in the adjacent lake waters. Pennak states that in 10 cc. of beach sand containing 2 to 3 cc. of water there were 4,000,000 bacteria, 10,000 protozoans, 400 rotifers, and many other microscopic metazoans such as tardigrades, nematodes, copepods, and oligochaetes.

The semisessile bdelloids and the sessile rotifers of the families Flosculariidae and Collothecidae are important members of the benthic and littoral fauna of ponds and lakes. The ecology of the latter two families has been studied by Edmondson (1940, 1944, 1945), who finds a general preference for attachment to plants with finely divided leaves. The bladderwort, *Utricularia*, is particularly favored by sessile rotifers and as many as 25,000 may be attached to a sprig of *Utricularia* occupying a space equivalent to 1 liter. Different rotifer species tend to select particular plants for attachment and some species are never found except on certain plants; under experimental conditions in which they are given a choice of a number of aquatic plants, the motile young of these species will settle on a particular kind of plant. Some sessile rotifers are almost invariably found on algae, especially the blue-green alga *Gloeotrichia* and certain epiphytic green algae. Certain species also select particular locations along the axis of an aquatic plant, some placing themselves distally, others proximally. The slow-moving *Cupelopagis vorax* shows a preference for broad-leaved plants. The sessile rotifers are also sensitive to the chemical composition of the water and may avoid water of high bicarbonate content or having a pH outside certain limits. Populations of sessile rotifers reach a maximum by the middle of the summer, then decline and disappear in autumn, passing the winter as dormant eggs.

The pelagic or limnetic rotifers are among the most characteristic members of the open waters of lakes and large ponds where they average about 1000 per liter (Ahlstrom, 1933). They swim continuously and therefore have a locomotory corona which may also assist in food capture although many plankton rotifers seize their prey by protruding the mastax. The limnetic rotifers exhibit certain common features that are adaptive to a pelagic life such as thinness of cuticle, transparency, stout or sacciform shape, loss, reduction, or ventral displacement of the foot, and buoyant devices such as oil drops, long projecting spines (Fig. 28), or a jelly hull (Fig. 63*B*). The eggs must also be prevented from sinking and this is accomplished by the mother's carrying them or fastening them to other plankton organisms, even other rotifers; or they may be provided with spines, air cells, jelly hulls, etc. The pelagic rotifers belong to the Ploima, the Testitudinellidae, and the Conochilidae and have a very wide distribution; netting the open waters of lakes throughout the world will generally yield the same few species of plankton rotifers. Among the most characteristic and widespread species are: *Polyarthra trigla* (= *platyptera*, Fig. 28*D*), *Trichocerca cylindricus* (Fig. 29*E*), *Chromogaster testudo, Brachionus pala, Brachionus angularis, Keratella cochlearis* (Fig. 34*B*), *Keratella aculeata, Notholca longispina* (Fig. 28*B*), *Ploesoma truncatum* and *hudsoni* (Fig. 27*A*), species of *Synchaeta* (Fig. 29*B*) *Asplanchna priodonta* (Fig. 68*A*, *B*), *Conochilus unicornis* (Fig. 63*D*), *Filinia longiseta* (Fig. 28*A*), *Pedalia mira* (Fig. 28*C*), and *Pompholyx complanata* and *sulcata* (Fig. 61*E*).

Some of the planktonic Ploima, notably species of *Keratella, Brachionus, Notholca,* and *Asplanchna,* occur in a number of form variations, formerly thought to be distinct species, that may appear in a definite succession, apparently related to season, that is, external conditions. These variations consist in alterations of body proportions, and especially in length of the projecting spines of the lorica (Fig. 67*D–F*). Numerous papers have been written on the subject of the causes of these form changes, or *cyclomorphoses*, as Lauterborn termed them. Wesenberg-Lund (1900) concluded that the rotifers (and other plankton organisms) tend to enlarge their surfaces during summer by body or spine elongation as a means of increasing their buoyancy with decline of specific weight of the water brought on by rising temperature. Dieffenbach and Sachse

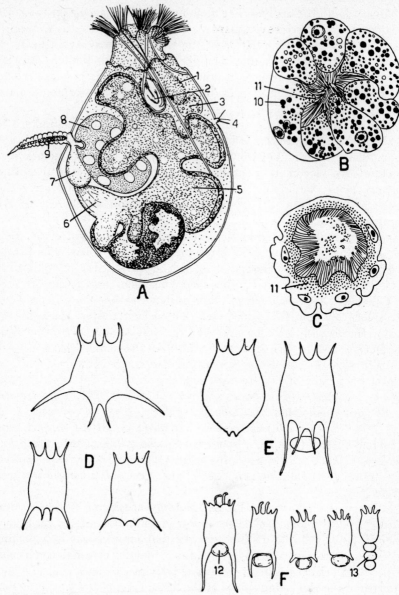

Fig. 67.—Physiology, ecology. *A. Gastropus stylifer*, with lobulate stomach (*after Wesenberg-Lund*, 1930). *B*. Section through the stomach of *Epiphanes* 2 hours after the cessation of feeding, showing protein balls. *C*. Same as *B* 10 hours after the cessation of feeding; protein balls have disappeared. (*B, C, after Beauchamp*, 1909.) *D, E*. Variants of shape of the lorica of *Brachionus pala* (*after Wesenberg-Lund*, 1930). *F*. Cycle of form changes of the lorica of *Keratella aculeata* from first parthenogenetic generation (left) to mictic female (right) (*after Krätschmar*, 1908). 1, brain; 2, mastax; 3, gastric gland; 4, dorsal antenna; 5, stomach; 6, intestine; 7, bladder; 8, germovitellarium; 9, foot; 10, protein spheres; 11, spheres of waste material; 12, parthenogenetic egg; 13, mictic eggs.

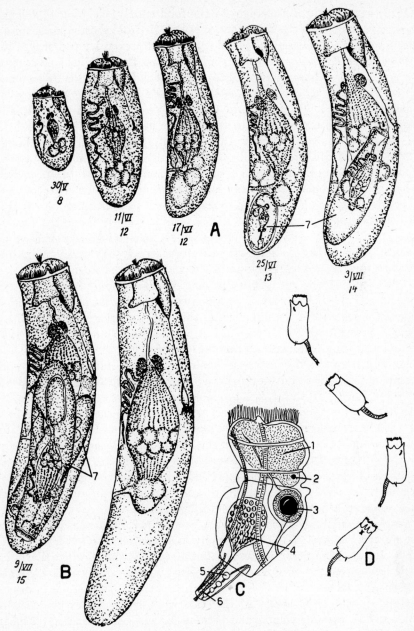

Fig. 68.—Ecology. *A, B.* Succession of form change of *Asplanchna priodonta* from May to July (*after Wesenberg-Lund*, 1930).   *C.* Male of *Keratella aculeata* (*after Krätschmar*, 1908).   *D.* Helicoidal path of swimming *Brachionus pala* (*after Viaud*, 1940); dorsal surface is kept facing outside of path.   1, brain; 2, cerebral eye; 3, oil drop; 4, testis; 5, pedal glands; 6, cirrus; 7, embryos.

(1912) attributed form changes to the food supply, claiming that long-spined forms appear when the food supply is rich and shortening of spines accompanies a decrease in the food supply.   However, Lauterborn (1900, 1904), using *Keratella cochlearis*, concluded that the terminal spine grows progressively shorter in successive generations from winter to summer (Fig. 67*F*) and Krätschmar (1908) confirmed this finding on *Keratella aculeata*.   The long-spined form (Fig. 34*C*) hatches from the dormant eggs and with successive parthenogenetic generations the spine gets shorter and shorter and may altogether disappear (Fig. 34*B*).   Long-spined forms can produce all other spine lengths but not vice versa. Consequently cyclomorphosis is a phenomenon related to successive parthenogenetic generations and is not attributable to external factors. This result was confirmed for *Keratella aculeata* by Hartmann (1920) and for *Asplanchna* by Lange (1913–1914).   As previously found by Wesenberg-Lund (1900), *Asplanchna* (Fig. 68*A, B*) increases greatly in size and length from spring to fall.   It therefore seems that many plankton rotifers undergo a progressive form change during the season.

Whitney (1916) was able to change *Brachionus pala* into what was considered another species of *Brachionus* by rearing its parthenogenetic eggs in a solution of sodium silicate; the experiment fails with fertilized eggs.   Powers (1912), Mitchell (1913), and Mitchell and Powers (1914) found that the small saccate form of *Asplanchna brightwellii* (= *amphora*) hatching from the dormant egg would give rise to larger humped and campanulate types and they believed they had induced these forms by means of diet.   However, it is probable that all these authors were really dealing with inherent cyclic form changes similar to the foregoing.

The terrestrial rotifers inhabit moss and lichen cushions adjacent to streams and lakes, also growing on glaciers, roofs, rocks, and trees.   They are active only during such times as these cushions are permeated with water and hence really lead an aquatic life in the water films between the plant parts.   They consist chiefly of bdelloids, especially callidinids, but also include a very few Ploima of such genera as *Lecane, Monostyla, Diaschiza,* and *Encentrum*.   These moss-dwelling rotifers are often spiny or warty (Fig. 52*A, B*) and, especially in alpine regions, frequently of a red color, resulting from carotenoids in the stomach and germovitellarium. The ecology of the moss-dwelling rotifers has been discussed by Heinis (1910) and Dobers (1915).   These creatures endure long periods of desiccation, up to 3 or 4 years.   At the onset of desiccation they contract to the smallest possible volume and become shriveled and wrinkled (Jacobs, 1909; Hickernell, 1917, Fig. 69).   Generally there is no secretion of a protective cyst but in recent years true encystment has been observed in a few bdelloids (Koning, 1929; Bryce, 1929; Bartos, 1942).   The survival in the desiccated condition is most successful if the rotifer was well-fed and if the drying occurs slowly. Upon the advent of water, the dried creatures swell, unfold, and resume activities in periods varying from minutes to several hours. Almost any bit of dried sphagnum will be found to contain desiccated rotifers. Reproduction generally follows rapidly on return to active life.

A number of rotifers lead epizoic and parasitic existences; they were considered above in the account of the orders and a useful review has been furnished by Budde (1925). Parasitism eventuates in the reduction of the head, corona, sense organs, and mastax, in the loss of activity, and the alteration of the foot into an organ of adhesion.

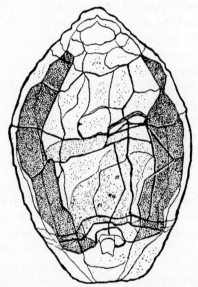

Fig. 69.—*Philodina roseola* in desiccated condition (*after Hickernell*, 1917).

Apart from the epizoic *Seison* and *Zelinkiella synaptae* which have no near relatives in fresh water, the marine rotifers are closely similar to fresh-water forms and belong to the same genera or species. They are free-swimming littoral or pelagic forms, chiefly Ploima. About 200 species have been recorded from brackish or salt water (Myers, 1936a) but the majority of the littoral ones are really fresh-water rotifers that occasionally occur along ocean shores and are able to adapt to a certain amount of salinity (Hofsten, 1912). There are probably less than 50 species that occur only or predominantly in the sea and most of these have littoral habits. They include species of *Synchaeta*, *Encentrum*, *Colurella*, *Lecane*, *Monostyla*, *Pleurotrocha*, *Notholca*, and *Testudinella* (only nonploimal marine genus). There are about 15 strictly marine pelagic Ploima, mostly of the genus *Synchaeta;* others belong to *Trichocerca* and *Keratella*. They seem to occur mainly in northern waters about 400 m. down (Zelinka, 1907).

The rotifers are in general cosmopolitan, that is, the same species occur throughout the world (Rousselet, 1909). Thus Murray (1911) examining collections of bdelloids from Australia, New Zealand, Fiji, Hawaii, British Columbia, and South Africa found the majority of the species identical with those of Europe and the British Isles, although a few peculiar ones were noted from Fiji and Hawaii. Of course the species inhabiting any particular pond are correlated with the chemical conditions and the plant life of that pond, but give the same type of pond in other parts of the world and the identical species are apt to be found therein. The universal distribution of rotifers is usually attributed to the fact that the dormant eggs and the adults in the desiccated state are readily blown about or carried by animals, and remain viable for long periods under extreme conditions.

As already mentioned, sexually dimorphic rotifers usually display pronounced reproductive cycles more or less related to seasonal conditions; such cycles have been particularly studied by Wesenberg-Lund (1930). Simple cycles obtain in the case of species inhabiting small temporary pools as *Epiphanes senta*. The dormant eggs hatch in spring with the advent of water; the population, consisting at first of amictic females, rapidly increases until myriads are present; mictic females then appear producing about 50 males each; and after copulation and laying of dormant eggs, the entire population dies off. This cycle occupies several weeks and for the rest of the year the species is represented only by the dormant eggs. Similar cycles obtain for some rotifers of small permanent ponds; the population reaches a maximum early in the season, males appear, and dormant eggs are laid; but some amictic females persist throughout the year, reproducing parthenogenetically. It would seem that in such species there is an inherent tendency for the production of mictic females after a limited number of generations of amictic forms. A good many rotifers of permanent water are summer forms, that is, the population gradually increases, reaching a maximum at the height of the summer, then gradually declines and disappears, leaving the dormant eggs to initiate a new cycle the following spring. The sessile rotifers of the families Flosculariidae and Collothecidae as well as a number of Ploima belong to this category. The most striking cycles are exhibited by the typical planktonic Ploima which have one or more population maxima accompanied by male production annually but are present throughout the year. Rotifers that remain active throughout the year are termed perennial. As discussed above, their cycles seem to be controlled to some extent by external conditions. The bdelloids that inhabit permanent waters are acyclic and perennial as a rule and may attain great numbers in winter under ice (Wesenberg-Lund, 1930).

The parthenogenetic eggs of rotifers hatch in 1 to 3 days but the dormant eggs when simply left in water require 6 to 8 weeks to hatch. In laboratory conditions the dormant eggs often fail to hatch. Hertel (1942) induced immediate hatching of the dormant eggs of *Epiphanes senta* on return to culture water after being kept 3 days in a desiccator. Lite and Whitney (1925) found that aeration of dormant eggs of *Brachionus* and *Asplanchna* causes the embryo to develop but the latter is unable to break the shell and escape. Preliminary treatment of several days with stale water weakens the shell so that hatching occurs promptly after return to aerated water. Presumably the dormancy of the fertilized eggs results from the imperviousness of the hard shell which is weakened by conditions such eggs meet in nature, as drying and freezing. Possibly until acted on by such factors the shell does not admit oxygen; it is, however, pervious to water (Lite and Whitney, 1925).

The rate of growth was measured for *Brachionus pala* by Chu (1934), for *Proales decipiens* and *Euchlanis dilatata* by Liebers (1937), and for a number of bdelloids by Dobers (1915); all give the usual growth curve, rapid increase in length at first with gradual decline and eventual cessation. All parts of *B. pala* were found to grow at the same rate. On the other hand *Floscularia conifera* was found to increase in length uniformly at a rate of 0.15 to 0.33 mm. per day (Edmondson, 1945); carmine added to the water was incorporated into the pellets of the tube and the zone of colored pellets served as a base for measuring increase in tube length.

Numerous studies have been made in laboratory cultures of the length of life of rotifers, the number of eggs laid, etc. Some of the available data for amictic ploimate and flosculariacean females are: *Asplanchna sieboldii*, 2 to 3 weeks (Tannreuther, 1919); *Proales decipiens*, 3 to 8 days, 20 eggs in winter, 30 in summer (Noyes, 1922); 12 days, 13 to 15 eggs, maximum, 23 (Liebers, 1937); *Cupelopagis vorax*, 40 days, about 40 young (Cori, 1925); *Euchlanis triquetra*, 21 days, 24 eggs (Lehmensick, 1926); *Lecane inermis*, 8 to 9 days, maximum 14, about 14 eggs (Finesinger, 1926; Miller, 1931); *Proales sordida*, 8 to 9 days, maximum, 22, 24 to 28 eggs, maximum, 34 (Jennings and Lynch, 1928; Lynch and Smith, 1931); *Testudinella*, five eggs (Luntz, 1926); *Epiphanes senta*, 8 days, 45 eggs, maximum, 66 (Ferris, 1932); *Brachionus pala*, 12 to 19 days (Chu, 1934); 6 days, about four eggs (Kolisko, 1938a); *Euchlanis dilatata*, 13 to 15 days, maximum 23, 7 eggs, maximum, 18 (Liebers, 1937); *Keratella aculeata*, 22 days, maximum, 29, eight eggs, maximum, 15 (Kolisko, 1938a); *Epiphanes brachionus*, 8 days, maximum, 17, about four eggs (Kolisko, 1938a); and *Floscularia conifera*, 4 to 6 days, maximum, 18, one or two eggs daily (Edmondson, 1945). In some species, the mictic females live longer than the amictic ones and produce more eggs, but usually the survival times of the two kinds of females are similar. Edmondson (1945) surprisingly found that aggregates of *Floscularia conifera* grow to about twice the length, live twice as long, and produce more eggs than solitary individuals.

It has been noticed by several of the above observers (see especially Jennings and Lynch, 1928) that the earlier and later eggs produced by a given female tend to be smaller and less viable and to give rise to smaller rotifers of reduced reproductive capacity. Often the last laid eggs fail to develop. In general the best developed and most viable and fecund young are derived from the middle reproductive period of mothers. Apparently these properties of the young depend upon the size of the egg from which they come and this presumably determines the amount of stored food available for the nutrition of the embryo.

In these laboratory cultures evidences of senescence are very noticeable; they include general sluggishness and reduction of activity, cessation of feeding, degeneration of internal organs, cessation of egg laying, increasing opacity and granularity in most cases, transparency in some.

The bdelloid rotifers appear in general to live longer than the Monogononta. Some data are: *Philodina roseola*, 10 days; *P. citrina*, 21 days; *P. megalotrocha*, 17 days; *Rotaria macrura*, 58 days; *R. rotatoria*, 20 to 50 days, mostly 35, one to nine young, mostly four (Spemann, 1924); callidinids, 5 months (Zelinka, 1891); *Adineta vaga*, 15 to 19 days, maximum, 22, maximum of ten eggs; *A. barbata*, maximum of 21 days, two eggs; *Habrotrocha constricta*, maximum of 34 days, six or seven eggs; *Macrotrachela quadricornifera*, 2 months, *Mniobia russeola*, over 30 days (Dobers, 1915). If one counts the months spent by callidinids in the desiccated or frozen condition, then they can undoubtedly live up to several years. The longest survival on record is that of a callidinid recovered from dry moss specimens kept 59 years in an herbarium (Rahm, 1923); however, there is no certainty that dust and fragments from other specimens were excluded. Increased reproductivity is reported following recovery from desiccation (Dobers, 1915).

In general no decline in vigor or fecundity is seen in rotifers bred parthenogenetically for many generations. However, inbreeding, that is, fertilization of mictic females by the males they produced, results in decreased vigor and fecundity in the parthenogenetic lines reared from such fertilized eggs (Whitney, 1912b; Hertel, 1942); outbreeding restores the original properties.

Experiments on the reactions of rotifers to external factors concern chiefly endurance of temperature extremes and of desiccation. In the active state, rotifers can endure temperatures to about 45°C. (Spemann, 1924). Numerous reports of the occurrence of rotifers in hot springs were made by Issel (1900, 1901, 1906), who found *Philodina roseola* at

46°C.; *Notommata najas* at 45°C.; *Lecane gissensis* and *Lepadella ovalis* at 42°C.; and *Rotaria rotataria, Monostyla cornuta, Adineta vaga,* and *Diaschiza gibba* at temperatures between 35 and 39°C. The identifications of some of these species are probably dubious, but evidently a number of different Bdelloidea and Ploima can live at rather high temperatures. In the desiccated condition, callidinids stand temperatures up to 151°C. for 35 minutes and 170 to 200°C. in an electric oven for 5 minutes (Rahm, 1923). Equally astounding is the resistance of bdelloids to cold. Murray (1910) reported that the two most common bdelloids of antarctic lakes, *Philodina gregaria* and *Adineta grandis,* could in the active state be repeatedly frozen and thawed without damage and could endure a temperature of −78°C. for hours. In the desiccated state the resistance to cold is almost unlimited (Rahm, 1923); desiccated callidinids withstood the temperature of liquid helium (−272°C.) for nearly 8 hours. Desiccated bdelloids are not damaged by being exposed to drying agents in desiccators or to a vacuum but cannot endure the total absence of oxygen (Rahm, 1923). This indicates that even in the state of extreme desiccation some metabolism is in progress.

According to Jennings (1906) the general behavior of the rotifers and their reactions to environmental factors are very similar to those of ciliate Protozoa. Many rotifers swim in a spiral helicoidal path like ciliates with body rotation such that one surface always faces the outer side of the spiral (Jennings, 1902; Viaud, 1940, Fig. 68*D*). Jennings has related the asymmetrical torsion of the body of the Trichocercidae to the spiral method of swimming; but while rotation to the right in this family is undoubtedly conditioned by reduction of the right side, nevertheless perfectly symmetrical rotifers also swim a spiral path involving body rotation (Viaud, 1940). Some rotifers swim a straight path without rotation (Viaud, 1940) as *Asplanchna,* for instance.

A very exact study of the reactions of rotifers to light has been made for several species by Viaud (1940, 1943). Whereas some species are indifferent to light, many show a highly positive reaction; in general the pelagic rotifers are more responsive to light than are those of benthic habits. Reaction to light in rotifers is mediated both by a general body sensitivity to light or *dermatoptic* sense and by the eye or eyes (visual sense). The former evokes a general locomotion toward the light, the speed of which increases with decreasing wave length. The exact orientation to light in which the animal proceeds toward (or away from) the light keeping its body at a certain angle toward the light rays is mediated by the eye and in rotifers is dependent on the morphological development of the eye. Rotifers with poorly functioning eyes or eyeless members of a species normally provided with good eyes show positive phototropism but proceed toward the light in an irregular, imprecise manner. In orientation mediated by the eye the speed of locomotion toward the light increases up to wave length 540 millimicrons and then declines. Rotifers with red or orange eyes are insensitive to the red end of the spectrum whereas *Polyarthra trigla* with a violet eye is more sensitive to the red end of the spectrum than other species tested. Species with a good visual sense will take a resultant path between two equal lights at an angle to each other.

24. Relationships.—In the history of zoology, the rotifers have been allied in turn to almost every invertebrate group, especially the arthropods and annelids. The idea of arthropod affinity was based on certain resemblances such as the cuticularized surface, the apparent segmentation, and the presence of jaws (trophi), and at the time was strengthened by the discovery of *Pedalia* whose movable bristle-bearing arms suggest the appendages of a crustacean larva. Long before it became evident that *Pedalia* is simply a highly modified flosculariacean, the arthropod relationship had been abandoned in favor of Hatschek's trochophore theory, still promulgated in some textbooks. This theory compares rotifers with the trochophore larva and concludes that rotifers are simply annelids that have remained in a larval state. At present this hypothesis is based chiefly on the rotifer *Trochosphaera* whose ciliary girdle, bent intestine, and excretory organs resemble topographically the similar parts of the trochophore. But, as already remarked, *Trochosphaera* is merely a peculiar rotifer. The girdle type of corona seen in the Flosculariacea and superficially resembling the prototroch of the trochophore is a highly modified corona. The primitive corona was a large ventral ciliated field in no way resembling the ciliary circlets of the trochophore. The annelid theory must therefore be regarded as without foundation, as concerns the trochophore resemblance. It is probable, however, that rotifers are related to the annelid-mollusk stem, and as shown in Chap. IX the rotifers and the trochophore stand at about the same grade of organization.

The embryology of rotifers, although still imperfectly known, suggests that these animals are primitive, not derived by the retrogression of higher forms. No trace is seen in the development of a coelom or an entomesoderm. The anatomy and embryology both incline to the origin of the rotifers from some low-grade creeping bilateral type such as a primitive flatworm. The primitive type of corona may well be the remnant of a former complete or ventral ciliation such as obtains in the Turbellaria. The formation of cuticularized parts as the trophi is common among the Turbellaria. The strongest point of resemblance between rotifers and turbellarians is, however, the protonephridial system which is practically identical with that of rhabdocoels. The presence of this type of excretory system practically precludes the derivation of the rotifers from any higher group since none of the latter have protonephridia with flame bulbs.

The retrocerebral organ is probably homologous with the frontal organ of Turbellaria. The division of the female gonad into ovary and vitellarium is another resemblance to flatworms. On the other hand, the rotifers differ from flatworms in the presence of an anus and the lack of a subepidermal muscle sheath and of the subepidermal nerve plexus so characteristic of the Turbellaria. Their small size, however, probably makes such an accessory nerve plexus unnecessary and their nervous system in general bears some similarity to that of flatworms. On the whole the Rotifera show a greater resemblance to the Turbellaria than to any other invertebrate group and may be considered as relating the Aschelminthes to the Platyhelminthes.

Within the rotifer class itself, the Seisonacea appear to occupy the most primitive position as judged by characters enumerated above (page 107). An early divergence of the bdelloid branch is also indicated by their paired germovitellaria, despite various specializations found in this group. The Monogononta with a single germovitellarium are presumably derived from a stem line having paired gonads. From such an ancestral form the Ploima branch in one direction with the notommatids as their most primitive forms while the Flosculariacea and Collothecacea diverge in another. The close relationship of these two sessile orders is evidenced by the strong similarity of their young stage and their males. These sessile types are undoubtedly derived from free-swimming rotifers whose appearance is reflected in the young and males.

V. CLASS GASTROTRICHA

1. Historical.—The gastrotrichs, being common microscopic animals, were naturally seen by the early microscopists and O. F. Müller in his *Animalcula infusoria fluviatilia et marina* (1786) gave several figures of "Infusoria" that are readily recognized as gastrotrichs. Ehrenberg (1838) created the names *Chaetonotus* and *Ichthydium* for common fresh-water gastrotrichs but regarded them as rotifers. Schultze (1853) established another genus, *Turbanella*, raised objections to the idea of rotifer affinity, and proposed the group name Ichthydina for the gastrotrichs known at that time. He regarded the gastrotrichs as most nearly allied to the Turbellaria. The idea of turbellarian affinity was rejected by Metschnikoff (1864) who returned to the conception of rotifer relationship, proposed the name Gastrotricha, in reference to the ventral ciliation, and suggested the union of gastrotrichs and rotifers into one class. Ludwig (1875) noticed the striking resemblance of the digestive tract of gastrotrichs to that of nematodes and considered the gastrotrichs as intermediate between rotifers and nematodes. A union of gastrotrichs with echinoderids under the name Nematorhyncha was suggested by Bütschli in 1876. Zelinka (1889) made the first detailed study of gastrotrich anatomy and returned to the idea of rotifer affinity, proposing the name Trochelminthes to cover the combination of rotifers and gastrotrichs. This name derives from the trochophore and expresses Zelinka's belief that the structure of both rotifers and gastrotrichs is referable to that of the trochophore. The Trochelminthes concept, usually with the addition of the echinoderids, met with much favor and was widely promulgated in textbooks.

After the work of Zelinka very little was added to our knowledge of the Gastro-tricha apart from taxonomic descriptions until recent years when A. Remane took up the study of the microscopic marine fauna of European shores.   Nearly the whole of modern knowledge of the Gastrotricha is owing to his labors.   He summarized this knowledge in his accounts of the Gastrotricha in the *Handbuch der Zoologie* and in Bronn's *Klassen und Ordnungen des Tierreichs.*   Valuable contributions have also been made by de Beauchamp (1929–1934).

2. Definition.—The Gastrotricha are free-living microscopic Aschel-minthes with ciliation limited to certain areas, with one or more types of cuticular specializations in the form of scales, spines, and bristles, with one or more pairs of adhesive tubes (sometimes wanting), and with excretory organs, when present, in the form of a pair of protonephridia, each with one flame bulb.

3. External Features.—The Gastrotricha are minute animals of fresh and salt water that vary in length from less than 0.1 to 1.5 mm., being usually less than 0.6 mm. long.   They are elongated, ventrally flattened, usually bristly or spiny creatures that glide about on ventral cilia much in the manner of a rhabdocoel.   In the commonest type of body shape, especially characteristic of the order Chaetonotoidea, the rounded lobe-like head is set off by a slightly constricted neck from the moderately elongated trunk terminating in a forked posterior end (Fig. 70A).   In the order Macrodasyoidea, the anterior end is usually not delimited as a head lobe, the sides are parallel, and the body varies from a short broad to a long slender shape (Fig. 70B).   The posterior end is generally forked but may be pointed, rounded, or truncate, and in a few species is drawn out into a slender tail (Fig. 70C).   The dorsal surface is usually convex but may be flattened also and in a few forms both surfaces are convexly curved so that the cross section is nearly circular.   One or two pairs of red pigment spots, presumably ocelli, occur on the sides of the head lobe in a few Macrodasyoidea, and one or two pairs of tentacles or palps are present in some genera (Fig. 71J).   The Gastrotricha are colorless and transparent but ingested food may lend color to the digestive tract.

Cilia occur on the head lobe and usually also on the ventral surface of the trunk.   The trunk ciliation may extend the entire length of the ventral surface in one broad band as in *Macrodasys* (Fig. 71D) or in two narrow longitudinal bands as in *Chaetonotus* (Fig. 71B) and *Turbanella* (Fig. 71G) or as a number of transverse bands as in *Thaumastoderma* (Fig. 71E) or as small patches arranged in two longitudinal rows as in *Dasydytes* and *Setopus* (Fig. 71C); or it may be limited to the anterior part of the trunk (Fig. 71A, F, H).   Trunk ciliation is altogether lacking in some cases.   The trunk ciliation usually continues onto the ventral surface of the head lobe which is also provided with its own ciliation on both surfaces in the form of sparsely set cilia, or tufts, patches, transverse groups, or

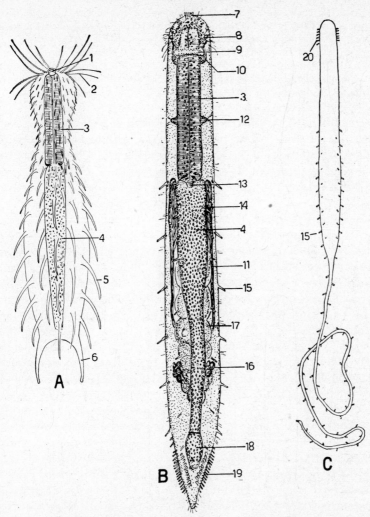

FIG. 70.—Types of Gastrotricha. *A. Chaetonotus*, fresh-water gastrotrich, from life. *B. Macrodasys*, marine gastrotrich, with lateral adhesive tubes. *C. Urodasys*, marine gastrotrich, with long tail. (*B, C, after Remane*, 1926.) 1, buccal capsule; 2, sensory bristles; 3, pharynx; 4, stomach-intestine; 5, cuticular spines; 6, tail forks; 7, mouth hooks; 8, piston pit; 9, dorsal brain commissure; 10, brain ganglion; 11, sperm duct; 12, pharyngeal pores to surface; 13, pharyngeal plug; 14, testis; 15, lateral adhesive tubes; 16, ovary; 17, eggs in uterus; 18, rectum; 19, posterior adhesive tubes; 20, anterior adhesive tubes.

partial girdles. Commonly, especially in the chaetonotoids, the head lobe bears, in addition to such ordinary cilia, tufts or short bands of very long cilia or bristles that may be motile or motionless and probably act primarily in a sensory capacity (Fig. 70*A*). Two or three such tufts or short bands on each side of the head lobe is a frequent arrangement in

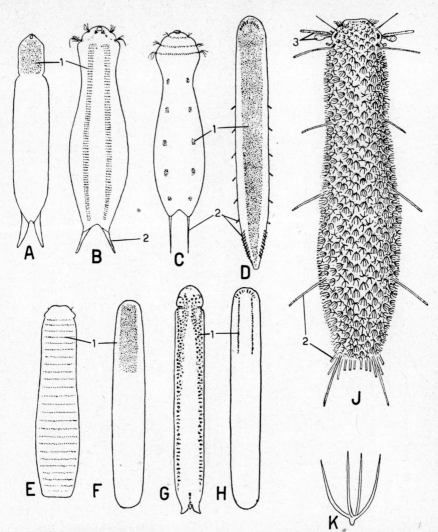

Fig. 71.—Distribution of cilia, scalation. *A–H,* ciliary arrangement in various gastrotrichs, ventral views. *A. Proichthydium. B. Chaetonotus. C. Setopus. D. Macrodasys. E. Thaumastoderma. F. Hemidasys. G. Turbanella. H. Lepidodasys. J. Thaumastoderma* with two pairs of palps and four-pronged scales. *K.* Single scale of *Thaumastoderma.* (*All after Remane,* 1926.) 1, ciliary tract; 2, adhesive tubes; 3, palps.

fresh-water genera as *Chaetonotus, Dasydytes, Ichthydium, Stylochaeta,* etc. (Fig. 72*A, D*). One or two rows of long cilia across the dorsal surface of the head lobe occur in *Turbanella, Proichthydium,* and others (Fig. 72*B*). *Xenotrichula* is peculiar in that the cilia of the ventral surface of head and trunk are transformed into cirri that are employed in running about like the cirri of the hypotrichous ciliates.

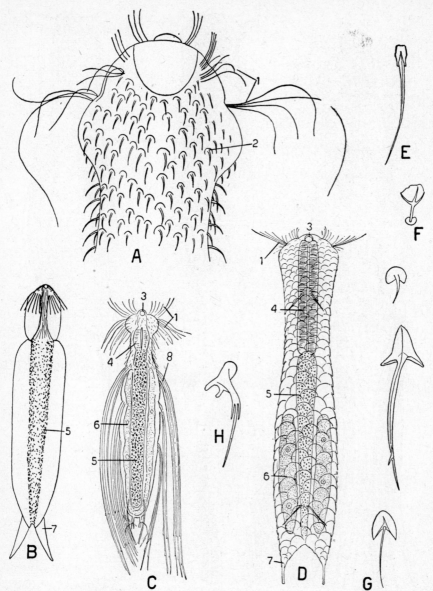

Fig. 72.—Scalation. *A.* Anterior end of *Chaetonotus*, showing sensory bristles and spined scales (*after Zelinka*, 1889). *B. Proichthydium* (*after Cordero*, 1918), with a ciliary row across the head. *C. Stylochaeta*, from life, with bunches of long spines. *D. Lepidodermella*, from life, clothed with spineless scales. *E-H.* Types of spined scales (*after Zelinka*, 1889; *and Voigt*, 1904). *F.* Stalked type of scale. 1, bunches of sensory bristles; 2, spined scale; 3, buccal capsule; 4, pharynx; 5, stomach-intestine; 6, ovary; 7, adhesive tubes; 8, bunches of spines.

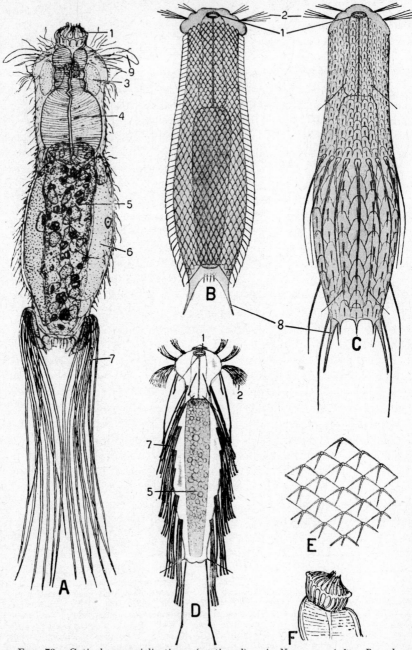

FIG. 73.—Cuticular specializations (continued). *A. Neogossea* (*after Beauchamp*, 1933) with terminal bunches of long spines. *B. Aspidiophorus* covered with stalked scales. *C.* Species of *Chaetonotus* with scales and spines of various sizes. *D. Dasydytes*, with bunches of spines. *E.* Surface of *Aspidiophorus*, enlarged, showing pattern formed by

The body surface consists of a thin cuticle that with rare exceptions forms one or more kinds of surface structures. These may consist of warty eminences but usually occur as scales, laid flat or overlapping, smooth or with a median keel or frequently provided with a conspicuous, posteriorly curved spine (Fig. 72). Such spined scales are characteristic of chaetonotoids and give the bristly appearance familiar in the common genus *Chaetonotus* (Figs. 70*A*, 73*C*). In some genera, as *Thaumastoderma* and *Tetranchyroderma*, the spines are subdivided into four or five prongs (Fig. 71*J*, *K*). Very curious are the double-decked or stalked scales consisting of two superimposed scales connected by a stalk (*Xenotrichula*, *Aspidiophorus*, Fig. 72*F*). The scale may be lost while the spines persist, set directly into the cuticle, as in *Dasydytes* (Fig. 73*D*). Such spines may be very long and may occur in bunches on the body sides (*Stylochaeta*, Fig. 72*C*, *Dasydytes*, Fig. 73*D*) or at the posterior end (*Neogossea*, Fig. 73*A*). The spines of the marginal scales may be longer than those elsewhere, or only marginal spines may be present. A complete covering of spineless scales is seen in *Lepidodermella* (= *Lepidoderma*, Fig. 72*D*). Larger cuticular thickenings termed plates, sometimes formed by the fusion of scales, may be present, especially on the ventral surface and on the head lobe of chaetonotoids. The head plates comprise typically an unpaired *cephalion* anterior to the mouth, an unpaired *hypostomium* behind the mouth, and a pair of lateral *pleurions*, each of which may be subdivided.

Highly characteristic gastrotrich structures are the adhesive tubes, most abundant in the Macrodasyoidea but also present in the Chaetonotoidea except the pelagic families Dasydytidae and Neogosseidae. They are projecting cylindrical cuticular tubes, movable by means of one or more delicate muscles and supplied by an adhesive gland cell containing one to three nuclei (Fig. 77*B*). The sticky secretion furnished by the gland and emitted from the tube is employed in adhering to objects. In the macrodasyoids, the tubes, numbering up to 250, occur in lateral longitudinal series at or near the lateral margins, in longitudinal or transverse rows or in clusters on the ventral surface of the head, and in bunches on the tail forks or along the sides of unforked tails (Figs. 70*B*, 79, 80*A*). In *Turbanella* each lateral tube is accompanied by a long motile sensory cilium (Fig. 74*A*). Among the chaetonotoids, the adhesive tubes are limited to one or two on each tail fork, where they may constitute the greater part of the fork (Fig. 70*A*) or may be situated terminally on the elongated forks, sometimes termed toes in analogy with rotifers and clothed in some species with a many-ringed cuticle (Fig. 80*B*).

---

three-spined outer end of stalked scales. (*B–E, after Voigt*, 1904.) *F*. Buccal capsule of *Neogossea* (*after Beauchamp*, 1933). 1, buccal capsule; 2, sensory bristles; 3, brain ganglia; 4, pharynx with bulbs; 5, stomach-intestine; 6, eggs; 7, bunch of spines; 8, adhesive tubes; 9, palp.

4. Internal Structure.—As in rotifers the cuticle is underlain by a syncytial epidermis, mostly thin throughout in chaetonotoids, much thickened laterally in macrodasyoids (Fig. 77A). Epidermal glands comprise the adhesive glands already mentioned and the dorsal glands of the macrodasyoids; the latter are numerous, dorsolaterally situated, rounded bodies of a homogeneous or granular material, each provided with a pore.

A subepidermal muscle sheath is lacking but delicate circular fibers, devoid of nuclei and continuous with the epidermis, occur in or just to the inner side of the epidermis. They furnish the muscles of the lateral adhesive tubes and of movable bristles. They may also take a transverse or dorsoventral direction. Longitudinal muscles are also present, chiefly as a ventrolateral group that extends the body length and operates the anterior and posterior adhesive tubes, inserting on the mouth region and pharynx (Figs. 74B, 75A). Finer dorsal longitudinal bands, two to six on each side, occur along most or part of the dorsal wall and likewise insert on mouth region and pharynx (Fig. 74C). The longitudinal muscles are nucleated and of the smooth type except in *Dactylopodalia* where cross striations occur. The great similarity of the muscle system to that of rotifers will be noted.

Only slight spaces exist between the body wall and the viscera. These are presumably of the nature of a pseudocoel as they have no definite lining but their embryonic origin is as yet unknown. In macrodasyoids, the pseudocoel is divided by membranes derived from the epidermis and sometimes containing muscle fibers into a central compartment enclosing the digestive tract and ripe eggs, and paired lateral spaces housing the gonads (Fig. 77A). There are no free amoeboid cells in the pseudocoel.

The mouth is terminal or slightly ventral and may be bordered by numerous small curved hooks (Fig. 75B). In the chaetonotoids a short cuticular buccal capsule bearing longitudinal ridges and sometimes projecting teeth and protrusible to some extent intervenes between mouth and pharynx (Figs. 73F, 74D–H, 75C–E). Among the macrodasyoids, the thin-walled distal end of the pharynx possibly corresponds to a buccal capsule. The gastrotrich pharynx is a characteristic feature having no resemblance to the rotifer mastax but remarkably similar to the nematode pharynx. It is an elongated tube, one-sixth to one-third the body length, having in most chaetonotoids one or more bulbous enlargements (Fig. 75D–F), as many as four in *Neogossea* (Fig. 73A). The pharyngeal lumen is three-angled as in nematodes (Fig. 76C) and the angles are oriented as in nematodes in the chaetonotoids (one midventral, others dorsolateral); but the opposite orientation is found in macrodasyoids (one middorsal, others ventrolateral, Fig. 76C). The histological structure is also very like that of the nematode pharynx. The wall consists of a columnar

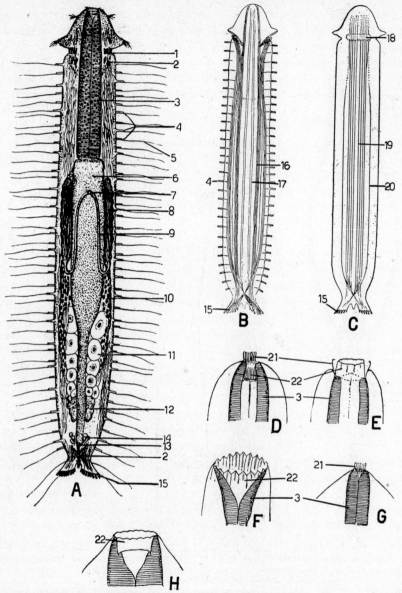

Fig. 74.—Muscles, mouth armature. *A. Turbanella*, with a long cilium accompanying each lateral adhesive tube (*after Remane*, 1925). *B.* Ventral view of *Turbanella*, showing longitudinal muscles. *C.* Same, dorsal musculature. *D–H.* Various types of mouth armature and buccal capsules in macrodasyoids. *D. Macrodasys*, buccal capsule retracted. *E. Macrodasys*, capsule protruded. *F. Ptychostomella. G. Dactylopodalia. H. Turbanella.* (*B–H, after Remane*, 1926.) 1, anterior adhesive tubes; 2, adhesive glands; 3, pharynx; 4, lateral adhesive tubes; 5, cilia; 6, stomach-intestine; 7, male gonopore; 8, testis; 9, sperm duct; 10, yolk gland; 11, eggs; 12, ovary; 13, anus; 14, anal glands; 15, posterior adhesive tubes; 16, ventrolateral muscles; 17, ventral muscles; 18, dorsal brain commissure; 19, dorsal muscle; 20, dorsolateral muscle; 21, mouth hooks; 22, buccal capsule.

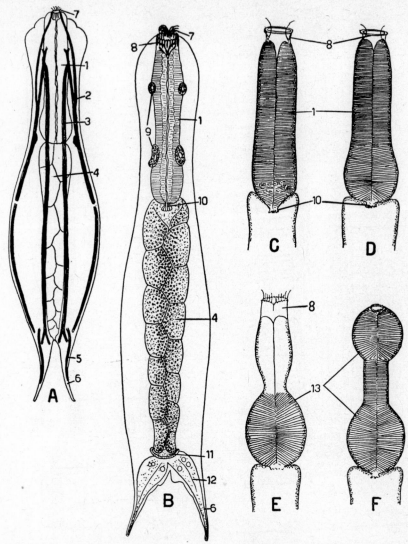

FIG. 75.—Musculature, digestive tract. *A.* Musculature of *Chaetonotus*, ventral. *B.* Digestive system of *Chaetonotus*. (*A, B, after Zelinka*, 1889.) *C–F.* Types of chaetonotoid pharynx (*after Remane*, 1926). *C. Heterolepidoderma*. *D, F. Chaetonotus*. *E. Dasydytes*. 1, pharynx; 2, lateral muscles; 3, ventral muscles; 4, stomach-intestine; 5, tail muscles; 6, tail forks; 7, mouth bristles; 8, buccal capsule; 9, salivary glands; 10, pharyngeal plug; 11, anus; 12, adhesive glands; 13, pharyngeal bulb.

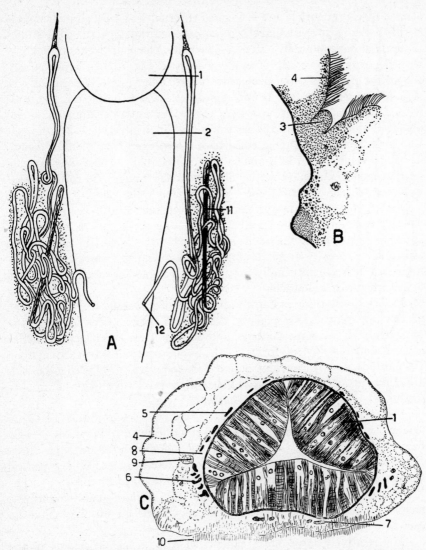

Fig. 76.—Sensory, excretory, and digestive systems.   A. Protonephridia of *Chaetonotus* (*after Zelinka*, 1889).   B. Section through a piston pit of *Macrodasys*.   C. Section through the pharynx of *Macrodasys*.   (*B, C, after Remane*, 1926.)   1, pharynx; 2, stomach-intestine; 3, piston; 4, epidermis; 5, dorsal muscles; 6, ventrolateral muscles; 7, ventral muscles; 8, pseudocoel; 9, nerve cord; 10, ventral ciliated tract; 11, flame bulb; 12, nephridiopore.

epithelium containing cross-striated radial muscle fibers (Fig. 76C), best developed in the bulbous regions.   These fibers are part of the epithelium. Some of the epithelial cells of the pharynx wall are specialized into gland cells and in a few chaetonotoids the pharynx bears two pairs of large projecting cells supposed to be salivary glands (Fig. 75B).   The pharynx is lined by a thin cuticle and is covered externally by thin circular muscle fibrils that are also epithelial extensions; they are aggregated at the mouth to form an oral sphincter.   In macrodasyoids, the pharynx communicates with the exterior by a pair of *pharyngeal pores* (Fig. 70*B*).   The posterior end of the pharynx often projects into the midgut as a *pharyngeal plug* (Fig. 75*B*).   The midgut or stomach-intestine is a simple straight tube without external glands in which the wider anterior stomach is not definitely delimited from the narrower posterior intestine.   The midgut wall lacks a cuticular lining, consists of a one-layered cuboidal or columnar epithelium (Fig. 77*A*), and is clothed externally with a fine layer of circular muscle fibers.   Circular fibrils next the lumen as in rotifers occur in *Polymerurus*.   Certain clear or granular cells, lacking inclusions, located chiefly in the anterior end of the stomach but also occurring elsewhere are believed to be gland cells secreting digestive enzymes.   The anus is ventral in the macrodasyoids, situated between the bases of the tail forks terminally or sometimes slightly dorsal or ventral, in chaetonotoids.   The anus is usually provided with a sphincter muscle and lined by inturned surface cuticle.

Practically nothing is known about digestion in Gastrotricha but the process apparently takes place in the midgut lumen.   The food consists of bacteria, protozoans, diatoms, and other minute organisms as well as general detritus.   Most forms move about continuously seeking food which is ingested by a sucking action of the pharynx.   Some chaetonotids are said to attach by the adhesive tubes of the tail forks and gather minute food objects by means of ciliary currents.

Protonephridia are limited to the order Chaetonotoidea.   To either side of the middle part of the digestive tract occurs a single nonnucleated flame bulb with a very long flame, resembling a flagellum (Fig. 76*A*). From each bulb a much coiled tubule leads to an opening on the ventral side at about the body middle.   There is no urinary bladder.   The Macrodasyoidea lack protonephridia but one or more pairs of granular masses opening ventrally and known as ventral glands may have an excretory function.

The relatively large brain consists of a mass on either side of the anterior part of the pharynx and a broad or narrow dorsal connection between the two masses (Fig. 70*B*).   From the brain a pair of lateral nerves containing ganglion cells extends the body length.   Sensory structures include the tufts of long cilia on the chaetonotoid head lobe which are continuous with ganglion cells incorporated into the brain, single motile or stiff tactile hairs or bristles scattered over the body, numerous in the macrodasyoids, fewer in the chaetonotoids, the lateral sense organs of the head, and pigment ocelli.   The lateral organs in chaetonotoids consist of a pair of ciliated pits on the head lobe just behind the most posterior

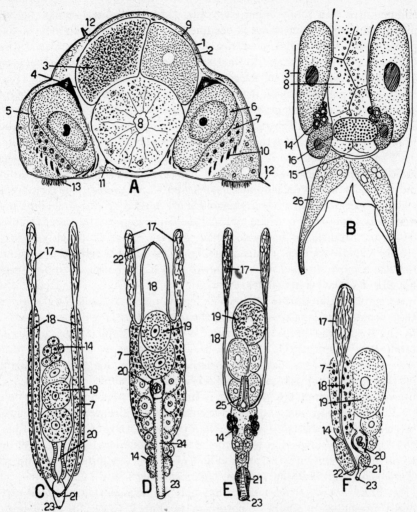

FIG. 77.—Digestive and reproductive systems. A. Section through the stomach-intestine of *Turbanella*. B. Reproductive system of *Chaetonotus* (*after Zelinka*, 1889). C. Reproductive system of *Cephalodasys*. D. Same of *Turbanella*. E. Same of *Macrodasys*. F. Same of *Thaumastoderma*. (*A, C–F, after Remane*, 1926.) 1, cuticle; 2, epidermis; 3, ripe eggs; 4, central compartment of pseudocoel; 5, lateral compartment of ·pseudocoel; 6, young egg; 7, yolk gland; 8, stomach-intestine; 9, dorsal muscles; 10, ventro-lateral muscles; 11, ventral muscles; 12, adhesive tube; 13, ciliated tract; 14, ovary; 15, anus; 16, organ X; 17, testes; 18, sperm ducts; 19, uterus containing ripe eggs; 20, seminal receptacles; 21, copulatory bursa; 22, male gonopore; 23, female gonopore; 24, oviduct; 25, penis papilla; 26, adhesive glands.

ciliary tufts.   In many macrodasyoids, these take the form of piston pits in which the pit bottom is occupied by an unciliated eminence, the piston (Fig. 76*B*).   Disappearance of pit and cilia and elongation of the piston results in the lateral tentacles or palps found in certain genera, as *Thaumastoderma* (Fig. 71*J*) *Neogossea* (Fig. 73*A*), and *Xenotrichula* (Fig. 80*B*).   The pigment ocelli, present in only a few species, consist of aggregations of red pigment granules inside some of the brain cells.   A static function is suspected for groups of highly refringent bodies found in the brain cells or the cells of the ciliated pits.

The Gastrotricha were apparently originally hermaphroditic but the male system has degenerated in the Chaetonotoidea so that in this order only females occur (except in *Xenotrichula*) and the eggs develop parthenogenetically.   The Macrodasyoidea are hermaphroditic but some are markedly protandric and one genus, *Dactylopodalia*, can be male, female, or hermaphroditic.   The reproductive system is not thoroughly understood.   There are one or two ovaries, consisting of a cell mass without definite capsule situated in the posterior part of the body.   As no mitoses have been observed in the ovary, the number of ovocytes (less than 25) is presumably fixed during embryonic development.   As the eggs ripen they become free in a space termed the uterus (Fig. 77) situated anterior to the ovary and probably provided with a thin wall although this is often not demonstrable.   Where the pseudocoel is subdivided into central and lateral compartments, the larger eggs lie alongside the midgut in the central compartment (Fig. 77*A*).   The connections of ovary, uterus, and oviduct are not clear.   In the Macrodasyoidea, the single oviduct usually presents an anterior enlargement, the seminal receptacle, often containing a mass of sperm, and a posterior, thicker walled swelling, the copulatory bursa, that leads to the female gonopore, opening anterior to or in common with the anus (Fig. 77*C*, *F*).   The bursa is missing in *Turbanella* (Fig. 77*D*) and the seminal receptacle is wanting in *Macrodasys* (Fig. 77*E*).   A nutritive tissue, that may be termed yolk gland, is generally present as a single or paired mass (Fig. 77*C*, *D*, *F*).   A definite oviduct has not been identified in the majority of the Chaetonotoidea but a simple or bifurcated sac, the so-called organ X, is present posteriorly, opening ventrally by a pore, and seems to represent a copulatory bursa (Fig. 77*B*).

The male system in macrodasyoids comprises a pair of testes or a single right testis, from each of which a sperm duct proceeds caudad or turns anteriorly (Fig. 77*C–F*).   Generally there is a single median male gonopore but when paired the sperm ducts sometimes open by separate pores.   The male gonopore or pores may open close to the female pore or in common with it or may be more or less anteriorly located.   A penis-like structure terminates the male system in *Macrodasys* (Fig. 77*E*) and *Urodasys*.   Traces of testes occur in a few chaetonotoids.

5. Breeding Habits and Development.—Fresh-water gastrotrichs, especially *Lepidodermella squamatum*, can be grown in protozoan-type cultures, best in 0.1 per cent malted milk (Packard, 1936; Brunson, 1949). Under such conditions, *L. squamatum* was found to live 8 to 21 days, and to lay up to five eggs, mostly three or four.   From the available evidence, it appears that all Chaetonotoidea produce two kinds of eggs as in rotifers, subitaneous and dormant, both of which develop parthenogenetically. The eggs are oval and enclosed in a shell that is thicker in the dormant eggs and in both kinds of eggs is usually ornamented with bristles or blunt spines, sometimes only on one side.   The eggs are laid in selected spots, often on the surface film or near an object, and hatch in 1 to 3 days into a small gastrotrich similar to the adult, that requires about 3 days to reach sexual maturity.   Some integumental structures as the adhesive tubes may increase in number after hatching.

Knowledge of the embryology is limited to Beauchamp's incomplete account of *Neogossea* (1929).   Cleavage is holoblastic and somewhat determinate and results in a coeloblastula of subequal cells.   Two ventral cells pass into the interior by a gastrulation process and while their fate has not been followed they probably produce the midgut (Fig. 78*A*, *B*). In front of the blastopore cells are proliferated into the interior to form the pharynx, which is therefore a stomodaeum, and anus and terminal intestine arise similarly and hence are proctodaeal (Fig. 78*D*, *E*).   About this time two ventroposterior cells become conspicuous as the primordial germ cells that pass into the interior and become the ovaries (Fig. 78*E*, *F*). No further details of the embryology are available.

6. Order Macrodasyoidea.—The members of this order have elongated vermiform bodies with or without a head lobe, with anterior, lateral, and posterior adhesive tubes, pharyngeal pores, and male reproductive system, but lack protonephridia.   They are exclusively marine and inhabit shore waters chiefly in sand, less often in the vegetation zone.   In addition to the usual ciliary gliding, the macrodasyoids can move in leech-like fashion by alternately attaching anterior and posterior adhesive tubes.   They may become temporarily sessile for long periods, fastening themselves by the rear adhesive tubes.   At present they are known only from European coasts but presumably will be found elsewhere, when proper search is made.   The author, however, failed to find them on the New England Coast or in Puget Sound.

The families and genera have been reviewed by Remane (1936). Among the genera may be mentioned: *Cephalodasys* (Fig. 80*A*) and *Lepidodasys* with rounded tail lobe edged with adhesive tubes; *Acan-*

thodasys covered with spined scales; *Macrodasys* (Fig. 70*B*) with pointed posterior end bordered with adhesive tubes, and with anterior and lateral tubes in addition; *Urodasys* (Fig. 70*C*) with a very long slender tail bearing adhesive tubes, and without intestine or anus; *Dactylopodalia*

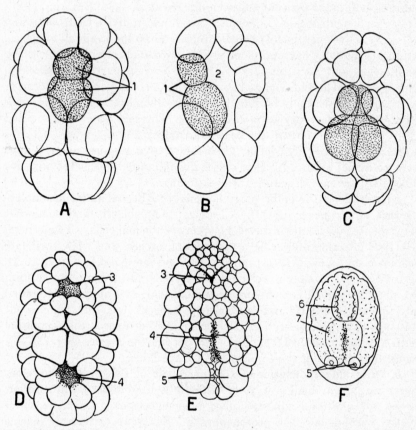

Fig. 78.—Embryology. *A.* Beginning gastrulation, two invaginating cells stippled. *B.* Sagittal section of *A.* *C.* Later stage, invaginated cells have divided to four. *D.* Formation of stomo- and proctodaeum. *E.* Stomo- and proctodaeum completed, primordial germ cells differentiated. *F.* Advanced embryo in eggshell. (*All of Neogossea, after Beauchamp,* 1929.) 1, invaginating cells; 2, blastocoel; 3, stomodaeum; 4, proctodaeum; 5, primordial germ cells; 6, pharynx; 7, stomach-intestine.

(= *Dactylopodella*) with rounded tail forks beset with adhesive tubes (Fig. 79*A*); *Turbanella* (Fig. 74*A*) with similar tail forks and with a long cilium accompanying each of the many lateral adhesive tubes; *Thaumastoderma* (Fig. 71*J*) with two pairs of palps and covered with four-pronged spines; *Tetranchyroderma* with similar spines but lacking palps; and *Platydasys* (Fig. 79*B*) with single testis, lateral adhesive tubes in two series, anterior row of tubes, and rounded posterior end edged with tubes.

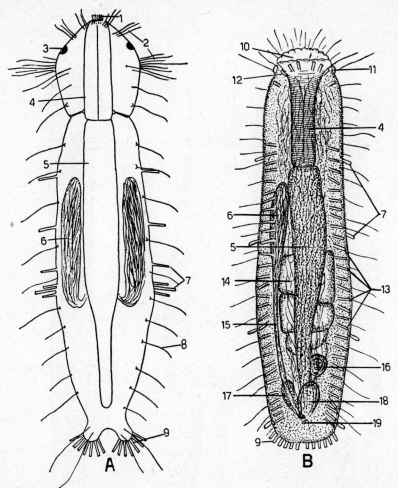

Fig. 79.—Macrodasyoidea. *A. Dactylopodalia. B. Platydasys.* (*Both after Remane,* 1926, 1927.)   1, mouth hooks; 2, sensory bristles; 3, eyes; 4, pharynx; 5, stomach-intestine; 6, testes; 7, lateral adhesive tubes; 8, long cilia; 9, posterior adhesive tubes; 10, buccal capsule; 11, piston pit; 12, anterior adhesive tubes; 13, ventrolateral adhesive tubes; 14, eggs in uterus; 15, sperm duct; 16, seminal receptacle; 17, gland; 18, copulatory bursa; 19, anus (also female gonopore).

7. Order Chaetonotoidea.—In this order the body is usually fusiform with a head lobe provided with tufts of long sensory cilia or bristles. Pharyngeal pores are lacking and a male reproductive system is absent except in *Neodasys* and *Xenotrichula*.   Adhesive tubes are limited to one or two pairs on the tail forks except in *Neodasys* (Fig. 80*C*) where there are lateral tubes accompanied by a long cilium.   A pair of protonephridia is present.   The chaetonotoids are mostly fresh-water inhabitants with benthic habits, dwelling among the vegetation of ponds and lakes, in

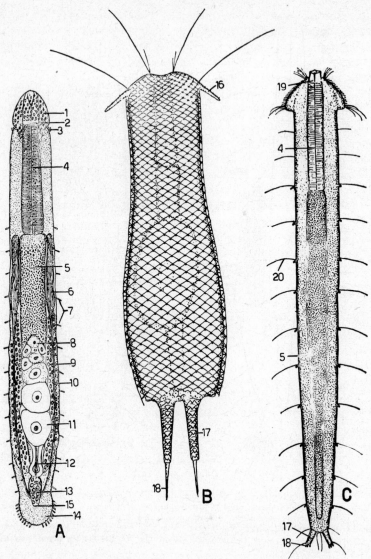

Fig. 80.—Macrodasyoidea, Chaetonotoidea. *A. Cephalodasys (after Remane*, 1926). *B. Xenotrichula. C. Neodasys. (B, C, after Remane*, 1927.) 1, head lobe; 2, brain commissure; 3, anterior adhesive tubes; 4, pharynx; 5, stomach-intestine; 6, testis; 7, lateral adhesive tubes; 8, ovary; 9, yolk gland; 10, sperm duct; 11, eggs in uterus; 12, seminal receptacle; 13, copulatory bursa; 14, tail lobe with adhesive tubes; 15, anus; 16, palps; 17, tail forks; 18, terminal adhesive tubes; 19, buccal capsule; 20, cilia accompanying adhesive tubes.

fouling materials, and in moss pools and bog waters. Species of *Chaetonotus* are among the commonest microscopic animals of ponds and are often seen in protozoan cultures. Many chaetonotoids are cosmopolitan.

Neodasys, marine, resembles the macrodasyoids, having an elongated band-like body (Fig. 80*C*), lateral adhesive tubes as well as several on the tail forks, and a male reproductive system. *Xenotrichula*, also marine, has a typical chaetonotoid appearance (Fig. 80*B*) with head lobe, dorsal covering of stalked scales, and adhesive tubes limited to the tail forks but retains portions of the male system. All other chaetonotoids exist only as parthenogenetic females, and the majority belong to the family Chaetonotidae with the genera *Chaetonotus*, with many species, provided wholly or partly with scales (Figs. 70*A*, 73*C*), some or all of which bear a spine; *Ichthydium* (Fig. 81*A*), without any cuticular specializations; *Lepidodermella* (= *Lepidoderma*), clothed dorsally with simple scales, lacking spines or keels (Fig. 72*D*); *Polymerurus* (Fig. 81*B*) with very long ringed tail forks; *Heterolepidoderma* with keeled scales; and *Aspidiophorus* (Fig. 73*B*) with stalked scales. Although the Chaetonotidae are primarily fresh-water animals, some species are marine. Some other chaetonotoid genera are: *Proichthydium* (Fig. 72*B*), with head lobe bearing a transverse row of long bristles and set off from the trunk by a deep transverse groove; *Neogossea* (Fig. 73*A*) with two bunches of long bristles at the rear end; *Dasydytes* (Fig. 73*D*) with regularly spaced bunches of long bristles along the sides of the trunk; and *Stylochaeta* (Fig. 72*C*), similar to *Dasydytes*, but with a terminal pair of short styles.

8. Relationships.—The Gastrotricha are usually considered to be closely related to the Rotifera with which group they are often united under the name Trochelminthes. The accounts of the two classes should suffice to demonstrate the wide anatomical differences between them. The common possession of cilia cannot be regarded as indicative of anything beyond descent from some common ciliated ancestor, presumably the Turbellaria. The most important resemblances between the Gastrotricha and the Rotifera are the integument and musculature and the presence in both groups of protonephridia with flame bulbs. On the other hand, the Gastrotricha differ widely from the Rotifera in their cuticular specializations, digestive tract, and reproductive system. In particular the digestive tract shows no resemblance to that of rotifers but is almost identical with that of nematodes even to minute histological details of the pharynx structure. Other nematode similarities of gastrotrichs are the cuticular spines and bristles, the adhesive tubes represented by the stilt bristles of the draconematid and epsilonematid nematodes, the lateral sense organs of the head, apparently corresponding to the amphids of nematodes, and the shape and relations of the brain. Caudal adhesive glands are common to rotifers, gastrotrichs, and nematodes, and also occur in priapulid larvae.   It may be concluded that the Gastrotricha are more closely related to the Nematoda than to any other invertebrate group, and that both, together with the Rotifera, stem, if rather remotely, from the Turbellaria.

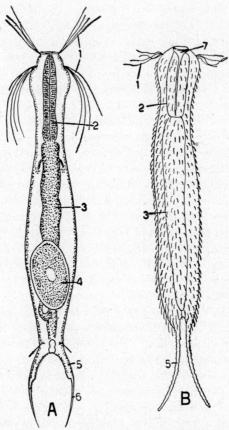

Fig. 81.—Chaetonotoidea.   *A. Ichthydium (after Remane, 1927).   B. Polymerurus (after Marcolongo, 1914).*   1, sensory bristles; 2, pharynx; 3, stomach-intestine; 4, egg; 5, tail forks; 6, adhesive tubes; 7, buccal capsule.

VI. CLASS KINORHYNCHA

1. Historical.—Members of this class were first seen in 1841 among algae on the channel coast of France by Dujardin who, however, did not publish his discovery until 1851.   He recognized the uniqueness of the creatures, proposed for them the name *echinodere*, and regarded them as intermediate between worms and crustaceans. Claparède in 1863 refound the animal seen by Dujardin and proposed the name *Echinoderes dujardinii* for it, at the same time describing another species.   Metschnikoff found echinoderids at Helgoland in 1865 and several observers soon reported them from various points on European coasts.   Greeff (1869) gave a considerable description of the animals and discovered the ovaries, thereby proving that the creatures were sexually mature animals, not larvae, as supposed by some observers. The protonephridia were discovered by Reinhard (1881) and this same observer, rejecting various proposed alliances for the echinoderids and recognizing their distinctive characters, created for them (1887) the name Kinorhyncha (Greek, *kineo* movement, *rhynchos*, snout, referring to the method of locomotion). Schepotieff (1907, 1908) added some points to the knowledge of the anatomy, but the greater part of our information about the Kinorhyncha is owing to the labors of Zelinka who summarized the existing knowledge in his 1928 monograph. Valuable accounts of the group have been published by Remane in the *Handbuch der Zoologie* (1929) and in Bronn's *Klassen und Ordnungen des Tierreichs* (1936).

2. Definition.—The Kinorhyncha or Echinodera are microscopic marine Aschelminthes devoid of cilia, with a regularly segmented spiny body of 13 or 14 joints, with a retractile head covered with circlets of spines, and with one pair of short protonephridial tubules each beginning in a single flame bulb.

3. External Characters.—The Kinorhyncha are minute marine animals, less than 1 mm. in length, of more or less bristly or spiny appearance, with a jointed body yellowish or brownish in color. The elongated body is divisible into the round head armed with spines, a single neck segment of about the same width as the trunk, and a jointed trunk usually bearing conspicuous terminal spines and often also lateral and middorsal spines (Fig. 82*A, B*). The trunk is flat below, arched above with almost parallel sides, and truncate or tapering at the posterior end. The body joints are called *zonites* by Zelinka to avoid implications of the word segment, but it appears to the author that these joints are segments of the superficial type found in Acanthocephala and Nematoda. The body surface is devoid of cilia and consists of a thick cuticle of which the various surface specializations are formed.

The approximately spherical head constitutes the first zonite; it bears a central terminal mouth and five to seven circlets of posteriorly directed spines, the *scalids* of Zelinka (Fig. 82*D*). The mouth is situated on the end of a protrusible eminence, the *mouth cone*, which is armed with a circlet of spines or thorns, the *oral styles* (Fig. 82*D*). Additional girdles of smaller spines or teeth may occur on the mouth cone or in the furrow between cone and head, as accessory to the oral styles. The scalids are hollow cuticular projections filled with epidermis (Fig. 84*C*) and consist of a basal part, the *socket*, and a scythe-like blade (Fig. 82*E*). The socket, typically bearing one, sometimes several, small spines (Fig. 82*E, F*), is separated from the blade by a circular fold lending flexibility. There are generally 10 to 20 scalids in each circlet, of decreasing size in successive circlets. In many Kinorhyncha some or all of the scalids in the most posterior circlet are beset with bristles, hence termed *trichoscalids* (Fig. 82*G, H*). The trichoscalids are each borne on a cuticular

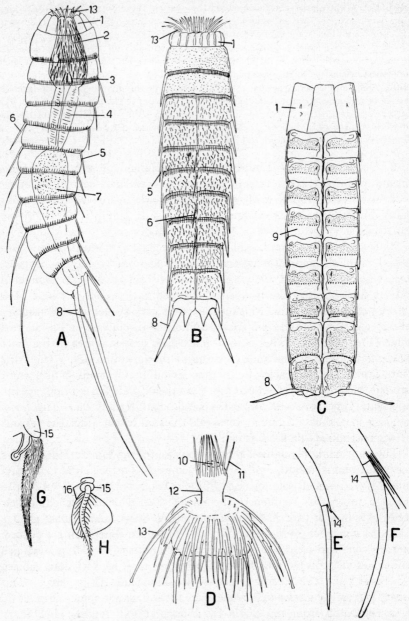

FIG. 82.—Types of kinorhynchs, spination. *A.* A cyclorhagous kinorhynch (*Echino-derella*), side view. *B.* Another cyclorhagous kinorhynch (unidentified). (*A, B, from life,* Puget Sound.) *C.* An homalorhagous kinorhynch, *Pycnophyes frequens,* from life, Maine. *D.* Head of *A* protruded, showing oral styles and scalids, from life. *E.* Scalid of *D,* enlarged. *F.* Scalid of *Semnoderes* with several basal styles. *G.* Trichoscalid of *Campyloderes.* *H.* Trichoscalid and accompanying plates of *Echinoderes.* (*F–H, after*

plate or scale and in *Echinoderes* these scales occur in sets of three, one before and one behind the middle one bearing the trichoscalid (Fig. 82*H*).

The entire head is withdrawable into the second or third zonite. The second zonite or neck is covered with large plates or *placids* whose arrangement differs in the three suborders. The placids are best developed in the cyclorhagous forms where there is a circlet of 14 (*Campyloderes*) or 16 (*Echinoderes*) triangular or trapezoidal plates (Fig. 82*A, B*) that close over the end when the head is withdrawn into the neck. In the other two suborders, the neck placids are only slight thickenings of the thin cuticle, mostly four ventrally and four or six dorsally, and do not act as a closing apparatus, being withdrawn with the head into the third zonite.

The remaining zonites, 11 in number except in *Campyloderes* where there are 12 (Fig. 83*B*), constitute the trunk. They are typically flattened below with a mid-ventral groove, arched above, and covered with one large dorsal or *tergal* plate and two ventral or *sternal* plates (Fig. 82*A–C*). In those cases in which the neck does not bear a closing apparatus, this is found instead on the third zonite. In the conchorhagous forms represented by *Semnoderes*, it consists of a pair of curved lateral plates that come together like the valves of a clam shell (Fig. 83*A*), and in the homalorhagous group (*Trachydemus, Pycnophyes*), a closing ring is formed by the large tergal plate and three sternal plates of the third zonite (Fig. 82*C*). Each zonite overlaps the succeeding one by means of a fold of thin cuticle that permits some flexibility, and similar thin cuticle occurs between the various plates. The trunk plates are usually thickened anteriorly, striated posteriorly, and tergal and sternal plates may articulate laterally by a peg-and-socket arrangement. Typically each trunk zonite bears middorsal and lateral spines jointed into the cuticle but not independently movable (*Echinoderes, Campyloderes*, Fig. 83*B*) or else unjointed tooth-like projections (*Pycnophyes*, Fig. 82*C*). Consequently the trunk is characterized by more or less complete middorsal and marginal rows of spines or teeth, hollow and filled with epidermis. Closely set or scattered fine bristles are also of frequent occurrence. On the ventral surface of the third or fourth zonite there occurs a pair of adhesive tubes like those of the Gastrotricha, each with a large gland cell at its base (Fig. 84*B*). The last tergal plate may bear on each side in addition to the regular marginal spine (when present) a conspicuous lateral end spine, movable by special muscles, and a similar median end spine occurs in *Centroderes* and *Campyloderes* (Fig. 84*A*).

Zelinka, 1928.) 1, placids; 2, retracted head; 3, pharynx crown; 4, pharynx; 5, lateral spines; 6, dorsal spines; 7, stomach-intestine; 8, lateral end spines; 9, sternal plates; 10, mouth; 11, oral styles; 12, mouth cone; 13, scalids; 14, basal style of scalid; 15, basal plate of scalid; 16, accompanying plates.

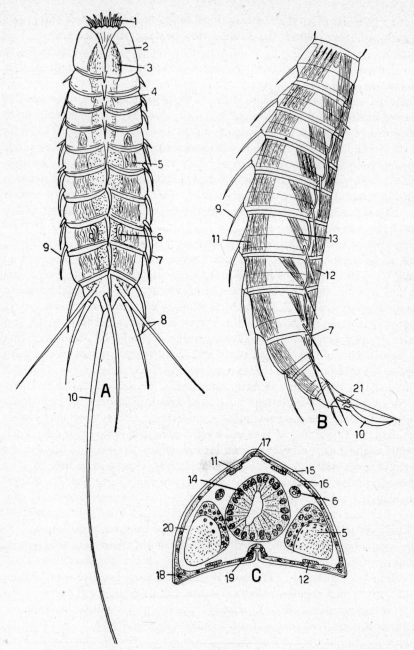

Fig. 83.—Kinorhynch structure. *A.* Conchorhagous kinorhynch, *Semnoderes*. *B. Campyloderes*, from the side, showing musculature. *C.* Section through the intestinal region of *Pycnophyes*, showing general structure. (*A–C, after Zelinka, 1928.*) 1, protruding scalids; 2, placids; 3, pharynx; 4, salivary glands; 5, testes; 6, protonephridia; 7,

4. Internal Anatomy.—Beneath the cuticle lies a more or less syncytial epidermis that extends into the cuticular spines and projects into the pseudocoel as cushion-like thickenings especially noticeable at the bases of the scalids; it further forms middorsal and lateral longitudinal thickenings or chords similar to those of nematodes (Fig. 83*C*). These chords show an enlargement in each zonite. Laterodorsal chords also occur.

The musculature resembles that of rotifers and gastrotrichs but is segmentally arranged in correlation with the body division into zonites (Fig. 83*B*). As in the groups mentioned there is no definite subepidermal muscle sheath. Ring muscles occur in the first two zonites and are altered in the trunk zonites into dorsoventral bands running on each side in each zonite from the tergal to the sternal plates (Fig. 84*C*). Their contraction compresses the body and causes protrusion of the head. In the lateral trunk regions is found a similar series of diagonal muscle bands extending from the anterior edge of one zonite diagonally forward to that of the preceding zonite (Fig. 83*B*). The longitudinal muscle bands are also divided up into segments attached to the thickened anterior edges of the cuticular plates (Fig. 83*B*). There is a pair of such longitudinal bands dorsolaterally and another pair ventrolaterally. Anteriorly these split up to assist as retractors of the head and posteriorly they furnish the muscles that operate the terminal spines. The head retractors consist of outer and inner longitudinal bands that extend from the inner surface of the head cuticle and base of the mouth cone to various posterior levels of the trunk (Fig. 84*C*). The muscle fibers of the Kinorhyncha insert directly on the cuticle; all are nucleated and all except the ring muscles of head and neck are cross-striated.

The digestive tract resembles that of gastrotrichs and nematodes. The cavity of the mouth cone (buccal cavity) is lined by a syncytial epithelium that also clothes the outer surface of a thick cuticular ring projecting from the anterior end of the pharynx into the buccal cavity (Fig. 85*A–C*). This ring, the *pharynx crown* (Fig. 85*C*), constitutes the anterior end of the pharynx. The pharynx proper is a muscular fusiform body whose wall consists of a cuticular lining, a syncytial epithelium, and an outer thick layer of radial muscle fibers arranged in a longitudinal series of rings (Fig. 84*D*). In possessing a lining epithelium, the kinorhynch pharynx differs from that of gastrotrichs and nematodes, in which the muscle fibers are in the epithelium and the latter is not a distinct layer. At the posterior end of the pharynx the radial fibers form a sphincter. The pharyngeal lumen is three-angled in some kinorhynchs

lateral spines; 8, lateral end spines; 9, dorsal spines; 10, median end spine; 11, dorsolateral muscles; 12, ventrolateral muscles; 13, diagonal muscle bands; 14, intestine; 15, cuticle; 16, epidermis; 17, dorsal chord; 18, lateral chords; 19, ganglion of the ventral chain; 20, pseudocoel; 21, fourteenth zonite.

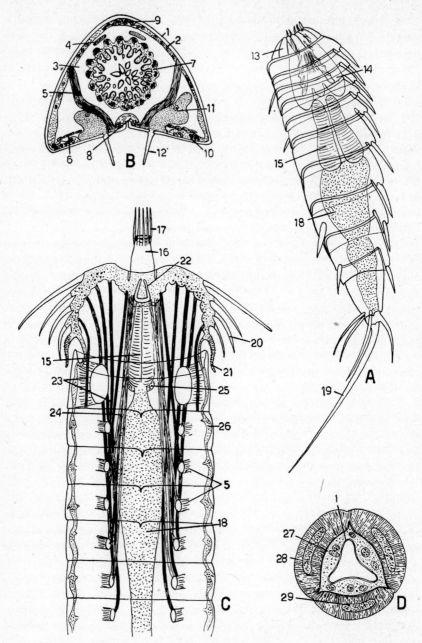

Fig. 84.—Internal structure. *A. Centroderes*. *B*. Section through the fourth zonite of *Pycnophyes*, showing the adhesive tubes. *C*. Frontal section of *Pycnophyes*, showing head retractors. *D*. Section through the pharynx of *Pycnophyes*. (*All after Zelinka, 1928*.) 1, cuticle; 2, epidermis; 3, pseudocoel; 4, dorsolateral muscles; 5, dorsoventral muscles; 6, ventrolateral muscles; 7, section of retracted head and scalids; 8, ganglion of

(Fig. 84*D*), rounded or flattened in others. Externally the pharynx is covered by a layer of about 10 protractor muscle bands extending from its posterior end to the base of the mouth cone (Fig. 85*B*).

The remainder of the digestive tract (Fig. 85*A*) is a simple, straight tube divided into esophagus, stomach-intestine, and end gut, all composed of a cuboidal or columnar nonciliated epithelium continuous with the lining epithelium of the pharynx. The esophagus is a slender tube to which are attached two dorsolateral and two ventrolateral syncytial masses regarded as salivary glands (Fig. 85*B*). The esophagus is lined by a continuation of the pharyngeal cuticle and hence both these parts of the digestive tract presumably represent a stomodaeum. At the junction of esophagus and stomach are found two or more so-called pancreatic glands similar to the salivary glands. The widened stomach-intestine (Fig. 83*C*) lacks a cuticular lining and gland cells, and is covered externally by a loose net of circular and longitudinal muscle fibers, of which the latter continue over esophagus and end gut. A sphincter occurs between stomach-intestine and end gut and another is located between the anteriorly expanded and posteriorly narrowed parts of the end gut. The end gut posterior to this sphincter is lined by cuticle, hence presumably represents a proctodaeum, and leads to the terminal anus, found between the tergal and sternal plates of the last zonite.

A spacious pseudocoel exists between the digestive tract and the epidermis. It is filled with a fluid containing numerous active amoebocytes that appear to originate from the wall of the digestive tract.

In the tenth zonite there occurs on either side of the intestine a large multinucleate flame bulb of which the flame consists of one long flagellum or a long and a short one (Fig. 85*D*). A short tube provided with driving flagella leads directly from each flame bulb to its own nephridiopore on the tergal plate of the eleventh zonite. The pore consists of a sieve plate.

The nervous system is so similar histologically to and so closely in contact with the epidermis that the two are distinguishable only with difficulty. The brain completely encircles the base of the mouth cone or the anterior part of the pharynx and may be in contact with the head cuticle (Fig. 85*A*). In this circumenteric nerve ring, the ganglion cells are more or less absent ventrally and are aggregated chiefly in the anterior, inner middle, and posterior parts. From the anterior ganglionic mass ganglion cells extend forward into the epidermal cushions at the bases of the scalids. From the nerve ring springs a ventral ganglionated cord that runs in contact with the epidermis in the mid-ventral line just inside

the ventral chain; 9, dorsal chord; 10, lateral chords; 11, adhesive gland; 12, adhesive tube; 13, placids; 14, retracted head; 15, pharynx; 16, mouth cone; 17, oral styles; 18, stomach-intestine; 19, median end spine; 20, scalids; 21, trichoscalids; 22, pharynx crown; 23, outer head retractors; 24, inner head retractors; 25, salivary glands; 26, lateral chords; 27, epithelial lining; 28, muscle layer; 29, nuclei.

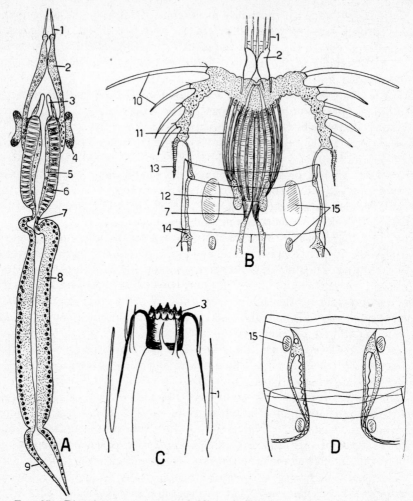

Fig. 85.—Digestive tract, protonephridia. *A*. Digestive tract of *Pycnophyes*. *B*. Anterior end of *Pycnophyes*, showing pharyngeal muscles. *C*. Pharynx forced out by pressure to show pharynx crown. *D*. Protonephridia of *Pycnophyes*. (*All after Zelinka*, 1928.) 1, oral styles; 2, mouth cone; 3, pharynx crown; 4, brain ganglia; 5, epithelial lining of pharynx; 6, muscle layer of pharynx; 7, esophagus; 8, stomach-intestine; 9, end gut; 10, scalids; 11, protractor muscles of pharynx; 12, salivary glands; 13, trichoscalids; 14, lateral chords; 15, dorsoventral muscles.

the mid-ventral groove of the body surface. This trunk presents a ganglion in the middle of each trunk zonite whereas between the zonites the cord consists of fibers only without ganglion cells (Fig. 86*A*). The lateral and middorsal epidermal chords also contain in each zonite a group of ganglion cells but these do not seem to be connected by fibers into definite longitudinal nerve cords. What appear to be ganglion cells also occur in each zonite in the epidermis between the chords.

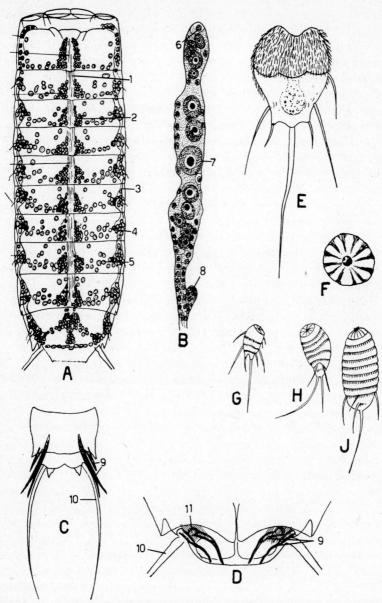

Fig. 86.—Nervous system, reproduction. *A. Pycnophyes*, showing nervous system.
B. Echinoderid ovary.   *C.* Rear end of male *Echinoderes*, showing the copulatory spicules.
D. Rear end of male *Pycnophyes*, with copulatory spicules. (*A–D, after Zelinka*, 1928.)
E–J. Stages in the development of *Echinoderella* (*after Nyholm*, 1947).   *E.* Earliest stage.
F. Anterior end of same showing primordia of placids.   *G, H,* Later stages.   *J. Hapalo-deres* stage.   1, ventral nerve cord; 2, ganglionic swellings of same; 3, lateral chord; 4, ganglion cells in lateral chord; 5, ganglion cells between chords; 6, apical cell; 7, developing ova; 8, seminal receptacle; 9, copulatory spicules; 10, lateral end spines; 11, gonopore.

Sense organs comprise the eyes of *Echinoderes*—cup-shaped masses of red pigment enclosing a lens-like body—and the sensory bristles, found in longitudinal rows on the trunk. Each bristle has a cuticular exterior enclosing a plasmatic strand continuous with a sensory nerve cell situated in the epidermis.

The Kinorhyncha are dioecious but the two sexes are usually indistinguishable externally. In *Trachydemus* and *Pycnophyes* only the males possess adhesive tubes and there are some further differences between the sexes in these genera in the edges of the plates of the last zonite. The female of *Echinoderes dujardinii* has more end spines than the male. The gonads are a pair of sacciform bodies opening separately on the thirteenth zonite. At the anterior end of each gonad is found an apical cell that gives rise to all the other cells of the gonad: germ cells, nutritive cells (female only), and epithelial wall. The ovary is at first a syncytium containing ovocytic and nutritive nuclei; later ova differentiate from the mass and absorb the nutritive syncytia (Fig. 86*B*). From the posterior end of each ovary a short oviduct provided with a seminal receptacle as a dorsal diverticulum extends to the genital pore. The testis wall consists of a flat epithelium and on the side next the intestine an inner layer of spermatogonia; the interior is filled with cells in various stages of spermatogenesis. From the posterior end of each testis a short sperm duct leads to the genital pore armed with two or three penial spicules, which may be accompanied by additional hairs, spines, or bristles (Fig. 86*C, D*). The penial spicules presumably serve in copulation but the latter process has not been observed. The sperm are large with a short tail and a broad elongated head containing mitochondria and a rod-like nucleus.

5. Development.—The laid eggs are unknown and hence the embryonic development has never been studied. Since the youngest females always contain sperm in the seminal receptacle, the eggs are presumably always fertilized and do not develop parthenogenetically. Sexual reproduction appears to occur at all seasons of the year. The eggs hatch into larvae that show little resemblance to the adults and pass through a metamorphosis comprising several larval stages separated by molts before attaining the adult anatomy. Nyholm (1947) has worked out the postembryonic development of cyclorhagous kinorhynchs and finds that the earliest stage consists of a minute larva without definite divisions into zonites and also lacking head, scalids, placids, pharynx, and anus (Fig. 86*E*). The mouth is surrounded by an area with radiating grooves suggestive of the closing apparatus (Fig. 86*F*) and the anterior body half is clothed with fine bristles. The spine arrangement on this larva suggests that it consists of three zonites. The development was followed through stages previously termed *Hapaloderes* in which the number of zonites gradually increases (Fig. 86*G–J*) and other differentiations occur, eventuating in adults of the genus *Echinoderella* (Fig. 82*A*). The homalorhagous kinorhynchs appear to hatch into a more advanced larval stage with six to seven zonites and bear a greater resemblance to the adults. The development of *Pycnophyes* was followed through *Leptodemus*, *Centrophyes*, and *Hyalophyes* stages; sexual reproduction may occur in the *Hyalophyes* stage. Various other late larval or, better, juvenile stages of kinorhynchs to which names have been given have not been traced to the adult form. These juveniles differ from the adults in their softer, transparent cuticle, not yet thickened into definite plates, fewer zonites (11 to 13), and fewer cuticular teeth, spines, and bristles.

In molting, the entire cuticle is shed from the mouth styles to the posterior end, including the proctodaeal lining. The new cuticle has already formed beneath the old one. The process of molting requires several days during which the animal by body contortions gradually frees itself from the old cuticle and ruptures this in the region of the mouth cone, then creeping out through this rupture (Zelinka, 1928).

6. Systematic Survey.—The Kinorhyncha are divided into three groups, possibly meriting the rank of suborders: Cyclorhagae, Conchorhagae, and Homalorhagae. In the first, only the first zonite can be retracted and the placids of the second zonite then close over this. *Echinoderes* with two eyespots and *Echinoderella* without them (Fig. 82*A*) are provided with lateral but no median end spines. A median end spine occurs in *Centroderes* (Fig. 84*A*) and *Campyloderes* (Fig. 83*B*). The latter, from the antarctic, differs from other kinorhynchs in having 14 zonites but the fourteenth zonite is merely the base of the end spine and hence of no morphological significance (Nyholm, 1947). The conchorhagous type comprises only the genus *Semnoderes* (Fig. 83*A*) in which the third zonite bears a closing apparatus in the form of a pair of shells. In the homalorhagous type, the closing apparatus is also borne on the third zonite and consists of one tergal and three ventral plates (Fig. 82*C*). The members of this group are less spiny and more truncate at the ends than the preceding genera. There are two homalorhagous genera: *Pycnophyes* with lateral end spines (Fig. 82*C*) and *Trachydemus* without them. In addition to the foregoing genera, a number of generic names have been given to juveniles.

7. Ecology.—The Kinorhyncha are exclusively marine, being generally found in mucky bottoms in the littoral zone, usually in rather shallow water. The known species have been taken chiefly on European coasts—in the Mediterranean, the Baltic, the North Sea, and off the British Isles—but the occasional finding of species in other, widely separated localities (Zanzibar, Japan, the antarctic) indicates that the group is extensively distributed throughout the world. They have simply not been sought for in an intensive manner. Kinorhycha were unknown on the coasts of the Americas until 1930 when Blake found three species (*Echinoderella remanei, Pycnophyes frequens* (Fig. 82*C*), and *Trachydemus mainensis*) off Mount Desert Island, Maine. The author refound the second of these Maine species without difficulty and also obtained two or three kinds of kinorhynchs at the first attempt in Puget Sound (Fig. 82*A, B*) but failed to discover any elsewhere on North American coasts.

The Kinorhyncha have benthonic habits dwelling in slime and mud or less often among algae. They are unable to swim but move about in worm-like fashion with the aid of the scalids. First the head is fully protruded and the scalids take hold on the substratum; the trunk is then brought forward by the contraction of the longitudinal muscles; and through this advance the head is withdrawn and is then thrust forward again for the next step. This method of locomotion is necessarily slow and laborious. The role of the adhesive tubes in locomotion has not been ascertained. Sidewise bendings are also possible and bendings of the head in a searching manner during locomotion are customary. When disturbed the animals withdraw the head completely, protecting it with the closing apparatus, and remain motionless.

The species that live among algae feed chiefly on diatoms while the others eat fine detritus and bottom material. In feeding the mouth cone is extended fully and the mouth styles spread open and thrust into the food material which is then ingested by a sucking action of the muscular pharynx. Nothing is known of the process of digestion. Zooxanthellae occur in the epidermis and also elsewhere in a number of species and are said to be devoured by the amoebocytes of the pseudocoel during periods of starvation.

In laboratory cultures kinorhynchs have been observed to live for half a year to more than a year.

8. Relationships.—Dujardin, the discoverer of the Kinorhyncha, recognized the unique character of the animal, while at the same time noting likenesses in its anatomical details to various groups—copepods, sipunculids, acanthocephalans, rotifers, tardigrades, and nematodes. Many zoologists have regarded the Kinorhyncha as allied to arthropods or intermediate between annelids and arthropods. This opinion rests on the external segmentation, the fact of molting, and the general similarity to an insect larva. As regards the kinorhynchid segmentation this appears to be of the superficial type already seen in rotifers and acanthocephalans, involving primarily the cuticle. The segmentation goes farther in the Kinorhyncha than in other pseudocoelomate groups except Priapulida since it extends not only into the musculature (also seen in Acanthocephala) but also into the nervous system. There is a further resemblance to annelid-arthropod segmentation in that during larval growth new segments form in front of the terminal segment. However, kinorhynchid segmentation differs fundamentally from annelid-arthropod segmentation in that the latter begins in the mesoderm and progresses toward the surface whereas in the pseudocoelomates it begins in the cuticle and progresses inward to a variable extent in different groups. It is impossible to maintain any relation of kinorhynchid segmentation to that of the annelids and arthropods. The structural characteristics of the Kinorhyncha, the lack of a coelom, the absence of a definite muscle layer in body and intestinal walls, the presence of protonephridia with flame bulbs, the close association of the nervous system with the epidermis, all bespeak a relatively low grade of organization, much below that of annelids. The affinities of the Kinorhyncha are undoubtedly to be sought among the classes of the Aschelminthes. With most of these the Kinorhyncha present similarities of structure. The segmented cuticle, syncytial epidermis with cushions, muscle arrangement, and retractile anterior end occur in common with rotifers and some of these points are also found in gastrotrichs. Other similarities to gastrotrichs are the spines and other cuticular specializations, the adhesive tubes, the single pair of flame bulbs, and the general construction of the digestive tract. Comparison of the mouth cone of the Kinorhyncha with the buccal tube of the Chaetonotoidea does not seem warranted. Strong affinity to nematodes is seen in the whole anatomy of the digestive tract, the division of the epidermis and musculature into longitudinal chords, the circumenteric form of the brain, the presence of a single mid-ventral nerve cord, the limitation of germ-cell formation to the beginning of the gonad, the molting of the cuticle in larval stages, and the copulatory spicules of the male. The similarity of the pharynx in Gastrotricha, Kinorhyncha, and Nematoda has already been emphasized although it must be noted that the kinorhynchid pharynx differs from the others in having an epithelial lining. Altogether the kinorhynchs appear to be most nearly allied to the nematodes and gastrotrichs while not directly derivable from either. It may be concluded that Gastrotricha, Kinorhyncha, and Nematoda are offshoots from some common stem.

VII. CLASS PRIAPULIDA

1. Historical.—The animal now called *Priapulus caudatus* is common in northern European waters and has been known to zoologists since the days of Linnaeus. It appears in Linnaeus's *Systema Naturae* first under the name *Priapus humanus*, later under the name *Holothuria priapus*, placed under the group Vermes Mollusca, a heterogeneous assemblage of soft-bodied invertebrates. The name *Holothuria priapus* was also employed by Fabricius (1780), who recorded the animal from Greenland waters, and by O. F. Müller (1806), who described and figured it from Danish waters. The animal was generally believed to be related to echinoderms. Lamarck in 1816 realized that the animal is not a holothurian and gave it the name now in use, *Priapulus caudatus;* but it appears to the author, as also remarked by Theel, that *Priapus* is the valid generic name, not *Priapulus*. Cuvier continued to call the creature *Holothuria* *priapus* and to place it among the footless echinoderms, close to *Sipunculus*. In 1847, Quatrefages created the group Gephyrea for the echiuroids and sipunculoids and suggested that *Priapulus* should also be included in this group, which he considered transitional between worms and echinoderms. The concept of a phylum Gephyrea for the three groups, priapuloids, sipunculoids, and echiuroids, has obtained in zoology to recent times, although students of these groups regard them as unrelated, requiring to be placed in separate phyla. There is a present tendency to erect a separate phylum for each of the three groups but the author feels that grounds exist for the inclusion of the Priapulida in the phylum Aschelminthes. Zoologists who feel, after reading the evidence herein presented, that the grounds are insufficient, should not hesitate to separate the priapuloids as a distinct phylum.

During the last hundred years, additional species of *Priapulus* have been described but it appears that actually there are only two distinct species, *caudatus* and *bicaudatus*. Von Siebold in 1849 described another priapulid from the Baltic under the name *Halicryptus spinulosus*. These three species therefore constitute the entire class.

A general discussion of the group is given by Baltzer in the *Handbuch der Zoologie*, Band II, part 2. The best accounts of the anatomy are those of Ehlers (1862) and Apel (1885) and splendid figures have been furnished by Theel (1906, 1911).

2. Definition.—The Priapulida are marine Aschelminthes of cylindroid shape and warty appearance, with an introversible presoma, a superficially segmented trunk, a more or less straight digestive tube with terminal mouth and anus, and a pair of urogenital ducts, each continuous with a gonad and a solenocytic protonephridium and opening by a separate pore near the anus.

3. General Structure.—The priapulids are animals of modest size, up to 8 cm., and drab coloration. The cylindroid warty body is divisible into an anterior shorter region, the *presoma*, and a longer *trunk;* in the genus *Priapulus* the posterior end bears one or two conspicuous warty appendages (Fig. 87*A*, *B*), wanting in *Halicryptus*. The presoma constitutes about one-third the body length in *Priapulus* and is somewhat plumper than the trunk, from which it is demarcated by an evident constriction; in *Halicryptus*, it occupies one-sixth or less the body length and is of the same diameter as the trunk, from which it is less definitely delimited (Fig. 88*A*). The terminal mouth is surrounded by an area armed with formidable spines (Figs. 87*D*, 88*B*), arranged in concentric pentagons, five to seven in number in *Priapulus* (Fig. 88*C*), three or four in *Halicryptus;* the spines increase in size from the mouth outward, then decrease again in the outer pentagons. The spiny circumoral region is ordinarily invaginated into the interior, in which condition the spines point backward; but when in use, as in the capture of prey, the region is everted whereupon the spines point forward. Posterior to the spine-bearing area, the location of the nerve ring is indicated on the surface as a circular band or collar in *Priapulus* (Fig. 87*D*), but is not distinctly set off in *Halicryptus*. Posterior to this comes the main part of the presoma,

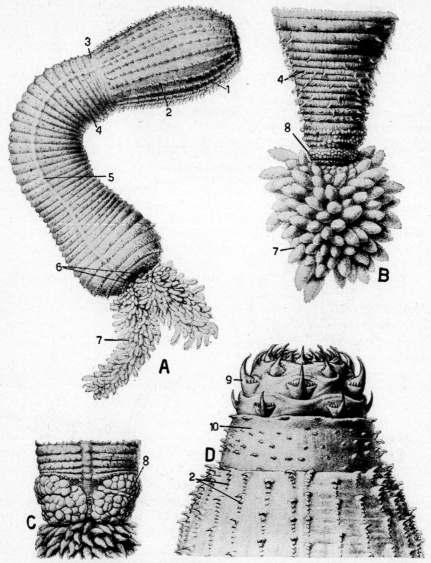

Fig. 87.—Priapulida. *A. Priapulus bicaudatus.* *B.* Rear end of *Priapulus caudatus.*
C. Posterior end of the trunk of *P. caudatus,* showing warts. *D.* Anterior end of *Priapulus*
with circumoral spiny area everted. (*All after Theel,* 1906, 1911.) 1, proboscis; 2, ribs of
papillae on proboscis; 3, constriction between presoma and trunk; 4, trunk rings; 5, ventral
nerve cord, 6, urogenital pores; 7, caudal appendages; 8, warts; 9, spines of circumoral area;
10, collar containing nerve ring.

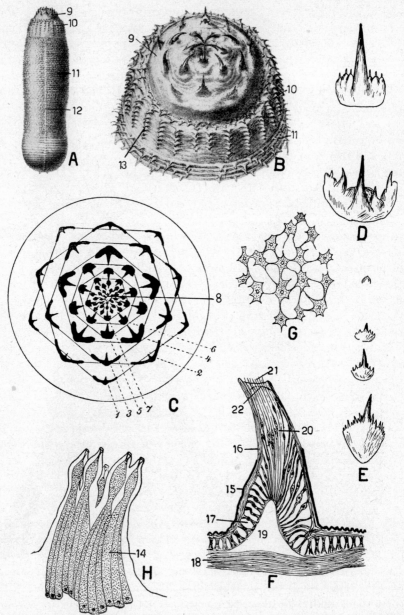

Fig. 88.—Priapulida (continued). *A. Halicryptus spinulosus. B.* Anterior end of *H. spinulosus.* (*A, B, after Theel,* 1906.) *C.* Scheme of the arrangement of spines on the circumoral area of *Priapulus. D.* Two spines of the circumoral area of *Priapulus. E.* Succession of spines down the pharynx. (*C–E, after Theel,* 1911.) *F.* Section through a papilla of the proboscis of *Priapulus,* showing also structure of the body wall. *G.* Section across the epidermis of *Halicryptus* (*after Apel,* 1885). *H.* Section through the warts of *Priapulus.* (*F, H, after Scharff,* 1885.) 1–7, pentagons of spines around the mouth of

usually called *proboscis*, a somewhat bulbous region in *Priapulus* (Fig. 87*A*), provided in both genera with 25 longitudinal ridges or ribs composed of a row of papillae. The proboscis can be invaginated into the interior but is usually exposed, constituting the anterior part of the animal. It is more or less demarcated from the trunk by a constriction.

The trunk is irregularly strewn with small spines and papillae and is annulated into rings, about 30 to 40 in *Priapulus*, around 100 in *Halicryptus*. These rings express the same kind of superficial segmentation seen in kinorhynchs and nematodes. Along the mid-ventral line of the trunk and also extending along the proboscis is seen a whitish longitudinal band caused by the underlying nerve cord (Fig. 87*A*). In *Priapulus*, the last trunk rings are beset with wart-like eminences (Fig. 87*C*) except mid-ventrally where the zone of the nerve cord is free from them.

The posterior end of the trunk bears three openings, the anus and the two urogenital pores, and is provided with a caudal appendage in *Pr. caudatus*, two in *Pr. bicaudatus;* but as a rudiment of the second appendage is present in the former species, it would appear that two is the original number. In *Pr. caudatus*, the caudal appendage is centrally located on the posterior end, and hence the anus is displaced laterally, to either side, apparently, without regularity; the anus is central in *Pr. bicaudatus*. The caudal appendages are hollow stems thickly beset with hollow rounded or oval vesicles, both having the same structure as the body wall. Their function is unknown; the former belief that they act as respiratory organs has been disproved by the experiments of Lang (1948). No evident effects follow their removal.

The body wall consists of cuticle, epidermis, circular and longitudinal muscle layers, and lining membrane. The cuticle is composed of a thin homogeneous outer stratum and a thicker lamellate inner layer (Fig. 88*F*). The epidermis is a one-layered epithelium of tall slender cells, whose ends make contact and seem to anastomose but which elsewhere are separated by fluid-filled spaces (Scharff, 1885, Fig. 88*G*). Beneath the epidermis lies the circular muscle layer composed of separate rings and beneath that the longitudinal muscle layer (90*A*), of separate strands in *Priapulus* but forming a continuous stratum in *Halicryptus*. Under each of the ribs of the proboscis is found a special longitudinal muscle (Fig. 89), situated to the outer side of the circular stratum; the latter is therefore attached to the epidermis only between the ribs so that each rib muscle is underlain by a space continuous with the body cavity and

---

Priapulus; 8, pharyngeal teeth; 9, spiny circumoral area; 10, proboscis; 11, trunk; 12, ventral nerve cord; 13, ribs of papillae on proboscis; 14, gland cells of warts; 15, homogeneous layer of cuticle; 16, lamellate layer; 17, epidermis; 18, circular body-wall muscle layer; 19, space under proboscis rib; 20, sensory part of papilla; 21, sensory hairs of papilla; 22, membrane over end of papilla.

filled with the same fluid as the latter. Presumably movements of this fluid play a role in the eversion and introversion of the proboscis. The body wall is lined internally by a very thin, structureless, nonnucleated membrane.

The papillae, spines, and warts of the body surface are either sensory or glandular structures. According to Scharff (1885), the papillae along the proboscis ribs are little truncate cones whose tip is devoid of cuticle and covered instead with a delicate membrane; inside is a bundle of especially long and slender epidermal cells with hair tips that pierce the membrane (Fig. 88F). These papillae presumably function as tango-receptors. The papillae of the trunk are similarly constructed. The warts on the posterior end of *Priapulus* contain masses of altered epidermal cells, apparently of glandular nature (Fig. 88H), and are permeated with the pores of these gland cells (Hammarsten and Runnström, 1918).

The mouth leads into a muscular pharynx composed of circular and radial muscles, clothed externally with a thin layer of longitudinal fibers and lined by epidermis and a cuticle covered with spines or teeth continuous with the spines around the mouth and gradually decreasing in size posteriorly (Fig. 90A). Around the anterior end of the pharynx are attached a circle of retractor muscles that originate on the body wall and accomplish the invagination of the proboscis (Figs. 89, 90A). The retractors consist of two series, the short retractors that originate at the junction of proboscis and trunk and the long retractors that originate on the trunk wall and act to pull in the proboscis. In *Priapulus*, there are up to 25 short retractors and 8 long ones; in *Halicryptus*, both sets are much shorter than in *Priapulus* and consist of about 10 bands each. Longitudinal bands also course along the outer surface of the pharynx. When the proboscis is invaginated, the pharynx invaginates into the midgut.

The intestine or midgut forms a straight or slightly curved tube occupying the center of the interior of the trunk. Its wall consists of a lining epithelium, followed by circular and longitudinal muscle layers (Fig. 90B). The intestinal epithelium is thrown into conspicuous circular folds, caused by variations in its height, and consists of columnar cells, very tall on the folds. The epithelium is said by some authors to be ciliated but no clear statement on this point was found. The midgut is separated by a constriction from the short end gut or rectum that leads to the anus and has the same histological construction as the midgut except that it is lined with cuticle.

Between the body wall and the digestive tube there exists a considerable space the nature of which is unknown and can be elucidated only by embryological studies, unfortunately still lacking. This space is everywhere lined by a very thin structureless membrane, usually called peritoneum; but as it lacks nuclei, its peritoneal nature is doubtful. This membrane forms the innermost layer of the body wall and the outermost layer of the intestinal wall and also webs the intestine and the urogenital organs to the body wall (Fig. 89) by extensions similar to mesenteries of coelomate animals. Although the presence of complete circular

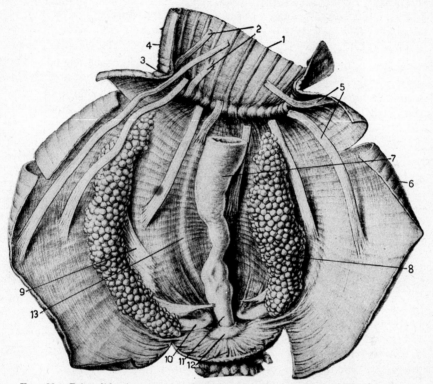

Fig. 89.—Priapulida (continued). Dissection of *Priapulus* (*after Theel*, 1911). 1, muscle along proboscis rib; 2, short retractors; 3, constriction between proboscis and trunk; 4, proboscis; 5, long retractors; 6, trunk rings; 7, intestine; 8, urogenital organ; 9, supporting membrane of urogenital organ; 10, urogenital duct; 11, rectum; 12, muscles around rectum; 13, ventral nerve cord.

and longitudinal muscle layers in both body and intestinal walls and of membranes connecting the viscera with the body wall are certainly suggestive of coelomate animals, it is known regarding the supporting membrane of the urogenital complex that this is not a true mesentery but an extension of the covering epithelium of the gonad. It is hence improbable that the body space of priapulids is a true coelom but decision on this point must await embryological studies.

The body cavity, also the cavity of the caudal appendages, and the

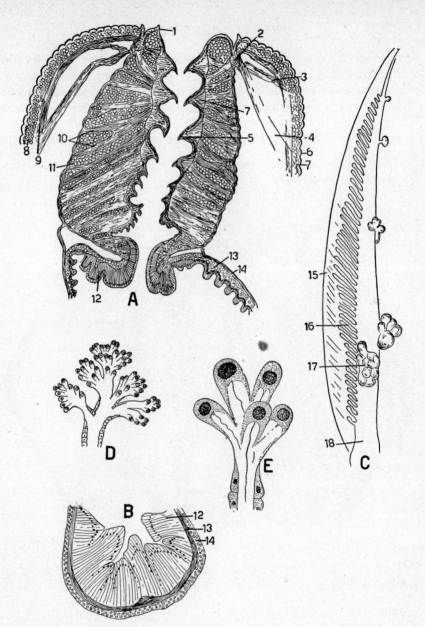

FIG. 90.—Priapulida (continued). *A*. Longitudinal section of the pharynx of *Halicryptus*. *B*. Cross section of the intestine. (*A, B, after Apel*, 1885.) *C*. Young stage of the urogenital organ of *Halicryptus* (*after Hammarsten*, 1915). *D*. Cluster of solenocytes of *Halicryptus*. *E*. Some solenocytes enlarged. (*D, E, after Moltschanov*, 1908.) 1, spines around mouth; 2, nerve ring; 3, short retractors; 4, long retractors; 5, teeth down pharynx; 6, cuticle; 7, epidermis; 8, circular muscles of body wall; 9, longitudinal muscles of body wall; 10, radial muscles of pharynx; 11, circular muscles of pharynx; 12, intestinal epithelium; 13, circular muscles of intestinal wall; 14, longitudinal muscles of intestinal wall; 15, supporting membrane of urogenital organ; 16, developing gonad tubules; 17, clusters of solenocytes; 18, urogenital duct.

spaces in the body-wall musculature are filled with a fluid in which float numerous rounded cells. These seem to be of the nature of athrocytes; they take up injected carbon or carmine particles (Moltschanov, 1908; Hammarsten, 1915) and according to the latter author deposit them in the protonephridia.

The nervous system (Fig. 91*B*) is simply constructed and strikingly similar to that of echinoderids. It consists of a circumenteric ring, situated at the beginning of the pharynx, and a mid-ventral cord, located in the epidermis of which it forms a thickening. The circumenteric ring, also continuous with the epidermis, is composed of fibers and ganglion cells but shows no ganglionic enlargements. The ventral cord contains ganglion cells throughout its length, is slightly broadened in each trunk annulus, and terminates in a thickening. The peripheral nerves are so delicate that they can be followed only with difficulty and have not been thoroughly worked out. According to Apel (1885), a pair of main lateral nerves springs from each annular thickening of the ventral cord and runs in the base of the epidermis around the body. Other nerves from these annual thickenings were also seen by Apel in a fragmentary manner. The last pair of lateral nerves, originating from the terminal thickening of the ventral cord, is stouter than the others in *Priapulus* and probably supplies the caudal appendages in this genus. From the nerve ring there spring 13 pairs of nerves that run backward in the epidermis of the proboscis, probably in the ribs, and four nerves that supply the pharynx, proceeding posteriorly in the epidermis of the latter and establishing contact by several ring connections (Fig. 91*B*). It is to be noted that the entire nervous system lies in a very primitive situation, in the epidermis (Fig. 91*A*), and is continuous with the latter.

In the body cavity lies a pair of urogenital organs, one to either side of the intestine (Fig. 89); each is an elongated, warty body supported by a mesentery composed of the lining of the cavity. The urogenital organ consists of the urogenital duct bearing the gonad on the side next the mesentery and clusters of solenocytes on the other side (Fig. 90*C*). The sexes are separate; each gonad is a fairly compact body composed of numerous tubules that often anastomose into a network. The protonephridial part of the urogenital complex takes the form of several large clusters of solenocytes opening into the urogenital duct by collecting canals. Each cluster consists of thousands of nucleated solenocytes (Fig. 90*D, E*). A solenocyte, it will be recalled, is a type of protonephridial end bulb that is provided with a flagellum instead of a tuft of cilia. An excretory function of the solenocytes is indicated by an experiment of Moltschanov (1908), who found that injected ammoniacal carmine is taken up by the solenocytes. The urogenital canal of each side opens separately by a pore at the posterior end of the animal (Fig. 87*A*).

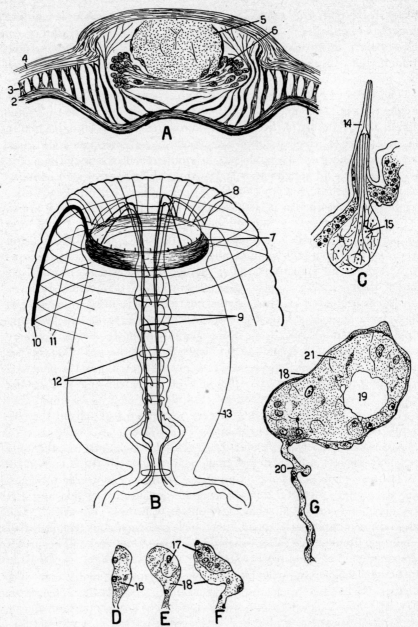

Fig. 91.—Priapulida (continued). *A.* Section across ventral body wall, showing nerve cord (*after Scharff,* 1885). *B.* Scheme of the nervous system of *Halicryptus* (*after Apel,* 1885). *C.* Adhesive gland on presoma of *Halicryptus* larva (*after Hammarsten,* 1915). *D–G.* Stages in the development of the gonad of *Halicryptus* (*after Lüling,* 1940). 1, homogeneous layer of cuticle; 2, lamellate layer of cuticle; 3, epidermis; 4, circular muscle of body wall; 5, nerve cord; 6, nerve cells; 7, circumenteric nerve ring; 8, nerves from ring to

4. Development.—Hardly anything is known of the embryology of the priapulids but the postembryonic development has been the subject of several satisfactory studies (Hammarsten, 1913, 1915; Eggers, 1925; Lang, 1939, 1948b; Lüling, 1940; Purasjoki, 1944). Lang (1939), who studied the early cleavage, reports that there is a 3-cell stage as in nematodes and a 16-cell stage consisting of four tiers of approximately equal cells, as in rotifers. No further information is available on the embryonic development Apparently there is a direct hatch into a minute larva that is very similar to the adult in general anatomy but possesses several features that are subsequently lost or altered. Chief among these is the encasement of the larval trunk in a cuticularized lorica or armor, consisting of a dorsal and a ventral plate and three long narrow lateral plates (Fig. 92*C*); in *Priapulus* there are two additional plates in the form of very small dorsal and ventral pieces in front of the main plates (Fig. 92*B*). From the lorica projects the presoma of the larva consisting of a spiny region followed by a narrowed neck. Both are invaginable into the interior as in the adult. The *Halicryptus* larva is noteworthy in that the last circlet of spines on the presoma, 12 instead of 25 in number, are the outlets of gland cells and recall the adhesive tubes of gastrotrichs (Fig. 91*C*); these are wanting in the adults and also in the *Priapulus* larva. On the other hand, the *Priapulus* larva has certain features wanting in the larva of *Halicryptus*, namely, two pairs of tactile spines (Fig. 92*A*, *B*) strongly resembling in position and structure the lateral antennae of rotifers, and a terminal foot ending in two toe-like projections (Fig. 92*D*), also highly suggestive of rotifers. This foot gives rise to the caudal appendages of the adult, which therefore appear homologous with the foot of rotifers, and it is supplied by a pair of caudal gland complexes. These caudal glands are also present in the *Halicryptus* larva which lacks the foot and they appear to persist as the glands of the warts of the adult *Priapulus*. The internal structure of these larvae is similar to that of the adults (Fig. 92*A*) except that the urogenital system is not fully developed. The development of the urogenital system has been followed by Eggers (1925) and Lüling (1940). Each urogenital complex arises from a small group of cells at the posterior end of the animal, apparently of ecthdermal origin. This grows inward and its cells soon differentiate into two groups, one of which becomes the covering epithelium of the complex while the other sprouts out the clusters of solenocytes on one side and the gonadal tissue on the other (Fig. 91*D–G*). The covering

body wall; 9, nerves from ring to pharynx; 10, ventral nerve cord; 11, segmental nerves from cord to trunk wall; 12, nerve rings in pharynx; 13, pharynx; 14, adhesive tube; 15, gland; 16, urogenital primordium; 17, inner mass separated off; 18, outer epithelium; 19, lumen of urogenital tube; 20, supporting membrane formed from outer epithelium; 21, inner mass, forms gonad and solenocytes.

epithelium also produces the so-called mesentery that attaches the urogenital complex to the body wall as well as other minor supports; it is
therefore indicated that these supports cannot be of the nature of true
coelomic mesenteries. The hollowing out of the interior mass produces

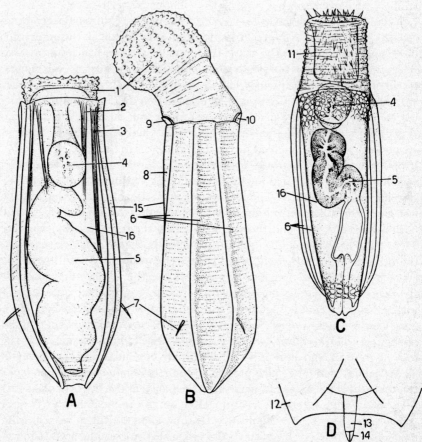

Fig. 92.—Priapulida (concluded), development. *A, B.* Larva of *Priapulus caudatus.*
C. Larva of *Halicryptus spinulosus.* (*A–C, after Lang,* 1948.) *D.* Posterior end of
Priapulus larva, showing rotifer characteristics (*after Lang,* 1939). 1, presoma; 2, short
retractors; 3, long retractors; 4, pharynx; 5, intestine; 6, lateral plates of lorica; 7, lateral
tangoreceptor; 8, ventral plate of lorica; 9, small ventral plate; 10, small dorsal plate; 11,
presoma invaginated; 12, dorsal plate of lorica; 13, foot; 14, toes; 15, trunk; 16, pseudocoel.

the urogenital canal. The development of the gonad is seen to be
identical with that of nematodes in that the covering epithelium, the
germinal tissue, and the genital duct are all derived from the same small
group of cells. The continuity of the genital duct with the gonad is also
characteristic of nematodes.

The priapulid larvae live in the bottom muck along with the adults, apparently feeding on detritus, and seem to pass about 2 years in the loricate condition. They then molt, shedding the lorica, and emerge as juvenile priapulids, identical in structure with the adults. The priapulids, like the echinoderids and nematodes, continue to molt throughout juvenile life; adults also molt.

5. Ecology and Physiology.—The priapulids live buried in soft bottoms in the littoral, including the intertidal, zone of colder seas, down to about 500 m. In the north they are found from Massachusetts northward around to Russia and Siberia, including the shores of Greenland, Spitsbergen, the Scandinavian coasts, and the Baltic and North Seas westward to Belgium. *Priapulus caudatus* or a slight variant thereof also inhabits the antarctic, being found along the shores of Patagonia, the Falkland Islands, and South Georgia. This species therefore exhibits the phenomenon of bipolarity, that is, occurrence at both poles and absence elsewhere, a distribution offering difficulties for the zoogeographer.

The animals live buried in the bottom muck but do not form definite tubes lined with secretion. According to Lang (1948a) when hungry they plow the mud in all directions, apparently seeking food; otherwise they lie quiescent in a vertical position with the widely opened mouth on a level with the surface. But according to Langeloh (1936), priapulids investigate the surroundings only by movements of the proboscis and when they burrow, they dig downward, manifesting a positive geotaxis. Burrowing is accomplished by alternate invagination and evagination of the proboscis and is much more vigorous in *Priapulus* than in *Halicryptus*. In *Priapulus* the rear end forms a ring-shaped expansion during digging that is used as anchorage and the body-wall musculature cooperates with the proboscis movements; whereas *Halicryptus* lacks anchorage and moves largely with the aid of peristaltic waves that progress in both directions from the anterior part of the trunk (Friedrich and Langeloh, 1936). No water current is maintained through the burrows.

The older workers believed that the priapulids ate the bottom muck but the observations of Lang (1948a) show that the animals are highly predaceous, attacking such forms as polychaetes and other priapulids with their teeth and swallowing them whole. Similar feeding habits were previously reported by Wesenberg-Lund (1929). Only slowly moving prey can be captured. Nothing is known of the digestive processes. Apparently the need for food is small as Lang kept specimens for 6 weeks without food and saw no appreciable change.

According to Lang, spawning on the Scandinavian Coast occurs in winter. The sex cells are shed into the sea water, where fertilization takes place.

The caudal appendages are regenerated if removed, provided that the sphincter at their attachment to the body is not injured. Injury of the sphincter permits the body fluid to escape and results in the death of the animal. Obviously the full complement of body fluid is necessary for the activities of the animal since muscular contractions can be effective only by putting the fluid under pressure.

The reactions of the priapulids to simple stimuli have been reported by Langeloh (1936). As the animals habitually live buried in the substratum and are never found on the surface they are presumably highly thigmotactic. Light tactile stimulation evokes vigorous burrowing movements; stronger stimulation causes the animals to pass into a short, very contracted state which seems to represent both an escape and a quiescent attitude. During activities, the body is customarily relaxed and extended. As noted above, positive geotaxis is operative in the burrowing process; this response is disturbed when the container of the animals is held at an angle of less than 60 degrees with the substratum, and disappears when the angle is reduced to 30 degrees. Exposure to sudden illumination causes *Halicryptus* to cease burrowing and assume the shortened state, and return to normal activity follows only after some lapse of time; no definite reaction is given by *Priapulus*. Both genera are somewhat negative to light and if illuminated on one side while burrowing, will deviate from the vertical toward the side away from the light. Reaction to light would seem to be of no significance in the normal life of the priapulids. The experiments of Langeloh were carried out in an artificial translucent slime made of agar-agar, which permitted observations on the burrowing animals. By altering the consistency of the agar-agar, it was shown that burrowing is possible only in a medium of adequate consistency.

6. Relationships.—All recent students of the Priapulida are agreed on their close relationship to other aschelminths, especially the kinorhynchs. In the imposition of a radial symmetry of the anterior end on a fundamental bilateral symmetry, the priapulids resemble the kinorhynchs and nematodes. The rounded invaginable anterior end covered with spines is very suggestive of the kinorhynchs. The characteristic of superficial segmentation also occurs in common with the kinorhynchs and nematodes. The identity of the central nervous system with that of kinorhynchs is certainly very striking. The presence of membranous supports in the body cavity seems to find its counterpart in the partitions dividing the pseudocoel of gastrotrichs. Protonephridia with flagella also occur in gastrotrichs and kinorhynchs. The larval stage of priapulids presents striking resemblances to rotifers in the presence of a lorica, a foot supplied with caudal glands, and lateral sense organs. The adhesive tubes that form such a prominent feature of gastrotrichs and that are also present in kinorhynchs and certain nematodes are seen in the *Priapulus* larva as a circlet on the anterior end. The development of the gonad and its duct are identical in priapulids and nematodes. The foregoing very specific resemblances appear to justify the alignment of the Priapulida among the Aschelminthes. On the other hand, the Priapulida do not appear derivable from any particular aschelminth group, although apparently most nearly related to the Kinorhyncha.

VIII. CLASS NEMATODA

1. **Historical.**—The larger parasitic nematodes were naturally well known to the ancients but the free-living nematodes, which are mostly microscopic, were not discovered until after the invention of the microscope when the vinegar eel and other so-called eelworms were seen by early microscopists. Linnaeus in his *Systema Naturae* (1758) placed roundworms along with many other kinds of worms in the order Intestina under his class Vermes and mentioned several prominent nematode genera as *Ascaris, Trichocephalus, Filaria, Strongylus,* and *Cucullanus* although he had of course only vague ideas of the limitations of these genera. The greatest advance in the eighteenth century was made by Goeze, who studied the vinegar eel and other nematodes and first began clearly to distinguish between the various kinds of worms. Cuvier and Lamarck, as previously noted, made some attempts at classifying worms but used insufficient criteria. Zeder, however, in 1800 utilized Goeze's notes and correctly distinguished several types of worms to which he gave common names, including nematodes which he termed roundworms (Rundwürmer). Rudolphi began to study the parasitic worms about 1793 and showed a much better understanding of them than most of his contemporaries. He adopted Zeder's groups based on Goeze's work and gave them scientific names, calling the roundworms Nematoidea. This spelling is retained by some zoologists to the present time but is usually altered to Nematoda. In his *Entozoorum synopsis* published in 1819 Rudolphi listed 11 genera and about 350 species of nematodes. No satisfactory placing of the nematodes in the animal kingdom was achieved until 1859 when Gegenbaur following the lead of Vogt created the class Nemathelminthes under the phylum Vermes. This class embraced two orders, Acanthocephla and Nematoidea, and the latter was subdivided into Nematodes and Gordiacei. The name Nemathelminthes won general acceptance, and although Gegenbaur himself later removed the Acanthocephala as a separate class, the association of the three groups of worms of cylindrical shape (nematodes, gordiaceans, and acanthocephalans) has been maintained to the present time usually with various untenable additions. The idea of associating all groups with protonephridia originated with T. H. Huxley, was accepted by Hatschek, and has lead to the classification here adopted.

During the nineteenth century parasitic worms were intensively studied, especially under the leadership of Leuckart, and many valuable contributions to the anatomy and life cycles of parasitic nematodes were made by a long list of distinguished helminthologists, as Van Beneden, Blanchard, Braun, Calandruccio, Cobbold, Diesing, Grassi, Leidy, Leuckart, von Linstow, Looss, Parona, Railliet, Rohde, Schneider, Stossich, and Zacharias. The available knowledge to that date was assembled by Schneider in 1866 in his well-known *Monographie der Nematoden*. The free-living nematodes, zoologically more important than the parasitic ones, were mostly neglected until the present century when our knowledge of them was greatly augmented by the studies of Allgen, Cobb, de Coninck, Daday, Ditlevsen, Filipjev, de Man, Micoletzky, Schuurmans-Stekhoven (hereafter shortened to Stekhoven), and Steiner. Study of the parasitic nematodes has continued with mounting intensity and a vast literature has accumulated, among the leading contributors to which may be mentioned Alessandrini, Alicata, Baylis, Bovien, Cameron, Fülleborn, Godfrey, Goldschmidt, Goodey, Hoeppli, Ihle, Jägerskiöld, Kreis, Lane, Leiper, Maplestone, Martini, Mönnig, Ortlepp, Rauther, Sandground, Seurat, Skrjabin, Spindler, Sprehn, Wetzel, Yamaguti, Yokogawa, Yorke, and Zavadovski abroad, and Ackert, Artigas, Augustine, Chandler, the Chitwoods, Christie, Cort, Cram, Dikmans, Faust, Hall, Lucker, Ransom, Schwartz, Stewart, Stiles, Stoll, Thorne, Travassos, Walton, and Ward in the Americas.

The outstanding account of the nematodes is *An introduction to nematology* (1937–   ) by the Chitwoods and collaborators, unfortunately still incomplete. *A synopsis of the families and genera of nematodes* by Baylis and Daubney (1926) and *The nematode parasites of vertebrates* by Yorke and Maplestone (1926) are useful taxonomic aids. The phytoparasitic nematodes have been treated by Filipjev and Stekhoven in *A manual of agricultural helminthology* (1941) which also contains valuable general information. Only a beginning has been made of the account of the nematodes by Stekhoven in Bronn's *Klassen und Ordnungen des Tierreichs* but the published part includes a useful bibliography of over 8000 titles to 1935. Other helpful accounts are those of Rauther in the *Handbuch der Zoologie*, Baylis in the *Fauna of British India*, and Wülker and Stekhoven in *Die Tierwelt der Nord- und Ostsee.*

2. Definition.—The nematodes are vermiform Aschelminthes of cylindrical shape, without cilia or flame bulbs, with four main longitudinal epidermal chords, a three-angled pharynx, circumenteric nerve ring, copulatory spicules, and one or two tubular gonads opening separately in the female, into the rectum in the male.

3. External Characters.—The nematodes, or roundworms,[1] are vermiform animals of long cylindrical shape, circular in cross section. There are two general types of body form, the *fusiform* and the *filiform* (Fig. 93*A*, *C*). The fusiform shape is that of an elongated spindle, widest through the middle and tapering toward the blunt or pointed ends; the posterior end is generally more tapering and pointed than the anterior end and in some species as *Rhabditis filiformis* (Fig. 93*E*) is very slender. In the filiform type, less common than the fusiform but illustrated in the Mermithidae, the Filarioidea, and the trichuroid genus *Capillaria* (Fig. 93*C*), the body is thread-like and of uniform diameter throughout, not diminishing toward the ends. Other variations are the short, plump, pyriform or oval shape assumed by certain ripe females as the phytoparasitic *Heterodera* (Fig. 93*F*), and the trichurine type in which the body is filiform anteriorly, fusiform posteriorly (Fig. 93*D*). The posterior end of the two sexes frequently differs in shape and external features, being generally curved in the male, and provided with papillae, alae, etc., lacking in the female.

[1] The author admits to no patience with Cobb's attempt to popularize the term "nema" for these worms and asks what is wrong with "nematode"? Some other terms coined by Cobb are objectionable as exaggerating the importance of the structures in question.

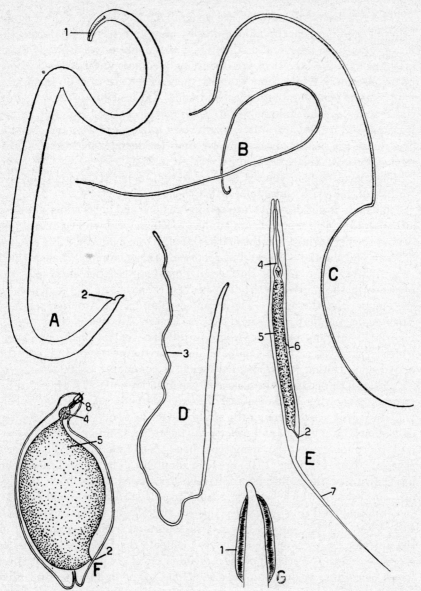

Fig. 93.—Types of nematodes. *A.* Fusiform type, dog ascarid, *Toxascaris leonina,* original. *B, C.* Filiform type, *Capillaria brevis* (*after Ransom,* 1911); *B,* male; *C,* female. *D. Trichuris trichiura,* partly filiform, partly fusiform, original. *E. Rhabditis filiformis* with slender tail (*after Bütschli,* 1873). *F. Heterodera schachtii,* mature female (*after Strubbel,* 1888). *G.* Anterior end of *A,* showing cervical alae. 1, cervical alae; 2, anus; 3, anterior slender part; 4, pharynx; 5, intestine; 6, vulva; 7, tail; 8, spear.

The free-living nematodes are generally microscopic or very small, below 1 mm. in length; among fresh-water and terrestrial forms the maximum length is several millimeters, but the marine nematodes, which are in general the largest of the free-living members, may attain a length up to 50 mm. While some parasitic nematodes are also of small size, many reach considerable length and some are excessively long. Thus the females of the kidney worm, *Dioctophyme renale*, and the guinea worm, *Dracunculus medinensis*, may attain a length of a meter or more. The males are nearly always smaller than the females and this size difference between the sexes is quite marked in some species.

The nematodes in general lack coloration, being transparent or of a whitish or yellowish tint conferred on them by the cuticle.

The body is not divisible into definite regions and lacks a distinct head although this term is sometimes applied to the anterior end to a level just behind the nerve ring. In the marine family Draconematidae the swollen anterior end simulates a head but represents the entire pharyngeal region (Fig. 138*A*). The ventral surface of nematodes is identifiable by the presence in the mid-ventral line of the excretory pore, the gonopore in the female, and the anus. The excretory pore has an anterior position. The female gonopore, also called *vulva*, is usually situated in the posterior body half but may occur anywhere in the mid-ventral line. The anus, which also serves as male gonopore, lies near the posterior end, and the body region behind it, or postanal region, is commonly called *tail*.

The mouth occupies the center of the anterior tip and is encircled by structures showing a pronounced hexamerous or biradial arrangement. Only in recent years through the study of marine nematodes by Filipjev, de Coninck, Stekhoven, and others, has an understanding of the generalized morphology of the nematode head been attained. The views especially of de Coninck (1942) are here adopted. The work of these men has shown that the mouth is primitively surrounded by six lobes, the *lips* or *labia*, each of which bears a sensory papilla, the *inner labial papilla*, sometimes altered to a bristle; the lips are laterally located, three on each side. The area bearing the lips may be separated from the remainder of the anterior tip by a circular groove. Outside the inner labial circle of six sense organs is a second or *outer labial* circle of six papillae or bristles, which, according to de Coninck, also belong to the lips but are regarded as cephalic by others. This is followed by an outer circle of four bristles or papillae which lie outside the labial region, and hence are termed *cephalic*. There are thus recognized as typical and primitive parts of the nematode head three circlets or crowns of sense organs of the nature of bristles or papillae, to a total number of 16 (Fig. 94). This condition obtains in many marine nematodes (Fig. 94) but several variants occur. The outer or cephalic crown of four bristles may move forward and join the outer labial crown of six bristles, making one circlet of ten bristles (Fig. 95), the compound nature of which, however, is usually indicated by the differing size of the two components, as the cephalic bristles are usually shorter than the outer labial bristles (Fig. 95). The number of bristles is sometimes augmented by doubling or by the forward migration of body sensory bristles. On the other hand, the number of head sense organs is often reduced in parasitic and terrestrial nematodes. The lips

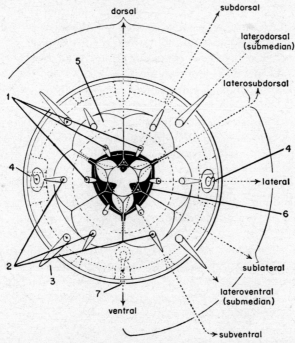

Fig. 94.—Scheme of the anterior end of a generalized nematode (*after de Coninck*, 1942). 1, inner labial papillae or bristles; 2, outer labial bristles; 3, cephalic bristles; 4, amphids; 5, lips; 6, buccal capsule; 7, excretory pore. The central triradiate figure represents the pharynx.

in these forms may be fused in pairs to form three lips, one dorsal and two ventrolateral (Fig. 96D), or be reduced to two lateral lips or be altogether wanting. The six inner labial papillae are usually retained, however, so that in such cases there are two or three per lip or else they simply encircle the mouth opening. Small lobes termed *interlabia* are sometimes present between the lips. In parasitic and terrestrial nematodes the sensory bristles of the two outer circlets are usually altered to papillae, the outer labial and the cephalic papillae, and in fact bristles and papillae are to be regarded as interchangeable structures. In such nematodes the two outer circlets are usually concentrated into one circlet and are frequently reduced in number by loss or fusion. There are thus in terrestrial and parasitic nematodes usually only two circlets of sense organs present, which may conveniently be termed the inner or internal and the outer or external circlets. In parasitic nematodes the inner circlet is also often wanting or vestigial (*Ascaris*, Fig. 96*D*) although its nerve supply can usually be traced histologically.

From the foregoing it is evident that a marked hexamerous or biradial symmetry pervades the anterior end of primitive nematodes; this sym-

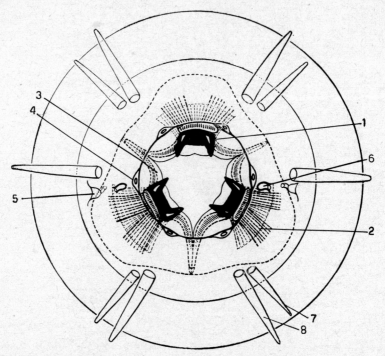

Fig. 95.—Scheme of the anterior end of *Enoplus* (order Enoploidea), showing two outer circlets of bristles combined to one of ten bristles (*after de Coninck*, 1942). 1, jaw; 2, jaw muscles; 3, lips; 4, labial papillae; 5, amphid; 6, cephalic slit; 7, cephalic bristles; 8, outer labial bristles.

metry is exhibited by the lips, the two labial circlets of sense organs, and the anterior part of the digestive tract. It is indicative of the superposition of a radial symmetry on an original bilateral symmetry and supports the conclusion of Steiner (1921) that nematodes originally led a semisessile life, fastened to objects by their posterior tip by means of the adhesive secretion of the caudal glands and waving about in the water (Fig. 96*A*). The four cephalic sense organs of the outer circlet retain their bilateral symmetry and are the anteriormost members of body sense organs or cuticular structures, which tend to be arranged in four or eight longitudinal rows.

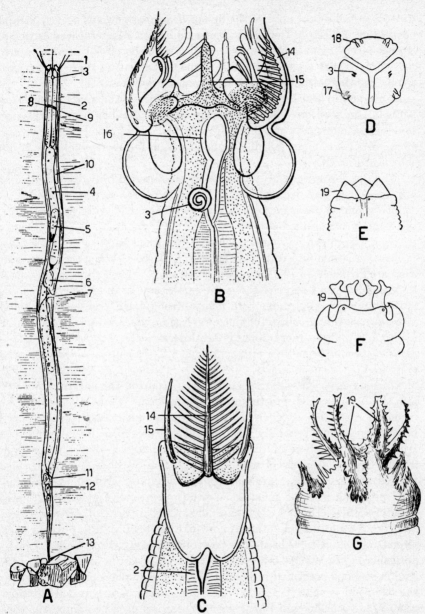

Fig. 96.—General nematode structure; lip variants. *A*. Nematode undulating in attached position (*after Steiner*, 1921b). *B, C*. Two views of the anterior end of *Wilsonema* (order Araeolamoidea), showing lip excrescences (*after Steiner*, 1921b). *D*. Scheme of the lips of *Ascaris* (*after Hesse*, 1892). *E–G*. Types of probolae of *Acrobeles* (*after Thorne*, 1925; *Steiner*, 1929a). 1, head bristles; 2, pharynx; 3, amphid; 4, intestine; 5, ovary; 6, uterus; 7, vulva; 8, nerve ring; 9, excretory pore; 10, renette; 11, anus; 12, caudal adhesive glands; 13, adhesive tube; 14, dorsal and ventral excrescences; 15, lateral excrescences; 16, buccal capsule; 17, outer labial papillae; 18, cephalic papillae; 19, probolae.

It is notable that none of the lips or head sense organs occupy medial positions. Their positions may be designated in a general way as dorsolateral, lateral, and ventrolateral. In the cephalic circlet it is the lateral sense organs that are absent and it seems probable that these were primitively wanting although some nematodes exist in which there are six sense organs in the cephalic circlet. To indicate the exact position of parts in the head circlets an elaborate terminology has been devised by some nematodologists as the Chitwoods (*An Introduction to Nematology*, Chap. V). The more sensible terms proposed by de Coninck (1942) are shown in Fig. 94.

The lips not infrequently bear or are surrounded by various cuticular protuberances and excrescences. In certain terrestrial nematodes as *Acrobeles* and *Wilsonema* peculiar rigid lip excrescences termed *probolae*, three or six in number, project forward (Thorne, 1925; Steiner, 1929a); they vary from simple rounded, conical, or forked eminences to branched projections resembling antlers (Fig. 96*B*, *C*, *E–G*). When six are present they are arranged in two circlets of three each. Their function is uncertain; possibly they serve to shove the earth aside or in feeding but can be moved only by lip motions. In many Strongylidae, the lips are altered into an upstanding collar, the inner surface of which is subdivided into a few to many (40 or more) lobes or teeth termed the *leaf crown* (or *corona radiata*), accompanied in a number of genera by a similar *inner leaf crown* (Fig. 97*A*).

Various other cuticular specializations occur on the anterior end outside the lips, especially in the order Spiruroidea. Thus in the spirurine nematodes, the lips are encircled by a cuticular collar that is most prominent dorsally and ventrally where it may be extended into conspicuous *head shields* (considered interlabia by some) that arch over the lips (Fig. 97*B*). Several genera of the spiruroid family Physalopteridae also possess an upstanding cuticular collar or collaret around the anterior extremity that in some genera can withdraw into it (Fig. 97*E*). In still another spiruroid family, the Acuariidae, there are present anteriorly two, four, or six longitudinal cuticular cord-like thickenings or grooves termed *cordons* or *epaulets*. These may be straight, recurved, or form loops or horseshoes (Fig. 97*D*); in *Seuratia*, the free posterior edge of the four cordon scallops is formed into spines (Fig. 98*A*). Cordons also occur in the oxyuroid genera *Aspidodera* and *Pseudaspidodera*. In the ascaroid genera *Heterocheilus* and *Typhlophorus* there is a broad cuticular thickening behind the lips that is longitudinally ribbed in the latter. In several spiruroid genera there are fantastic cuticular ornamentations projecting from the head as four feathery appendages in *Ancyracanthus* (Fig. 98*E*), four pointed wings in *Schistorophus* (Fig. 181*C*), eight simple lobes in *Ancyracanthopsis* (Fig. 98*F*), two split into a number of secondary lobes

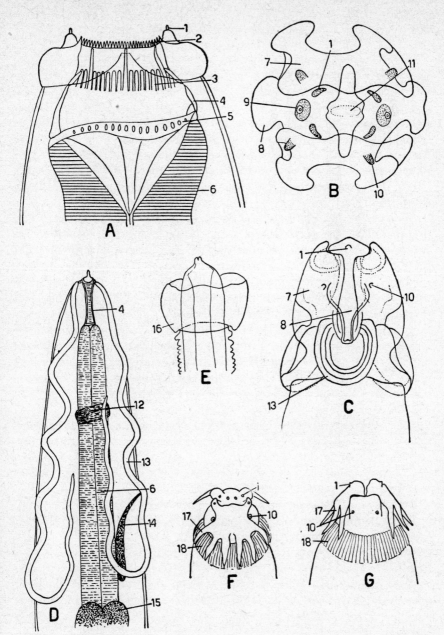

Fig. 97.—Head structures. *A.* Horse strongyle, *Poteriostomum*, with leaf crowns (*after Boulenger*, 1921), lateral view. *B, C.* Spiruroid *Parabronema*, from elephants, with head shields and cordons (*after Baylis*, 1921). *B. End face* view. *C. Lateral view. D. Dispharynx*, bird acuariid, with recurved cordons (*after Seurat*, 1916a). *E. Proleptus*, shark spiruroid, with cuticular collar (*after Lloyd*, 1920). *F, G.* Two views of the head of *Histiocephalus* (*after Gendre*, 1921). 1, lip papilla; 2, outer leaf crown; 3, inner leaf crown; 4, buccal capsule; 5, dorsal gutter (carries gland duct); 6, pharynx; 7, head shield; 8, lateral lips; 9, amphid; 10, external circlet of papillae; 11, mouth; 12, nerve ring; 13, cordon; 14, renette; 15, intestine; 16, collar; 17, head appendages; 18, cervical collar.

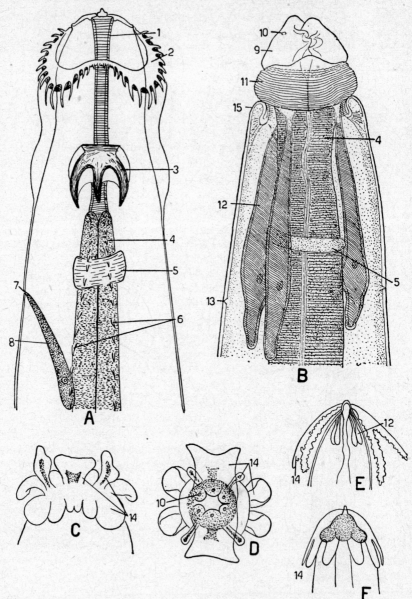

Fig. 98.—Head structures (continued). *A. Seuratia (after Seurat, 1916b)* with spiny cordons and body spines. *B. Tanqua (after Baylis and Lane, 1920)* with ballonets and cervical sacs. *C, D.* Two views of the head end of *Serticeps (after Drasche, 1883). E.* Anterior end of *Ancyracanthus (after Diesing, 1839). F.* Anterior end of *Ancyracanthopsis (after Drasche, 1883).* 1, buccal capsule; 2, cordon; 3, trident spine; 4, pharynx; 5, nerve ring; 6, rows of body spines; 7, excretory pore; 8, renette; 9, lip; 10, labial papilla; 11, head bulb; 12, cervical sacs; 13, cervical papillae; 14, head appendages; 15, collar.

in *Histiocephalus* (Fig. 97*F, G*), and a circle of variously shaped processes in *Serticeps* (Fig. 98*C, D*). Mention of other head ornamentations in spiruroids will be found under the order Spiruroidea in the discussions of the families Acuariidae, Schistorophidae, and Histiocephalidae.

It is common for the cuticle of the anterior end to be thickened or inflated through the presence of vesicles therein. In the spiruroid family Gnathostomidae, four cuticular inflations termed *ballonets* result in a swollen band just behind the lips called the *head bulb* (Fig. 99*A*). The head bulb is armed with circlets of spines in *Gnathostoma* and *Echinocephalus* (Figs. 99*A*, 100*A*) and with transverse striations in *Tanqua* in which it is subdivided externally into two or four swellings (Figs. 98*B*, 99*B*).

On the sides of the anterior end, just external to or level with the circlet of cephalic sense organs, occurs a pair of sense organs very characteristic of nematodes, the *amphids*, most conspicuous and best developed in aquatic nematodes, especially marine ones, but also present in a reduced and inconspicuous state in terrestrial and parasitic members. The amphids are cuticular excavations of three general shapes: *cyathiform*, *spiral*, and *circular* (Fig. 99*C–K*). The cyathiform type, found in the Enoploidea, has the shape of a pocket and is provided with a slit aperture (Fig. 99*C*). The spiral type, characteristic of the Chromodoroidea and Araeolaimoidea, occurs in many variants, ranging from a spiral of several turns to crescentic and loop shapes (Fig. 99*F–K*). The circular amphid has the form of a disk and is limited to the order Monhysteroidea (Fig. 99*D*). Students of free-living nematodes (Filipjev, de Coninck, and Stekhoven) have utilized the shape of the amphids as a basis for classifying nematodes (Stekhoven and de Coninck, 1933) and as their system appears to be the most satisfactory, it has been adopted here. The amphids are presumably chemoreceptors and are provided with a gland and nerve endings (Fig. 110*C*). In addition to and adjacent to the amphids, the Enoploidea have another pair of pouch-like cephalic sense organs, the *cephalic slits* (Fig. 95).

The general body surface may be smooth, especially in parasitic members, but often presents a variety of cuticular specializations such as bristles, spines, warts, papillae, punctations, striations, and ridges. Cuticular sensory bristles are often scattered irregularly and sparsely along the body length in marine nematodes. In *Greeffiella* (Fig. 100*E*) closely placed circles of bristles cover the entire body, giving the animal a very bristly appearance. In the marine families Epsilonematidae and Draconematidae the posterior part of the body bears a double row of large stiff hollow bristles, known as *stilt bristles* or *ambulatory setae*, employed in locomotion (Fig. 100*B*).

Transverse or longitudinal striations, thickenings, or ridges are of

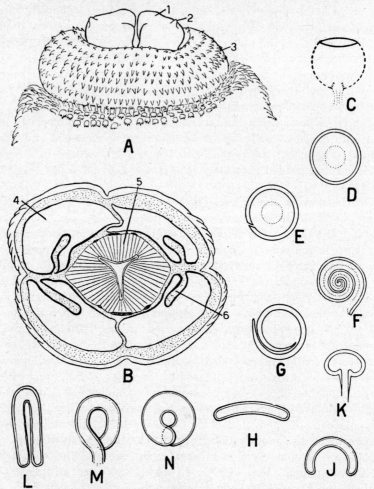

Fig. 99.—Head structures (continued). *A. Gnathostoma. B.* Section through the head bulb of *Tanqua,* showing the ballonets. (*A, B, after Baylis and Lane,* 1920). *C–N.* Types of amphids (*after Stekhoven and de Coninck,* 1933). *C.* Cyathiform type, Enoploidea. *D.* Circular type, Monhysteroidea. *E.* Variant of the circular type, transitional from spiral type (*Linhomeus*). *F.* Spiral type, Chromadoroidea. *G–N.* Variants of the spiral type. *G–K.* Chromadoroidea. *K. Plectus. L–N.* Araeolamoidea. 1, lip; 2, labial papilla; 3, head bulb; 4, ballonet cavity; 5, pharynx; 6, muscles.

common occurrence. In many nematodes fine transverse grooves, termed *striations,* occur at regular intervals; when these are deeper and more pronounced they are called *annulations,* and give the body a seg- mented appearance, dividing the cuticle into rings or *annules.* Such annulation is very conspicuous in the marine families Epsilonematidae (Fig. 100*B*), Draconematidae (Fig. 138*B*), and Desmoscolecidae (Fig. 100*D*). In the last family thick cuticular rings alternate with depressed

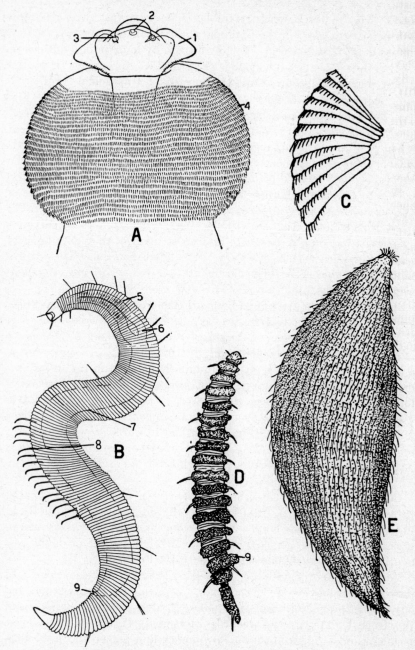

Fig. 100.—Cuticular structures (continued). *A. Echinocephalus (after Baylis and Lane, 1920). B.* An epsilonematid, from life, Puget Sound. *C.* Ventral bristle combs of an epsilonematid *(after Steiner, 1931). D. Desmoscolex (after Chitwood, 1936). E. Greeffiella (after Schepotieff, 1908).* 1, lip; 2, labial papillae; 3, papillae of outer circlet; 4, head bulb; 5, pharynx; 6, end bulb of pharynx; 7, intestine; 8, stilt bristles; 9, anus.

rings so that the worm greatly resembles an insect larva. Strongly annulated bodies also occur in the phytoparasitic criconematines (Fig. 101*C*). Annules may be stiffened in whole or in part by longitudinal flutings or rod-shaped or V-shaped thickenings (Fig. 136*C*). Incomplete or partial annules sometimes occur. Annules may be of trapezoidal form, with posterior edges that project over succeeding annules (*Thelazia*, Fig. 174*A*) and these edges may be spiny as in the parasitic genera *Goezia* and *Spinitectus* (Figs. 161*C*, 179*C*). In *Criconema* (= *Iota*, *Ogma*), the rear edge of each annule bears eight scales or in one species transverse rods (Taylor, 1936) that project over the succeeding annule and render the body very rigid, capable of motion only in the forward direction (Fig. 101*C*). In the curious marine family Epsilonematidae, ventral combs of spines are borne on the rear edges of the annules in the region just anterior to that provided with stilt bristles (Fig. 100*C*). The annules are cuticular thickenings that do not extend to interior structures; they may be solid or hollow or filled with a spongy or vacuolated material. They represent the same kind of superficial segmentation that occurs in rotifers and other aschelminths.

Spines apart from those already mentioned are of frequent occurrence, especially in the order Spiruroidea, as illustrated by: *Echinonema* (Fig. 175*A*) with circlets of spines on the anterior part of the body, *Pneumonema* with lateral rows of large hooks anteriorly; *Gnathostoma* with spines covering practically the entire body but diminishing posteriorly; and *Tetrameres*, *Rictularia*, *Rictularioides*, and *Echinuria* with two to four longitudinal rows of spines (Figs. 102*C*, 175*B*). Spines are also found in certain oxyuroids as in *Hystrignathus* and *Lepidonema* where they cover the anterior end of females (Fig. 153*H*) and in *Carnoya*, with circles of spines anteriorly (Fig. 157*A*). The dioctophymoid genus *Hystrichis* is also armed with small spines over the whole or the anterior part of the body (Fig. 192*D*).

Cuticular warts are sometimes present. In *Gongylonema*, inflated warts, also called plaques, are strewn over the anterior end (Fig. 101*B*), in some species on one side only. The best development of warts is seen in the curious terrestrial genus *Bunonema* which has a single or double row of cuticular warts along one side of the body (Fig. 101*A*).

Various types of longitudinal cuticular specializations also occur. In many trichostrongyles, as *Nematodirus*, *Cooperia*, and related genera the body is longitudinally ribbed; about 40 such ridges occur in *Oswaldocruzia leidyi* from the intestine of a tree frog (Steiner, 1924). Usually, however, the longitudinal ridges are fewer in number and higher and more pronounced, and are then termed *wings* or *alae*. Alae occur as *lateral* or *longitudinal* alae, one, two, or four in number usually extending the body length in lateral positions; as *cervical* alae, single or paired, on the anterior

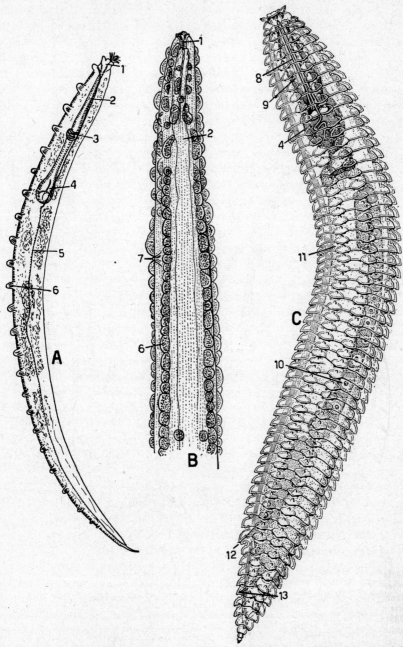

Fig. 101.—Cuticular structures (continued). *A. Bunonema* with lateral warts (after Jägerskiöld, 1905). *B.* Anterior end of *Gongylonema*, with placques (*after Ward*, 1916). *C. Criconema* (*from Taylor*, 1936, *after Cobb*, 1914a). 1, buccal capsule; 2, pharynx; 3, nerve ring; 4, end bulb; 5, lateral chord; 6, warts; 7, excretory pore; 8, buccal stylet; 9, muscles of stylet; 10, ovary; 11, intestine; 12, vulva; 13, anus.

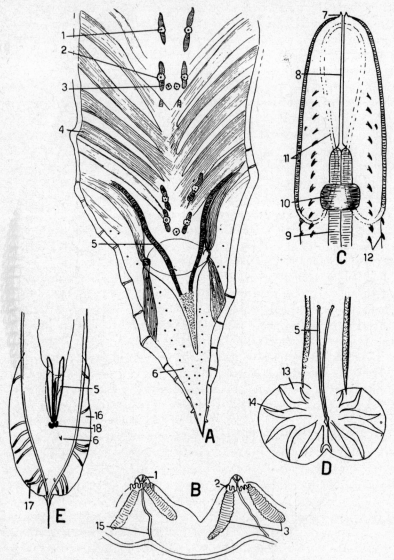

FIG. 102.—Cuticular structures, copulatory aids. A. Rear end of *Cosmocerca*, with plectanes. B. Two plectanes, enlarged, side view. (*A, B, after Drasche*, 1882.) C. Anterior end of *Echinuria* with cordons and four rows of spines (*after Seurat*, 1916c). D. Strongyloid bursa (*Longistriata, after Schwartz and Alicata*, 1935). E. Rear end of *Rhabditis maupasi*, with caudal alae and pedunculated papillae (*after Stekhoven and Teunissen*, 1938). 1, papilla; 2, frill around papilla; 3, plectane; 4, muscles; 5, spicules; 6, ordinary genital papillae; 7, lips; 8, buccal capsule; 9, pharynx; 10, nerve ring; 11, cordon; 12, rows of spines; 13, bursa; 14, muscle rays of bursa; 15, nerve to papilla; 16, caudal alae; 17, pedunculated papillae; 18, gubernaculum.

part of the body, as in the ascarid genera *Toxocara* and *Toxascaris* (Fig. 93*G*), and as caudal alae on the rear end of males. Caudal alae, although laterally situated, are not part of the lateral alae. They are employed in copulation and hence generally bear genital papillae. They are usually absent from marine nematodes but are of common occurrence among saprophagous and zooparasitic nematodes (Fig. 102*E*) where they vary from narrow ridges to wide expansions, sometimes confluent ventrally in front of the anus. They are usually purely cuticular but in the Strongyloidea the wide caudal alae, meeting posterior to the tail to form a copulatory bursa, are provided with characteristic muscle rays (Fig. 102*D*).

Finally mention may be made of a type of cuticular marking termed *punctation* (Fig. 134*C*, *F*). Punctations are minute depressed dots or ovals; they may occur in transverse or longitudinal rows and often are arranged in patterns. Sometimes transverse striations are found on higher magnification really to consist of rows of punctations; punctations may also occur between striations or in a row along ridges.

Papillae, presumably always of sensory nature, are among the common surface structures of nematodes. In addition to the labial and cephalic papillae already discussed the anterior region frequently bears in the vicinity of the nerve ring a pair of *cervical* papillae. These have been named *deirids* by Cobb but no reason is apparent for distinguishing them from other papillae by a special name. In *Chevreuxia*, the cervical papillae are covered by a backwardly directed cuticular fold (Fig. 104*A*). Various types of *genital* papillae, associated with copulation, occur on the ventral surface of the rear end of males. The ordinary genital papillae are a few to many small rounded cuticular elevations, arranged irregularly or in longitudinal rows, in both preanal and postanal locations, as well as on the caudal alae when present. They may be elevated on little stalks and are then termed *pedunculated* papillae (Fig. 102*E*). They are sometimes encircled by punctations forming a *rosette* or supported fore and aft by little cross-striated cuticular plates called *plectanes*. Both rosettes and plectanes occur in the oxyuroid family Cosmocercidae (Figs. 102*A*, 103). Various other papilliform copulatory aids are found near the anus in male nematodes. There may be a preanal mid-ventral row of *copulatory warts*, larger elevations with a central concavity (Fig. 104*B*, *C*). A single large sucker-like papilla, the *preanal sucker*, occurs in the mid-ventral line shortly anterior to the anus in several families of zooparasitic nematodes (Fig. 156*A*). In the oxyuroid family Heterakidae, this sucker has a definite cuticularized rim, lacking in the preanal suckers of the oxyuroid families Subuluridae and Kathlaniidae and the spiruroid family Cucullanidae. The sucker may be circular or oval and is supplied by muscle fibers.

There are still other caudal cuticular specializations in males that presumably act as copulatory aids such as scales and areas provided with transverse or longitudinal ridges. Flask-shaped excavations or cuticular

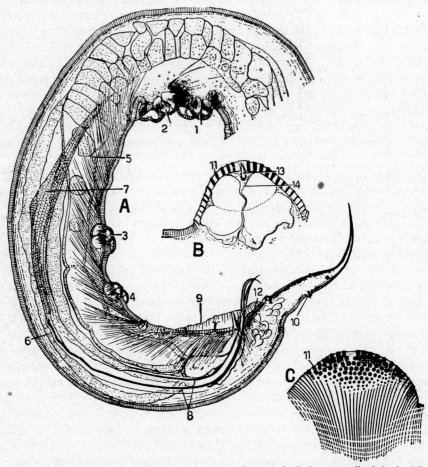

Fig. 103.—Copulatory aids (continued). *A.* Rear end of *Cosmocercella haberi* with rosetted copulatory warts. *B.* Section through a wart. *C.* Enlarged view of a wart. (*All after Steiner,* 1924.) 1–4, four pairs of copulatory warts; 5, sperm duct; 6, intestine; 7, spicule retractor; 8, spicules; 9, caudal alae; 10, ordinary genital papillae; 11, punctations of rosette; 12, depressor ani muscle; 13, sensory organ; 14, nerve.

tubes occurring singly or in a preanal row and serving as gland outlets also appear to function in copulation.

Near the posterior end of many nematodes there occurs a pair of cuticular pouches resembling the amphids (Fig. 104*E*). These are called *phasmids* by Cobb. They appear normally to be the outlets of the precaudal glands, and a surface papilla is often associated with them.

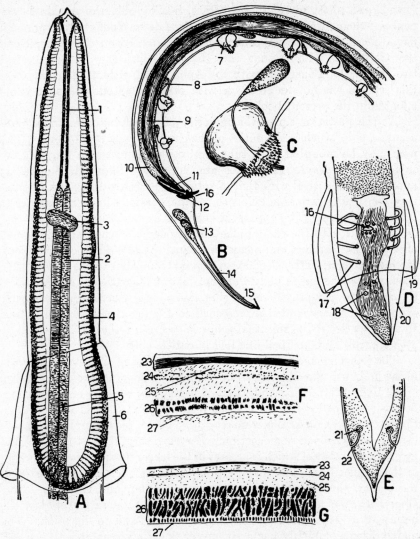

Fig. 104.—Cuticle (concluded). *A. Chevreuxia (after Seurat, 1916). B, C.* Copulatory warts of *Trilobus*, supplied by glands (*after Brakenhoff, 1914*). *D.* Rear end of *Physaloptera* with preputial fold over the caudal alae (*after Ortlepp, 1922*). *E.* Rear end of *Rhabditis*, showing phasmids (*after Chitwood, 1930*). *F.* Section through the cuticle of *Oxyuris* (*after Martini, 1916*). *G.* Section through the ascarid cuticle (*after Glaue, 1910*). 1, buccal capsule; 2, pharynx; 3, nerve ring; 4, cordon; 5, cervical papilla; 6, cuticular fold; 7, copulatory wart; 8, gland of same; 9, seminal vesicle; 10, intestine; 11, spicule; 12, gubernaculum; 13, caudal glands; 14, their duct; 15, adhesive tube; 16, anus; 17, pedunculated papillae; 18, ordinary papillae; 19, preputial fold; 20, caudal alae; 21, gland of phasmid; 22, duct of phasmid; 23, cortical layer; 24, fibril layer; 25, matrix; 26, fiber layers; 27, basement membrane.

Glands and phasmids may degenerate, leaving only the papilla as evidence of their former existence.   Phasmids occur chiefly in the parasitic nematodes.   So much importance has been placed on the phasmids by the Chitwoods (1937) that they have divided the Nematoda into two subclasses, Phasmidia with and Aphasmidia without phasmids.   As this scheme has not found favor with other nematodologists, it is not adopted in the present book.

At the posterior tip of the majority of free-living nematodes there occurs a pore which is the outlet of the caudal glands (see below).   This pore may be mounted on a tube, entirely comparable to the adhesive tubes of gastrotrichs and other aschelminths.[1]   This whole adhesive apparatus is identical with that of rotifers and gastrotrichs and its presence constitutes valuable evidence for the relationship of nematodes to these two classes.   The apparatus is absent in parasitic nematodes.

In addition to the caudal alae and strongyloid bursa already noted, other caudal terminal enlargements occur.   Males of the order Dioctophymoidea (Fig. 193*D*) also have a terminal bursa but this is formed of an expansion of the entire body wall, not just of the cuticle.   In females of the spiruroid genus *Simondsia* (Fig. 177*A*) the caudal end is greatly expanded into a rounded excrescence containing the distended uterus. In some species of the spiruroid genus *Physaloptera*, the tail is covered by a backwardly directed bell-like fold of cuticle (Fig. 104*D*).

The foregoing account by no means exhausts the variations of external forms and cuticular structure but should give some idea of their range.

4. Body Wall.—The body wall of nematodes consists of cuticle, epidermis (often called subcuticle), and muscle layer.   The cuticle, of which the external specializations were recounted above, is of complicated histological and chemical construction.   Histologically it consists of several layers the number of which is greater in the larger parasitic members than in the smaller forms but which are reducible to three kinds of material: the cortex, the matrix or homogeneous stratum, and the fiber layers (Fig. 104*F*, *G*).   The cortical layer consists of a dense material of the nature of a keratin and is resistant to solvents and to digestion.   The matrix layer commonly has a spongy or finely alveolar appearance and according to Chitwood (1936) consists of or contains a fibroid named matricin, rich in sulphur.   The matrix layer is often subdivided by one or more narrow strata of felt-like fibrils and just beneath the cortical layer may be more or less altered to form what is termed the internal cortical layer.   The innermost part of the cuticle consists of two or three fiber

---

[1] Cobb has termed the pore *spinneret;* this usage is objectionable, first, because spinneret is the long-established name of the spinning tubes of spiders, and, second, because this adhesive apparatus of nematodes is in no wise different from the adhesive apparatus of other aschelminths and does not require a special name.

layers of very dense connective tissue running in different directions in adjacent layers. Like vertebrate connective tissue, these fiber layers consist chiefly of collagen. Through the subdivision of the matrix layer by fibrillar membranes and the presence of the maximum number of fiber layers, as many as eight or nine layers may be counted in the cuticle of ascarids (Fig. 104*G*). The cuticle is bounded internally by a basement membrane. According to the chemical investigations of Chitwood (1936), the cuticle of *Ascaris* consists of 35 per cent matricin, 29 per cent collagen, and 2.2 per cent keratin, all reckoned as dry weight. Other substances found that could not be correlated with the histological layers were albumins (i.e., water-soluble proteins) and a glucoprotein (mucoid).

The layers of the cuticle participate to varying degrees in the formation of external cuticular structures. Transverse striations and annulations may or may not involve regularly repeated thinnings of the cortical layer. Cuticular outgrowths generally have a core of matrix. The alae consist of matrix covered by the cortical layer and cervical alae contain hard skeletal supports embedded in the matrix (Fig. 105*A*).

The epidermis (hypodermis, subcuticle) is a cellular or syncytial layer that bulges into the pseudocoel at four places to form four longitudinal ridges termed the *longitudinal chords*, middorsal, mid-ventral, and lateral in position (Fig. 105*C*). Of these the lateral chords are the most conspicuous and usually show on the surface as pale lines. In some nematodes, four subsidiary chords occur between the four main chords, in dorsolateral (subdorsal) and ventrolateral (subventral) positions. The chords are better developed anteriorly and tend to disappear posteriorly, except the lateral chords which commonly run the body length. The epidermal nuclei are situated in the chords and the epidermis between the chords (subcuticle of older authors) is devoid of nuclei (Fig. 105*C*). Typically there are three longitudinal rows of nuclei in the lateral chords (Fig. 105*D*) and zero to three rows in the median chords (Retzius, 1906; Martini, 1906–1909; Filipjev, 1928). The subsidiary chords and often also the dorsal chord lack nuclei but the ventral chord is generally provided with them. Cell walls are usually present in the epidermis. The cells of the central row of the lateral chords are cuboidal but the other epidermal cells are of peculiar shape, consisting of a nucleated bulging part situated in the chord and a flattened nonnucleated extension on one or both sides that forms the epidermis between the chords (Fig. 105*C*). The number of cells or nuclei in each longitudinal row is limited in juvenile nematodes and adults of smaller species, ranging from about 12 to 25. In the larger forms the epidermis tends to become syncytial in later life and the nuclei may divide to form large numbers of small nuclei.

In the free-living nematodes, unicellular epidermal glands are of frequent occurrence but are generally lacking in parasitic members.

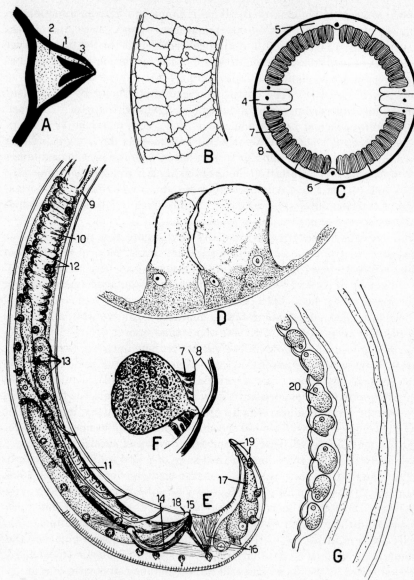

Fig. 105.—Body wall, epidermal glands. *A*. Section through the cervical alae of the cat ascarid (*after Glaue*, 1910). *B*. Surface view of the lateral chord, showing outlines of the epidermal cells (*after Retzius*, 1906). *C*. Schematic section through a marine polymyarian nematode (*after Filipjev*, 1924). *D*. Section through the lateral chord (*Cucullanus*, *after Martini*, 1909). *E*. Side view of rear end of male araeolamoid, showing lateral chord glands (*after Brakenhoff*, 1914). *F*. Lateral chord gland enlarged (*after Jägerskiöld*, 1901). *G. Axonolaimus*, with mid-ventral row of gland cells (*after de Coninck and Stekhoven*, 1933). 1, cortex; 2, matrix; 3, stiffening; 4, lateral chord; 5, dorsal chord; 6, ventral chord; 7, muscles; 8, cuticle; 9, intestine; 10, testis; 11, seminal vesicle; 12, lateral chord gland cells; 13, copulatory glands; 14, spicule; 15, gubernaculum; 16, muscles of male apparatus; 17, caudal glands; 18, anus; 19, ordinary genital papillae; 20, mid-ventral glands.

Gland cells usually accompany the amphids and phasmids and other sensory organs (see further below).   A single or double row of gland cells situated in the lateral chords and opening through the cuticle has been observed in many marine nematodes of the orders Enoploidea, Chromadoroidea, and Araeolamoidea (Jägerskiöld, 1901; Stewart, 1906; Brakenhoff, 1914, Fig. 105*E–F*).   Although the ordinary genital papillae lack glandular components, being apparently tangoreceptors, gland cells usually accompany the copulatory warts and other accessory copulatory structures of males (Fig. 104*C*).   A mid-ventral preanal row of gland cells occurs in males of some species of the araeolamoid genus *Axonolaimus* (de Coninck and Stekhoven, 1933, Fig. 105*G*) and a similar row provided with tubular exits is found in several chromadoroid genera (Ditlevsen, 1919, Schneider, 1927, Fig. 106*D*).   Caudal glands are generally present in the tail of free-living marine nematodes, usually lacking in others. They are long-stalked, pyriform cells, nearly always three in number, that open at the tip of the tail by a single pore, sometimes mounted on an adhesive tube (Fig. 106*A*).   The caudal glands are identical with the pedal glands of rotifers and like the latter secrete an adhesive cement by which the animal anchors itself to objects.

The cervical or ventral gland is generally regarded as of excretory nature and hence will be considered with that system.

Directly internal to the epidermis is the layer of body-wall musculature, consisting exclusively of longitudinal fibers.   This muscle layer is divided by the longitudinal chords into longitudinal strips, four, eight, or two in number, depending on the number of chords; but as the chords tend to die out posteriorly so the number of muscle strips may vary in different body regions of the same worm.   Very great weight was placed by A. Schneider (1860, 1866) on the form, number, and arrangement of the muscle cells as a taxonomic character and he coined the following terminology still in use.   In some nematodes, there seem to be no definite muscle cells but the muscle layer is continuous or at best divided into two zones by the lateral chords; to this type Schneider applied the term *holomyarian*.   It shows transitions to the formation of definite muscle cells, fusiform or rhomboid in shape, with their long axes parallel to the longitudinal body axis (Fig. 106*C*).   When there are only a few longitudinal rows of muscle cells, mostly two to five, in each longitudinal strip, as in *Oxyuris* (Martini, 1916), the condition is termed *meromyarian* (Fig. 106*C*) and when a larger number of rows is present in each strip, the term *polymyarian* is applied (Fig. 105*C*).   As transitions occur between these various conditions and as the number of muscle rows diminishes toward the body ends, Schneider's distinctions are no longer regarded as of particular importance and are certainly not indicative of relationship between nematode genera.   The number of muscle cells is constant in forms in

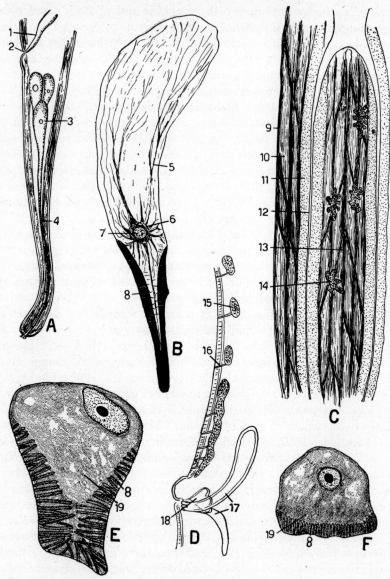

Fig. 106.—Epidermal glands, muscles. *A.* Caudal glands of a marine nematode (*Oncholaimus, after Kreis,* 1934). *B.* Details of a muscle cell (*Ascaris, after Bilek,* 1909). *C. Oxyuris equi* opened out along the ventral side to show arrangement of the muscle cells (meromyarian type, *after Martini,* 1916). *D.* Preanal row of copulatory tubes with attached glands of male *Parasabatiera (after Ditlevsen,* 1919). *E.* Coelomyarian type of muscle cell. *F.* Platymyarian type of muscle cell. (*E, F, after Chitwood,* 1931.) 1, rectum; 2, anus; 3, caudal glands; 4, their duct; 5, supporting fibrils; 6, perinuclear basket of supporting fibrils; 7, nucleus; 8, muscle bands; 9, ventral chord; 10, muscle cells; 11, lateral chord; 12, posterior excretory canal; 13, dorsal chord; 14, large pseudocoelocytes (four); 15, gland cells; 16, their tubular exits; 17, spicules; 18, gubernaculum; 19, cytoplasmic part of muscle cell.

which it has been investigated as *Oxyuris* (Martini, 1907, 1908) which has eight rows of muscle cells with six to nine cells in each longitudinal row, making a total of 65 cells. Similar numbers have been found in related forms.

The histology of the muscle cells of nematodes, especially of *Ascaris*, has been the object of numerous investigations, most recently by Roskin (1925) and Mueller (1929). The cell is of elongated fusiform or rhomboid shape and is composed of two zones, a fibrillar zone and a protoplasmic zone containing the nucleus (Fig. 106*E*). The fibrillar zone, situated next the epidermis, consists of longitudinal ribbons or bands of homogeneous contractile substance alternating with noncontractile material containing supporting fibrils. The protoplasmic part also contains a network of supporting fibrils (Fig. 106*B*) and often gives off processes toward nerve fibers or other structures. The muscle cells may be flat with the fibrillar region limited to a basal zone paralleling the epidermis, a condition termed *platymyarian;* or the protoplasmic zone may bulge into the pseudocoel with the fibrillar zone extending up its sides (Fig. 106*E, F*), a condition termed *coelomyarian.* It appears that the meromyarian and platymyarian conditions are the more primitive occurring in the simpler nematodes whereas the polymyarian and coelomyarian conditions are derived by development from the former, and characterize the larger parasitic nematodes such as the ascarids.

The muscles associated with the digestive and genital systems will be considered with those systems.

5. Pseudocoel.—The pseudocoel or space between the body wall and viscera is filled with fluid and usually contains fibrous tissue and fixed cells or nuclei, especially in parasitic nematodes. However, similar structures have been described in many free-living forms. Thus in *Thoracostoma* (Türk, 1903) and *Enoplus* and *Cyclolaimus* (Rauther, 1909), a network of nucleated strands covers the outer surface of the digestive tract and gonads (Fig. 107*B*). In *Oncholaimus* (Stewart, 1906) the pseudocoel is occupied by a fibrous nucleated network that forms membranes clothing the outer surface of the pharynx and the inner surface of the muscle layer. Distinct cells arranged more or less in rows may also occur, usually along one or more of the longitudinal chords. In parasitic nematodes there is often present dorsal to the pharynx a single large cell from which fenestrated membranes extend through the pseudocoel and over the viscera and muscle layer. Details of this condition for *Ascaris* (Fig. 107*A*) have been given by Goldschmidt (1906) and for *Oxyuris* by Martini (1916). A similar dorsal cell and a nucleated fibrous network covering the digestive tract and inner surface of the body wall and sending strands to the longitudinal chords have been described for the oxyuroid nematode, *Cephalobellus papilliger*, by the Chitwoods (1933b). These

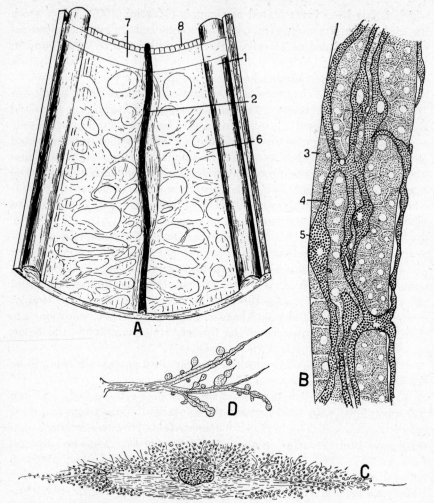

Fig. 107.—Membranes and cells of the pseudocoel. *A.* *Ascaris* opened out, showing fenestrated pseudocoel membrane (*after Goldschmidt*, 1906). *B.* Net over the intestine of *Enoplus* (*after Rauther*, 1909). *C.* One of the four large pseudocoelocytes of *Contracaecum*. *D.* Branch of the same, showing nodules. (*C, D, after Nassonov*, 1900.) 1, lateral chord; 2, ventral chord; 3, intestine; 4, network; 5, fatty granules; 6, fenestrated membrane; 7, nerve ring; 8, muscle cells.

authors further state (1937) that the pseudocoel cell or nucleus dorsal to the pharynx is common in parasitic nematodes and also in the free-living order Chromadoroidea, and that fibrous membranes in the pseudocoel are especially well developed in trichuroids and dioctophymatoids, notably in *Eustrongylides*. Common also in parasitic nematodes are two, four, or six large cells (Fig. 106*C*) occupying fixed constant positions, usually in relation to the longitudinal chords (four such cells in *Ascaris*,

Nassonov, 1897; Mueller, 1929; *Contracaecum*, Nassonov, 1900; *Oxyuris*, Martini, 1916, Fig. 106*C;* and cucullanids and camallanids, Törnquist, 1931). These cells are often highly branched or stellate with rounded nodules along the sides and ends of the branches (Fig. 107*C, D*). In free-living nematodes pseudocoel cells are generally smaller and more numerous. The *pseudocoelocytes*, as they may be called, and the fibrous strands and membranes associated with them may be regarded as a kind of mesenchyme.

The pseudocoelocytes are fixed and constant in position; there seem to be no free or wandering cells in the nematode pseudocoel. The pseudocoelocytes are neither phagocytic nor amoeboid and will not take up vital dyes (Hurlaux, 1947). Injected particles or bacteria adhere to them but are not phagocytized (Mueller, 1929; Hurlaux, 1947). The visible particles in them appear to be chiefly of the nature of enzymatic bodies. According to Hurlaux, the giant pseudocoelocytes of parasitic nematodes have an oxidative function (more later).

6. Nervous System.—The nervous system has been described for a number of nematodes, chiefly parasitic ones: for *Siphonolaimus* by zur Strassen (1904), for *Ancylostoma* by Looss (1905), for *Hexamermis* by Rauther (1906), for *Ascaris* by Goldschmidt (1908–1910), for *Oxyuris* by Martini (1916), for *Camallanus* and *Cucullanus* by Törnquist (1931), for *Cephalobellus* by the Chitwoods (1933b), for *Rhabditis terricola* by Chitwood and Wehr (1934), and for *Spironoura* and *Oesophagostomum* by the Chitwoods (1940). The main part of the nervous system consists of a ring, the *circumenteric ring*, encircling the pharynx, and of associated ganglia, of which the main ones are the paired lateral ganglia and the single or paired ventral ganglia. Others that may be present are a small dorsal ganglion, a pair of subdorsal ganglia, a pair of postlateral ganglia behind the lateral ganglia, and a pair of postventral ganglia behind the ventral ganglia (Figs. 108, 109*A*). The circumenteric ring is commissural, that is, consists chiefly of fibers with very few ganglion cells. It is evident that the lateral ganglia correspond to the cerebral ganglia of other Protostomia and the circumenteric ring represents the dorsal and ventral connections between the lateral ganglia. The various ganglia are close to the ring and are connected with it or each other by short commissures. From the ring there proceed forward six papillary nerves, two dorsolateral, two lateral, and two ventrolateral, to the sense organs of the anterior end of which it will be recalled there are three circlets with a total of 16 members. The ganglion cells of the papillary nerves are situated along the course of the nerves, usually near their entrance into the ring. The dorso- and ventrolateral papillary nerves on reaching the anterior end fork into three branches one of which supplies the inner labial papilla (or bristle) and the other two supply the outer labial and cephalic bristles

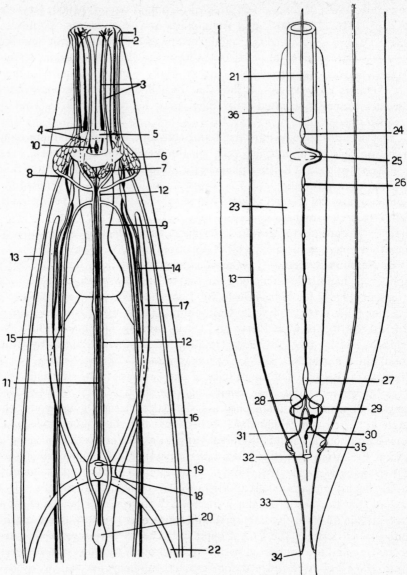

Fig. 108.—Nervous system of *Cephalobellus* (*after the Chitwoods*, 1933b). 1, amphid; 2, amphidial nerve; 3, papillary nerves; 4, papillary ganglion; 5, circumenteric nerve ring; 6, lateral ganglion; 7, ventral ganglion; 8, lateroventral brain connective; 9, pharynx; 10, ganglion cell of dorsal nerve; 11, dorsal nerve; 12, paired ventral nerves; 13, external lateral nerve; 14, internal lateral nerve; 15, ventrolateral nerves; 16, dorsolateral nerves; 17, anterior excretory canal; 18, transverse excretory canal; 19, excretory pore; 20, retrovesicular ganglion; 21, unpaired ventral nerve behind ganglion; 22, posterior excretory canal; 23, intestine; 24, prevulvar ganglion; 25, vulva; 26, postvulvar ganglia; 27, preanal ganglion; 28, intestinorectal sphincter; 29, rectal commissure; 30, dorsorectal nerve; 31, ventrolateral connectives; 32, anus; 33, caudal nerve; 34, phasmid; 35, lumbar ganglia; 36, vagina.

(or papillae) of that sector. The lateral papillary nerves (which seem to be absent in some parasitic nematodes as *Ancylostoma*) fork into only two branches as there are only two cephalic sense organs in the lateral sector. Although primarily sensory, the papillary nerves also contain motor fibers for the muscles that operate the bristles. The terminal branches of the papillary nerves are present even when the sense organs they originally supplied are absent or rudimentary as in many parasitic nematodes. There is also in the anterior end a pair of amphidial nerves from the amphids; they connect with the lateral ganglia, not with the circumenteric ring, and each also bears a ganglion (Fig. 109*A*). The amphidial nerves are larger with larger ganglia in the free-living nematodes.

From the nerve ring and associated ganglia there proceed posteriorly the following main nerves: a middorsal nerve, one to three pairs of lateral nerves, and a mid-ventral nerve (Fig. 108). The dorsal nerve originates from the middorsal region of the nerve ring, usually presents at once a small swelling, the dorsal ganglion, and then proceeds posteriorly in the dorsal chord as a motor nerve devoid of or poor in ganglion cells. The lateral somatic nerves originate mostly from the lateral ganglia and are of sensory nature with ganglionic swellings in their course along the lateral chords. They supply a sensory branch to the cervical papillae when present and posteriorly enter a pair of large ganglia in the anal region, the lumbar ganglia. Dorsolateral (also called subdorsal) nerves may occur between the dorsal and lateral nerves. The ventral nerve is the main body nerve and is in reality a ganglionated cord. It is usually paired at its origin from the ventral part of the nerve ring and the two nerves proceed posteriorly in the ventral chord to a point behind the excretory pore where they usually fuse to form a ganglion, the *retrovesicular* ganglion, behind which the single ventral nerve continues as a ganglionated cord to the anal region. Here it enters a single or paired *anal* or *preanal* ganglion from which a pair of connectives, the *anolumbar* or ventrolateral connectives extend to the lumbar ganglia. The ventral cord usually passes to the right of the vulva in females but in some nematodes remains paired to a point behind the vulva where fusion to one cord occurs in a ganglion called the *postvulvar* ganglion. In some nematodes as *Ascaris* (Fig. 110*A*, *B*) there are numerous ventrolateral connectives between the ventral and lateral nerves. Ventrolateral (subventral) nerves may also occur. The tail is supplied by nerves from the anal and lumbar ganglia and those from the latter also innervate the phasmids. There may be a pair of caudal ganglia in the tail. The innervation of the posterior end is more complicated in males than in females. The genital papillae are innervated from bipolar sensory nerve cells that form a longitudinal strand, the *bursal* nerve, on either side in or near the lateral chords (Fig. 110*A*). The axones of these cells enter the lateral nerve and

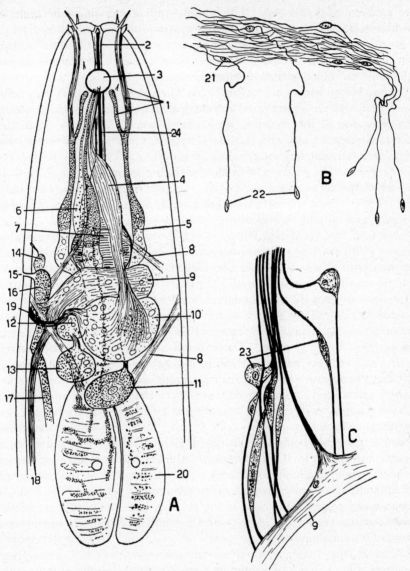

Fig. 109.—Nervous system (continued).   A. Brain and anterior nerves of *Siphono-laimus*, lateral view (*after Zur Strassen*, 1904).   B. Bursal nerve with bipolar neurones supplying genital papillae (*after Deineke*, 1908).   C. Papillary ganglion of an ascarid (*after Goldschmidt*, 1908).   1, three branches of papillary nerve (only three of the six papillary nerves shown); 2, buccal capsule; 3, amphid; 4, amphidial nerve; 5, papillary ganglion; 6, amphidial gland; 7, pharynx; 8, pharyngo-cutaneous muscles; 9, circumenteric nerve ring; 10, lateral ganglion; 11, postlateral ganglion; 12, ventral ganglion; 13, postventral ganglion; 14, gland attached to bristle; 15, excretory pore; 16, ampulla of renette; 17, renette; 18, ventral nerve; 19, ventrolateral brain connective; 20, end bulb of pharynx; 21, bipolar cells; 22, genital papilla; 23, ganglion cells of papillary ganglion; 24, odontostyle.

eventually reach the ventral nerve by way of the single or multiple ventrolateral connectives. The innervation of the bursa in bursate males has been described only for *Ancylostoma* in which there are two pairs of anal ganglia, a pair of cloacal ganglia, two pairs of ventrolateral connectives, and a chain of three lumbar ganglia (Fig. 111*A*); nerves from all these elements enter the bursa in which they branch.

The foregoing account is of general applicability to the various species for which the nervous system has been described but naturally the details differ in different species. The innervation of the anterior end is very similar in all but differences occur in the number of nerves behind the nerve ring. The greatest divergences from the usual plan are seen in *Ascaris* which is also the form in which the nervous system has been most thoroughly studied. *Ascaris* is peculiar in having a pair of subdorsal ganglia in addition to the single unpaired dorsal ganglion, in the subdivision of the lateral ganglia into six ganglia one of which is the ganglion of the amphidial nerve, in the large size of the paired ventral ganglia, and in the occurrence of numerous asymmetrical dorsoventral loops connecting the dorsal and ventral nerves throughout the body length (Fig. 110*B*). *Ascaris* also has a conspicuous pair of subdorsal and subventral nerves.

In addition to the body nervous system there are in nematodes two enteric (or sympathetic) systems, one in the pharynx and the other in the rectum. The pharynx system, connected directly with the ventral part of the circumenteric nerve ring, consists in general of three longitudinal strands, one in each sector of the pharynx wall. These strands contain nerve cells and are connected by two or three ring connectives. The rectal system in its simplest form consists of a pair of anorectal commissures extending from the anal ganglia to the dorsal surface of the rectum where they join a dorsorectal ganglion from which a median caudal nerve proceeds into the tail. In males the system is more complicated chiefly through the interpolation of a ganglion on each anorectal commissure from which ganglia nerves proceed to the cloaca. In *Ancylostoma* males, which have two pairs of anal ganglia, one behind the other, there are also two pairs of anorectal commissures and two dorsorectal ganglia in tandem arrangement (Fig. 111*A*).

An incredible amount of detail concerning the finer structure of the nervous system of *Ascaris* has been furnished by Goldschmidt. According to this and similar work, the nerve cells are constant in number, location, shape, and course of their fibers. Each ganglion contains a definite fixed number of cells, e.g., there are seven bipolar sensory cells in each of the papillary ganglia of *Ascaris* (Fig. 109*C*). The sensory neurones of nematodes are bipolar, with one branch (dendrite) coming from the sense organ and the other (axone) proceeding along a nerve trunk (Fig. 109*B*).

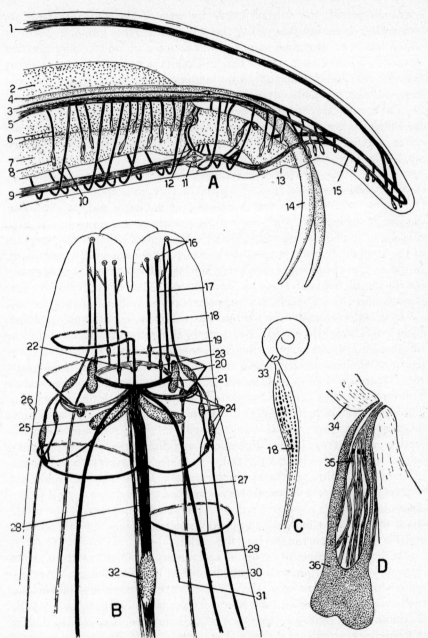

Fig. 110.—Nervous system (continued). A. Rear end of *Ascaris*, showing nervous system (*after Hesse*, 1892). B. Anterior part of the nervous system of *Ascaris* (*after Goldschmidt*, 1908). C. Amphid with amphidial nerve of an epsilonematid (*after Steiner*, 1931). D. Amphid of *Ascaris* (*after Goldschmidt*, 1903). 1, dorsal nerve; 2, intestine; 3, lateral nerve; 4, spicule sheath; 5, bursal nerve; 6, branch of bursal nerve to genital papilla;

7. Sense Organs.—As already noted, the nematodes, especially the free-living ones, are abundantly supplied with sense organs, chiefly in the form of bristles and papillae. Although the number and arrangement of the head sense organs has now been determined and depicted for a large number of nematodes by the study of *en face* preparations (see, for instance, the Chitwoods, Chap. V), very little exact information is available as to the histological construction of these organs. The labial and cephalic bristles are cuticular structures that are jointed to the cuticle. Each contains a nerve fiber that passes through an aperture in the cuticle to join the adjacent papillary nerve. Bristles may be supplied by a gland cell. The only satisfactory account of the structure of the labial and cephalic papillae is that of Goldschmidt (1903) for *Ascaris*. *Ascaris* has three lips formed by the fusion of the original 6 and each lip bears two papillae, each of which consists of 2 sense organs, making a total of 12 (Fig. 106*D*). It appears that in *Ascaris* the 6 inner labial papillae are wanting and therefore the 12 sense organs represent the 6 outer labial papillae, the 4 cephalic papillae, and the 2 amphids (formerly erroneously called lateral papillae in parasitic nematodes). The cuticle over each pair of sense organs is greatly thinned and marked off by a circular groove. The medial sense organ of each pair (i.e., the outer labial papilla) consists of a stout nerve fiber that ascends toward the surface, narrows, and terminates beneath the cuticle in a bulb-like ending (Fig. 111*D*). The outer papilla of the dorsolateral and ventrolateral pairs (i.e., the cephalic papilla) is similar but just beneath the cuticle has a lens-shaped expansion from which a canal, at first narrow, then wider, passes to the surface (Fig. 111*C*). A nerve fiber runs along the center of this canal. In both kinds of papillae there is, shortly before they reach the undersurface of the cuticle, a region that stains intensely, and in both the ascending nerve fiber is accompanied by two cells, an inner supporting cell that embraces the fiber and an outer accompanying cell that lies alongside the supporting cell. Despite these names, invented by Goldschmidt, the purpose of these cells is not clear nor can it be stated to what extent these descriptions for *Ascaris* apply to other nematodes.

The cervical papilla of *Ascaris* (Goldschmidt, 1903) is similar to the outer labial papilla of the same animal, consisting of an ascending nerve fiber terminating in a little elevation beneath the cuticle and also provided with a supporting and an accompanying cell (Fig. 112*A*). The

---

7, seminal vesicle; 8, genital papilla; 9, ventral nerve; 10, ventrolateral connectives; 11, preanal ganglion; 12, anorectal connectives; 13, anus; 14, spicules; 15, caudal nerves; 16, sensory papillae; 17, papillary nerves; 18, amphidial nerves; 19, papillary ganglion; 20, amphidial ganglion; 21, nerve ring; 22, dorsal ganglion; 23, subdorsal ganglion; 24, parts of the lateral ganglia; 25, ventral ganglia; 26, cervical papillae; 27, dorsal nerve; 28, ventral nerve; 29, dorsolateral nerves; 30, ventrolateral nerves; 31, dorsoventral connectives; 32, ganglion of ventral nerve; 33, amphid; 34, cuticle; 35, nerve endings; 36, supporting cell.

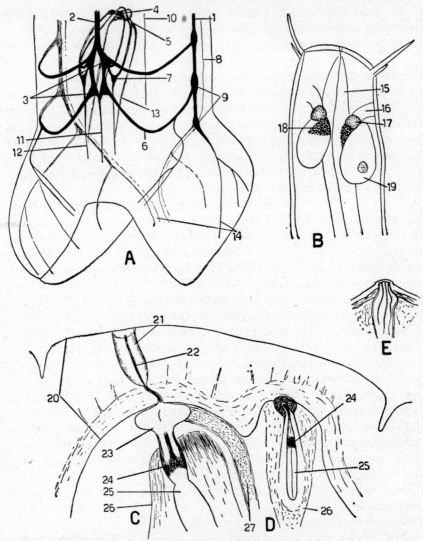

Fig. 111.—Nervous system (concluded), sense organs. *A.* Bursa of Ancylostoma, showing nerves (*after Looss,* 1905). *B.* Anterior end of marine enoploid (*Parasymplocostoma*), showing eyes (*after Schulz,* 1931). *C.* Cephalic papilla of *Ascaris.* *D.* Outer labial papilla of *Ascaris.* (*C, D, after Goldschmidt,* 1903.) *E.* Genital papilla of *Ascaris* (*after Hesse,* 1892). 1, ventrolateral nerve; 2, ventral nerve; 3, anal ganglia; 4, dorsorectal ganglia; 5, anorectal commissures; 6, ventrolateral connectives; 7, cloacal ganglion; 8, dorsolateral nerve; 9, lumbar ganglia; 10, dorsal nerve; 11, median caudal nerve; 12, cloacal nerve; 13, rectal nerves; 14, nerves to bursal rays; 15, pharynx; 16, pit leading to eye; 17, lens-like body; 18, pigment; 19, retinal cell; 20, cuticle; 21, canal; 22, nerve fiber; 23, lens-like thickening; 24, pigmented region; 25, papillary nerve; 26, supporting cell; 27, accompaying cell.

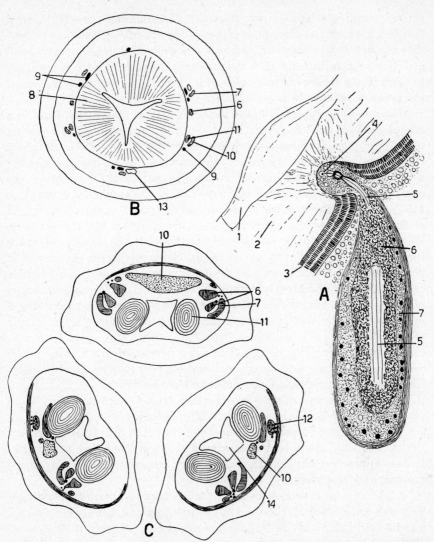

Fig. 112.—Sense organs (concluded), lip pulp. *A.* Cervical papilla of *Ascaris (after Goldschmidt*, 1903). *B.* Section through the pharynx of *Ascaris (after Hoeppli*, 1925), showing rear ends of the pulp cells. *C.* Section through the lips of *Ascaris (after Goldschmidt*, 1903), showing cell arrangement in the lip pulp. 1, cuticular cortex; 2, matrix; 3, fiber layers of cuticle; 4, sensory ending; 5, nerve; 6, supporting cell; 7, accompanying cell; 8, pharynx; 9, arcade cells; 10, fiber cells; 11, clavate cells; 12, sensory nerves; 13, filler cells; 14, cavity.

genital papillae (*Ascaris*) are wart-like elevations of greatly thinned cuticle with a central circular opening. The underlying sense organ consists of one to three ascending nerve fibers embedded in a supporting cell and terminating distally in a narrow canal that perforates the cuticle to open in the center of the papilla (Fig. 111*E*).   It is supposed that all the types of papillae of nematodes are of a tactile nature.

The amphids or lateral organs, as they were formerly called, occur in a lateral position outside the circlet of cephalic sense organs in free-living nematodes, usually incorporated into this circlet in parasitic members and hence erroneously mistaken for papillae. They are, as already noted, cuticular excavations of various shape; in the bottom of the excavation occurs a cluster of nerve endings of the amphidial nerve (Fig. 110*C*) and also the opening of the amphidial gland, a unicellular gland often of great length that proceeds posteriorly alongside the pharynx (Fig. 127*D*).   This description applies only to free-living nematodes in which the amphids are believed to serve as chemoreceptors.   In parasitic nematodes, the amphids are greatly reduced and have lost the cuticular cavity.   As described by Goldschmidt (1903) for *Ascaris* under the name of lateral papilla, the amphid consists of a bundle of nerve fibers embedded in a supporting cell and uniting to a single fiber that penetrates the cuticle (Fig. 110*D*).

The phasmids (Fig. 104*E*) when fully developed are a pair of unicellular glands that open by a canal and pore on either side of the tail. The two glands are called the precaudal or phasmidial glands.   From this condition various degrees of reduction to mere papillae occur.   The phasmids are presumably some sort of glandulo-sensory organ.   They are best developed in parasitic nematodes but it is not definitely established that they are absent in marine and other free-living nematodes. It does appear certain that they are absent whenever caudal glands are present, and vice versa.

A pair of eyes is present in a few fresh-water and marine nematodes. The eyes are located on the sides of the pharynx and usually consist of a lens-like cuticular body resting on a pigment cup (Steiner, 1916; Schulz, 1931).   Little is known of the nervous part of the eyes.   According to Schulz (1931) the lens and pigment mass in *Parasymplocostoma* rest upon a large cell of the nature of a sensory cell which probably has secreted the pigment (Fig. 111).   The eyes in this nematode are remarkable in being at the bottom of pits.   The resemblance of this eye to the cerebral eyes of rotifers is striking.   Schulz has also pointed out that in many nematodes what have been regarded as eyes are merely colored patches or areas of excretory nature in the pharynx walls.

Nematodes are also abundantly supplied with free nerve endings, presumably of sensory nature.   Some of these of regular occurrence in the anterior end of parasitic nematodes probably represent vanished sense organs of the head circlets.

8. Digestive System.—The mouth is terminal with rare exceptions and as already noted is bordered by the lips, six or fewer in number, sometimes altogether wanting, sometimes augmented by interlabia. Investigations of the interior tissue of the lips or *lip pulp* of ascarids have shown that this is composed of the distal ends of a definite number of unusually large, elongated cells, the main parts of which lie along the pharynx (Goldschmidt, 1903; Hoeppli, 1925). In addition to the supporting and accompanying cells of the sensory fibers of the head papillae, the cell group in question comprises *clavate* cells, *fiber* cells, *arcade* cells, and *filling* cells (Fig. 112*B*, *C*). The clavate cells, two in each lip, are long cells with a hollow interior, lamellate structure, and bulbous distal ends that fill the convexity of the lips. The fiber cells, so-called from their fibrous cytoplasm, are two in number in the dorsal lip (but fused distally) and single in the other lips. The arcade cells, nine in number, run along the pharynx, two opposite each angle, and one opposite each sector, and at the base of the lips are united by arches, whence the name arcade cells. From these arches processes extend into the lips but do not reach the main convexity of the latter which contains only the distal ends of the clavate cells. A few other cells are present as space fillers. In the anterior end of ascarids between the pharynx and the body wall, there are a total of 42 cells, the distal ends of most of which extend into the lips. According to the studies of Hoeppli (1925), the cell number and arrangement here is constant or practically so for a considerable number of parasitic nematodes but no comparable investigations on conditions in free-living nematodes are available.

The mouth leads into the *buccal capsule*, very variable in size, shape, and degree of differentiation in different nematodes. When well developed it is a cylindrical or prismatic tube, lined by cuticle often heavily sclerotized into ridges, rods, plates, and other stiffenings that often bear teeth of various sizes. In some genera as *Enoplus* (Fig. 95) there are three especially large and heavy teeth known as *jaws* or *gnathi*. The buccal capsule and its stiffenings often exhibit a triradiate arrangement corresponding with that of the pharynx. In some nematodes, especially rhabditoids, the buccal capsule is divisible into three sections (Steiner, 1933a): an anterior chamber enclosed by the lips, the *vestibule* or *cheilostom*, a middle and longest and most sclerotized portion, the *protostom*, and a small terminal chamber, the *telostom*, called *glottoid apparatus* in some nematodes (Fig. 113*E*). In some forms, the protostom is further subdivisible. For the sclerotizations the general term *rhabdions* was coined by Steiner. Whether this analysis of the structure of the buccal capsule, based on rhabditoids, is applicable to other groups of nematodes

is doubtful.   It follows the erroneous Chitwood theory that the rhabditoids are the most primitive existing nematodes whereas unquestionably
the free-living marine nematodes occupy this position.   In many marine
nematodes the buccal capsule is small and weakly developed and when
heavy sclerotizations occur, these seem to follow other structural plans
than that of rhabditoids.   Not infrequently the buccal capsule is wholly or
partly embraced by pharyngeal tissue, being then spoken of as *embedded*.

In certain groups of nematodes, the buccal capsule is armed with a
conspicuous protrusible *spear* or *stylet*, used to puncture plants and animal
prey.   This may be formed, as in tylenchoids, by the coming together of
the sclerotizations of the buccal capsule, so that it constitutes a *buccal
stylet* (Fig. 113D).   This is necessarily hollow and forms the path of food
intake.   In other cases, as in dorylaimoids, the spear represents an
enlarged tooth, that originates in the pharynx wall, may or may not be
hollow, and may or may not lie in the path of food ingestion (Fig. 113B).
This type will here be called *odontostyle*.

The pharynx (usually called esophagus by nematodologists) is one of
the most characteristic features of nematode anatomy.   It is a cylindrical
tube of considerable length lined by a thin cuticle and bounded externally
from the pseudocoel by a membrane; as noted above, the amphidial
glands and the elongated cells that accompany the sensory nerves and
contribute to the lip pulp embrace the anterior part of the pharynx (Fig.
112B).   The pharynx lumen is triradiate, being extended into three
symmetrically arranged longitudinal grooves that partially divide the
pharynx wall into three sectors, one dorsal and two ventrolateral (Fig.
113A).   The pharynx thus exhibits a marked triradiate structure continuous with that of the buccal capsule, lips, and head sense organs.   The
pharynx wall consists of a syncytial epithelium, which, however, is so
thickly permeated with muscle fibers and gland tissue as to be scarcely
demonstrable.   Numerous radial fibers, usually arranged in clusters,
extend from the lining cuticle to the bounding membrane (Fig. 113A).
From the outer ends of the three grooves fibers believed to be of elastic
nature ("marginal" fibers) proceed to the bounding membrane.   Three
highly branched uninucleate or multinucleate pharyngeal glands are
typically present in the pharynx wall, one dorsal and two ventrolateral.
They are so long and so greatly branched that portions of them are met
with in almost any section through the pharynx (Fig. 113A).   The main
cuticularized duct of each gland opens, often by way of an ampulla, into
the pharynx lumen, or may run forward into the buccal capsule to discharge there in connection with conspicuous structures as jaws or large
teeth.   It is usual for the dorsal gland to open much farther forward than
do the ventrolateral glands.   In the Enoploidea there are five or more
pharyngeal glands instead of the usual three.   In some tylenchoids, the

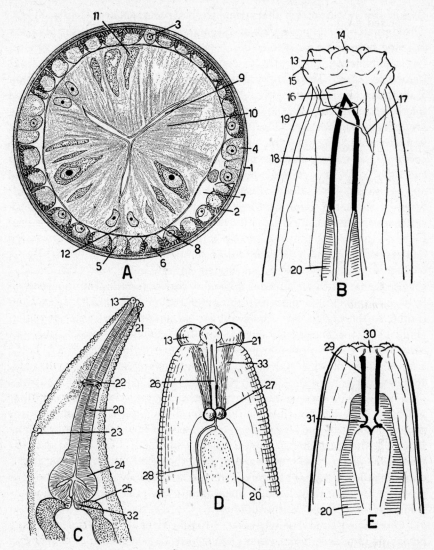

FIG. 113.—Pharynx and buccal capsule. *A.* Section through the pharynx (*after Chitwood*, 1931). *B. Dorylaimus*, showing odontostyle. *C.* Oxyuroid type of pharynx with end bulb (*Thelastoma, after Chitwood*, 1933). *D.* Tylenchoid buccal capsule with buccal stylet (*after Steiner*, 1936). *E.* Buccal capsule of *Rhabditis.* (*B, E, after Stekhoven and Teunissen*, 1938.) 1, cuticle; 2, epidermis; 3, dorsal chord; 4, lateral chord; 5, ventral chord; 6, muscle layer; 7, pseudocoel; 8, pharynx; 9, triradiate lumen; 10, muscle fibers of pharynx; 11, sections of pharyngeal glands; 12, marginal fibers; 13, lips; 14, labial papillae; 15, cephalic papillae; 16, amphid; 17, amphidial nerve; 18, odontostyle; 19, guide ring of odontostyle; 20, pharynx; 21, buccal capsule; 22, nerve ring; 23, excretory pore; 24, end bulb of pharynx; 25, intestine; 26, buccal stylet; 27, end knobs of stylet, derived from telostom; 28, duct of dorsal pharyngeal gland; 29, protostom; 30, cheilostom; 31, telostom; 32, pharyngo-intestinal valve; 33, protractor muscles of buccal stylet.

glands protrude from the pharyngeal wall into the pseudocoel (Fig. 114*B*). Three small protruding *cardiac* glands occur at the rear end of the pharynx in some free-living nematodes as *Trilobus*, *Tripyla*, and related genera.

The pharynx frequently presents one or more muscular swellings known as *bulbs*. These are considered true bulbs only when they contain a valvular arrangement (Fig. 114*A*) in the form of three more or less sclerotized swellings that can partially close the lumen; otherwise they are called *pseudobulbs* (Fig. 114*A*). Bulbs or pseudobulbs may be situated about the pharynx middle, then spoken of as *median*, or may occur at the rear end of the pharynx, then termed *posterior, cardiac,* or *end* bulbs. With regard to shape and the presence of bulbs, pharynges are classifiable as follows (Filipjev and Stekhoven, 1941): *cylindrical*, when of the same diameter throughout; *dorylamoid*, when slender anteriorly and wider posteriorly (Fig. 115*A*); *bulboid* or *oxyuroid*, when provided with an end bulb (Fig. 113*C*); *rhabditoid*, with an anterior wide region (*corpus*), usually leading into a median pseudobulb, followed by a narrowed region (*isthmus*), succeeded by an end bulb (Fig. 114*A*); *diplogasteroid*, with an anterior muscular region terminating in a median bulb, succeeded by a posterior glandular region (Fig. 115*B*); *tylenchoid*, similar to the diplogasteroid, except for the more slender anterior region (Fig. 114*C*); *aphelenchoid*, similar to the tylenchoid, except that the pharyngeal glands protrude posteriorly from the pharynx (Fig. 114*B*); and *mermithoid*, with a very long tubular, nonmuscular pharynx (Fig. 133*C*).

The Trichuroidea were formerly believed to have a very peculiar pharynx, supposed to consist of an intracellular lumen in a longitudinal row of large cells, the *stichocytes*, collectively termed the *stichosome* (Fig. 190). It has been shown, however, by Chitwood (1930, 1935) that the trichuroid pharynx, though slender, is of the usual muscular type and is only embedded in or contiguous with the stichosome (Fig. 189), the cells of which are pharyngeal glands opening into the pharynx. A stichosome is also present in the Mermithoidea.

The pharynx may be muscular throughout or its posterior part may be devoid of muscle fibers, being then spoken of as a glandular or *ventricular* region. A pharynx muscular anteriorly and glandular posteriorly is characteristic of the orders Spiruroidea and Filarioidea. In ascaroids, especially anisakines, the posterior part of the pharynx often gives off one or more blind, usually solid, diverticula or appendages (Fig. 160). This appendage or pharyngeal caecum is single and directed backward in *Raphidascaris, Contracaecum,* and *Goezia,* whereas in *Multicaecum, Polycaecum,* and *Typhlophorus,* all three of which are parasites of crocodilian reptiles, there are two anterior and three posterior pharyngeal caeca. No esophagus is present between the pharynx and the intestine but pharyngeal tissue usually projects into the beginning of the intestine as a pharyngo-intestinal valve.

The intestine or midgut, following directly upon the pharynx, is a simple straight tube formed of a one-layered cellular epithelium. In

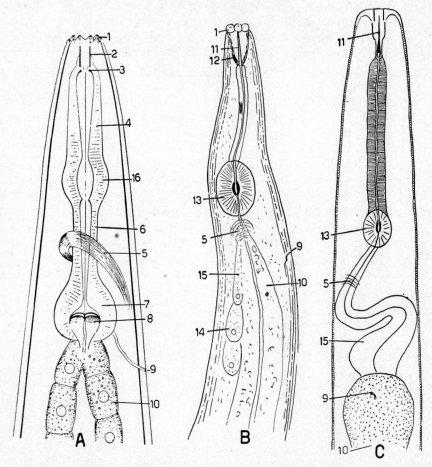

FIG. 114.—Pharynx (continued). *A*. Pharynx of *Rhabditis maupasi*, illustrating rhabditoid type (*after Reiter*, 1928). *B*. Aphelenchoid type of pharynx (*after Steiner*, 1935). *C*. Tylenchoid type of pharynx (*after Fuchs*, 1915). 1, lips; 2, protostom; 3, telostom; 4, corpus of pharynx; 5, nerve ring; 6, isthmus of pharynx; 7, end bulb of pharynx; 8, valve apparatus of end bulb; 9, excretory pore; 10, intestine; 11, buccal stylet; 12, protractor muscles of same; 13, median bulb of pharynx; 14, pharyngeal glands; 15, glandular part of pharynx; 16, median pseudobulb.

Contracaecum and several other anisakine ascaroids, its beginning gives off a blind hollow caecum that extends anteriorly alongside the pharynx (Fig. 160). The intestinal epithelium consists of large cuboidal or columnar cells packed with inclusions and provided with a conspicuous

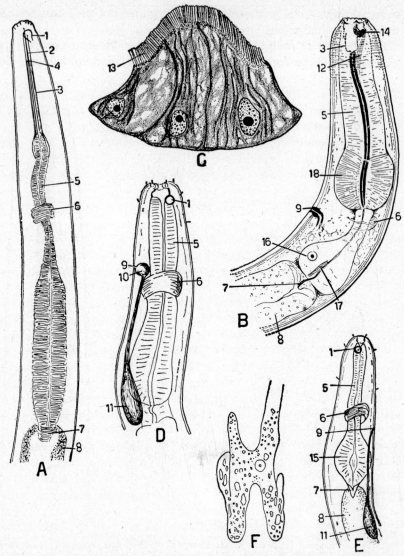

FIG. 115.—Digestive tract (concluded), excretory system. *A.* Dorylaimoid type of pharynx (*Dorylaimus, after Thorne,* 1936). *B.* Pharynx of *Diplogaster* (*after Steiner,* 1930). *C.* Section through nematode intestine (*after Chitwood,* 1931). *D.* Anterior end of *Linhomeus,* showing renette with ampulla. *E.* Anterior end of *Desmolaimus,* with simple renette. (*D, E, after Kreis,* 1929.) *F.* Lobulate renette of *Enoplus* (*after de Man,* 1886). 1, amphid; 2, odontostyle; 3, wall of buccal capsule; 4, ring guide of odontostyle; 5, pharynx; 6, nerve ring; 7, pharyngo-intestinal valve; 8, intestine; 9, excretory pore; 10, ampulla; 11, renette; 12, muscle of tooth; 13, rod border of intestinal epithelium; 14, tooth in buccal capsule; 15, end bulb of pharynx; 16, glandular part of pharynx; 17, cervical papilla; 18, median pseudobulb.

rod border that probably represents altered immobilized cilia (Fig. 115*C*). The number of intestinal cells is limited and in many of the smaller parasitic nematodes only two rows are present. In some strongyloids, the intestinal cells are multinucleate. The rear part of the intestine may be covered externally with a delicate muscle net similar to that of rotifers. At its junction with the rectum the intestine is provided with a uninucleate sphincter termed the intestinorectal valve. In the Mermithidae, the intestine has altered to a blind, food-storing cylinder, that lacks a lumen, is not connected with either pharynx or anus, and consists of two or more rows of large cells filled with food inclusions (Fig. 132*B*).

The rectum or hindgut is a short usually flattened tube provided with rectal glands in many parasitic nematodes; these are large unicellular glands, usually three in number in females, six in males. Being of proctodaeal origin, the rectum is lined by cuticle outside which is an epithelium of a few large cells covered externally by muscle tissue. The anus is a transverse slit operated by a *depressor ani* muscle, frequently H-shaped. This muscle acts to elevate the dorsal wall of the rectum and the posterior lip of the anal aperture thus assisting in defecation. Rectum and anus are lacking in the females of some nematodes, as the mermithids and the guineaworm, but are always present in males as they serve as the outlet of the male reproductive system. The sperm duct enters the ventral wall of the rectum in all nematodes except the Trichuroidea in which it enters dorsolaterally. The rectum is thus in whole or in part a cloaca in male nematodes in which sex it is provided with a spicular pouch that contains the copulatory spicules.

9. Excretory System.—This system is peculiar in nematodes, being totally unlike that of other Aschelminthes or other Protostomia, for that matter. It is devoid of flame bulbs or any current-producing mechanism. The structures that are usually considered to be excretory (evidence later) are of two sorts, glandular and tubular. The glandular type of excretory system is found in free-living marine nematodes, which are here regarded as the most primitive existing members of the class. It here consists typically of a single large gland cell, situated ventrally in the region of the posterior end of the pharynx or anterior part of the midgut (Fig. 115*E*). This cell is usually called the *ventral* or *cervical* gland but Cobb's term *renette* has met with some acceptance. The long or short neck runs forward from the cell and opens in the mid-ventral line by an excretory pore. This pore is generally located in the region of the nerve ring but may be more anterior, even at the level of the lips. An ampullary enlargement may occur prior to the pore (Fig. 115*D*). The renette is lobulate in *Enoplus* (Fig. 115*F*) and usually consists of a group of several cells in the Chromodoroidea. It is by no means present in all free-living marine nematodes. Little information is available as to its occurrence in fresh-water and terrestrial nematodes but those obviously related to marine forms are known to possess one.   The Dorylaimoidea, a group of terrestrial spear-bearing nematodes, generally lack a renette although the excretory pore may be detectable.   In the Mermithidae, a renette is present only in parasitic juvenile stages, not in adults, although these are free-living.   A two-celled renette occurs in *Rhabdias* (Fig. 116*A*) and many rhabditoids.   From this condition appears but a step to the canal system by way of long canal-like outgrowths from the renette cells as in juvenile *Ancylostoma* (Fig. 116*B*).   Later anterior outgrowths arise, and an H-shaped system results as in *Oesophagostomum* (Fig. 116*C*). The canals may pass through the renette cells as in *Oesophagostomum* or the renette cells may depend from a transverse connection between the limbs of the H as in certain species of *Rhabditis*.   In *Contracaecum* and other anisakine ascaroids there is but one renette cell and one canal (left), presumably through loss of the right part of the system; here the canal passes through the renette (Fig. 116*D*).   Finally the renette cells become unrecognizable as such and an H-shaped system of canals embedded in cytoplasmic material remains as in *Camallanus* (Fig. 117*A*) and oxyuroids.   When fully developed, the H-system thus consists of a longitudinal canal, the lateral excretory vessel, running in each lateral chord, a transverse canal connecting the lateral vessels by way of a bridge of lateral chord tissue, and a common stem leading from the transverse vessel to the excretory pore.   The posterior limbs, or parts of the lateral canal posterior to the transverse canal, are usually much longer than the anterior limbs (Fig. 117*A*).   The common stem may be enlarged to an ampulla or bladder-like reservoir, as in Fig. 116*B*.   Through loss of the anterior limbs, the H-system becomes altered to the shape of an inverted U (Fig. 117*D*).   In *Ascaris* (Fig. 117*C*), the H-system is present, but the anterior limbs are somewhat reduced and the transverse canal and adjacent parts of the lateral canals are altered into a network which is particularly evident on the left side where it contains the single nucleus of the system.   A greater development of the left than of the right lateral vessel often obtains and as already noted only the left posterior limb remains in anisakine ascaroids (Fig. 116*D*).   A loss of one lateral canal, either right or left, but usually left, is seen in the tylenchoids.   The H-system of canals obtains in adult Strongyloidea and Spiruroidea or the inverted U-type through loss of the anterior limbs.   The Trichuroidea and Dioctophymoidea are devoid of an excretory system in the adult stage but the inverted U-type is present in at least some Filarioidea.

On present evidence it is difficult to decide the relationship of the renette to the canal system.   Stekhoven (1937–1939) believes the two structures are wholly independent but may sometimes secondarily establish connections.   The Chitwoods consider the canal system to be the

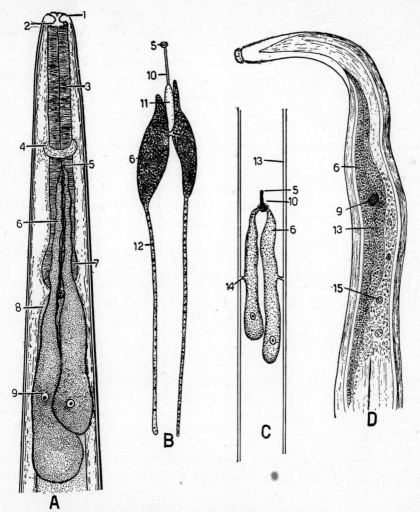

FIG. 116.—Excretory system. *A. Rhabdias* with two-celled renette. *B.* Juvenile *Ancylostoma* (*after Stekhoven*, 1927), with posterior canals developing from the renette cells. *C. Oesophagostomum*, with lateral connections of renette cells to canals. (*A, C, after Chitwood*, 1931.) *D. Contracaecum* (*after Nassonov*, 1900), with excretory system on one side only. 1, lips; 2, buccal capsule; 3, pharynx; 4, nerve ring; 5, excretory pore; 6, renette cells; 7, pharyngeal bulb; 8, intestine; 9, nucleus of renette cell; 10, common stem; 11, contractile ampulla; 12, posterior extensions of renette cells; 13, excretory canal; 14, connections between canals and renette cells; 15, pseudocoelocytes.

original one from which the renette type can be derived by way of forms regarded as transitional that have both systems concomitantly. On such a view the lateral canals would presumably represent protonephridia that have lost their flame bulbs. This is an attractive theory that would reconcile the excretory system of nematodes with that of other Aschel-

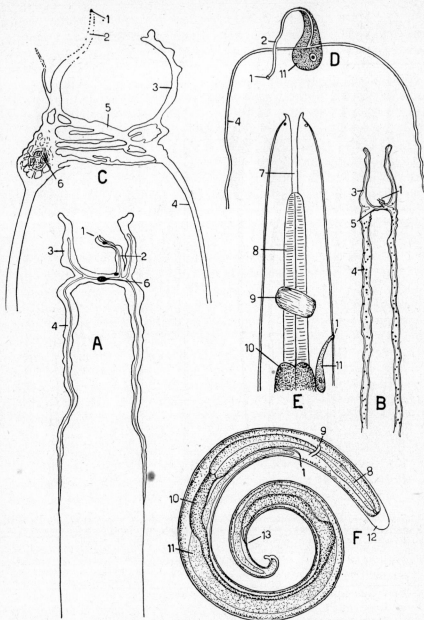

Fig. 117.—Excretory system (continued). *A.* H-type, *Camallanus.* *B.* H-type with many nuclei, *Cucullanus.* (*A, B, after Törnquist,* 1931.) *C.* H-type, horse ascaris (*after Mueller,* 1929), with transverse canal altered into a network. *D. Physaloptera,* fourth-stage juvenile, inverted U-type (*after Seurat,* 1919). *E.* Juvenile spiruroid (*Ascarops*) with one-celled renette (*after Seurat,* 1919). *F.* Juvenile strongyloid (*Metastrongylus*) with long one-celled renette (*after Alicata,* 1935). 1, excretory pore; 2, common canal; 3, anterior canal; 4, posterior canal; 5, transverse canal or network in *C*; 6, nucleus; 7, buccal capsule; 8, pharynx; 9, nerve ring; 10, intestine; 11, renette; 12, sheath; 13, anus.

minthes; but it meets the insuperable objection that the marine nematodes, which have the renette system, are undoubtedly the most primitive existing nematodes, ancestral to nematodes with a canal type of excretory system. That the renette is the original type of nematode excretory system is definitely proved by the fact that the juveniles of many parasitic nematodes, including oxyuroids, ascaroids, spiruroids, and strongyloids, have a typical one-celled renette, indistinguishable from that of marine nematodes (Stewart, 1918; Seurat, 1916, 1919; Alicata, 1935, Fig. 117*E*, *F*). Cobb (1890) followed the further history of this cell in *Enterobius* (an oxyuroid, with an H-type adult system) and found that the cell puts out two posterior processes (Fig. 118*A*, *B*) that undoubtedly become the posterior limbs of the lateral canals. This observation, plus the existence of transitional types that have both renette cells and canals (Fig. 116*B–D*), strongly indicates that the canals are intracellular outgrowths from the renette.

The vessels of the canal system are lined by a firm membrane outside of which is a layer of syncytial cytoplasm. Although sometimes containing numerous nuclei (*Cucullanus*, Fig. 117*B*), this cytoplasm is as a rule devoid of nuclei and the whole system usually bears a single nucleus, often very large, generally situated along the transverse canal, often on the left side (Fig. 117*D*). It thus appears to be a fact that in general the canal system represents channels in the cytoplasm of a single cell, presumably the altered renette. Additional nuclei along the common terminal duct (Fig. 117*A*) are probably those of epidermal cells invaginated to form this duct. The view is therefore here adopted that the canals are intracellular outgrowths of the renette, probably necessitated by increasing body size, and that they are unrelated to protonephridia, which have disappeared in the evolution of nematodes.

10. Reproductive System.—The nematodes as a rule are dioecious, existing as separate males and females. Males are readily distinguished externally from females by their smaller size, curvature of the posterior end, and presence of bursae, genital papillae, and other accessory copulatory structures. In marine and most parasitic nematodes, the sexes occur in equal proportions but this is not the case with terrestrial and fresh-water members. Micoletsky (1921) examined 50 to 500 individuals of some 45 species of terrestrial and fresh-water nematodes and found a preponderance of females in nearly all cases. In 15 species no males at all occurred in the material and there were fewer than 50 males per 100 females in 75 per cent of the terrestrial species and in 50 per cent of the fresh-water ones. The scarcity or absence of males indicates a tendency toward hermaphroditism or parthenogenesis in nematodes from these types of habitats. Hermaphroditism is in fact not uncommon among terrestrial nematodes, especially rhabditoids, as shown by the studies of

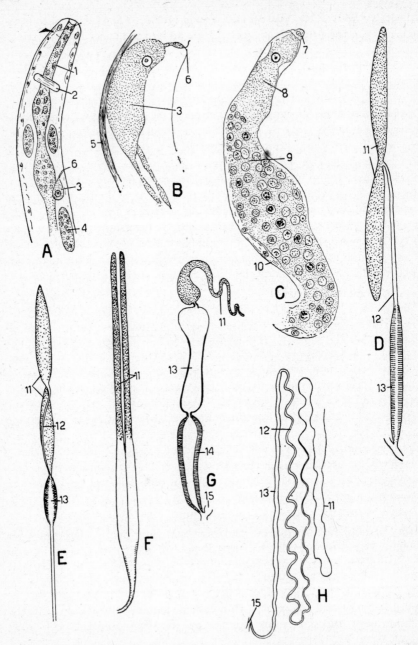

Fig. 118.—Excretory system (concluded), male reproductive system. *A. Enterobius* juvenile with one-celled renette. *B.* Same, later, with posterior canals growing from renette. (*A, B, after Cobb,* 1890.) *C.* Tip of gonad of pig ascaris (*after Musso,* 1930). *D.* Scheme of male system with two opposite testes. *E.* Male system of *Anticoma typica* with testes in tandem (*after Cobb,* 1890). *F.* Male system of *Heterodera marioni* with parallel testes (*after*

Maupas (1900), Potts (1910), and Honda (1925). The hermaphroditism is usually of the protandric type; the gonad first produces sperm that are stored and later fertilize the eggs subsequently developed by the same gonad. Hermaphroditism is usually called *syngony* in works on nematodes. Syngonic nematodes have the external appearance of females. It was shown by the above workers that genuine males occasionally appear in cultures of syngonic nematodes; in 13 species of rhabditoids, Maupas obtained 0.13 to 45 males per thousand females. Curiously enough, these males, although anatomically normal, have lost the sexual instinct and usually will not copulate; when they do so, the offspring contain many more males than is usual for the species. The sperm produced by syngonic females are usually insufficient to fertilize all the eggs matured by the ovary so that following a production of fertilized eggs there is a period of emission of sterile eggs. Sometimes the ovary again reverts to sperm production. In some hermaphroditic nematodes, however, the production of sperm continues throughout the egg-laying period, simultaneously with the production of eggs. In the experiments of Potts and Maupas, in which some syngonic species were bred for nearly 50 generations, there was no indication of deterioration as the result of such inbreeding.

The occurrence of parthenogenesis has been proved for several terrestrial nematodes, e.g., *Mermis subnigrescens* (Christie, 1929) and *Heterodera marioni*, the root-knot nematode (Tyler, 1933), although males are known in both species. Tyler bred 12 generations of females parthenogenetically in *H. marioni*. A remarkable kind of parthenogenesis has been recorded for *Rhabditis monhystera* by Belar (1924) and probably also exists in other species of *Rhabditis*. These species are dioecious and the eggs will not develop unless insemination by a male has occurred; but in those eggs that are to develop into females, the sperm merely acts as a stimulator to development and does not participate in the subsequent mitotic processes.

Intersexes, that is, females having some male characters, have been frequently reported in nematodes (Steiner, 1923) and seem to result from partial sex reversal under environmental influence.

Nematode gonads are of tubular shape, varying greatly in length, and may be straight, sinuous, reflexed, or coiled back and forth (Figs. 118, 121). As regards mode of germ-cell production, they are of two types, *telogonic* and *hologonic*. In hologonic gonads, limited to the orders Trichuroidea and Dioctophymoidea, proliferation of germ cells takes

---

Atkinson, 1889). *G.* Male system with one anterior testis (*Camallanus, after Törnquist*, 1931). *H.* Scheme of the male system of ascaris, with long coiled testis and duct. 1, pharynx; 2, nerve ring; 3, renette; 4, gonad primordium; 5, lateral chord; 6, excretory pore; 7, apical cell; 8, terminal cell; 9, germinal zone; 10, covering epithelium; 11, testis; 12, sperm duct; 13, seminal vesicle; 14, ejaculatory duct; 15, intestine. Spicules are omitted.

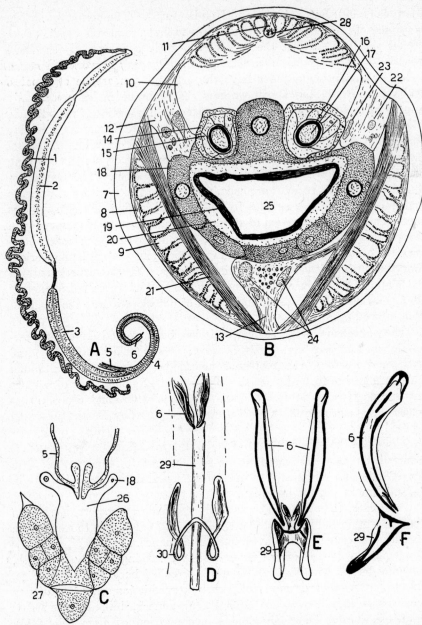

Fig. 119.—Male reproductive system (continued).   *A.* Male system of *Trichuris* (*after Rauther,* 1918).   *B.* Section through the rear end of ascaris (*after Voltzenlogel,* 1902).   *C.* Development of spicule sacs (*after Seurat,* 1920).   *D.* Male armature of a trichostrongyloid, with telamon (*after Hall,* 1921).   *E.* Spicules and gubernaculum of a chromadoroid.   *F.* Same from side view.   (*E, F, after de Man,* 1907.)   1, testis; 2, seminal vesicle; 3, ejaculatory duct; 4, cirrus; 5, intestine; 6, spicule; 7, cuticle; 8, epidermis; 9, muscle layer; 10,

place along the entire length of the gonad, either throughout its walls or in limited areas; in telogonic gonads, germ cells are proliferated only in the blind proximal end, termed the *germinal zone*, usually from a single large *terminal* cell (Fig. 118C). The germinal zone is succeeded by a *growth zone* in which the gametogonia enlarge and differentiate. They are here not loose but attached to a central cytoplasmic strand or *rachis* of uncertain function. Further distally, the gametocytes become free from the rachis and undergo maturation processes. The gonad is covered by a flat epithelium continuous with the epithelium that forms the gonoduct wall. At the proximal tip of the gonad, this covering epithelium may present a large *apical* cell (Fig. 118C), not to be confused with the true terminal proliferative cell.

Probably there were originally two gonads in all nematodes but in males a single testis is usually present and this extends anteriorly. However, two testes occur in many nematodes and these are oppositely oriented (Fig. 118D) except in *Heterodera marioni* (Fig. 118F) where they are parallel, and in *Anticoma typica* (Fig. 118E), in which they have a tandem arrangement (Cobb, 1890). The terms *diorchic* and *monorchic* are convenient for referring to the two-testes or one-testis condition, respectively. The free end of the testis is often convoluted or recurved and very long testes may be wound back and forth (Fig. 118H). There is a single sperm duct continuous with the surface epithelium of the testis. This proceeds posteriorly and usually presents a widened, somewhat muscularized region of varying length, the *seminal vesicle* (Fig. 118G), posterior to which, the terminal, often heavily muscularized part of the sperm duct, called *ejaculatory duct*, continues to its junction with the rectum (Fig. 118G). The various divisions of the sperm duct may be marked off by constrictions (Fig. 119A) and a sphincter may occur at the junction with the rectum. A varying number of prostatic glands, producing an adhesive secretion, may enter the distal end of the ejaculatory duct.

Male nematodes with very few exceptions (example, *Trichinella*) are provided with copulatory spicules secreted by and lodged in spicule pouches formed of cloacal evaginations (Fig. 119C) that have the same histological structure as the cloacal wall (Fig. 119B). The spicule pouches, usually two in number, unite prior to their entrance into the cloaca. The spicules consist of hard sclerotized cuticle with a cytoplasmic core (Fig. 119B). They are typically and primitively two in number, but single in some nematodes as a result of fusion or, less often, through

pseudocoel; 11, dorsal chord; 12, lateral chord; 13, ventral chord; 14, muscle layer of spicule pouch; 15, epidermis of spicule pouch; 16, spicule; 17, cytoplasmic core of spicule; 18, rectal glands; 19, cuticular lining of rectum; 20, lining epithelium of rectum; 21, copulatory muscle; 22, bursal nerve; 23, lateral nerve; 24, ventral nerve; 25, rectum; 26, cloaca; 27, evaginations to form spicule pouches; 28, dorsal nerve; 29, gubernaculum; 30, telamon.

the loss of one spicule.   The spicules are usually very short relative to
the body length but are sometimes very elongated and exceptionally
may equal or exceed the body length.   They present a great variety of
size and shape and may be styletiform, curved, flattened, provided with
flanges, blade-like, etc.   The two spicules may be equal in size and alike
in shape (Fig. 119E) or may exhibit various degrees of dissimilarity.
When unlike, the left spicule is usually long and slender, whereas the
right one is short and stouter (Fig. 177E).   Often the spicules are accompanied by an accessory piece, the *gubernaculum*, which is a sclerotization
of the dorsal wall of the spicule pouch, very variable in shape but characterized in general by incurved margins (Fig. 119E, F).   It acts to direct
the spicules toward the anus and to prevent their piercing the cloacal
wall.   In Strongyloidea there is sometimes present another piece, the
telamon, named and first described by Hall (1921); this is a slightly
sclerotized, immovable formation of complicated shape (Fig. 119D) in the
ventral and lateral cloacal walls that also aids in directing the spicules
during copulation.   The morphological variations of the spicules and
their accessory pieces furnish important taxonomic characters in nematodes, being utilized for generic and specific diagnoses in the same way
as are the trophi of rotifers.

The spicules serve in copulation primarily to spread open the female
gonopore and apparently do not act as conduits for the sperm.   They
are operated by retractor muscles extending from their proximal ends
forward to the lateral chords and protractor or exsertor muscles originating on the ventral body wall (Fig. 120A).   The gubernaculum is provided
with similar muscles.   Copulatory muscles in the form of a series of
bands in the ventrolateral body wall (Fig. 166A) in the anal region are of
common occurrence in nematodes.

The order Trichuroidea is unique among nematodes in that the very
long cloaca, often lined with spines, is eversible in males as a cirrus (Fig.
188C).   A single copulatory spicule accompanies the cirrus in the
Trichuridae but is absent in other Trichuroidea.

The sperm of nematodes are usually quite unlike those of other animals, being rounded, conical, lobulate, or elongated bodies (Fig. 120B–F)
that move slowly in amoeboid fashion.   Even when the external shape
approaches the flagellate type, the cytological structure characteristic
of flagellate sperm is wanting.

In females there are usually two ovaries oriented in opposite directions
and these may be straight, sinuous, reflexed, or if very long wound back
and forth (Fig. 121A, B).   The ovaries and ducts may also be arranged
in a parallel position (Fig. 121C), extending either anteriorly or posteriorly, and reduction to a single ovary and duct is not uncommon
(Fig. 121D).   The terms *monodelphic* and *didelphic* are convenient for

indicating the single and double condition of the female tract, respectively. The *polydelphic* condition, in which there are more than 2 (up to 10 or 11), also occurs, especially in the Physalopteridae (Spiruroidea).

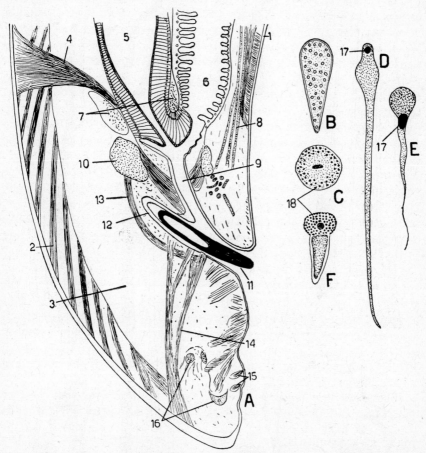

Fig. 120.—Male system (concluded). *A.* Section through the tail end of ascaris, showing relation of spicule to rectum (after *Voltzenlogel, 1902*). *B–F.* Types of nematode sperm. *B. Thoracostoma (after de Man, 1888).* *C. Anaplostoma (after de Man, 1907).* *D. Trilobus (after Chitwood, 1931).* *E. Passalurus (after Meves, 1920).* *F.* Horse ascaris. 1, cuticle; 2, copulatory muscles; 3, pseudocoel; 4, dilator of intestine; 5, intestine; 6, ejaculatory duct; 7, sphincter; 8, ventral nerve; 9, rectum; 10, rectal glands; 11, spicule; 12, spicule sheath; 13, protractor of spicule sheath (exsertor of spicule); 14, retractor muscles; 15, genital papillae; 16, nerve cells; 17, nucleus; 18, mitochondria.

The epithelial covering of the ovary continues distally as the oviduct which at first may be slender with a tall epithelium but which soon widens into a broad tube, the uterus, lined with a flat to cuboidal epithelium and provided with circular and oblique muscle fibers. The beginning of the uterus usually functions as a seminal receptacle in which

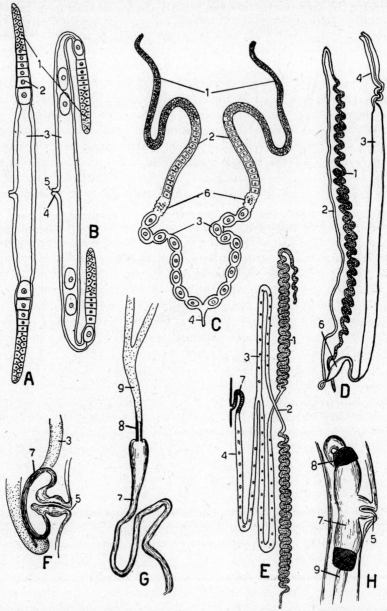

Fig. 121.—Female reproductive system. *A.* Scheme of female system with opposite straight ovaries. *B.* Scheme with opposite reflexed ovaries. *C. Heterodera,* with anterior parallel ovaries (*after Nagakura,* 1930). *D. Trichuris,* with single sinuous ovary (*after Rauther,* 1918). *E. Heterakis gallinae* (*after Baker,* 1936) with opposite sinuous ovaries and simple ovejector. *F.* Ovejector of *Oesophagostomum. G.* Ovejector of *Tetrameres* (*after Seurat,* 1920). *H.* Ovejector of *Nematodirus.* (*F, H, after Ransom,* 1911.) 1, ovary; 2, oviduct; 3, uterus; 4, vagina; 5, vulva; 6, seminal receptacle; 7, ovejector; 8, sphincter; 9, uterine vagina forming part of ovejector.

sperm are stored (Fig. 121*C*) and in which fertilization occurs; the seminal receptacle may also be otherwise located, often at or near the distal end of the female tract, sometimes as a lateral pouch. The seminal receptacle may have a distinctive epithelium, as in *Ascaris*, where it is provided with tall processes that almost fill the lumen and apparently serve to phagocytize excess sperm. The uterus functions for the storage of eggs which, as they pass distally along it, undergo fertilization, shell formation, and some degree of embryonic development, in some cases as far as the formation of juveniles. Distally the uterus or uteri enter a common muscularized tube lined with cuticle, the vagina, usually quite short, that opens to the exterior by the female gonopore or vulva. The true vagina, recognized by its cuticular lining, may be extended inward by appropriating the distal part of the uterus which then comes to resemble the vagina histologically except for the absence of the cuticular lining; this vaginal extension is sometimes called *vagina uterina* or *uterine vagina*. In many strongyloids and spiruroids, the terminal part of the female tract becomes heavily muscularized, forming the *ovejector* (also spelled *ovijector*), functioning in the expulsion of the eggs (Fig. 121*F–H*). This may involve only the true vagina or also the uterine vagina and may be entirely single or partly forked. In its most complicated form, the ovejector consists of three regions, the terminal muscularized region, a sphincter, and a nonmuscular proximal region (Fig. 121*H*) continuous with the uterus.

The female gonopore is a mid-ventral transverse slit with bulging lips that is usually situated along the middle third of the body but may be shifted anteriorly or to the vicinity of the anus. There is apparently only one nematode, *Rondonia rondoni*, a parasite of fishes, in which the vagina opens into the rectum (Travassos, 1919). Both vaginal and vulvar glands (Fig. 135*B*) may occur, chiefly in free-living marine nematodes. The vulvar glands consist of one to several pairs of gland cells situated anterior and posterior to the vulva. Dilator muscles in the form of radiating bands encircle the vulva in most nematodes.

A peculiar system of tubes, the *demanian* system, is found in the posterior part of many females of the marine family Oncholaimidae (order Enoploidea). This system, discovered by de Man in 1886, has since been investigated by Zur Strassen (1894), Cobb (1930), and Kreis (1934). It is variable in form and degree of development in different members of the family and reaches its highest complexity in *Metoncholaimus* and *Adoncholaimus*. In these (Figs. 127*E*, 128*C*), the system begins as a blind cell cluster in the dorsal wall of the midgut and runs posteriorly dorsal to the midgut as a thin-walled tube that gives off one or two connections into the adjacent uterus or uteri. These connections are encircled by a radiating cluster of gland cells termed the *rosette*. More posteriorly the tube forks and each fork, accompanied by a row of gland cells, the *moniliform* glands, opens to the exterior laterally shortly in front of the anus by a minute pore or set of pores.   In *Adoncholaimus* in addition to two uterine connections, there is also an outlet into the vagina (Fig. 128*C*).   In other oncholaims, the system is simpler with fewer parts and connections.   According to Cobb, the system emits an adhesive fluid, presumably playing some role in reproduction.

The female tract is in general much longer and more complicated in parasitic than in free-living nematodes, in relation to the greater egg production characteristic of parasites.   Especially the uteri and the growth zone of the ovary are greatly lengthened in parasitic nematodes.

11. Copulation and Reproductive Habits.—Although parthenogenetic and syngonic reproduction occur in nematodes, most species are dioecious and insemination by a male is necessary for the development of the eggs. In copulation, the spicules are inserted in the vulva and presumably the various accessory copulatory structures, as well as adhesive secretions, assist the process.   The male is usually oriented at an angle to the female and often coils around her (Fig. 148*C*).   In bursate males, the bursa folds over the female body.   The trichuroid worm, *Trichosomoides crassicauda*, parasitic in the urinary tract of rats, is notable in the animal kingdom in that the minute males, 1.5 to 3.4 mm. long, dwell in the vagina of the female, 10 to 13 mm. long, where they were originally taken to be young worms (Linstow, 1874; Hall, 1916; Thomas, 1924).

The sperm travel up the female tract to the seminal receptacle where they fertilize the ripe ovocytes as these proceed distally.   The entire sperm enters the egg.   As soon as fertilization has occurred, a fertilization membrane appears around the egg and this thickens to form a shell. To the inner side of this shell, the egg soon gives rise to an inner or *lipoid* membrane, thin and delicate.[1]   As the eggs pass along the uterus there is added outside the shell a third or *protein* membrane, a product of the uterine wall.   It is the protein membrane that furnishes the surface sculpturings, filaments, etc., present on some nematode eggs.   The nematode egg (Fig. 122*F*) is therefore typically surrounded by three membranes, the lipoid membrane, the shell, and the protein membrane; the last is not infrequently wanting.   The chemical composition of these membranes has been repeatedly investigated.   It was first shown by Krakow (1892) that the shell consists of chitin, something that is rather surprising in view of the complete lack of chitin elsewhere in the nematode body.   The manner of formation of the shell and the lipoid membrane was elucidated by Fauré-Fremiet (1912) and Wottge (1937).   The ripe ovocyte contains glycogen and lipoid globules and, immediately after

---

[1] Usually called vitelline membrane but this name should be reserved for the surface membrane of the ovocyte before fertilization.

fertilization, the glycogen globules move to the surface where they break down into glucose from which glucosamine, the chief constituent of chitin, is synthesized. Next globules of saponified lipoid material move to the egg surface and become the lipoid membrane which when finished is

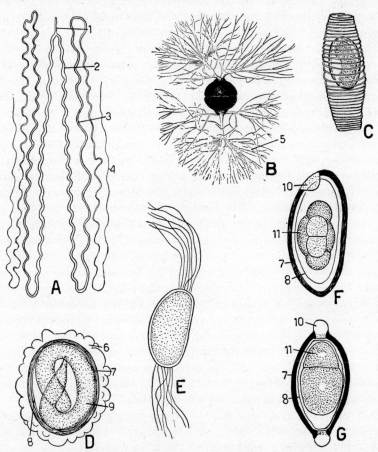

Fig. 122.—Female reproductive system, egg membranes. *A.* Scheme of the female system of ascaris. *B.* Mermithid egg (*after Christie,* 1937). *C. Pseudonymus* egg enclosed in spiral filaments (*after Györy,* 1856). *D.* Ascaris egg (*after Alicata,* 1935). *E.* Egg of *Tetrameres* with polar filaments (*after Seurat,* 1920). *F.* Oxyuroid egg (*Dermatoxys veligera*) with one opercular plug (*after Seurat,* 1920). *G.* Trichuroid egg (*Trichuris suis*) with two opercular plugs (*after Alicata,* 1935). 1, vagina; 2, uterus; 3, oviduct; 4, ovary; 5, byssus; 6, protein membrane; 7, shell; 8, lipoid membrane; 9, juvenile; 10, opercular plug; 11, embryo.

composed of a sterol, cholesterol in at least some nematodes. Chitwood (1938) and Jacob and Jones (1939) verified these results and also proved the protein nature of the outermost membrane.

The shell enclosing the ripe egg is usually of rounded, oval, or elliptical

shape with a smooth, spiny, or warty surface (Fig. 122). A single fila-
ment occurs at each pole of the shell in *Citellina*, a bunch of filaments
similarly located in *Tetrameres* (Fig. 122*E*) and some other spiruroids,
and in mermithoids there is at each pole an elaborately branched projection, the *byssus* (Fig. 122*B*). These projections of the protein membrane seem to function for attaching the eggs to objects. The eggs of
Pseudonymus, an oxyuroid parasite of water beetles, are encircled by
spirally coiled filaments (Fig. 122*C*) that on contact with water unroll
and become entangled in water plants. In some nematodes, provision
is made for the easy escape of the young worm by a hiatus in the shell
filled in with a soft opercular plug, single in oxyuroids (Fig. 122*F*),
present at both poles in trichuroids and dioctophymoids (Fig. 122*G*).

Little seems to be known of the reproductive habits of free-living
marine nematodes; apparently they lay a small number (less than 50)
of relatively large eggs into their habitat, sometimes conglomerating
them into masses by means of an adhesive secretion. Similar habits
obtain in terrestrial nematodes, except that usually more eggs are laid,
up to several hundred. Phytoparasitic nematodes often lay their eggs
in plant tissues or inside the plant galls that they evoke or accumulate
them in their bodies which then dry up to form cysts. The zooparasitic
nematodes are usually oviparous, discharging their eggs inside the host
body. The eggs may be unsegmented on leaving the female or may
undergo various degrees of development inside her uterus, up to the formation of juvenile worms. Development to young worms may also
occur in the host body during the passage of the eggs to the exterior. A
good many zooparasitic nematodes are ovoviviparous, that is, the eggs
hatch to juvenile worms in the maternal uterus; the egg membranes are
then more delicate than in oviparous forms and the protein membrane
is usually absent. Whether true viviparity, the nourishing of embryos
by the uterus, occurs in nematodes is doubtful.

It is usual for nematodologists to speak of eggs containing embryos
or young worms as *embryonated*. While this term is convenient it is more
exact to use the expression ovic embryos or juveniles.

12. Embryology.—The embryology of nematodes has been investigated
by a number of zoologists and in fact has been the subject of several
classical studies in cytology and germ-cell lineage. Although the cleavage does not follow the typical spiral plan, the development is nevertheless highly determinate in character and the fate of each cell can be definitely followed. There is further in nematodes a very early segregation
of the germ-cell line, at the first cleavage, in fact. The principal embryological studies are those of Zur Strassen (1896), Boveri (1899), and
Müller (1903) on *Parascaris equorum* (= *Ascaris megalocephala*), Neuhaus
(1903) on *Rhabdias bufonis* (= *Rhabditis nigrovenosus*), Martini (1903,

1906) on *Camallanus lacustris* (= *Cucullanus elegans*), and Pai (1928) on *Turbatrix aceti* (= *Anguillula aceti*).

The egg is of oval form and in *Turbatrix* one pole bears the micropyle through which the sperm enters; this pole becomes the anterior end. The first cleavage occurs transverse to the egg axis and produces two cells of about equal size, an anterior cell called $S1$ and a posterior cell $P1$ which is the ancestor of the germ cells. At the second division $S1$ divides into A and B, and $P1$ divides into $S2$ and $P2$. In *Parascaris*, these four cells are at first arranged in a T-shape (Fig. 123A) but later shift to the rhomboid shape characteristic of the four-cell stage of other nematodes (Fig. 123B). In this rhomboid, A is anterior, B, dorsal, $S2$, ventral, and $P2$, posterior. The $S1$ cell is the primary somatic cell and the descendants of its offspring A and B produce the ectoderm of the entire body except the posterior end. The $S2$ cell, also called $EMSt$ or entodermal-mesodermal-stomodaeal cell, divides into E and MSt (Fig. 123C, D). E is the entoderm cell and gives rise to the entire entoderm, which in nematodes is the midgut epithelium. MSt divides into M and St (Fig. 123E). M is the mesoderm cell and produces the body-wall musculature and the cells of the pseudocoel. St gives rise to the pharynx. St, M, and E lie in this order from anterior to posterior in the ventral side of the embryo (Fig. 123F) and are gradually brought into the interior by a process of gastrulation (Fig. 123H). Here the E cell proliferates a chain of cells that becomes the midgut. The offspring of M form a strand on either side of the midgut (Fig. 123J, K). St proliferates a mass of cells that in *Parascaris* passes into the interior by a regular process of stomodaeal invagination (Fig. 124A) but in other nematodes there is no or little trace of such a process and the stomodaeal mass is brought into the interior during gastrulation, later connecting with the surface ectoderm anteriorly, and the midgut posteriorly. After these processes have occurred, a frontal section (Fig. 124B) will show the embryo to consist of an ectodermal epithelium enclosing a central column consisting anteriorly of the stomodaeal mass, and posteriorly of the midgut cylinder with a strand of mesoderm to either side. The germ layers are thus clearly defined at this time. In the meantime divisions have continued in the P line of cells (propagative or germ-cell line). $P2$ divides into $S3$ and $P3$, and $P3$ into $S4$ and $P4$ (Fig. 123D, E). $S3$ and $S4$ are generally ectodermal, furnishing the epidermis of the rear part of the body and of the proctodaeum, but in *Parascaris*, their offspring contribute to the mesoderm. This contribution, which may be regarded as an ectomeso-derm, adds itself to the rear end of the previously formed mesoderm, which is clearly an entomesoderm, and functions like the latter. The cell $P4$, which meantime is brought into the interior by the gastrulation process and lies behind and below the midgut, is the source of the repro-

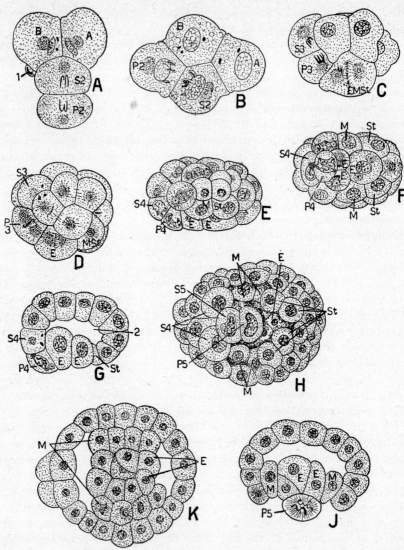

Fig. 123.—Embryology. *A.* T-shaped four-celled stage. *B.* Later four-cell stage, rhomboid shape. *C.* Seven-cell stage. *D.* 18-cell stage. *E.* Later stage, about 30 cells. *F.* Same as *E,* ventral view. *G.* Section through the blastula, sagittal. *H.* Gastrula, ventral view. *J.* Cross section through early gastrulation stage. *K.* Frontal section of the gastrula. (*All of Parascaris equorum, after Boveri,* 1899.) 1, polar body; 2, blastocoel.

ductive tract except its distal ectodermal parts. In *Turbatrix* in which the fate of *P*4 has been followed more precisely than in other nematodes, *P*4 divides into two cells, *S*5 and *P*5. The offspring of *S*5 produce the epithelium that covers the gonad and forms the wall of the gonoduct and *P*5 proliferates the germ cells. Similar observations were made for

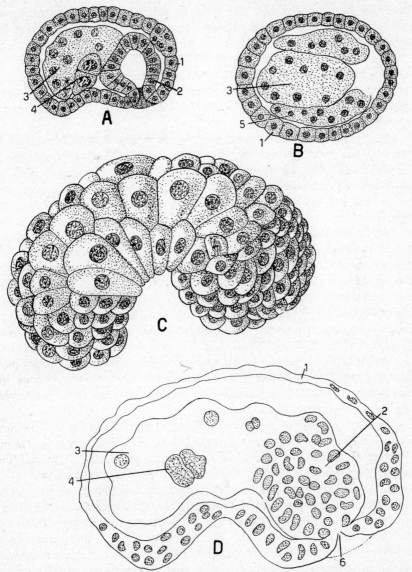

Fig. 124.—Embryology (continued). *A*. Sagittal section, showing formation of the stomodaeum. *B*. Frontal section of similar stage, showing mesodermal bands to either side of entoderm mass. *C*. Later stage of the embryo, worm shape now evident. *D*. Sagittal section of same, showing digestive tract indicated. (*All of Parascaris equorum, A, B, after Boveri*, 1899; *C, D, after Müller*, 1903.) 1, epidermis; 2, stomodaeum; 3, midgut entoderm; 4, germ cells; 5, mesoderm bands; 6, future mouth.

Rhabdias by Neuhaus and the common origin of both germ cells and epithelial wall of the reproductive tract from $P5$ probably obtains throughout nematodes. The nervous system and sense organs are formed from the same cells that furnish the anterior epidermis, probably $S1$ as a rule. Little definite information is available as to the origin of the excretory canals but in *Turbatrix*, which has a one-celled renette, this is one of the offspring of $S1$, or, in other words, the renette is an epidermal gland cell.

As the fate of the individual cells has now been followed, it remains to consider the more general embryonic processes. Cleavage results in a coeloblastula (Fig. 123G), which, however, is generally dorsoventrally flattened and elongated in the anteroposterior direction. The dorsal and lateral walls of the blastula consist chiefly of the descendants of $S1$ with some additions from $S3$ and $S4$, whereas the flat or even concave ventral surface is composed of *EMSt* and $P4$ or their offspring. Gastrulation occurs mostly by epiboly; the ectodermal sides grow down and push the ventral surface into the interior. As the embryo is of elongated shape, the blastopore takes the form of an elongated groove that soon closes over completely. The invaginated material forms an oval mass extending anteroposteriorly in the blastocoel and consisting of the stomodaeum, the midgut, and the gonad primordia with the mesoderm to either side (Figs. 124B, D, 125B–E). It is clear that the pseudocoel of nematodes is a persistent blastocoel. By the process of gastrulation the previously flattened embryo is altered to a cylindroid shape. It continues to elongate and is soon recognizable as a juvenile worm curved inside the egg membranes (Fig. 125A).

The development of the pharynx is rather puzzling in view of the fact that this structure is generally regarded as a stomodaeum, i.e., as of ectodermal nature, as evidenced by its cuticular lining. But all the accounts of nematode embryology agree in deriving the pharynx or at least its main primordium from the same stem cell that gives rise to the entoderm and entomesoderm. Some authors do indicate a later participation of ectoderm in the formation of the pharynx as Boveri (1899) for *Parascaris* and Martini (1903) for *Camallanus* but others deny this. However, it must be recalled that the pharynx consists mainly of muscle fibers, presumably mesodermal, and that its epithelial component is demonstrable with difficulty. This fact probably explains the minor role played by the ectoderm in the embryonic development of the pharynx.

It was discovered by Boveri (1887) for *Parascaris equorum* and since confirmed for other nematodes that not only is the germ-cell line segregated from the somatic cells at a very early stage but also this line is distinguishable from other cells by the behavior of its chromosomes. Only in the germ-cell line do the chromosomes reappear of normal size

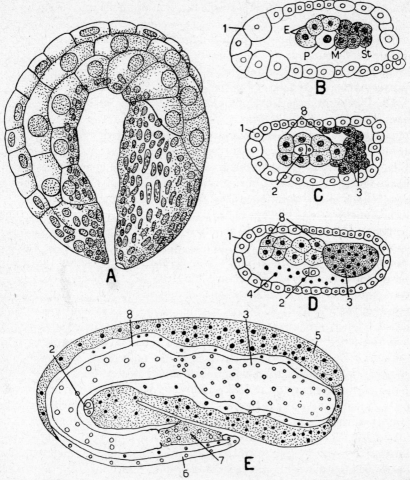

Fig. 125.—Embryology (concluded). *A*. Advanced embryo of *Parascaris equorum* (*after Müller*, 1903). *B–E*. Development of *Turbatrix aceti* (*after Pai*, 1928), anterior end to right, sagittal sections. *B*. 141-cell stage, after gastrulation. *C*. 171-cell stage, stomodaeum forming, 7 E-cells, 4 M-cells on each side. *D*. Later stage, stomodaeum formed. *E*. Sagittal section of a young worm, digestive tract completed. 1, epidermis; 2, primordium of reproductive system; 3, stomodaeum; 4, pseudocoelocytes; 5, epidermis derived from S1 (stippled); 6, epidermis derived from S3 (blank); 7, proctodaeum derived from S4 (stippled); 8, midgut, derived from E-cells.

and shape at each mitosis; in the somatic cells chromatin is continuously cast off and the chromosomes appear in a broken and reduced state. This process of chromatin loss from the nuclei of somatic cells is termed *diminution* and will be found discussed in works on cytology.

Cell multiplication ceases in all the organs except the reproductive system during late embryonic development and the number of cells or nuclei present at that time remains constant throughout the life of the nematode except that amitotic fragmentation of nuclei may occur in the larger species.

Experiment confirms the highly determinate mosaic nature of nematode development. If one blastomere is destroyed in the two-cell stage, the other develops as it would have in a normal embryo and gives little if any evidence of regulatory power (Schleip, 1923).

13. Postembryonic Development and Life Cycle in General.—Nematodes hatch as juvenile worms, erroneously called larvae[1] by workers on nematodes. These juvenile worms are usually fully developed at hatching except as regards size and the reproductive system together with accessory reproductive structures. At hatching, the gonad usually consists of four cells, two inner ones, products of $P5$, which are the primordial germ cells, and two outer encircling ones, products of $S5$, which give rise to the gonoducts and the epithelial covering of the gonad. During their growth to the adult size, the juveniles undergo some changes of form, especially of the posterior end and of the buccal capsule. A marked alteration of body form is limited to certain females as in the genus *Heterodera* (see later). A remarkable feature of the postembryonic growth of nematodes is the occurrence of molts in which the entire cuticle, including the lining of the buccal capsule, pharynx, rectum, and vagina, is shed. There are probably always four molts and the nematode emerges from the fourth molt as a fully developed adult although growth may continue. In some cases the juvenile worm may enter on a quiescent phase inside the shed cuticle which thus serves as a cyst. In other cases one or two molts may be passed while the young worms are still within the egg membranes so that the juveniles after hatching appear to undergo fewer than the usual number of molts. This is the case with many of the Filarioidea which tend to hatch in a somewhat embryonic undeveloped state. Here the young worms, called microfilariae, are enclosed in a sheath while still within the egg membranes. Although the nature of this sheath is disputed the sheath is probably the cast-off cuticle of the first molt so that on hatching the microfilaria is really a second-stage juvenile.

The life cycle of nematodes presents far more variation than is the case with trematodes and cestodes, and all degrees of entoparasitism occur; there are, however, no true ectoparasites among nematodes. The terminology that has grown up with regard to nematode cycles is often objectionable and does not conform to usage in other groups of invertebrates. As already noted, the so-called larvae are really juveniles and will be so designated. Those that have not yet molted are first-stage juve-

---

[1] A larva is a postembryonic, independently existing stage that differs markedly from the parents in morphology and attains the adult morphology by a process of metamorphosis.

niles, those after the first molt are second-stage juveniles, and so on. The stage at which the juveniles enter the host is termed the *infective* stage. In many cases, the molted cuticle remains as a protective covering around the juvenile worm enabling it to withstand adverse conditions. Such juveniles are said to be *ensheathed* or *encysted;* the former term is considered preferable. Juveniles inside the egg membranes, usually referred to as embryonated or larvated eggs or ova, will here be termed ovic juveniles. From the shape of their pharynx, juveniles may be designated as rhabdiform, filariiform, etc. Details of the cycles of specific nematodes will be given in the account of the orders, and at this point only a general picture of the numerous variations will be presented.

a. Direct Cycle.—In free-living aquatic and terrestrial nematodes, juveniles after hatching grow and undergo minor changes as in other invertebrates, except that molts occur as in echinoderids and arthropods. Growth may be more or less uniform or may show sudden increases after each molt.

b. Early Stage of Phytoparasitism.—Juveniles may attach to the roots or other parts of plants, piercing the tissue by the spear or other armature of the buccal capsule and feeding on plant sap and tissues, but do not enter the plant.

c. Later Stage of Phytoparasitism.—The juveniles penetrate into the plant, living in the tissues, or in cavities where their activities have caused the death of tissues, or in galls evoked by their presence. In these sites sexual reproduction occurs and the juveniles after hatching escape to infect new plants.

d. Final Stage of Phytoparasitism.—Whereas in the foregoing cases the nematode often retains the ability to live free in the soil, feeding on plant remains, nematodes in this category, belonging chiefly to the genus *Heterodera*, are obligatory phytoparasites. Here also the juveniles penetrate into plants where they evoke gall formation. The males retain their vermiform appearance but the females alter to a plump, lemon-like form, and eventually become a skin filled with eggs. These cysts released into the soil by the disintegration of the affected part of the plant are very resistant to adverse conditions. They eventually emit juveniles that migrate through the soil to infect new plants. Species of *Heterodera* may require insemination by males or may reproduce parthenogenetically.

e. Early Stage of Zooparasitism.—Here the nematode leads a free existence as males, females, and young but the latter on reaching the infective stage require to be transported as ensheathed juveniles by insects to fresh food supplies, before they can continue their development.

f. Saprophagous Type of Zooparasitism.—The nematode leads a free existence in the soil but in lack of adequate organic food the juveniles enter an invertebrate host where they live ensheathed or free without much development until the host dies from other causes, whereupon the juveniles feed upon the carcass and develop to sexual maturity; one or more generations may be passed in the carcass until it is consumed.

g. Zooparasitism in Juvenile Stages Only.—Juvenile nematodes develop to advanced stages within an invertebrate host, chiefly an insect, then leave, and develop to sexual maturity as free-living soil inhabitants, for several generations in some species; but eventually an infective stage, either an ensheathed or ovic juvenile, must be taken into the invertebrate host again. This type of cycle is characteristic of mermithids which do not feed in the adult stage.

h. Combination of Saprophagous Juveniles with Zooparasitic Adults.— In this type of cycle, the nematodes grow to sexual maturity in the invertebrate host, mate, and produce offspring; these remain in the host until it dies whereupon they feed on the carcass. Third-stage ensheathed juveniles constitute the infective stage which is ingested by the invertebrate host.

i. Zooparasitism in Adult Females Only.—Here the juveniles are free-living and grow to sexual maturity in the soil. After mating the males die and the impregnated females penetrate an invertebrate host where they produce a new generation of juveniles.

j. Combination of Phytoparasitic Juveniles with Zooparasitic Adults.— Gravid female nematodes in the invertebrate host produce juveniles that enter the reproductive system of the host and are deposited by the latter in the plant tissue that is parasitized by the host larvae (insects). The juvenile nematodes live in and feed on the plant tissue in company with the host larvae, develop to sexual maturity, and the gravid female nematode then penetrates the host larva, remaining therein as the latter metamorphoses to an adult insect.

k. Combination of Phytoparasitic Adults with Zooparasitic Juveniles.— Here the juvenile stages occupy the invertebrate host, which is a plant-parasitic insect. The juveniles emerge into the plant tissues where they become adult and breed; the juveniles thus produced gain access to the invertebrate host.

l. Combination of Phyto- and Zooparasitism with Parthenogenesis in the Zooparasitic Phase.—The offspring of adult female nematodes inhabiting an invertebrate (insect) host develop into parthenogenetic females. The offspring of these mature in the soil or in a plant and after mating, the males die, while the impregnated females penetrate an insect larva.

m. Combination of Phyto- and Zooparasitism with Parthenogenesis in the Phytoparasitic Phase.—The young produced by the gravid female nematodes in the female host fly are deposited by the latter in a plant where they develop to parthenogenetic females; several parthenogenetic generations may ensue. Eventually there is produced a gametogenetic generation and the impregnated females penetrate the fly larvae within the plant.

n. Continuous Zooparasitism without Free Stage.—Only one nematode is known, the oxyuroid *Probstmayria vivipara* (Ransom, 1907) inhabiting the intestine of horses, that lives generation after generation in the host without the necessity of passing any stage to the exterior.

o. Typical Zooparasitic Cycle.—The nematode gains access to the invertebrate or vertebrate host in a young stage, develops to sexual maturity, usually in the intestine but also in other organs, and its eggs or ovic embryos or juveniles or free young pass to the exterior where they exist for varying periods and may undergo further development. Eventually, however, an infective stage is reached which must enter new individuals of the same host species either by active penetration or through being ingested. After such entry the young worm may proceed directly to the site parasitized by the adult or may undergo more or less extensive wandering through the host body, especially through the lungs, before settling down to become a sexual adult. This cycle may be regarded as an alternation of parasitic and free stages.

p. Alternation of Zooparasitic Hermaphroditic or Parthenogenetic Females with Free-living Adults.—The offspring of the parasitic females on reaching the exterior may or may not, apparently depending on conditions, develop into one or more free-living generations of sexual adults. This cycle is considered an alternation of homogonic and heterogonic generations; it occurs in *Strongyloides stercoralis* and other Rhabdiasoidea.

q. Optional Use of Transport Host.—Infective juveniles may be ingested by various invertebrates in which they encyst without further development, and reach maturity only when the transport host is ingested by the appropriate definitive host.

r. Zooparasitism with Obligate Intermediate Host.—Here some young stage of the nematode is swallowed by the intermediate host or penetrates it, reaches an infective stage in this host, and develops no further until it gains access to the definitive host.

s. Zooparasitism with Two Obligate Intermediate Hosts.—In this cycle, known for *Gnathostoma*, the first intermediate host is *Cyclops*, the second a fish, frog, or snake, and the definitive host a carnivorous mammal.

14. Histological Peculiarities of Nematodes.—An outstanding anatomical feature of nematodes is their cell constancy; as already noted cell division in general ceases at hatching except in the reproductive system and there is usually no further increase in the number of nuclei. Cell or nuclear constancy has been studied in detail in several nematodes, in *Oxyuris equi* by Martini (1907, 1908, 1916), in *Turbatrix aceti* by Pai

(1928), and in *Rhabditis longicauda* by Schönberg (1943). Martini found cell constancy in all structures of *Oxyuris* except the reproductive tract, the midgut, and the epidermis. Pai was unable to determine the number of nuclei in the epidermis or reproductive system but listed a total of 434 for other body parts as follows: 251 nerve cells, one excretory cell, 18 cells in the midgut, 64 in the body-wall musculature, 59 in the pharynx, 5 in the esophagus, 20 in the rectum, and 16 mesenchyme cells in the pseudocoel. In the female *Rhabditis*, Schönberg counted 68 muscle cells in the body wall, about 200 nerve cells, 120 epidermal cells, and 172 cells in the digestive tract. The number of muscle cells in the body wall seems to be remarkably similar for a large number of nematodes, being usually 64, 65, or 68. In the horse ascaris, Goldschmidt (1908–1910) reported a total of 162 nerve cells.

As there is usually no cell multiplication after birth in nematodes despite very considerable increase in size, it follows that many cells become very large and elongated. This is notably the case with the muscle cells of the body wall, the cells of the pseudocoel, the cells of the excretory canals, etc. In the larger nematodes, muscle cells may be several millimeters in length, possibly more than 10 mm. in some cases. There is also evidenced a tendency toward the formation of syncytia. Nuclear or cell increase during juvenile phases certainly seems to obtain in some nematodes especially in the digestive tract; thus Moorthy (1938) records for *Camallanus sweeti* a steady augmentation in the number of intestinal cells during postembryonic life from 35 in first-stage juveniles to about 200 in the adult. Whether mitotic division is involved is not stated but it seems more probable that the nuclei multiply by amitosis or fragmentation.

15. Order Enoploidea.—This order was formerly considered a family Enoplidae and what are now regarded as its families were then listed as subfamilies. The enoploids are free-living, chiefly marine, nematodes, and are treated in any of the larger studies of marine nematodes as those of Allgen, de Man, Filipjev (especially 1925), Micoletzky, Stekhoven, Steiner, etc. They are worms of small to moderate size with a smooth cuticle, typically with cyathiform amphids, and with a narrowed, strongly cuticularized anterior end that may be set off as a cephalic capsule by a groove. The full complement of head sense organs is present, namely, six labial papillae, and one circlet of 10 (sometimes 12) bristles or sometimes two circlets of 6 bristles each (Fig. 95). Subcephalic and cervical bristles are of common occurrence and furnish the two extra bristles of the cephalic circlet present in some forms. Additional sense organs in the form of a pair of cephalic slits are present. The buccal capsule, weak or well-developed, is typically embraced by the anterior end of the pharynx which is then attached to the inner surface of the cephalic capsule. The pharynx is a simple straight tube lacking bulbous enlargement except in *Polygastrophora* (= *Bolbella*) in which the rear part of the pharynx is provided with six or eight bulbs (Fig. 126*A*). A one-celled renette and three caudal glands (Fig. 127*C*) are present. The female system is usually didelphic with reflexed ovaries and the male may bear a few genital papillae.

Only some of the several families are mentioned here. The Leptosomatidae with weakly developed lips and buccal capsule are exemplified by *Anticoma* (Fig. 126*D*) with a cluster of bristles on each side in the cervical region, *Synonchus* (Fig. 126*C*) with slightly scalloped cephalic capsule and body beset with bristles anteriorly, and *Thoracostoma* (Fig. 126*B*) with cephalic capsule scalloped posteriorly into six conspicuous lobes. *Thoracostomopsis*, only genus of its family, is characterized by the long spear in the buccal cavity, the deeply scalloped cephalic capsule, and the exceptionally long head bristles (Fig. 127*A*). The Oxystomatidae are filiform worms without buccal capsule so that the pharynx is broadly attached around the mouth; the various genera (*Thalassolaimus, Trefusia, Oxystomatina, Halalaimus*, Fig. 126*E*) are distinguished chiefly by the shape of the amphids. In the Enoplidae there are three lips and the large buccal cavity is provided with three strong movable jaws (Fig. 127*B*). Labial papillae are present in *Enoplus* (Figs. 95, 127*B*), whereas in the other enoplids (*Enoploides, Enoplolaimus*, and others) the inner labial sense organs take the form of bristles. The Oncholaimidae are a large and important family of marine nematodes, comprising some 30 genera and nearly 100 species, monographed by Kreis (1934). This family is characterized by the large buccal capsule, not embraced by the pharynx and provided in most genera with one to three large immovable teeth; females possess a demanian system (page 251). There are six lips provided with papillae but some or all of the head bristles (6 or 10 in number) may be converted into papillae, often very reduced and inconspicuous. The amphids show a good many variations from the cyathiform shape and may be circular or biconvex. The teeth are perforated by the ducts of the pharyngeal glands. Of the genera may be mentioned *Pelagonema* (Allgen, 1929, Fig. 127*D*) without teeth in the buccal cavity and known only as females, *Monocholaimus* (Fig. 129*B*) with one tooth, *Paroncholaimus* with three equal teeth, and *Oncholaimus, Metoncholaimus, Oncholaimium, Adoncholaimus*, and *Viscosia* with three unequal teeth (Fig. 128*A, B*). Of the last five genera, the first three are monodelphic, the last two didelphic, and *Viscosia* (Fig. 129*A*) lacks the demanian system. *Metoncholaimus pristiurus*, found in marine mud on both North American and European coasts, has been suggested by Cobb (1932) as a laboratory type for the study of free-living nematodes. In this species there are six lips, each carrying a labial papilla, one circlet

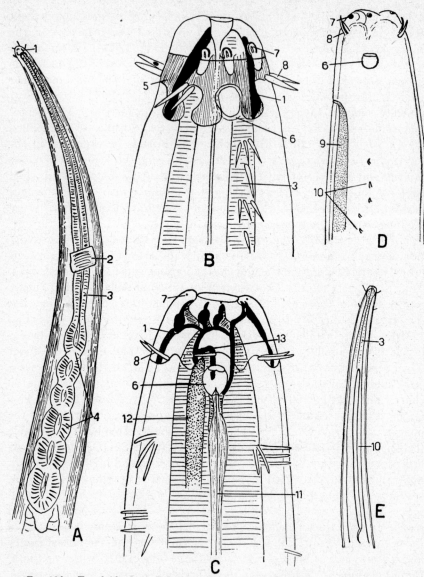

Fig. 126.—Enoploidea. *A. Polygastrophora (after Kreis, 1929). B. Thoracostoma. C. Synonchus. (B, C, after Stekhoven and Adam, 1931.) D. Anticoma (after Filipjev, 1918). E. Halalaimus (after Filipjev, 1925).* 1, buccal capsule; 2, nerve ring; 3, pharynx; 4, pharyngeal bulbs; 5, head capsule; 6, amphid; 7, labial papillae; 8, outer circlet of bristles; 9, renette; 10, cervical bristles; 11, amphidial nerve; 12, duct of pharyngeal gland; 13, tooth.

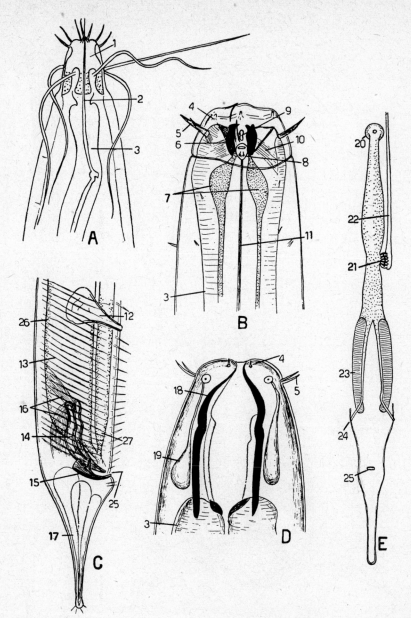

Fig. 127.—Enoploidea (continued).   *A. Thoracostomopsis (after Ditlevsen, 1919).   B. Enoplus communis (after de Man, 1886).   C.* Posterior end of male *Enoplus (combined after Bastian, 1865, and de Man, 1886).   D. Pelagonema (after Kreis, 1934).   E.* Demanian system of *Metoncholaimus (after Cobb, 1930).*   1, head capsule; 2, spear; 3, pharynx; 4, labial papillae; 5, outer circlet of bristles; 6, jaws; 7, pharyngeal gland outlets; 8, amphid; 9, cephalic slit; 10, jaw muscles; 11, amphidial nerve; 12, accessory copulatory organ; 13, copulatory muscles; 14, spicules; 15, gubernaculum; 16, muscles of spicules; 17, caudal glands; 18, buccal capsule; 19, amphidial gland; 20, beginning of system in intestinal wall; 21, rosette; 22, duct to uterus; 23, moniliform glands; 24, pores; 25, anus; 26, intestine; 27, ejaculatory duct.

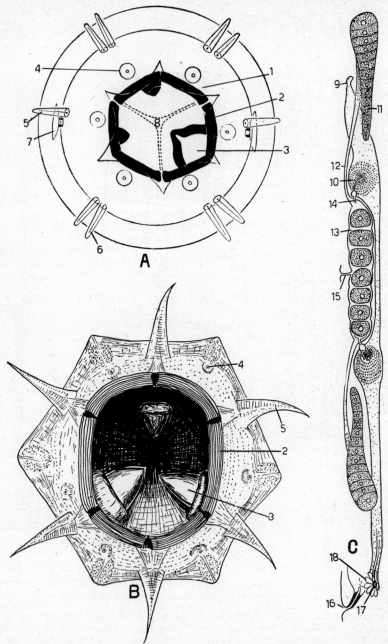

Fig. 128.—Enoploidea (continued). *A.* Scheme of the anterior end of *Oncholaimus* (*after de Coninck*, 1942). *B.* Head end of *Adoncholaimus* (*after Kreis*, 1934). *C.* Demanian system of *Adoncholaimus* (*after Cobb*, 1930). 1, lips; 2, buccal capsule; 3, teeth in buccal capsule; 4, inner labial papillae; 5, outer labial bristles; 6, cephalic bristles; 7, amphids; 8,

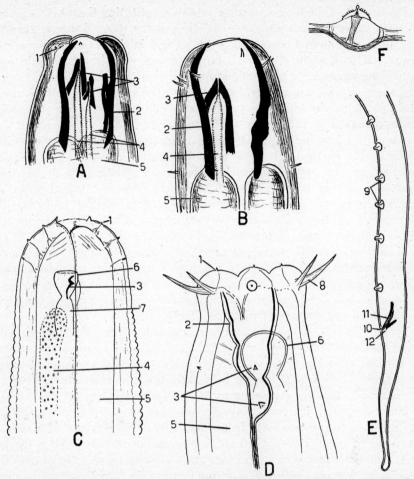

Fig. 129.—Enoploidea (continued). *A. Viscosia. B. Mononcholaimus.* (*A, B, after Kreis,* 1934.) *C. Tripyla. D. Trilobus. E.* Posterior end of *Trilobus,* showing row of preanal copulatory warts (*after Filipjev,* 1931). *F.* Copulatory wart, enlarged. (*C, D, F, after Micoletzky,* 1925.) 1, labial papillae; 2, buccal capsule; 3, teeth; 4, ducts of pharyngeal glands; 5, pharynx; 6, amphid; 7, amphidial nerve; 8, outer circlet of bristles; 9, copulatory warts; 10, anus; 11, spicule; 12, gubernaculum.

of 10 bristles, and well-developed cyathiform amphids. The sclerotized buccal capsule bears in its posterior part the three teeth, one dorsal, and two ventrolateral, of which the left ventrolateral is much the largest. Each tooth is the outlet of a long, branched, unicellular pharyngeal gland. There are three long-stalked caudal glands opening by a pore at the tip of the tail. The excretory pore situated shortly behind the anterior end

mouth; 9, beginning of system in intestinal wall; 10, rosette; 11, ovary; 12, oviduct; 13, uterus, 14, duct from demanian system into uterus; 15, vagina; 16, anus; 17, exit pore of demanian system; 18, moniliform glands.

is the outlet of the long-stalked gland cell constituting the renette.   The female system is monodelphic consisting of the reflexed ovary, narrow oviduct, wide uterus containing a row of eggs in single file, short vagina provided with small gland cells, and vulva provided with conspicuous radiating muscles.   The demanian system is of the type in which a long canal runs forward from the rosette to the uterus and the intestinal canal behind the rosette forks into two tubes accompanied by a row of moniliform glands (Fig. 127*E*).   In the male there are two opposite elongated testes and a long multinucleate gland opens from in front into the beginning of the sperm duct.   The genital armature consists of two equal slender spicules and a reduced gubernaculum.   Externally the flexible curved male tail is provided with one preanal papilla, paired postanal rows of setae, and a mid-ventral row of about 10 papillae.   The family Enchelidiidae, markedly slenderized anteriorly, without lips but with six labial papillae, and 10 bristles in the outer circlet, is exemplified by *Polygastrophora* with several pharyngeal bulbs (Fig. 126*A*) and *Parasymplocostoma* (Fig. 111*B*) and *Enchelidium* with highly developed eyes. Many species of this family exhibit a marked sexual dimorphism in that the males lack a buccal capsule whereas females have a roomy one provided with one large and two smaller teeth.

Some enoploids have spread into brackish water and brackish soil and thence into terrestrial and fresh-water habitats.   These nonmarine forms fall into the family Trilobidae, split by some into two or three families.   Here belong *Tripyla* with three lips and weak buccal capsule bearing a tooth-like projection at the entrance into the pharynx (Fig. 129*C*); *Trilobus* with buccal capsule embraced by the pharynx and provided with one or two teeth in pockets (Fig. 129*D–F*); and *Mononchus* with large, heavily sclerotized tooth-bearing buccal capsule (Fig. 130*A–C*), sometimes placed in a separate family Mononchidae.   *Mononchus*, or the mononchs, as Cobb (1917) terms them in his interesting account, is a genus of predatory nematodes dwelling in fresh water and moist soil, represented by a large number of species.   *Mononchus* has six lips, and six inner and six outer labial papillae; but the cephalic circlet is wanting. The strongly sclerotized buccal capsule generally bears one large dorsal tooth and often in addition two small ventrolateral teeth or denticulate ridges or areas (Fig. 130*A*); sometimes also another denticulate area (Fig. 130*C*).   The females are didelphic with opposite ovaries and are usually syngonic, that is, protandrous hermaphrodites.   Males are rare and unknown in many species; they are diorchic with equal copulatory spicules, a gubernaculum of two pieces, and a preanal row of tubular copulatory papillae (Fig. 130*D*), together with some ordinary papillae.

16. Order Dorylaimoidea.—Formerly considered a family Dorylaimidae under the order Enoploidea, this group was raised to super-

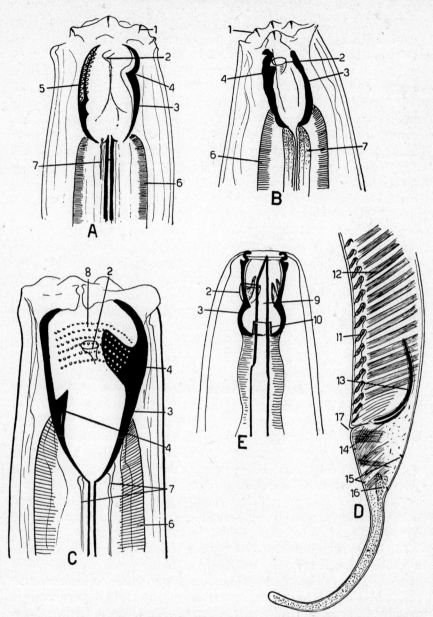

Fig. 130.—Enoploidea (concluded), Dorylaimoidea. *A–C.* Three common species of *Mononchus* (*after Stekhoven and Teunissen*, 1938). *A. Mononchus muscorum*, with one tooth and two dentigerous ridges. *B. M. papillatus*, with one tooth. *C. M. lacustris* with three teeth and a dentigerous area. *D.* Rear end of male *Mononchus*, showing preanal row of tubular copulatory aids (*after Cobb*, 1917). *E. Actinolaimus* (*after Filipjev*, 1931). 1, labial papillae; 2, amphid; 3, buccal capsule; 4, tooth; 5, dentigerous ridges; 6, pharynx; 7, duct of pharyngeal gland; 8, dentigerous area; 9, odontostyle; 10, guide ring; 11, tubular copulatory aids; 12, copulatory muscles; 13, spicule; 14, gubernaculum; 15, ordinary genital papillae; 16, caudal glands; 17, anus.

family rank with five families by Thorne and Swanger (1936) and Thorne (1939) in their monographs. The dorylaims are among the most common nematodes of soil and fresh water. They are characterized by the dorylaimoid type of pharynx (Fig. 115*A*) and by the protrusible hollow spear in the buccal cavity (Fig. 113*B*). This spear originates in a cell in the ventrolateral pharynx wall and hence is an odontostyle but typically lies axially in the buccal cavity. It is a hollow tube with an oblique terminal aperture through which food (plant and animal juices) is sucked. The spear is held in place by cuticularized thickenings of the buccal wall in the form of a guide ring or collar (Fig. 113*B*). All 16 head sense organs take the form of papillae, arranged in two circlets of 6 and 10 each, and the head end is often separated from the cervical region by a pronounced groove. The amphids are cyathiform with slit openings. The renette seems to be absent or rudimentary and there are no caudal glands but lateral chord glands occur in three families. Many dorylaims exist only as females and these are apparently parthenogenetic rather than synogonic. There are one or two reflexed ovaries; the eggs are laid in an unsegmented condition. The males are monorchic or diorchic with two approximately equal spicules, a gubernaculum of three pieces, and prominent copulatory muscles. They are well supplied with genital papillae in the form of a preanal mid-ventral row of tubular papillae, a pair of adanal papillae alongside the anus, and two or four longitudinal series of ventrolateral papillae.

The main genus *Dorylaimus* with nearly 200 species has a simple slender spear with a guide ring (Fig. 113*B*). Some other genera that may be mentioned are: *Tylencholaimus* with proximal flanges or knobs on the spear (Fig. 131*B*); *Actinolaimus* with four buccal teeth in addition to the spear (Fig. 130*E*); *Nygolaimus* with, instead of a spear, a spear-like solid tooth in the left ventrolateral wall of the very long plicated buccal cavity (Fig. 196) and with three cardiac glands at the proximal end of the pharynx; *Xiphinema* with very long slender spear (Fig. 131*A*); and *Axonchium*, slenderized anteriorly and with a muscular sheath around the proximal part of the pharynx.

17. Order Mermithoidea.—This group is also frequently placed under Enoploidea and is generally regarded as related to the Dorylaimoidea (Steiner, 1917). The mermithoids are smooth filiform worms often of considerable length (to 50 cm., but usually shorter) that are parasitic in juvenile stages in terrestrial or fresh-water invertebrate hosts, usually insects, but free-living in soil or water in the adult condition. The sense organs, of which the entire 16 are usually present, are reduced to papillae, and the amphids vary from large cyathiform types to minute pores. The digestive tract offers many peculiarities. A buccal capsule is wanting and the pharynx proceeds directly from the mouth opening (Fig.

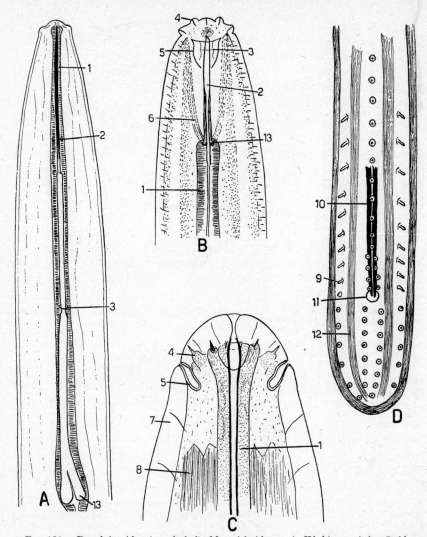

FIG. 131.—Dorylaimoidea (concluded), Mermithoidea. *A. Xiphinema (after Stekhoven and Teunissen*, 1938). *B. Tylencholaimus (after Thorne*, 1939). *C.* Anterior end of a mermithid. *D.* Posterior end of a male mermithid. (*C, D, after Hagmeier*, 1912.) 1, pharynx; 2, spear; 3, guide ring; 4, labial papillae; 5, amphid; 6, protractor muscles of spear; 7, cuticle; 8, body-wall musculature; 9, genital papillae; 10, spicules; 11, anus; 12, muscles; 13, knobs at proximal spear end.

131*C*).   The pharynx is long and tenuous, reaching half or more the body length in some mermithids, and consists of a cuticular tube embedded in a thin cytoplasmic layer.   Posteriorly there are attached to it a varying number of variously arranged stichocytes (Figs. 132*A*, 133*C*).   The pharynx does not communicate with the intestine although sometimes

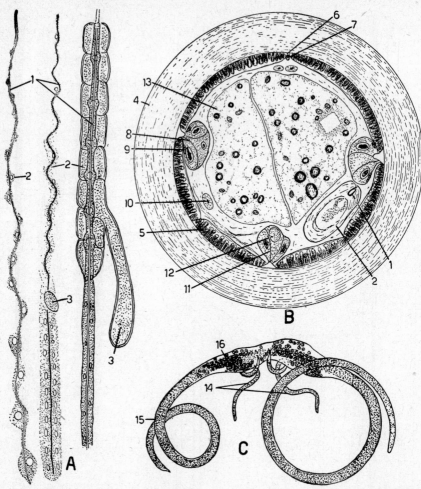

Fig. 132.—Mermithoidea (continued). *A.* Three types of stichosome arrangement (*schematic, based on Meissner,* 1854; *Müller,* 1931; *Linstow,* 1892). *B.* Cross section through a mermithid, showing the trophosome (*after Rauther,* 1916). *C. Tetradonema* in copulation (*after Hungerford,* 1919). 1, pharynx; 2, stichosome; 3, especially large stichocyte; 4, cuticle; 5, muscle layer; 6, dorsal chord; 7, dorsal nerve; 8, lateral chord; 9, lateral nerves; 10, fat cells in pseudocoel; 11, ventral chord; 12, ventral nerve; 13, trophosome (intestine); 14, males; 15, female; 16, accumulation of eggs near gonopore.

adhering to it.   The intestine is also peculiar, being transformed into a trophosome that consists of two or more rows of greatly enlarged cells packed with food reserves (Figs. 132*B,* 133*C*).   The trophosome lacks an anal outlet and serves to nourish the adults, which probably do not feed. Some species possess a very anteriorly located gland, probably representing the renette.   The didelphic female system is of the opposite type. The males, much smaller than the females, are usually diorchic with one

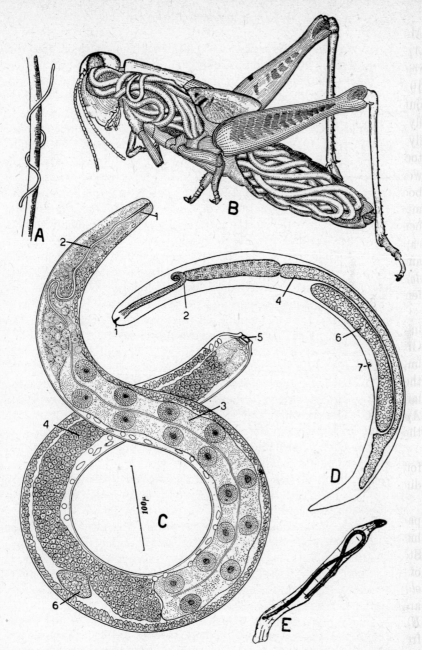

FIG. 133.—Mermithoidea (concluded). *A. Mermis subnigrescens* ascending a grass blade to lay eggs (*after Christie, 1937*). *B.* Grasshopper infected with juvenile *Agamermis decaudata*. *C.* Juvenile *Agamermis* after 6 days in the host. (*B, C, after Christie, 1936.*) *D. Aproctonema entomophagum*, young female (*after Keilin and Robinson, 1933*). *E.* Soil dipterous larva infected with a juvenile mermithid (*after Hagmeier, 1912*). 1, spear; 2, pharynx; 3, stichosome; 4, trophosome (intestine); 5, breaking joint; 6, genital primordium; 7, vulva.

or two spicules and with numerous genital papillae on their posterior ends (Fig. 131*D*).   Reproduction is bisexual or parthenogenetic.

The order comprises two families, the Tetradonematidae and the Mermithidae.   The former contains three species, *Tetradonema plicans*, *Aproctonema entomophagum*, and *Mermithonema entomophilum*, generally regarded as primitive mermithoids.   *Tetradonema*, seen only once (Cobb, 1919; Hungerford, 1919), is, unlike other mermithoids, parasitic throughout life, inhabiting all stages, but especially the soil-dwelling larva, of a fly *Sciara*, which may be infected with 2 to 20 worms of both sexes.   The fly maggots apparently become infected by eating the eggs of the nematode.   These hatch in its digestive tract (also in water) and the juvenile worms penetrate into the host's haemocoel where they devour the fat body and other organs.   Mature female worms are 5 mm. long, males 1 mm.   After copulation within the host (Fig. 132*C*) the eggs are laid beneath the cuticle of the female's gonoporal region which thus acts as a capsule.   Disintegration of the host frees the female with her egg burden and her death then allows dispersal of the eggs in the soil.   Adult *Tetradonemas* have the typical mermithoid digestive tract including in the female a stichosome of four very large conspicuous cells.

A similar cycle obtains for *Aproctonema* (Keilin and Robertson, 1933) in which also juvenile worms of both sexes inhabit the larvae of *Sciara*. Growth to maturity and copulation occur in the insect host but the impregnated females escape to the exterior where they die after expelling their eggs.   The eggs hatch in the decaying wood inhabited by the fly larvae and the latter are penetrated by second-stage juveniles.   Juvenile *Aproctonema* have a dorylaimoid type of pharynx provided with a stylet; the stylet persists in the adults (Fig. 133*D*).

Mature adults of both sexes of *Mermithonema entomophilum* were found by Goodey (1941) in a female fly (*Sepsis cynipsea*) whose reproductive system they had damaged.   No further details are available.

The typical mermithoids comprise the family Mermithidae which as parasites of insects are of considerable economic importance and hence have been the subject of several general (Rauther, 1906; Hagmeier, 1912; Steiner, 1924; Müller, 1931) and many special studies.   Good accounts of this family are given in Filipjev and Stekhoven's *Agricultural Helminthology* and by Christie in *An Introduction to Nematology*.   The mermithids are parasitic in juvenile stages in invertebrates, chiefly insects (Fig. 133*B*; *E*), but also crustaceans, spiders, and snails, whereas the adults lead a free existence, often of some duration, in soil or fresh water.   The hosts become infected either by eating mermithid eggs or through being penetrated by juvenile worms.   The parasites dwell in the haemocoel where they are very destructive to the viscera and fat body, killing the host or rendering it incapable of metamorphosis and reproduction.   Juvenile mermithids are provided with a dorylaim type of stylet (Fig. 133*C*), generally wanting in the adult; the peculiarities of the digestive tract, including the absence of an anus, are present during all stages of the life cycle (Fig. 133*C*). Those juveniles that infect by penetration often show a propelling modification of the posterior part of the body to assist penetration and this region may break off at a preexistent node (Fig. 133*C*) and be left outside. A considerable number of genera and species of mermithids have been described and a number of life cycles have been elucidated of which a few of the best known examples will now be given.

Paramermis contorta (Kohn, 1905; Comas, 1927) is an example of an aquatic mermithid. It parasitizes the larvae of the midge *Chironomus*, emerging when mature and settling into the bottom mud where copulation and egg-laying ensue, followed by the death of the adults, which live at most 4 or 5 days. The eggs hatch into young worms in 14 to 16 days and these swim about, dying in a few hours unless they make contact with a *Chironomus* larva, which they can penetrate if it has recently molted and has a soft cuticle. Unless the mermithid makes the attempt near the anterior end of *Chironomus*, the latter is apt to reach around and destroy it. Usually the *Chironomus* larva harbors only one *Paramermis* juvenile but rarely two or three may be present. Aquatic dipterous larvae of the genus *Simulium* are also much subject to infection with mermithids (Strickland, 1921).

A well-worked-out life cycle is that of *Agamermis decaudata*, parasitic in grasshoppers (Cobb, Steiner, and Christie, 1923; Christie, 1929, 1936). The adults live in cavities in the soil 5 to 15 cm. below the surface, usually coiled in groups consisting of one female and several males. The females (to 46.5 cm. long) lay large numbers of eggs into these soil cavities, from June to the onset of cold weather. Although development begins after laying, hatching is generally deferred until the next spring or summer. One molt occurs inside the egg membranes so that second-stage juveniles are released into the soil. These are well-developed little worms, 5 to 6 mm. long, with a conspicuous dorylaim stylet and a breaking node at about the middle of the body. They migrate to the surface of the soil and after rains or dews climb wet vegetation where when opportunity affords they penetrate into newly hatched grasshopper nymphs through thin places in the body wall of the latter. During penetration the body breaks at the node and the whole posterior half or more is left outside; or if it should enter the host, it atrophies. After reaching the haemocoel of the grasshopper host, the young mermithids grow rapidly, developing a conspicuous stichosome (Fig. 133*B*, *C*). They remain in the host 1 to 3 months, then emerge head first through the intersegmental joints of the host, and enter the soil, mostly during August to October; each worm remains isolated in a soil cavity until the following June when a molt occurs (only two molts have been observed) and the males seek and impregnate the females. Eggs are deposited during the rest of this summer and throughout the whole of the following summer. By the end of their second reproductive summer the females have exhausted the food supply in their trophosomes with resulting body transparency and probably die during their third winter in the soil.

Mermis subnigrescens, also a parasite of grasshoppers, likewise inhabits cavities in the soil to 60 cm. below the surface, nearly always in isolation (Christie, 1937). Copulation occurs occasionally but the females are capable of parthenogenetic reproduction. In the early morning on rainy days during June and July, they emerge from the soil and climb the vegetation (Fig. 133*A*), to which they attach their eggs by way of the byssus of the protein membrane (Fig. 122*B*). The females probably die after oviposition but may live much longer if prevented from laying. When the eggs are eaten by grasshopper nymphs they hatch in the latter's intestine into juveniles that by the aid of their stylet penetrate into the grasshopper's haemocoel where they complete their growth in 4 to 10 weeks. They then emerge and enter the soil, where the final molt occurs the following spring and the females then become filled with eggs by fall but retain these until the following summer. A similar cycle obtains for *Mermis nigrescens*, a closely related if not identical species, that is parasitic in earwigs (Baylis, 1944, 1947).

A number of mermithids parasitize ants but in no case has a complete cycle been elucidated. In *Allomermis myrmecophila* observed by Crawley and Baylis (1921) the advanced juveniles emerge from the ants by the anus or through the body wall in the latter part of the year and enter the soil. The eggs enclosed in a gelatinous secretion are laid into the molting cuticle. It is supposed the ants become infected by eating the eggs. Vandel (1934) studied a species of *Hexamermis* that lives in the soil around the nests of certain ants and lays its eggs in these earth cavities. Penetration of late ant larvae by the juvenile mermithids was postulated. The striking changes induced in ants by mermithid parasites are discussed later.

An environmental determination of sex has been established for several mermithids (*Paramermis contorta*, Caullery and Comas, 1928; *Mermis subnigrescens*, Christie, 1929; *Amphimermis zuimushi*, Kaburaki and Iyatomi, 1933). The determining factor in all observed cases is the number of juveniles per host insect. When the host is infected with only one or a few mermithids, these are nearly always females, but with heavy infections of 25 or more worms per host, the juvenile mermithids develop preponderantly or wholly into males.

18. Order Chromadoroidea.—This is a group of mostly marine nematodes with spiral amphids and usually a ringed cuticle marked with round or oblong punctations or other ornamentations. The buccal capsule is often armed with teeth and the pharynx is provided with a posterior bulb. The reproductive system is double with reflexed gonads and the rear part of males generally bears a preanal row of genital papillae or other copulatory aids. In the families Cyatholaimidae and Choanolaimidae there are conspicuous spirally wound amphids, six lips with papillae, and 10 bristles or papillae arranged in one circlet. The Cyatholaimidae with a circle of longitudinal rib-like thickenings in the wall of the buccal capsule and tubular preanal copulatory aids include *Paracyatholaimus* and *Paracanthonchus* (Fig. 134*C*) with a large forwardly directed dorsal tooth, and *Seuratiella*, *Cyatholaimus* (Fig. 134*F*), and *Choniolaimus* without such a tooth. *Seuratiella* has four preanal tubes of which the most anterior one is especially large (Fig. 134*D*, *E*). *Achromadora* and *Ethmolaimus* (Fig. 134*A*, *B*) are fresh-water genera belonging to this family. The Choanolaimidae are represented chiefly by *Halichoanolaimus* (Fig. 135*A*) with carnivorous habits and comb-like teeth in the buccal capsule. In the Desmodoridae the head bristles are arranged in two or three circlets (Fig. 135*C*). The most common genera are *Desmodora* (Fig. 135*E*) with armored head, *Monoposthia* with a circular amphid and with V-shaped stiffenings interrupting the cuticular rings (Fig. 136*C*) and *Spirina* with amphid spiral reduced to one turn (Fig. 135*D*). The Microlaimidae, with six labial papillae, six labial bristles, four cephalic bristles, amphids usually reduced to one turn, and toothed buccal cavity, are represented by the small *Microlaimus* (Fig. 136*B*) with a number of species. In the Chromadoridae, the cuticle is conspicuously ornamented, the amphids are spiral, crescentic, or elliptical, and the head sense organs are arranged in the usual three circlets. The family embraces a number of genera formed by revision of the old genera *Spilophora* and *Chromadora*. *Spilophora* proper, now called *Spilophorella*, is distinguished by the double pharyngeal bulbs (Fig. 136*D*). The genera derived from *Chromadora* under such names as *Chromadorina*, *Prochromadorella*, *Chromadorella* (Fig. 136*A*), *Prochromadora*, *Chromadorita*, *Neochromadora*, and *Dichromadora* are distinguished chiefly by the cuticular ornamentations and the structure of the buccal capsule, which usually contains one large dorsal tooth and smaller ventrolateral teeth. The genus *Chromadora* as now restricted has a large immovable dorsal tooth and a row of dots along each cuticular ring; four of these dots situated along the body sides are much larger than the others (Fig. 137*A*). In *Richtersia* (Fig. 137*B*), only genus of the Richtersiidae, there are numerous longitudinal rows of small cuticular hooks. The Comesomidae with large spirally coiled amphids, less conspicuous cuticular ornamentations, two circles of head papillae and an outer circlet of four bristles are exemplified by *Sabatieria* (Fig. 137*C*) with small mouth opening and small dorsal tooth.

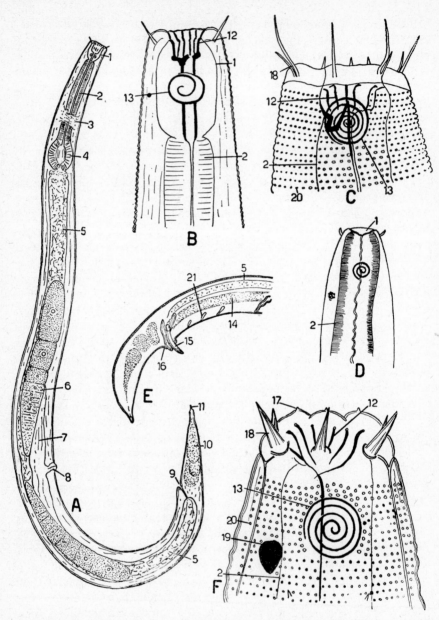

Fig. 134.—Chromadoroidea. *A. Ethmolaimus. B.* Head of *Ethmolaimus.* (*A, B,* after *Höfmanner and Menzel*, 1915.) *C. Paracanthonchus (after Stekhoven and Adam,* 1931). *D. Seuratiella. E.* Rear end of male *Seuratiella.* (*D, E, after Ditlevsen,* 1919.) *F. Cyatholaimus (after de Man,* 1890). 1, buccal capsule; 2, pharynx; 3, nerve ring; 4, pharyngeal bulb; 5, intestine; 6, ovary; 7, uterus; 8, vulva; 9, anus; 10, caudal glands; 11, adhesive tube; 12, ribs of buccal capsule; 13, amphid; 14, ejaculatory duct; 15, spicule; 16, gubernaculum; 17, labial papillae; 18, bristles of external circlet; 19, eye; 20, cuticular punctations; 21, tubular copulatory aids.

The order Chromadoroidea also includes two families of marine nematodes of peculiar appearance, the Draconematidae and the Epsilonematidae, both provided with stilt bristles. In the Draconematidae (= Chaetosomatidae, studies by Claparéde, 1863; Metschnikoff, 1867;

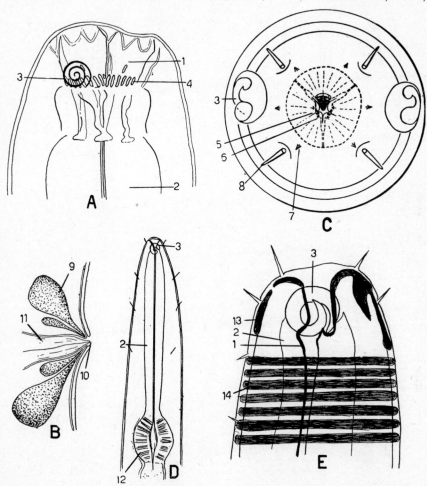

FIG. 135.—Chromadoroidea (continued). *A. Halichoanolaimus.* B. Vulvar glands of same. (*A, B, after Ditlevsen,* 1919.) *C.* Scheme of the anterior end of *Desmodora* (*after de Coninck,* 1942). *D. Spirina* (*after de Man,* 1890). *E. Desmodora* (*after Allgen,* 1929). 1, buccal capsule; 2, pharynx; 3, amphid; 4, teeth; 5, lips; 6, labial papillae; 7, outer labial bristles; 8, cephalic bristles; 9, vulvar glands; 10, vulva; 11, vagina; 12, pharyngeal bulb; 13, head capsule; 14, cuticular ornamentations.

Schepotieff, 1908; Irwin-Smith, 1917; Cobb, 1913, 1929; Kreis, 1938), the enlarged anterior end containing the short pharynx simulates a head and is followed by a slender neck-like region of varying length; the body then broadens somewhat and finally tapers to a short pointed tail (Fig. 138*A*).

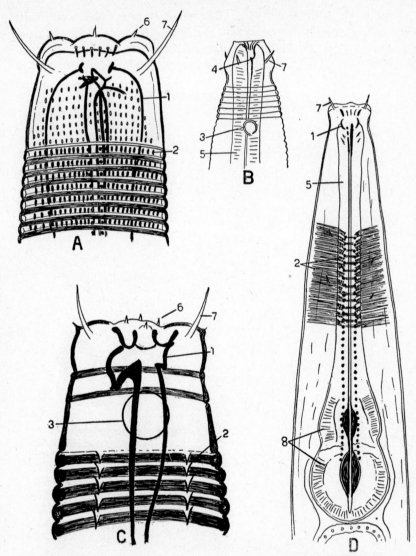

FIG. 136.—Chromadoroidea (continued). *A. Chromadorella (after de Man*, 1890). *B. Microlaimus (after de Coninck and Stekhoven*, 1933). *C. Monoposthia (after Steiner*, 1916a). *D. Spilophorella (after de Man*, 1888). 1, buccal capsule; 2, cuticular ornamentations; 3, amphid; 4, tooth in buccal capsule; 5, pharynx; 6, labial bristles; 7, cephalic bristles; 8, pharyngeal bulbs.

The body as a whole is more or less ringed and bristly. The "head" is divisible into a smooth distal part bearing the amphids and a set of hollow adhesive bristles, a middle heavily ringed zone, and a proximal smooth or slightly ringed part that encloses the pharyngeal bulb (Fig. 138*B*). The amphids vary from a spiral to a crook-like shape (Fig. 138*B*). The stilt

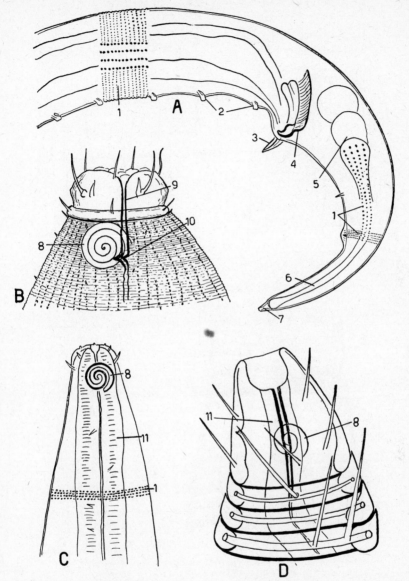

Fig. 137.—Chromadoroidea (continued). *A*. Tail of male *Chromadora*. *B*. *Richtersia* *after Steiner*, 1916a). *C*. *Sabatieria*. (*A, C, after de Coninck and Stekhoven*, 1933.) *D*. Anterior end of *Epsilonema* (*after Steiner*, 1931). 1, cuticular ornamentations; 2, tubular copulatory aids; 3, spicule; 4, gubernaculum; 5, caudal glands; 6, duct of caudal glands; 7, adhesive tube; 8, amphid; 9, buccal capsule; 10, teeth; 11, pharynx.

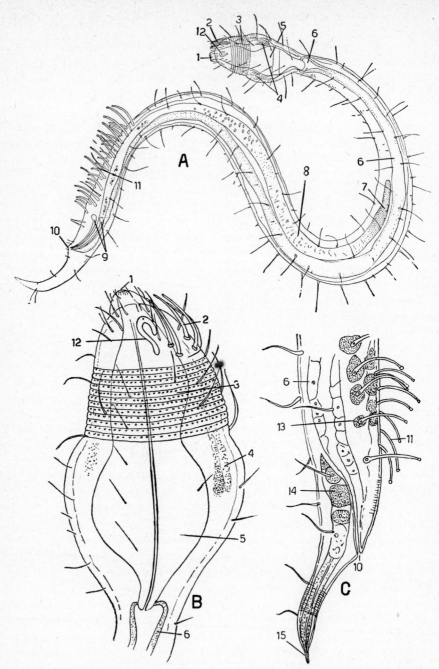

FIG. 138.—Chromadoroidea (concluded). *A*. A male draconematid. *B*. Head of same. *C*. Tail of female draconematid. (*A–C, after Irwin-Smith*, 1917.) 1, mouth; 2, anterior adhesive bristles; 3, ringed zone of head; 4, glands; 5, pharyngeal bulb; 6, intestine; 7, testis; 8, sperm duct; 9, spicules; 10, anus; 11, stilt bristles; 12, amphid; 13, glands of stilt bristles; 14, caudal glands; 15, adhesive tube.

bristles are arranged in two or four longitudinal rows situated ventrally directly in front of the anus (Fig. 138*A*). They are hollow, provided with adhesive glands (Fig. 138*C*), and together with the adhesive bristles of the head are employed by the worm to accomplish locomotion in a leech-like manner (Fig. 195*A*–*F*). The Epsilonematidae (= Rhabdogasteridae, magnificiently monographed by Steiner, 1931) carry the heavily ringed body bent into a shape resembling the Greek letter epsilon (Fig. 100*B*). The smooth, strongly cuticularized anterior end (Fig. 137*D*) bears the spiral amphids and two circlets of sensory bristles; the stilt bristles, here solid, are located just behind the middle body bend (Fig. 100*B*).

19. Order Araeolaimoidea.—This order was created by de Coninck and Stekhoven (1933) for several families characterized by four conspicuous cephalic bristles (Fig. 139) well set off from the labial circlets, which consist of papillae or reduced bristles. Other features are the spiral or loop-like amphids, the lack of cuticular ornamentation, and the absence of preanal copulatory aids. The Plectidae are fresh-water or terrestrial araeolaimoids with a very muscular pharyngeal end bulb; in this family may be mentioned *Plectus* with a long tubular buccal capsule (Fig. 140*A*) and *Wilsonema* (Cobb, 1914a) with strange cuticular expansions on the head, that reach great ◾omplication in *W. cephalatum* (Fig. 96*B*, *C*). The other families lack a pharyngeal bulb. In the Diplopeltidae, the amphids, shaped like a shepherd's crook, are mounted on cuticular shields. The Axonolaimidae, with smooth surface and normal amphids, include *Odontophora* with tooth-like plates in the buccal cavity, and *Axonolaimus* and *Araeolaimus* without such teeth; *Axonolaimus* is provided with the shepherd's crook type of amphid (Fig. 140*C*) and *Araeolaimus* has spiral amphids (Fig. 140*B*). The Camacolaimidae with principal genus *Camacolaimus* (Fig. 140*D*) are characterized by a finely ringed cuticle, spiral amphids shoved anteriorly among the cephalic bristles, and a spear-like thickening in the buccal wall. The Tripyloididae, a family hitherto of uncertain position, seem best placed under the Araeolaimoidea, although they differ from other families of this order in the well-developed external labial bristles; their amphids, however, are typically araeolaimoid, of loop form. The family has recently been monographed by Allgen (1947) who regards it as an araeolaimoid group transitional to Chromadoroidea. The chief tripyloid genera are *Bathylaimus* with two-chambered buccal capsule, and teeth in the posterior chamber (Fig. 141*C*), and *Tripyloides* with three- or four-chambered buccal capsule (Fig. 140*E*).

20. Order Monhysteroidea.—This order is characterized by the circular amphids; it includes aquatic and terrestrial, but mostly marine, nematodes with smooth or slightly ringed cuticle, often bearing scattered bristles, with single or double outstretched ovaries, and often with preanal papillae in males.   In the Cylindrolaimidae, the chief genus *Cylindrolaimus* (Fig. 141*D*) is a soil or fresh-water nematode with a long cylindrical buccal capsule.   *Siphonolaimus* (= *Anthraconema*, study by Zur Strassen, 1904), representing the Siphonolaimidae, marine, is characterized by the presence of a buccal stylet (Fig. 141*E*).   Members of *Sphaerolaimus*, main genus of the Sphaerolaimidae, are short, plump marine worms with head and body bristles and large, globose buccal capsule with lateral

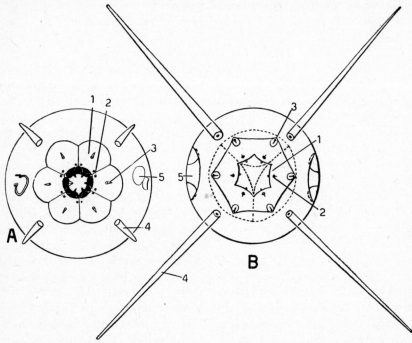

FIG. 139.—Araeolaimoidea.   *A, B*. Scheme of the araeolamoid head.   *A. Plectus. B. Ascolaimus.   (After de Coninck*, 1942.)   1, lips; 2, labial papillae; 3, outer labial bristles; 4, cephalic bristles; 5, amphids.

stiffenings and several subdivisions (Fig. 141*A*).   In the Limhomoeidae and Monhysteridae, the buccal capsule lacks special characteristics. The former family without lips and with amphid incompletely circular includes *Metalinhomoeus* with six labial papillae and four bristles, and *Paralinhomoeus* (Fig. 141*B*) and *Linhomeus* with all 16 head sense organs in the form of bristles.   In the Monhysteridae with six definite lips and oval or circular amphids, the chief genera are *Theristus* with slightly ringed cuticle and 10 head bristles (Fig. 142*D*) and *Monhystera* with smooth cuticle and mostly six head bristles (Fig. 194*A–C*).   Both *Theristus* and *Monhystera* may be provided with eyes.   *Steineria* is notable for the very long body bristles (Fig. 142*A*).

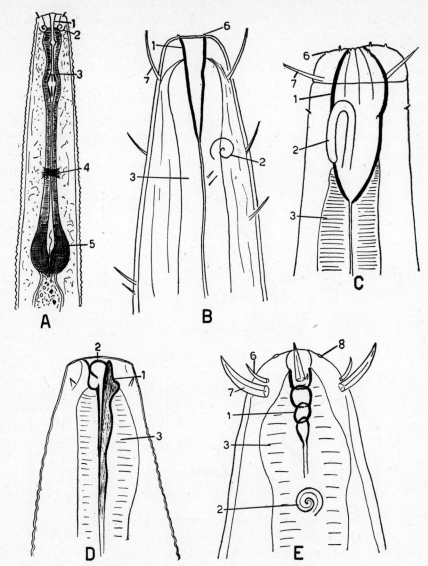

Fig. 140.—Araeolaimoidea (continued). *A. Plectus (after Hofmänner,* 1913). *B. Araeolaimus (after Steiner,* 1916a). *C. Axonolaimus (after Stekhoven and Adams,* 1931). *D. Camacolaimus (after de Man,* 1889). *E. Tripyloides (after de Coninck and* Stekhoven, 1933). 1, buccal capsule; 2, amphid; 3, pharynx; 4, nerve ring; 5, pharyngeal bulb; 6, outer labial bristles; 7, cephalic bristles; 8, labial papillae.

21. Order Desmoscolecoidea.—This order comprises a few short, plump, marine nematodes with heavily ringed and more or less bristly bodies, hemispherical amphids, and armored head (Fig. 142*B*) distinctly set off from the body and provided with four bristles; a differentiated

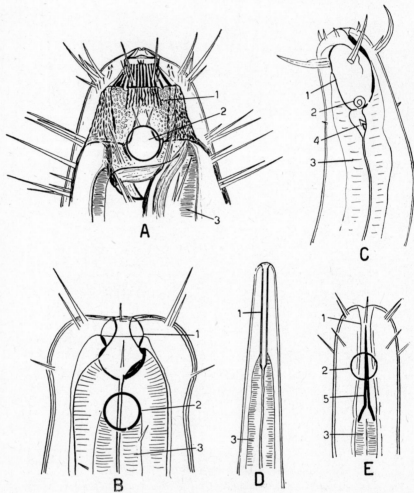

Fig. 141.—Araeolaimoidea (concluded), Monhysteroidea. *A. Sphaerolaimus. B. Paralinhomeus.* (*A, B, after de Man,* 1907.) *C. Bathylaimus* (*after de Coninck and Stekhoven,* 1933). *D. Cylindrolaimus* (*after Ditlevsen,* 1912). *E. Siphonolaimus* (*after de Man,* 1893). 1, buccal capsule; 2, amphid; 3, pharynx; 4, teeth; 5, spear.

buccal capsule is wanting. There are two families, the Desmoscolecidae and the Greeffiellidae. In the former (studies by Schepotieff, 1907; Chitwood, 1936; Kreis, 1934, 1938), the body is sparsely provided with bristles and the coarse annulation is therefore conspicuous, producing a

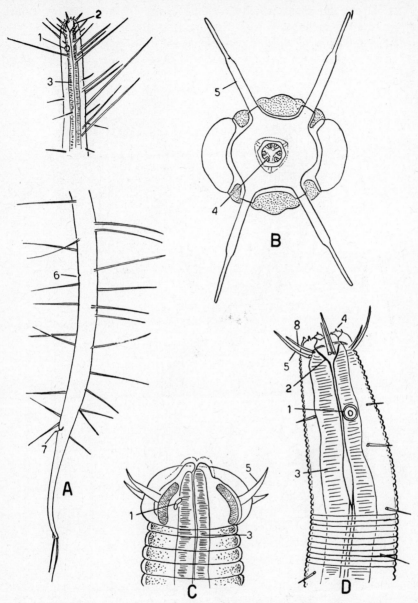

FIG. 142.—Monhysteroidea (concluded), Desmoscolecoidea. *A. Steineria (after Stek-hoven*, 1935). *B.* Scheme of the anterior end of *Desmoscolex (after de Coninck*, 1942). *C. Tricoma (after Kreis*, 1938). *D. Theristus (after de Coninck and Stekhoven*, 1933). 1, amphid; 2, buccal capsule; 3, pharynx; 4, labial papillae; 5, cephalic bristles; 6, vulva; 7, anus; 8, outer labial bristles.

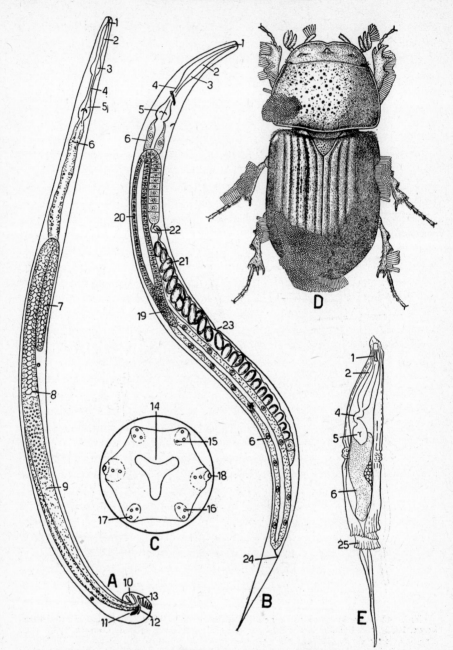

Fig. 143.—Rhabditoidea. *A. Rhabditis elegans*, male. *B. Rh. elegans*, female. (*A, B, after Maupas*, 1900.) *C.* Scheme of the anterior end of *Rhabditis* (*after de Coninck*, 1942). *D.* Dung beetle, *Aphodius*, with numerous attached ensheathed juveniles of *Rh. coarctata*. *E.* One of the ensheathed young. (*D, E, after Triffitt and Oldham*, 1927.)   1, buccal capsule; 2, corpus of pharynx; 3, median bulb; 4, isthmus; 5, end bulb; 6, intestine; 7, testis;

resemblance to an insect larva. The chief genera are *Desmoscolex* with alternating inflated and depressed body rings (Fig. 100*D*) and *Tricoma* with body rings all alike (Fig. 142*C*). In 1935, a species of *Desmoscolex* was reported from a Yugoslavian cave (Stammer, 1935), the first finding of a nonmarine desmoscolecid. The Greeffiellidae, with one genus *Greeffiella* (= *Trichoderma*) are clothed with bristles arranged in circlets attached to the rear borders of the annules (Fig. 100*E*).

22. Order Rhabditoidea or Anguilluloidea.—This is a large and important assemblage of small to moderately sized nematodes with the head sense organs all in the form of papillae and the amphids reduced to small pockets (Fig. 143*C*). The pharynx generally presents one or two bulbs, generally two, of which one is a pseudobulb and the other a valvulated bulb (Fig. 114*A*). Phasmids are present but caudal glands are wanting. The excretory system is usually symmetrical with or without two renette cells and with lateral and transverse canals. The female reproductive system is usually didelphic with reflexed ovaries (Fig. 143*B*) but not uncommonly monodelphic and lacks heavily muscled regions; in males caudal alae forming a bursa supported by genital papillae are often present (Fig. 102*E*). The spicules are equal and similar and accompanied by a gubernaculum (Fig. 102*E*). The life cycle may be direct but frequently includes an infective sheathed juvenile stage (*dauerlarva* of German workers, Fig. 143*E*), that requires to be transported in or on an invertebrate, usually an insect (Fig. 143*D*); sometimes development in an intermediate host is a necessary part of the life cycle. The rhabditoid nematodes are usually terrestrial, preferably dwelling in sites rich in organic decay, as decaying plants, decomposing animal carcasses, dung, compost piles, manure, etc., and for this reason are often easily cultivated on organic nutrients. From such saprophagous habits, transitions are easy to partial or complete phyto- or zooparasitism. Less frequently rhabditoids may be found living free in aquatic habitats.

In the family Rhabditidae (= Anguillulidae), the buccal wall is sclerotized in three distinct sections (Fig. 113*E*) but lacks teeth and the characteristic pharynx (rhabditoid or rhabdiform type) consists of a distal cylindrical part, the *corpus*, a median pseudobulb, then a narrowed region, the *isthmus*, and finally a valvulated end bulb (Fig. 114*A*). The genus *Rhabditis*, without head or body excrescences (Fig. 143*A*, *B*), has numerous species, many free-living, others with semiparasitic habits. Many that inhabit animal droppings have acquired the habit of utilizing coprophagous insects as vehicles for transport to new food supplies, and

---

8, sperm duct; 9, seminal vesicle; 10, bursa; 11, spicule; 12, gubernaculum; 13, papilla; 14, lips; 15, inner labial papillae; 16, outer labial papillae; 17, cephalic papillae; 18, amphid; 19, ovary; 20, oviduct; 21, uterus with eggs; 22, seminal receptacle; 23, vulva; 24, anus; 25, sheath (cuticle of second molt).

such transport is obligatory in some species. Thus the third-stage
juveniles of *Rhabditis coarctata* (Fig. 143*E*) cannot develop further unless
transported to fresh dung by dung beetles to whose body they adhere
(Fig. 143*D*) in the ensheathed state (Leuckart, 1891; Steiner, 1919;
Triffit and Oldham, 1927). They will not adhere to dead beetles. On
arrival at fresh dung, they emerge from their sheaths, enter the dung, and
there develop to sexual maturity. *Rh. mutatoria* is another coprophagous
species that uses dung bettles for transportation in juvenile stages
(Fuchs, 1937). Other *Rhabditis* species employ as transports dipterous
insects that feed on dung or rotting plant material (Aubertot, 1923a;
Menzel, 1924). In some *Rhabditis* species, the stage requiring transport
is morphologically distinct. Thus in *Rh. dubia* (Bovien, 1937), the entire
cycle may be passed in cow dung but at times special third-stage juveniles
appear that attach themselves to dung-feeding psychodid flies, winding
themselves around the intersegmental furrows of the flies and leaving
when the flies contact fresh dung. A step toward parasitism is seen in
Rh. obtusa (Fuchs, 1915, 1937) which lives and may pass its entire life
cycle in the debris in the tunnels of bark beetles. At times, however,
special third-stage juveniles, differing from the regular young in their
more slender shape, appear and these enter the hindgut of the beetles for
transport to new tunnels; they may reside in the beetle, showing growth
but no development, for considerable periods and may pass from the gut
into the haemocoel.

Invertebrates other than insects are also utilized by juvenile *Rhabditis*.
The best investigated form is *Rh. maupasi* (= *pellio*), the well-known
earthworm nematode (Johnson, 1913; Otter, 1933, Figs. 102*E*, 114*A*).
Active juveniles inhabit the nephridia or in the ensheathed state occur in
the brown bodies found posteriorly in the coelomic cavities but undergo
no development until the earthworm dies, whereupon the nematodes feed
on the carcass and attain maturity. *Rh. maupasi* usually breeds as a
protandric hermaphrodite, although males occur and copulations have
been witnessed. The young bred in the earthworm carcass wander
about and pass much time in the soil, repeatedly entering and leaving
earthworms by way of the nephridiopores, dorsal pores, or sex openings.
Rhabditid juveniles have repeatedly been found in terrestrial snails but
details of the cycles are unknown.

An epizoic habit, possibly semiparasitic, is exhibited by *Rh. ocypodis*,
habitually found on the gills of crabs (Chitwood, 1935).

Some other rhabditids worthy of mention are *Bunonema* with one or
two ventrolateral longitudinal rows of warty protuberances (Fig. 101*A*,
Jägerskiöld, 1905; Cobb, 1915) and *Diploscapter* with dorsal and ventral
digger hooks on the lips (Cobb, 1893; Steiner, 1921b, Fig. 194*D*, *E*). Both
genera are soil dwellers.

The small family Angiostomatidae resembles the Rhabditidae in the shape of the pharynx and the presence of a bursa formed of the caudal alae, supported by papillae, but differs in the absence of a valve in the end bulb. The family has been treated by Chitwood (1933) who notes species of *Angiostoma* in the intestine of the salamander *Plethodon* and in snails.

The family Cylindrocorpidae is characterized by the long slender buccal capsule, the absence of a distinct median bulb, and the presence of a nonvalvulated end bulb (Fig. 144C). Remarks on this family have been made by Chitwood (1933), Steiner (1933), and Goodey (1939); the latter showed the necessity of altering the former name Cylindrogasteridae. This family is mostly saprophagous or coprophagous (Goodey, 1927, 1930a, 1935) but one species is parasitic in the stomach of a snake (Chitwood, 1933).

In the Diplogasteridae, the short broad buccal capsule may be provided with one or more teeth and in the typical genus *Diplogaster*, with numerous species in damp soil and decaying material, there is a valvulated median bulb combined with a weak and glandular end pseudobulb (Fig. 115B). Some diplogasterids have acquired semiparasitic habits in relation to insects (Fig. 144A, B). Thus *D. butschlii* inhabits the galleries of bark beetles and as ensheathed juveniles attaches for transport under the elytra of the beetles (Fuchs, 1915, Fig. 144B); other species utilize dung and staphylinid beetles (Bovien, 1937). Such habits easily lead to invasion of internal organs and diplogasterid juveniles often crowd the intestine and haemocoel of beetles (Merrill and Ford, 1916; Bovien, 1937); a diplogasterid (*Pristionchus aerivora*, Fig. 148C) occurs in the head of termites (Merrill and Ford, 1916) and also in other insect material. These nematodes usually cause the death of the host, whereupon they feed and mature in the carcass; consequently they can be reared in cultures containing fragmented insects. *Cephalobium microbivorum* (Ackert and Wadley, 1921) is a true endoparasitic diplogasterid, inhabiting as adults the intestine of crickets; the eggs ejected in an early stage develop outside and presumably crickets become infested by ingesting juvenile stages.

In the family Cephalobidae, the elongated buccal capsule has a more or less chambered appearance; according to Thorne's analysis of this family (1937), there are two main types of buccal structure: the panagrolaimoid, with principal genus *Panagrolaimus*, in which only a short rear part of the capsule is narrowed and embraced by the pharynx (Fig. 45A), and the cephaloid type in which most of the capsule is so narrowed and embraced (Fig. 145B). In the latter group, the chief genera are *Cephalobus* (Fig. 145B) without and *Acrobeles* (monographed by Thorne, 1925) with probolae of various grades of complexity (Fig. 96E–G). The

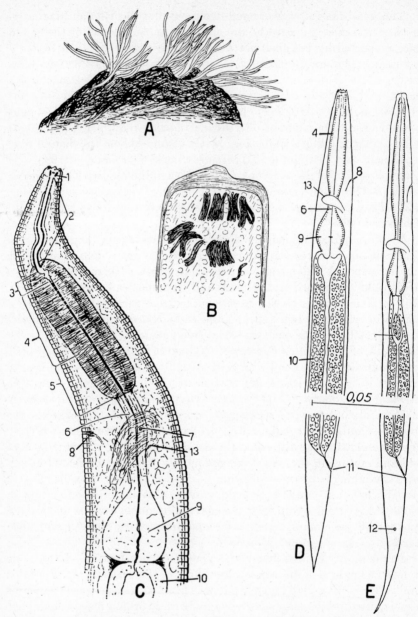

Fig. 144.—Rhabditoidea (continued). *A.* Infective juveniles of *Diplogaster*, extended on cow dung, awaiting arrival of a dung beetle (*after Bovien*, 1937). *B.* Underside of elytron of a bark beetle, with attached *Diplogaster bütschlii* juveniles (*after Fuchs*, 1915). *C. Cylindrocorpus* (*after Steiner*, 1933). *D, E.* Third-stage juveniles of *Neoaplectana bibionis* (*after Bovien*, 1937). *D.* Normal free-living type. *E.* Special infective type, requiring transportation. 1, cheilostom; 2, protostom; 3, telostom; 4, corpus of pharynx; 5, part corresponding to the median bulb; 6, isthmus; 7, cervical papilla; 8, excretory pore; 9, end bulb; 10, intestine; 11, anus; 12, phasmid; 13, nerve ring.

Cephalobidae generally live in soil in the vicinity of plant material or in the debris of insect burrows, etc. According to Goodey (1943b), the vinegar eel, formerly *Anguillula aceti*, favorite object of study of early microscopists, and related nematodes belong to the Cephalobidae. The name *Anguillula* is considered invalid by Peters (1927), although still accepted by some nematodologists; he proposed *Turbatrix* for the vinegar eel and later Goodey (1945) placed the species *redivivus*, found in sour paste, in the genus *Panagrellus*. Related forms occur in the exudations ("slime flux") of oak trees (de Man, 1910) and in the felt mats placed under beer mugs in certain parts of Germany (de Man, 1914). The anatomy of *Turbatrix aceti* has been described by de Man (1910) and Peters (1927). The worms, to 2.4 mm. in length, are of smooth slender shape with a long pointed tail. They are so permeated with fat globules as to hinder observation of internal structure. The mouth is encircled by six minute papillae and leads into a cuticularized buccal capsule of three successive chambers of which the second is provided with three ridges and the third with three small teeth (Fig. 145*D*). The pharynx (Fig. 145*E*) lacks a distinct median bulb and terminates in a true end bulb. The reproductive system is single in both sexes, extending anteriorly and there reflexed; the male lacks caudal alae and has five pairs of very small genital papillae. The females are ovoviviparous, producing up to 45 young, and live up to 10 months. Although found only in old vinegar, the vinegar eel appears not to require a highly acid medium and may be cultivated on rotting fruits and vegetables.

The Steinernematidae are characterized by the degeneration of the buccal capsule, the lack of a distinct median bulb, and the weak valvulation of the end bulb (Fig. 144*D*, *E*). The best known genus is *Neoaplectana*, semiparasitic in insects. *N. glaseri* (Steiner, 1929b) has attracted attention as a possible agent of control of the Japanese beetle. Like other rhabditoids already mentioned, this nematode is a facultative parasite; it may complete its cycle repeatedly in insect carcasses but in the absence of adequate food supplies produces a special third-stage infective juvenile, lacking in the nonparasitic cycle, and this requires entry into a Japanese beetle larva or adult or other insects (Glaser, 1932; Glaser, McCoy, and Girth, 1940). These infective juveniles may live at least 18 months in the soil without food. After ingestion by a suitable host, they develop in the host's digestive tract to sexually mature worms that copulate. The females are ovoviviparous, usually producing about 15 young. The host generally dies and the young nematodes then feed and develop in its carcass. *N. glaseri* is cultivable in artificial media (see later) and the infective stage can be evoked by withdrawing food. More typical rhabditoid cycles are exhibited by *N. bibionis* (Fig. 144*D*, *E*) and *N. affinis* in which the infective stage adheres to flies of the genus

Bibio but development to maturity usually occurs only in insect carcasses where the whole cycle may be passed with omission of the infective stage (Bovien, 1937).

The family Tylenchidae is characterized by the presence of a conspicuous buccal stylet or spear and by the asymmetrical form of the excretory system with canals on one side only. In recent years there has been evident a tendency to make a separate order of this family and raise its subfamilies to the rank of family (see Throne, 1949). While such an arrangement will probably stand, we here retain the family Tylenchidae in a broad sense. The tylenchids or tylenchoids include the most important phytoparasitic nematodes and these are treated at length in Filipjev and Stekhoven's *Agricultural Helminthology*. These phytoparasites feed by piercing plant tissues and cells with their spear and sucking out the juices. As they occur in vast numbers and as the objects of their attacks are frequently plants of great economic or esthetic importance, a voluminous literature has accumulated concerning them. It is possible here to mention only the most prominent species. The tylenchid pharynx is characterized by a median muscular bulb and a posterior glandular swelling and is divided by Filipjev and Stekhoven into two types: the *tylenchoid*, in which the glandular swelling forms a compact bulb (Fig. 114*C*) and the *aphelenchoid* in which it projects backward as a lobe over the anterior part of the intestine (Fig. 114*B*). This usage does not correspond with that of Thorne (1949). In some tylenchids the dorsal pharyngeal gland opens at the base of the spear and in others into the median bulb. Some genera with the tylenchoid type of pharynx are *Tylenchus* (= *Anguillulina*), *Ditylenchus*, and *Anguina*. Species of *Tylenchus* (Fig. 114*C*) are mostly soil inhabitants where they feed on fungi and other plants; the common and widespread *T. davainei* is usually associated with mosses and liverworts. *Ditylenchus dipsaci*, the stem-and-bulb eelworm, is an important phytoparasite, attacking a large number of plants, among them rye, oats and other grasses, clover and alfalfa, as well as numerous bulbs such as those of lilies, hyacinths, onions, gladiolus, and narcissi (Fig. 146*B*). In the genus *Anguina* may be mentioned *A. agrostis* that produces galls in the inflorescences of grasses, and *A. tritici*, the wheat-gall nematode, that transforms wheat grains into galls (Fig. 145*F–J*). These galls contain dormant juveniles that as the galls soften and decay in the spring rains escape and migrate in the soil to new wheat plants. They enter the developing inflorescence, evoking galls within which they develop to maturity, breed, and produce young.

Some phytoparasitic genera with the aphelenchoid type of pharynx are *Rotylenchus*, *Aphelenchus*, *Aphelenchoides*, and *Heterodera*. *Rotylenchus similis* is an important plant pest in tropical and subtropical

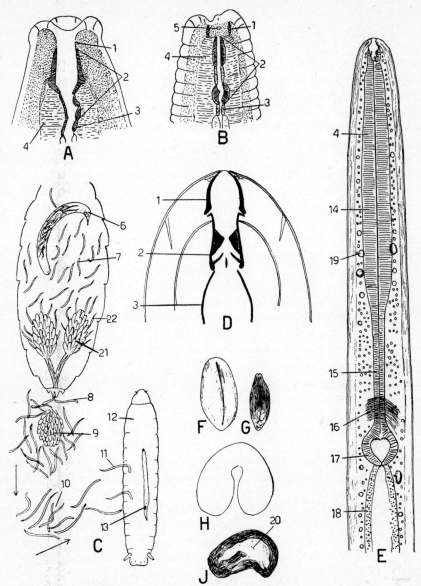

Fig. 145.—Rhabditoidea (continued). *A. Panagrolaimus. B. Cephalobus.* (*A, B, after Thorne,* 1937.) *C.* Cycle of *Scatonema Wülkeri* in fly (*after Bovien,* 1937). *D.* Buccal capsule of *Turbatrix aceti. E.* Anterior end of *Turbatrix aceti.* (*D, E, after de Man,* 1910.) *F–J.* Work of the wheat gall nematode, *Anguina tritici* (*after Byars,* 1920). *F.* Normal wheat grain. *G.* Infested wheat grain. *H.* Section through a normal grain. *J.* Section through infested grain (gall) showing interior mass of nematodes. 1, cheilostom; 2, protostom; 3, telostom; 4, pharynx; 5, amphid; 6, mature female nematode in fly; 7, young produced by 6; 8, young emerging with egg mass; 9, egg mass; 10, free-living adults; 11, impregnated females enter fly larva; 12, fly larva; 13, enlarged female in fly larva; 14, corpus of pharynx; 15, isthmus; 16, nerve ring; 17, end bulb; 18, intestine; 19, fat globules; 20, mass of nematodes; 21, fly ovary; 22, nematodes entering ovary.

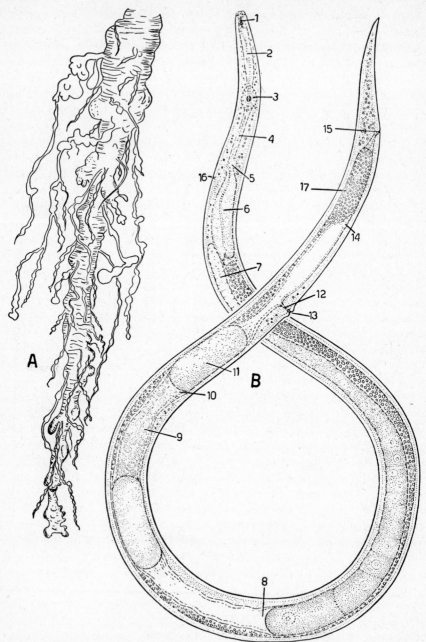

Fig. 146.—Rhabditoidea, tylenchoids. *A.* Root of parsnip, infected with galls of *Heterodera marioni* (*after Atkinson*, 1889). *B.* The stem-and-bulb eelworm, *Ditylenchus dipsaci* (*after Thorne*, 1945). 1, stylet; 2, corpus; 3, median bulb; 4, isthmus; 5, nerve ring; 6, glandular part of pharynx; 7, anterior ovary; 8, oviduct; 9, seminal receptacle with sperm; 10, uterus; 11, egg in uterus; 12, vagina; 13, vulva; 14, abortive posterior ovary; 15, anus; 16, excretory pore; 17, intestine.

countries, attacking the roots of coffee, tea, banana, pepper, sweet potato, pineapple, and other food plants. *Aphelenchus avenae* occurs on the roots of a number of plants, but apparently chiefly in association with fungus infections. Of the many species of *Aphelenchoides* may be mentioned: *A. cocophilus* which produces a diseased ring in the trunk of the coconut and other palms; *A. olesistus*, causing brown spots on the leaves of ferns; *A. fragariae*, causative agent of the bunch disease of strawberries, characterized by stunting and dwarfing of the plants; and *A. ritzemabosi*, the chrysanthemum eelworm, whose infestations are very destructive.

The genus *Heterodera* (broad sense) contains the most important phytoparasitic nematodes and those showing the greatest alteration for a parasitic existence and the highest degree of sexual dimorphism. Penetration of the host plant is effected by second-stage juveniles that pierce and suck cell contents and usually evoke a gall, dwelling therein to sexual maturity. With successive molts, generally three, the females become more and more plump, eventually assuming a pyriform, gourd, or lemon shape (Fig. 147*A–C, E*); they remain in the gall or may partially protrude from it. They mature 200 to 500 eggs or more and then degenerate, leaving their cuticle (plus in some species a gelatinous exudation) as a protective cyst for the eggs. These cysts become free in the soil by disintegration of affected parts of the plant host and remain viable for long periods, withstanding adverse conditions. Within them development occurs to second-stage juveniles that escape into the soil where they may live for many months without feeding. The males in their development also pass through three additional molts but retain a typical nematode appearance (Fig. 147*D, H*). They usually escape from the parent gall and wander through the soil to find and fertilize females on other plants, thereupon dying.

The principal species of *Heterodera* are *schachtii*, *rostochiensis*, and *marioni* (= *radicicola*). *H. schachtii*, the sugar-beet eelworm, attacks mainly sugar beets but also a variety of other plants of the families Chaenopodiaceae and Cruciferae. The female (Fig. 93*F*) partially protrudes from the gall when mature (being then inseminated by the male, shown in Fig. 147*H*), and secretes from the vulva a gelatinous material or egg sac into which some of the eggs are extruded (Fig. 147*F*) and which forms part of the cyst (Fig. 147*G*). Accounts of the life cycle have been given by Strubbel (1888) and Thorne and Giddings (1922), and the morphology is treated by Triffitt (1928). *H. rostochiensis*, the golden potato eelworm, attacks chiefly this plant throughout the world and is highly injurious, as up to 40,000 nematodes may occur on the roots of one potato plant. The life cycle is similar to that of *H. schachtii*, of which *H. rostochiensis* is regarded as a variety by some workers. The

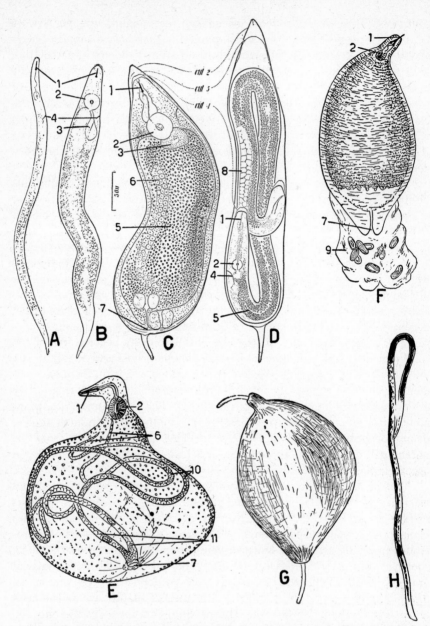

FIG. 147.—Rhabditoidea, tylenchoids. *A–D.* Root-knot nematode, *Heterodera marioni* (*after Christie and Cobb,* 1931). *A.* Second-stage female. *B.* Third-stage female. *C.* Fourth-stage female. *D.* Fourth-stage male inside third cuticle. *E.* Mature female, *H. marioni* (*after Atkinson,* 1889). *F. Heterodera schachtii,* female exuding egg mass (*after Strubbel,* 1888). *G.* Mature "cyst" of *H. schachtii,* with young escaping. *H.* Mature male, *H. schachtii.* (*G, H, after Thorne,* 1922.) 1, spear; 2, median bulb of pharynx; 3, glandular pharynx; 4, excretory duct; 5, intestine; 6, ovary; 7, vulva; 8, testis; 9, egg mass; 10, oviduct; 11, uterus.

root-knot eelworm, *H. marioni,* inhabits galls that it evokes on the roots
(Fig. 146*A*) of a great variety of plants (850 species, according to Buhrer,
1933). Life cycle studies have been made by Christie and Cobb (1941)
and Tyler (1944). Roots are penetrated by second-stage juveniles; the
galls, which may reach a diameter of an inch, are inhabited by all stages
of the nematode (Christie, 1936). The gourd-shaped female (Fig. 147*E*)
deposits in the gall or in the adjacent soil a gelatinous mass containing
500 to 1000 eggs, so that in this species the female body does not become
a cyst for the eggs. On account of this fact, Chitwood has recently
(1949) proposed to remove this species from the genus *Heterodera* and
has revived for it the genus *Meloidogyne.* The taxonomic tangles thus
involved cannot be considered here. The males of *marioni* usually
emerge from the galls and seek females elsewhere but *marioni* females
are regularly parthenogenetic (Tyler, 1933).

An interesting fact about the phytoparasitic tylenchids is that they
often occur in a number of biological strains or races. These strains are
morphologically indistinguishable but often those attacking one kind of
plant will not penetrate the roots of other plant sorts that are hosts to
other strains, or else will survive only temporarily therein (Steiner, 1925;
Hodson, 1931; Goodey, 1931a; Christie and Albin, 1944).

There are also some tylenchids that parasitize insects to varying
degrees. Species of *Tylenchus* inhabit the galleries of bark beetles and
may seek transportation on the bodies or under the elytra of these
beetles (Fuchs, 1915). A whole series of forms formerly placed in the
genus *Aphelenchus* also lives in association with bark and other beetles
(Fuchs, 1929, 1930, 1937, 1938) and juveniles inhabit the haemocoel or
Malpighian tubules of such beetles although complete cycles have not
been worked out.

Included in the Tylenchidae is the subfamily Criconematinae, extensively treated by Taylor (1936). The criconematines are free-living soil
inhabitants but are usually found around the roots of plants. They have
annulated bodies and the annules are heavily developed in the genera
Criconema and *Criconemoides.* *Criconema* (= *Ogma, Iota*) is of morphological interest because of the teeth or scales projecting caudad from the
posterior edge of each annule (Figs. 101*C*, 148*A, B*) and arranged in
eight longitudinal rows.

The family Allantonematidae of uncertain relationships differs from
the Tylenchidae in the degeneration of the pharynx musculature. The
members of this family have a parasitic phase in insects and a free-living
phase in plants attacked by the insect hosts. The impregnated female
nematode penetrates the larval stage of the insect host and dwells in the
haemocoel, there producing ovoviviparously numerous young of both
sexes. At the time of host egg laying, these young nematodes exit by

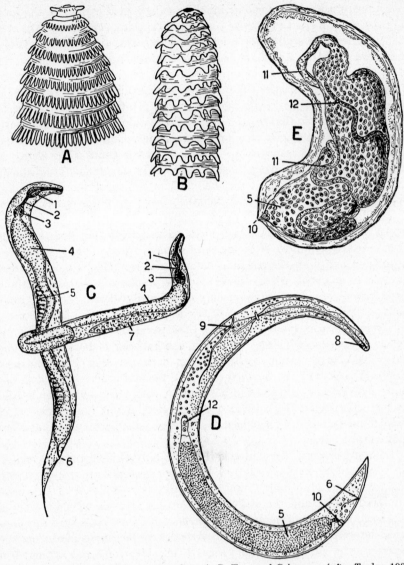

Fig. 148.—Rhabditoidea (continued). *A, B.* Types of *Criconema* (*after Taylor*, 1936). *C. Pristionchus aerivora* in copulation (*after Merrill and Ford*, 1916). *D.* Free-living impregnated female of *Allantonema mirabile* (*after Wülker*, 1923). *E.* Same, after becoming parasitic (*after Leuckart*, 1887). 1, median bulb; 2, isthmus; 3, end bulb; 4, intestine; 5, uterus; 6, anus; 7, testis; 8, spear; 9, excretory duct; 10, vulva; 11, oviduct; 12, ovary.

way of the anus or female gonopore into the plant tissues parasitized by the host's larvae where they attain sexual maturity (Fig. 145*C*). The males die after inseminating the females and the latter penetrate host larvae where they undergo considerable alteration, losing their digestive tract and becoming distended into a sausage or oval shape by the expanded uterus full of developing young (Fig. 148*D*, *E*). Detailed life histories are known for only a few allantonematids. *Tylenchinema oscinellae* (Goodey, 1930c, 1931b) inhabits as adult impregnated females the haemocoel of the frit fly, usually bringing about an inhibition of the reproductive system of the host. The nematodes give birth to numerous young that, after undergoing considerable growth, pass from the haemocoel into the host digestive tract and are deposited by way of the host anus into oat panicles parasitized by the fly. Here the nematodes live with the fly larvae in the damaged plant tissues until sexually mature; the males die after impregnating the females, and the latter enter fly larvae, probably penetrating the body wall. Similar cycles obtain for *Allantonema mirabile* (Fig. 148*D*), parasitic in the haemocoel of the pine weevil (Wülker, 1923; Bovien, 1937); *Scatonema wülkeri* (Fig. 145*C*) in the haemocoel of the fly *Scatopse fuscipes* (Bovien, 1932); and *Howardula benigna* in cucumber beetles (Cobb, 1921). In the first, the extreme alteration of the parasitic female into an oval sac containing only the reproductive system (Fig. 148*E*) is noteworthy. The life cycle of *Scatonema* differs in that the parasitic larvae enter the reproductive tract and pass out with the eggs (Fig. 145*C*). The males of *Scatonema* lack the stylet and pharyngeal glands conspicuously present in the female. The life cycle of *Chondronema passali* found in the haemocoel of the horned *Passalus* beetle differs from the typical allantonematid cycle in that only the juvenile stages occur in the host beetle; the adults lead a free existence in the galleries in decaying wood occupied by all stages of the beetle. The female nematode, however, shows the same degenerative changes as do other allantonematid females.

More complicated cycles with the interpolation of one or more parthenogenetic generations occur in some allantonematids. *Fergusobia curriei* lives in galls of the flower and leaf buds of *Eucalyptus* evoked by the larvae of the fly *Fergusonina*. In these galls, the nematodes breed parthenogenetically until autumn when males appear and two adult fertilized female nematodes penetrate into female fly larvae (never males) and dwell in the haemocoel, producing a large number of young worms that pass into the reproductive system of the fly host and are deposited into the host plant along with fly eggs (Currie, 1937). *Heterotylenchus aberrans* parasitizes the onion fly whose larvae are a serious pest of onions in Denmark (Bovien, 1937). Fertilized female worms in infected flies give rise to smaller females that lay parthenogenetic eggs in the host haemocoel. These hatch into juveniles of both sexes that when nearly grown escape to the exterior by way of the host's reproductive tract. Males die after fertilizing the females and these enter larval onion flies. In this species, both male and female flies are parasitized but apparently the nematodes are unable to escape from male hosts.

A small group of allantonematids belonging to the subfamily Sphaerulariinae are characterized by the fact that in the parasitic female the uterus gradually everts through the vulva forming a large protrusion in which the eggs develop and which also usually contains the intestine altered into a food reservoir. The known species of this group are *Sphaerularia bombi* in queen bumblebees (Leuckart, 1885, 1886a, 1887) in which the everted uterus has a tubular shape (Fig. 149*A, B*), *Tripius* (= *Aproctonema*) *gibbosus* in the fly *Cecidomyia pini* (Leuckart, 1886b, 1887) with a sacciform protrusion (Fig. 149*C–E*), and *Proatractonema sciarae* in the larvae of sciarid flies (Bovien, 1944). The sphaerulariine nematodes have a typical allantonematid life cycle: the parasitic female inhabits the host haemocoel, gives rise to numerous juveniles that enter the soil and there develop to adults that copulate, and the impregnated female penetrates the host insect.

23. Order Rhabdiasoidea.—The members of this order are frequently placed under the Rhabditoidea which they resemble anatomically but their complicated life cycles and adoption of vertebrate hosts constitute grounds for separating them into a distinct order. As in the case of many rhabditoids described above, the life cycle includes parasitic and free-living phases but differs in that the parasitic form is either a protandrous hermaphrodite or a parthenogenetic female. The eggs from this hatch to free-living young which may develop directly into the parasitic form, in which case the cycle is said to be direct or *homogonic;* or they may develop into free-living males and females, the offspring of which proceed to the parasitic phase so that the cycle is then indirect or *heterogonic.* In this direct cycle males are altogether wanting. The order includes two families, the Rhabdiasidae, parasitic in the lungs of amphibians and reptiles, and the Strongyloididae, in the intestine of mammals.

The essential features of the rhabdiasoid life cycle were discovered in 1865 by Metschnikov and Leuckart, working with *Rhabdias bufonis* (= *Rhabditis nigrovenosa*), the familiar lung nematode of frogs and other amphibians. This worm lives in the lungs as a protandrous hermaphrodite (Fig. 150*A, F*) with the structure of a female; the sperm produced in the early and evanescent male phase of the reproductive system are stored in a seminal receptacle. The developing eggs pass into the host's buccal cavity and thence are swallowed into the digestive tract where they hatch into rhabdiform young, so called because of the rhabditoid form of their pharynx (Fig. 150*B*). These young accumulate in the cloaca and exit in the feces, developing in contaminated soil into free males and females (Fig. 150*D*, *E*). The females after impregnation produce viviparously filariform young (i.e., with a long tubular pharynx lacking bulbs, Fig. 150*C*) that devour the contents of their mother and

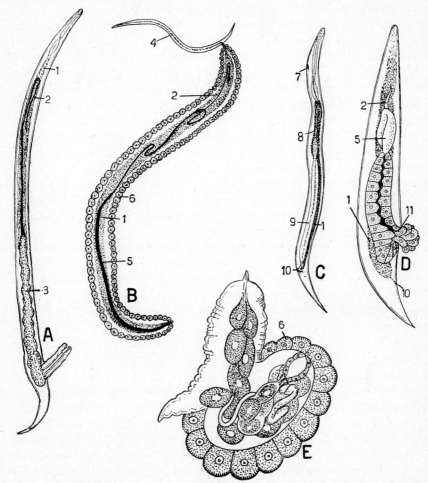

FIG. 149.—Rhabditoidea, Allantonematidae. *A, B. Sphaerularia bombi.* *A.* Female with beginning uterine eversion. *B.* Eversion completed. *C–E. Tripius gibbosus.* *C.* Male. *D.* Young female with beginning eversion of the intestine. *E.* Mature female; everted intestine forms a sac containing the reproductive system. (*All after Leuckart,* 1887.) 1, intestine; 2, ovary; 3, uterus; 4, remains of original worm; 5, oviduct; 6, uterus turned inside out; 7, excretory duct; 8, testis; 9, seminal vesicle; 10, anus; 11, vulva.

then escape as infective ensheathed juveniles. These require penetration into frogs for their further development. They penetrate the skin (Fülleborn, 1928), enter the lymph channels, and from these lodge in various organs; but only those that gain the lungs achieve maturity.

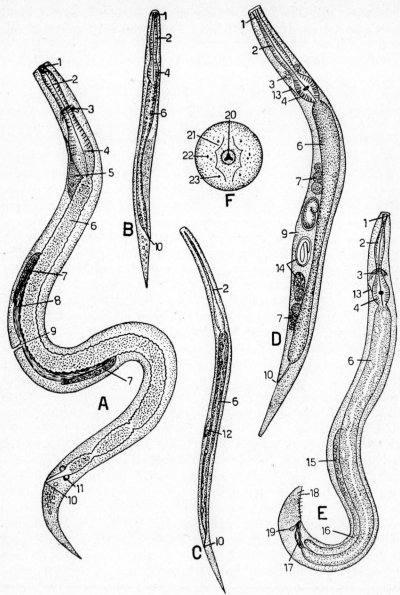

Fɪɢ. 150.—Rhabdiasoidea, *Rhabdias.* *A–E. Rhabdias bufonis (after Metschnikoff,* 1865). *A.* Parasitic female. *B.* Rhabdiform young. *C.* Filariform young. *D.* Free-living female. *E.* Free-living male. *F.* Scheme of the anterior end *(after Chu,* 1936). (*A* should be twice as large relative to the others.) 1, buccal capsule; 2, pharynx; 3, nerve ring; 4, end bulb; 5, renette cell; 6, intestine; 7, ovary; 8, uterus; 9, vulva; 10, anus; 11, anal glands; 12, primordium of reproductive system; 13, excretory duct; 14, embryos in uteri; 15, testis; 16, sperm duct; 17, spicules; 18, genital papillae; 19, gubernaculum; 20, mouth; 21, lips; 22, amphids; 23, external circlet of papillae.

The infective juveniles may also use snails as transport hosts. A similar heterogonic cycle obtains for *R. fülleborni* in the lungs of toads (Travassos, 1926).

The cycle of a reptilian rhabdiasoid is exemplified by *Rhabdias* and its varieties from the lungs of garter and other snakes (Goodey, 1924; Chu, 1936). Here the rhabdiform young produced by the parasitic hermaphrodites develop in soil to ensheathed infective juveniles (also rhabdiform) or occasionally under favorable conditions to a few free-living males and females that in turn give rise to similar infective young. The infective juveniles after ingestion by snakes migrate through the host tissues to the lungs. Whereas it is probable that any species of *Rhabdias* may employ either the homogonic or heterogonic type of life cycle, it appears that the latter dominates in species parasitizing amphibians and the former in those employing snake hosts.

The Rhabdiasidae also include the genus *Entomelas*, differing from *Rhabdias* in that the parasitic phase is a parthenogenetic female. The cycle of *E. dujardinii* in the lungs of the blindworm *Anguis* (amphibian) includes free-living males and females; the latter after impregnation give birth to rhabdiform young that devour them and become ensheathed infective juveniles. These probably employ snails and earthworms as transport hosts that are eaten by *Anguis* (Seurat, 1920).

The chief representative of the family Strongyloididae is *Strongyloides stercoralis*, an intestinal parasite of man and other mammals, in tropical and subtropical countries. The main features of the life cycle of this worm were elucidated by Grassi in 1878 and Leuckart in 1882 and numerous studies on this parasite have since appeared (Van Durme, 1902; Looss, 1905; Leichtenstern, 1905; Fülleborn, 1914, 1927; Sandground, 1926; Nishigori, 1928; Faust, 1933, 1935). The parasitic phase, living more or less embedded in the intestinal mucosa, consists of parthenogenetic females (Fig. 151*D*). Their eggs hatch in the host to rhabdiform young (Fig. 151*C*) that are voided with the feces and develop in contaminated soil either into unsheathed infective filariform juveniles (Fig. 151*B*) or into free-living rhabdiform males and females (Fig. 151*A*) whose rhabdiform young grow into infective filariform juveniles indistinguishable from those produced in the homogonic cycle. The infective juveniles creep to favorable elevations where they await contact with the skin of the host through which they penetrate. Obviously, barefoot humans walking about in areas infested with this parasite are liable to penetration; infection can also occur through the mouth cavity. After penetration into the host the juveniles enter the circulatory system and are carried to the lungs. Here they undergo a certain amount of development and such later stages migrate up the trachea to the pharynx whence they are swallowed, eventually reaching the intestine.

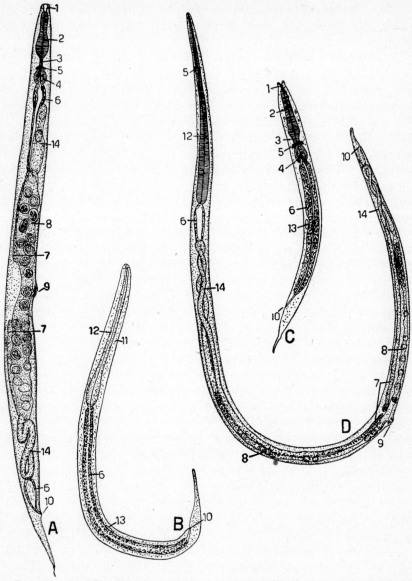

Fig. 151.—Rhabdiasoidea, *Strongyloides*. *A–D, Strongyloides ransomi (after Schwartz and Alicata*, 1930).   *A.* Free-living female, 1 mm. long.   *B.* Filariform young.   *C.* Rhabdiform young.   *D.* Parasitic female, 4 mm. long.   1, buccal capsule; 2, corpus; 3, isthmus; 4, end bulb; 5, nerve ring; 6, intestine; 7, ovary; 8, uterus; 9, vulva; 10, anus; 11, excretory duct; 12, pharynx; 13, reproductive primordium; 14, oviduct.

Much study has been expended on the question of what factors determine whether the life cycle of *Strongyloides stercoralis* (and other rhabdiasoids) shall be homogonic or heterogonic. The status of this question to date was reviewed by Sandground (1926), who concluded that the type of cycle is independent of external factors and is fixed in early stages of development. He failed, however, by means of selection to produce strains that would reproduce exclusively by one or the other method, but noted that the mode of development could be altered by breeding in an unusual host. In a series of studies on *Strongyloides ratti* in the rat, Graham (1936–1939) maintained homogonic and heterogonic strains by infecting rats with single juveniles of each type. Each strain produced predominantly juveniles of its own type but did give rise to some juveniles of the other type. The yield of heterogonic forms in homogonic strains was related to season, being greater in spring and summer and declining in fall and winter; the factors involved are apparently temperature and humidity acting on the rat host and so affecting the constitution of the eggs of the parasitic females. Inherent differences between the heterogonic and homogonic strains were demonstrated; thus the heterogonic females were more prolific and produced a much higher percentage of males than the homogonic ones but the latter have a longer reproductive life. Juveniles from the heterogonic strain were more successful in infecting rats than were homogonic juveniles. Later (1940) Graham studied a homogonic line derived from the heterogonic line and found that its characteristics closely resembled the latter. The preponderance of the evidence indicates that the type of life cycle is determined by genetic factors in the eggs of the parasitic females, but external factors may play some role as shown by Beach's studies on *Strongyloides simiae* in monkeys (1936), grown in various culture media. The poorer the osmotic and nutritional properties of the medium, the greater was the tendency for the rhabdiform juveniles to develop into infective filariform juveniles rather than into sexual adults; whereas favorable media produced exclusively free-living sexual forms. Every species of *Strongyloides* appears capable of reproducing by either the homogonic or the heterogonic method.

Cases of autoinfection by *S. stercoralis* in man, that is, of the development of juveniles directly into parasitic females within the host intestine without passage to the exterior, have been reported by Nishigori (1928) and Faust and De Groat (1940).

The claim of some authors that the parasitic females of *Strongyloides* are hermaphroditic rather than parthenogenetic appears to be discredited at the present time, and was definitely disproved for *S. ratti*, one of the species involved in this claim, by Chitwood and Graham (1940).

Some other species of *Strongyloides* of economic importance are

S. ransomi in swine (Fig. 151) and *S. papillosus* in sheep.   The life cycle of the former, investigated by Schwartz and Alicata (1930) and Lucker (1934), is identical with that of *S. stercoralis* except that the eggs of the parasitic generation hatch only after passage to the exterior.   In *S. papillosus*, males are very rare in the free-living generation (Ransom, 1911) and possibly the eggs of the free-living female develop parthenogenetically.

24. Order Oxyuroidea.—The members of this order are obligatory zooparasites, chiefly of vertebrates, with simple life cycle, involving only one host.   They are small to medium worms of fusiform shape with a long slender pointed tail in the female, sometimes also in the male.   The head organs are reduced to papillae, usually present in one circle of 8 or 10, and the amphids are represented by tubular pockets (Fig. 152*A*). There are generally three or six simple lips.   The buccal capsule, small and often devoid of cuticularized specializations, leads into a rhabdiform pharynx provided with a conspicuous valvulated end bulb and often also with a differentiated corpus or median bulb and isthmus (Fig. 152*B, C*).   The excretory system is of the H-type without accompanying renette cells.   The monodelphic or didelphic female system (Fig. 152*D*) often shows heavy muscularization of its terminal portions.   The eggs are generally of simple oval contour with a relatively thin shell.   Oviparity obtains and the ovic juveniles usually do not hatch until swallowed by an appropriate host.   Spicules are sometimes wanting but usually males are provided with one spicule or two equal spicules, also with genital papillae, often accompanied by caudal alae.

The Thelastomatidae with eight simple papillae in the external circlet (Fig. 152*A*) and one copulatory spicule or none in the male are parasites of the digestive tract of insects and some other arthropods.   Leading papers on this family are those of Christie (1931) and Chitwood (1932). The life cycle is best known for *Leidynema appendiculata* (Fig. 152*D*) found in the intestine of cockroaches (Dobrovolny and Ackert, 1934). The eggs laid by this nematode would not hatch in several media tried and are not infective until the contained embryo develops to an advanced stage.   Such ovic juveniles hatch in the midgut of the roach and develop to adults of both sexes.   In *Aorurus*, in millipedes and scarabaeid beetle larvae (Fig. 152*C*) and *Hammerschmidtiella* (Fig. 153*A*), in cockroaches, the female pharynx presents a pronounced median pseudobulb in addition to the end bulb.   In *Leidynema* (Fig. 152*D*), with several species in cockroaches, there is a well-indicated corpus, also an intestinal diverticulum.   The pharynx is uniformly cylindrical in the other genera to be mentioned except for a slight isthmus in front of the end bulb.   *Thelastoma* (Fig. 152*B*), with two ovaries and slender tail in both sexes, parasitizes cockroaches and scarabaeid beetle larvae; *Blatticola*, with one ovary and conical tail in both sexes, has one species *blattae* in the intestine

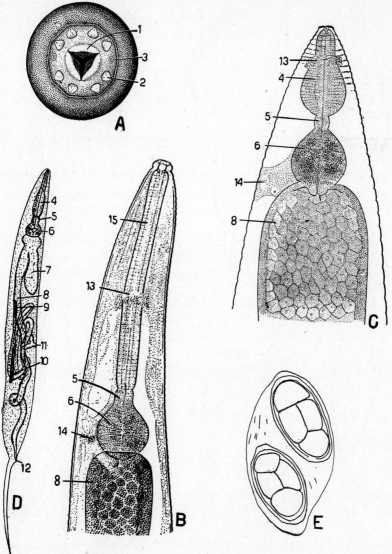

FIG. 152.—Oxyuroidea. *A. En face* view of anterior tip of *Thelastoma.* *B.* Anterior region of *Thelastoma.* *C.* Anterior region of *Aorurus.* (*A, B, C, after Christie,* 1931.) *D. Leidynema appendiculata (after Dobrovolny and Ackert,* 1934). *E.* Two embryos of *Binema* in a capsule (*after Travassos,* 1925). 1, lip; 2, sensory papilla; 3, amphid; 4, median bulb of pharynx; 5, isthmus; 6, end bulb; 7, intestinal caecum; 8, intestine; 9, anterior ovary; 10, posterior ovary; 11, vulva; 12, anus; 13, nerve ring; 14, excretory pore; 15, pharynx.

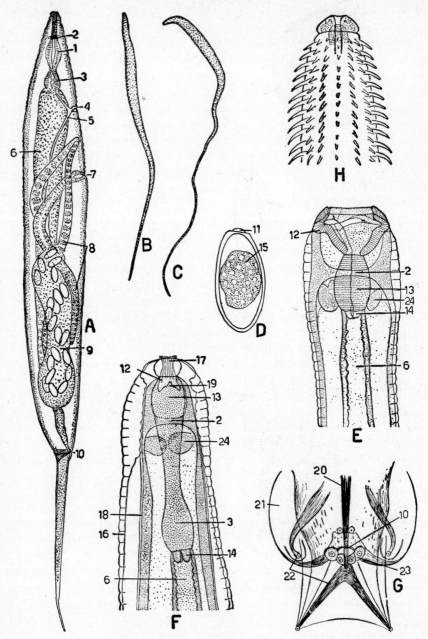

Fig. 153.—Oxyuroidea (continued). *A. Hammerschmidtiella diesingi* (*after Chitwood*, 1932). *B, C.* Short- and long-tailed females of *Oxyuris equi*. *D.* Embryo of *Oxyuris equi*. (*B, C, D, after Schwartz*, 1923.) *E.* Fourth-stage juvenile of *Oxyuris equi*. *F.* Same, molting to adult female. (*E, F, after Ihle and Van Oordt*, 1921.) *G.* Male tail of *Oxyuris equi* (*after Ehlers*, 1899). *H. Hystrignathus* (*after Christie*, 1934). 1, median bulb of pharynx;

of roaches; and *Scarabanema*, similar to *Thelastoma*, but with smaller amphidial openings and more posterior excretory pore, also occurs in scarabaeid beetle grubs. The life cycle of *Blatticola blattae* was investigated by Bozeman (1942) and found similar to that of *Leidynema*. A number of new genera and species of thelastomatids have been described for mole crickets by Basir (1942, 1948), who also furnishes a key to the genera of the family. The genera *Binema* in mole crickets (Travassos, 1925; Valkanov, 1936) and *Pseudonymus* in water beetles (Györy, 1856) have interesting egg characters; in the former the eggs in groups of two or three are enclosed in a capsule (Fig. 152E) and in the latter, the shell is embraced by the coils of two groups of filaments (Fig. 122C). *Hystrignathus* and the related *Lepidonema* and *Artigasia* (Artigas, 1926, 1928; Christie, 1934), all parasites of passalid beetles, are characterized by longitudinal rows of spines on the cervical region of females (Fig. 153H).

The Oxyuridae have four double papillae in the outer circlet (Fig. 154D) and usually one spicule in the male. The genus *Oxyuris*, formerly including a large number of species, has now been restricted to those oxyurids in which the buccal capsule is provided with a complicated array of cuticular bristles (Fig. 153F) plus teeth in females. As so defined, the genus parasitizes equines and the principal species is *O. equi* (= *curvula*) in the horse (Fig. 153B–G). This species is the subject of an exhaustive monograph by Martini (1916); other studies are those of Ehlers (1899), Jerke (1901), Railliet (1917), Schwartz (1923), and Wetzel (1930). *O. equi* occupies the colon and caecum of the horse; the females vary greatly in tail length (Fig. 153B, C) and those with very long tails are sometimes regarded as a separate subspecies *mastigodes*. Ripe females protrude from the anus and deposit their eggs around the anal region, fastening them by a gluey secretion. Exposure to air is necessary for the development of the eggs, which after reaching an advanced stage drop to the ground and are ingested by horses in grazing. Juvenile stages are passed in the horse intestine; the fourth stage (Fig. 153E, F) grasps a plug of mucous membrane in its pharynx and feeds on the cells of this plug. A similar cycle obtains for *Enterobius vermicularis*, the common pinworm of children, characterized by paired anterior vesicular expansions (Fig. 154A–C) and a pair of lateral alae. Numerous studies on oxyuriasis, as infestation with this nematode is called, in Washington were made by Cram and associates (summary in Cram, 1943). The small worms (females to 10 mm., males to 3.5 mm.) inhabit the terminal part of the colon. The ripe females make excursions out of

2, nerve ring; 3, end bulb; 4, excretory pore; 5, excretory canals; 6, intestine; 7, vulva; 8, ovaries; 9, uterus; 10, anus; 11, operculum; 12, buccal capsule; 13, pharynx; 14, pharyngo-intestinal valve; 15, embryo; 16, molted cuticle; 17, bristles of buccal capsule; 18, new cuticle; 19, teeth; 20, spicule; 21, caudal alae; 22, pedunculated papillae; 23, ordinary papillae; 24, cells of the lateral cord.

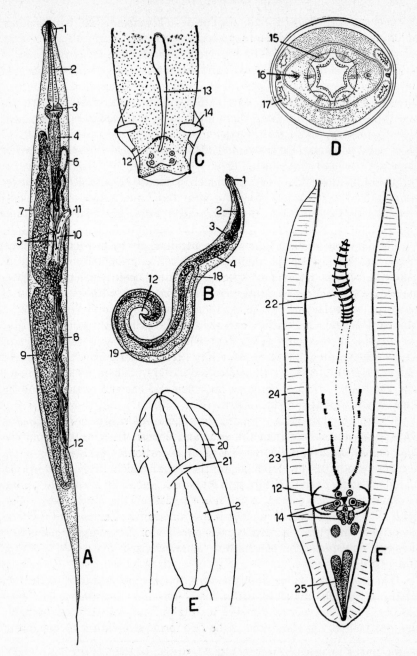

Fig. 154.—Oxyuroidea (continued). *A.* *Enterobius vermicularis,* female. *B.* Same, male. (*A, B, after Leuckart,* 1876.) *C.* Male tail of *E. vermicularis* (*after Seurat,* 1916). *D. En face* view of *Oxyuris equi* (*after Flözel,* 1869). *E.* Anterior end of fourth-stage juvenile of *Dermatoxys veligera* (*after Wetzel,* 1931). *F.* Male tail of *D. veligera* (*after*

the anus, mostly at night, to deposit eggs, being stimulated to oviposition by contact with air. Many females also rupture under these conditions, releasing showers of eggs. These eggs are already well advanced in development and on contact with air continue to the infective stage that must be swallowed by a human being. Juvenile stages inhabit the small intestine and appendix. Contaminated persons often reinfect themselves and infect other members of the family, as ovic juveniles occur on their hands, clothing, linens used by them, and even in the dust of the rooms they occupy (Nolan and Reardon, 1936), so that the parasite may be acquired by inhalation of such dust.

A number of Oxyuridae, previously assigned to the genus *Oxyuris*, inhabit the intestine of rabbits, hares, rats, mice, and other rodents (treated by Hall, 1916). *Dermatoxys* and *Passalurus* both have three teeth in the buccal capsule; the former is distinguished from the latter by the pronounced cervical alae and longitudinal series of short transverse ridges on the rear of the male (Fig. 154*F*). The chief species are *D. veliger* and *P. ambiguus* in rabbits; the fourth-stage juvenile of the former shows an interesting adaptation in the form of four hooks by which it buries its anterior end in the host's mucosa (Fig. 154*E*, Wetzel, 1931). *Aspiculuris tetraptera*, in rats and other rodents, is peculiar in lacking all copulatory pieces in the male (Fig. 155*F*). In *Syphacia* and *Wellcomia*, also in rodents, the male is transversely expanded just prior to the slender pointed tail (Fig. 155*C*). *Syphacia*, reviewed by Tiner (1948), is further characterized by two or three ventral cuticular bosses (mamelons) on the rear part of the male (Fig. 155*B*).

Several oxyurid genera, among which may be mentioned *Thelandros*, *Pharyngodon*, *Ozolaimus*, and *Macracis*, parasitize the intestine of reptiles, especially lizards; the first two are treated by Seurat (1917).

The small family Rhigonematidae, characterized by four double papillae in the external circlet, two equal copulatory spicules, and a short, thick pharynx, is parasitic in millipedes. The principal genera are *Rhigonema* (Fig. 155*A*) with three lips and seminal receptacle (Christie and Cobb, 1927; Artigas, 1926), *Dudekemia* with three lips but no distinct seminal receptacle (Artigas, 1930), and *Icthyocephalus* with two large lips (Artigas, 1926).

The Atractidae differ from the preceding family primarily in the long pharynx, usually divisible into a distal strongly muscular part, and a proximal less muscular part terminating in the end bulb. There is a general lack of alae and the males are provided with two copulatory

Seurat, 1915b). 1, cephalic expansions; 2, pharynx; 3, end bulb; 4, intestine; 5, ovaries; 6, anterior oviduct; 7, anterior uterus; 8, posterior oviduct; 9, posterior uterus; 10, vagina; 11, vulva; 12, anus; 13, spicule; 14, papillae; 15, lips; 16, amphid; 17, double papilla of outer circlet; 18, testis; 19, seminal vesicle; 20, hooks of juvenile; 21, nerve ring; 22, set of transverse ridges; 23, cuticular markings; 24, caudal alae; 25, caudal glands.

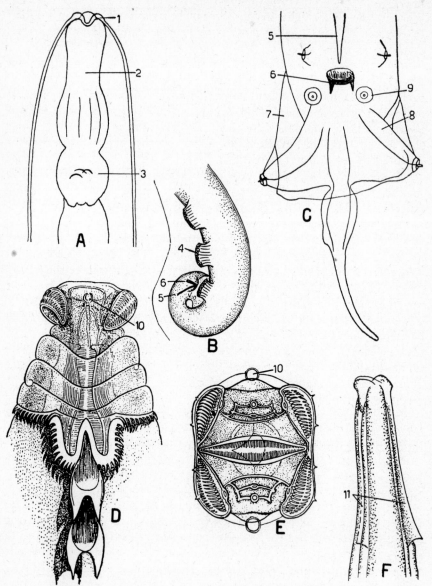

Fig. 155.—Oxyuroidea (continued). *A.* Anterior end of *Rhigonema* (*after Artigas*, 1926). *B.* Side view of posterior end of *Syphacia* (*after von Linstow*, 1884). *C.* Male tail of *Syphacia* (*after Tiner*, 1948). *D.* Anterior end of *Heth.* *E. En face* view of *Heth.* (*D, E, after Steiner*, 1921b.) *F. Aspicularis tetraptera* (*after Hall*, 1916). 1, lips; 2, pharynx; 3, end bulb; 4, mamelons; 5, spicule; 6, gubernaculum; 7, caudal alae; 8, pedunculated papillae; 9, ordinary papillae; 10, amphid; 11, cervical alae.

spicules. *Atractis* (Fig. 156*D*) with distal part of the pharynx longer than the proximal part, unequal spicules, a gubernaculum, and a tubular accessory organ, parasitizes the intestine of lizards and tortoises. *Labiduris*, with three prominent lips bordered posteriorly with fringes and with equal spicules, also inhabits turtles. *Probstmayria vivipara*, occurring by millions in the caecum and colon of horses, appears to be the only nematode that regularly reinfests its host without the necessity of passage to the exterior (Ransom, 1907). The female produces ovoviviparously a few large young that remain in the host intestine. Occasional passage of such young to the exterior, where they can survive for some time in feces, provides for the transfer of the parasite to new host individuals. Several atractid genera inhabit the intestine of millipedes, as *Ransomnema* with a preanal sucker in the male (Artigas, 1926), *Angra* with three-branched head appendages in the female (Travassos, 1929), and *Heth*, in which the female head is furnished with four fringed lobes and behind these a lobed collar edged with spines (M. B. Chitwood, 1935, Fig. 155*D*, *E*). Sexual dimorphism is very marked in *Heth*, so much so that the male was originally considered to belong to a distinct genus.

The remaining oxyuroid families (transferred to the Ascaroidea by the Chitwoods) have a simple lateral papilla adjacent to each amphid in addition to the four double papillae, and two copulatory spicules in the male. The Cosmocercidae with equal male spicules and a gubernaculum occur in mollusks, millipedes, amphibians, reptiles, and some other vertebrates. In some members parasitizing cold-blooded vertebrates, juvenile stages inhabit the lungs and later pass by way of the pharynx into the digestive tract where the mature parasite lives. This type of cycle is found in *Cosmocerca*, principal species *C. trispinosa* in salamanders; this genus is characterized by the presence in the male of two or four rows of genital papillae supported by plectanes (Fig. 102*A*, *B*). In *Cosmocercoides*, widely distributed in the intestine of terrestrial amphibians and reptiles (Holl, 1928; Wilkie, 1930; Harwood, 1930, 1932), there are several large genital papillae encircled by cuticularized tubercles ("rosettes," Fig. 103*B*). *Cosmocercella*, with a species in a tree frog (Steiner, 1924) also has rosettes, further a pair of caudal alae inflated by inner vesicles (Fig. 103*A*, *B*). *Aplectana*, in the intestine of amphibians and reptiles (Miranda, 1924; Walton, 1941b) differs from the foregoing genera in lacking special types of genital papillae. According to the Chitwoods (1937), several cosmocercids, apparently belonging to the genus *Cosmocercoides*, occur in the intestine of slugs and other terrestrial snails. These authors regard "*Angiostoma*" *helicis* from the genital apparatus of *Helix* (Conte and Bonnet, 1903) as a cosmocercid. The genera *Carnoya* (Fig. 157*A*) with circles of spines around the female

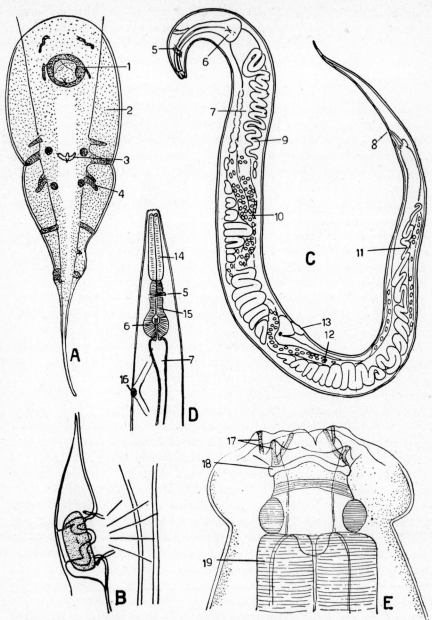

Fig. 156.—Oxyuroidea (continued). *A.* Male tail of *Heterakis gallinae.* *B.* Side view of preanal sucker of same. *C.* Female of *H. gallinae.* (*A, B, C, after Baker,* 1936.) *D. Atractis (after Thapar,* 1925). *E. Spironoura (after Baylis and Daubney,* 1922). 1, preanal sucker; 2, caudal alae; 3, anus; 4, papillae; 5, nerve ring; 6, end bulb; 7, intestine; 8, anus; 9, anterior ovary; 10, anterior uterus; 11, posterior ovary; 12, posterior uterus; 13, vulva; 14, anterior part of pharynx; 15, posterior part of pharynx; 16, excretory pore; 17, sensory papillae; 18, ring in buccal capsule; 19, pharynx.

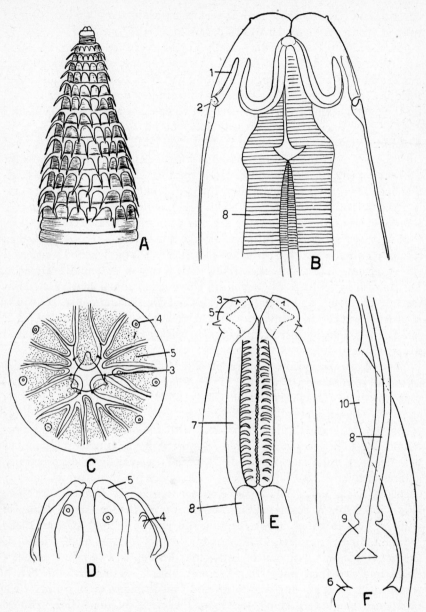

FIG. 157.—Oxyuroidea (continued). *A. Carnoya (after Gilson*, 1898). *B. Pseud-aspidodera (after Baylis and Daubney*, 1922). *C. Kathlania, en face* view. *D.* Same, side view. (*C, D, after Lane*, 1914.) *E. Cruzia,* buccal capsule. *F. Cruzia,* pharynx. (*E, F, after Maplestone*, 1930.) 1, cordons; 2, profile view of cordon; 3, labial papillae; 4, outer circlet of papillae; 5, lips; 6, intestine; **7,** buccal capsule with teeth; 8, pharynx; 9, end bulb; 10, intestinal caecum.

anterior end (Gilson, 1898) and *Rondonema* with instead two longitudinal rows of spines (Artigas, 1926) are parasites of millipedes.

In the family Kathlaniidae, chiefly parasites of turtles, there are three lips, often subdivided, a cuticularized buccal capsule, often provided with teeth, and a bulbous pharyngeal swelling just prior to the end bulb. The male is characterized by the presence of a rimless preanal sucker formed by the aggregation of ventral muscles; two equal or nearly equal spicules and a gubernaculum are present but caudal alae are wanting. In *Kathlania* (Lane, 1914) each lip is subdivided into one main and several subsidiary lips (Fig. 157*C, D*) and the buccal capsule bears three teeth. *Spironoura* (includes *Falcaustra*) with a number of species in various cold-blooded vertebrates has undivided lips and a cuticularized ring support-ing the buccal capsule (Fig. 156*E*). A preanal sucker is wanting in some species and in others there are one or more muscular convergences that may or may not present a sucker-like appearance. *Cissophyllus* has strongly cuticularized lips; the dorsal lip bears a large trilobed tooth and the two ventrolateral lips are armed with a row of cuticularized plates. Distinguishing features of *Cruzia* are three longitudinal rows of teeth in the buccal capsule and an anterior intestinal diverticulum (Fig. 157*E, F*); a preanal sucker is wanting. This genus, sometimes separated as a family Cruziidae, has been found in marsupials and pigs (Travassos, 1917; Maplestone, 1930).

The most distinctive feature of the Heterakidae, parasites of the intestine of amniote vertebrates, is the definite male preanal sucker pro-vided with a cuticularized rim (Fig. 156*A*). The buccal capsule is generally absent or undifferentiated and the pharynx lacks swellings other than the end bulb. *Heterakis*, with longitudinal alae and pro-nounced caudal alae in the male supported by a number of pairs of pedunculated papillae (Fig. 156*A–C*), parasitizes chiefly birds, especially gallinaceous birds, but a few species (sometimes put into distinct genera) occur in mammals. The most common species is *Heterakis gallinae* (Fig. 156*A–C*), a cosmopolitan inhabitant of the caeca of domestic poultry. As in other oxyuroids, the life cycle is direct (Uribe, 1922; Dorman, 1928; Clapham, 1933; Baker, 1935, 1936); the eggs, passed to the exterior in an unsegmented condition, develop to a certain stage out-doors and are then infective when swallowed. *Aspidodera*, in South American marsupials and edentates, and *Pseudaspidodera*, in gallinaceous birds, are characterized by the looped cervical cordons (Fig. 157*B*). *Strongyluris*, with truncate male tail provided with short broad alae supported by pedunculated papillae, and *Spinicauda*, with pointed male tail devoid of alae, parasitize reptiles. The genus *Ascaridia*, often regarded as an oxyuroid, is here referred to the Ascaroidea, and there is little doubt that the Heterakidae in general are closely allied to the ascaroids.

The family Subuluridae, often regarded as a subfamily of the Heterakidae, differs from the latter in having a buccal capsule provided with three teeth and a kathlaniid type of preanal sucker, an oval or fusiform muscular eminence without definite rim. The family parasitizes the intestine of birds and mammals. The main genus *Subulura* (Fig. 158*A*, *B*) is represented by numerous species in birds and mammals and the life cycle of one of these, *S. brumpti,* inhabiting the caeca of poultry, has been studied by Alicata (1939). This worm differs from other oxyuroids in requiring an intermediate host (insect) in which the ovic juveniles develop to an advanced stage infective to chickens that eat such infected insects. The developmental stage attained without sojourn in the insect host is not infective.

25. Order Ascaroidea.—This order is composed of relatively large stout nematodes that are obligatory parasites of the intestine of vertebrates. There are three prominent lips, sometimes with interlabia, and the papillae are arranged as in the higher oxyuroid families (Fig. 158*C*), i.e., there are four double papillae and a lateral papilla on each side accompanied by the amphid. A buccal capsule is wanting and the simple cylindrical pharynx usually lacks bulbous enlargements but is sometimes provided with an end bulb. The excretory system is of the H-type with more or less reduction of the anterior branches (Fig. 117*C*). The male is typically devoid or nearly so of caudal alae and has two equal or nearly equal spicules, usually not accompanied by a gubernaculum (Fig. 110*A*). Genital papillae, often very numerous, are present but prominent accessory copulatory structures are wanting (except in *Ascaridia*). In the female, the two (or more) uteri run parallel (Fig. 122*A*). The females are oviparous, producing large numbers of eggs in an unsegmented condition. These may undergo early development during their passage along the host intestine but complete development to the juvenile stage outside the host. It was previously customary to consider the order as constituted of one family, Ascaridae, divided into subfamilies; but Skrjabin and Karokhin (1945) raise these to family rank and recognize four families. Valuable articles on the Ascaroidea have been published by Baylis (1916, 1920, 1923).

The Ascaridae are characterized by the muscular pharynx, without or with a slight glandular region, and by the absence of digestive diverticula. The life cycle in the known cases is direct, without intermediate host, but the juveniles after hatching in the host intestine enter on a migratory phase involving a sojourn in the lungs. The genus *Ascaris,* smooth worms without interlabia or cervical alae and with a simple

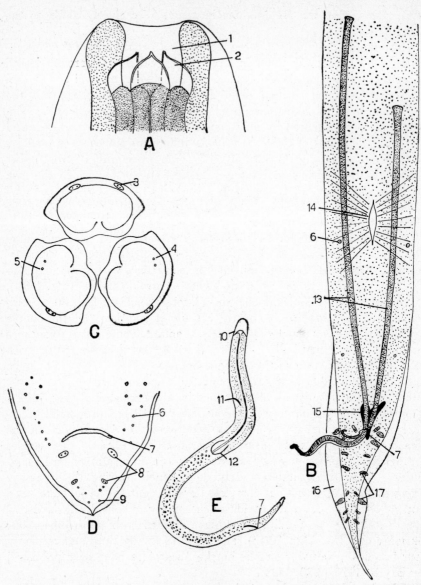

Fig. 158.—Oxyuroidea (concluded), Ascaroidea. *A.* Anterior end of *Subulura*. *B.* Male posterior end of *Subulura*. (*A, B, after Seurat*, 1914.) *C.* Lips of *Ascaris lumbricoides* (*after Thornton*, 1924). *D.* Rear end of male of *A. lumbricoides* (*after Goodey*, 1926). *E.* Newly hatched second-stage infective juvenile of *A. lumbricoides* (*after Ransom and Foster*, 1920). 1, buccal capsule; 2, teeth in buccal capsule; 3, double papillae of the external circlet; 4, amphid; 5, lateral papilla; 6, preanal papillae; 7, anus; 8, double postanal papillae; 9, single postanal papillae; 10, cuticle of first molt; 11, excretory pore; 12, pharynx; 13, spicules; 14, preanal sucker; 15, gubernaculum; 16, caudal alae; 17, postanal papillae.

cylindrical pharynx, formerly embraced a large number of species (nearly a thousand, according to some) but is now restricted to a few members, parasitic in mammals. *Ascaris lumbricoides* is one of the most common and most familiar of human helminths and has been noticed from early times because of its large size (females to 40 cm., males to 25 cm.). Its size has also made it a favorite type for class study of the Nematoda. The smooth fusiform body tapers to the ends without any demarcation of the three lips. The female system is double with a parallel arrangement (Fig. 122*A*) and is very long, beginning with the thread-like ovaries and winding back and forth as these pass insensibly into the oviducts and finally into the much wider uteri. The latter approach the vulva from behind and near the vulva unite to a short common uterine stem continuous with the short vagina. The vulva is situated about one-third the distance from the anterior end. The curved caudal end of the male bears ventrally 50 or more pairs of simple preanal papillae and five pairs of postanal papillae (Fig. 158*D*), of which the two anterior pairs are double; there is also a pronounced cushion-like eminence just anterior to the anus. The male reproductive system resembles that of the female but is single; a considerable length of the terminal part of the sperm duct is enlarged to a broad seminal vesicle that joins the intestine and spicule pouch just prior to the anus (Fig. 118*H*).

The characteristic oval eggs with a brown mammillated protein membrane (Fig. 122*D*) are unsegmented on issuance from the female. They develop to an infective (second-stage) juvenile (Fig. 158*E*) in the open and when swallowed by an appropriate host hatch in the latter's intestine. It was formerly believed that such juveniles then developed to maturity while remaining in the intestine. Following up evidence of juvenile migration obtained by Stewart (1916) through feeding ovic juveniles to rats and mice, Ransom and associates (Ransom and Foster, 1917, 1919, 1920; Ransom and Cram, 1921) were able to elucidate the true history of the juveniles in the human host. After hatching, the juveniles burrow into the intestinal wall and reach the branches of the portal vein by which they are carried to the liver. They then enter the branches of the hepatic veins which convey them into the postcaval vein and so into the heart whence they pass out to the lungs via the pulmonary arteries. Here they rupture the capillaries and escape into the alveoli of the lungs where they grow and molt. They then work their way up the trachea into the pharynx and down the digestive tract, finally reaching their definitive home, the small intestine.

A. lumbricoides also occurs in apes, pigs, cattle, sheep, and squirrels (Goodey, 1926); different specific names have been applied to some of these but the worms are morphologically indistinguishable. The question whether the pig ascaris is identical with the human ascaris has been

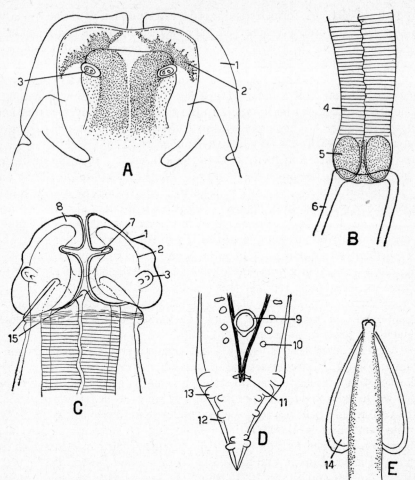

Fɪɢ. 159.—Ascaroidea (continued). *A.* Anterior end of *Ophidascaris (after Baylis,* 1920). *B.* Pharynx of *Neoascaris vitulorum (after Baylis and Daubney,* 1922). *C.* Anterior end of *Parascaris equorum (after Yorke and Maplestone, The nematode parasites of vertebrates, courtesy the Blakiston Co.).* *D.* Male tail of *Ascaridia galli.* (*B, D, after Baylis and Daubney,* 1922.) *E.* Head of *Toxocara mystax (after Taylor,* 1924.) 1, lip; 2, lip pulp; 3, double papillae of external circlet; 4, muscular part of pharynx; 5, glandular part of pharynx; 6, intestine; 7, groove; 8, lip lobule; 9, preanal sucker; 10, preanal papillae; 11, anus; 12, caudal alae; 13, postanal papillae; 14, cervical alae; 15, interlabium.

debated for years. It appears that the two forms are morphologically identical but are physiologically distinct in that the infective stage of the one will not develop in the other host and vice versa (Payne, Ackert, and Hartman, 1925; the Caldwells, 1926, 1928; Buckley, 1931). The pig ascaris is therefore often referred to as *A. lumbricoides suum* or *suilla.* *Ascaris columnaris* in the skunk has been studied by Goodey and Cameron (1923).

Other important ascarid genera in mammals are *Neoascaris*, with a short glandular region at the rear end of the pharynx (Fig. 159*B*), *Parascaris* (Fig. 159*C*) with small interlabia and a deep horizontal groove along the inner surface of the lips, and *Toxocara* and *Toxascaris* with cervical alae. The first is represented by *N. vitulorum*, cosmopolitan in bovines, especially young animals (some notes on the life cycle by Schwartz, 1922). *Parascaris equorum* (= *Ascaris megalocephala*) is a cosmopolitan parasite of the intestine of horses and other equines. *Toxocara* and *Toxascaris* parasitize carnivores; common cosmopolitan species are *Toxocara canis* in dogs, *T. mystax* (Fig. 159*E*) in cats, and *Toxascaris leonina* (Fig. 93*A, G*, life history in Wright, 1935a) in both, as well as in other carnivores (Baylis, 1924). In so far as known the life cycle of mammalian ascarids resembles that of *Ascaris lumbricoides* but juveniles of *T. leonina* remain in the intestinal wall, omitting the migration to the lungs, probably because they are too large to enter the small blood vessels (Wright, 1935a). Some ascarids inhabit snakes, lizards and other reptiles of which may be mentioned *Ophidascaris* with interlabia and lips constricted at their bases (Fig. 159*A*) and *Polydelphis* with four or six uteri (reptilian ascarids reviewed by Baylis, 1920). Walton (1936) has found encapsulated juveniles of *Ophidascaris* in the muscles and mesenteries of frogs and salamanders, which apparently act as transport hosts.

The genus *Ascaridia* differs from other ascarids in having a rimmed preanal sucker similar to that of the Heterakidae (Fig. 159*D*). This genus parasitizes chiefly birds and the principal species, *A. galli* (= *lineata, perspicillum*), a common parasite of the small intestine of chickens and other poultry, has been the object of intensive morphological and physiological studies by Ackert and associates in Kansas as well as by others (Ackert, 1931; Roberts, 1937). The juvenile worms in the host duodenum pass through a phase, presumably corresponding to the migratory phase of other ascarids, in which they bury their anterior ends in the mucous membrane; later they withdraw and live free in the lumen.

The Heterocheilidae are distinguished by cuticular ornamentations forming a collar behind the lips and by the presence of one or more intestinal caeca directed anteriorly. In *Heterocheilus*, in the manatee, backward folds from the lips participate in a broad cuticular collar and there is one intestinal caecum (Fig. 161*A*). *Crossophorus*, in *Hyrax*, has two intestinal caeca and a collar composed of fimbriae.

In the Anisakidae, the posterior part of the pharynx is often altered into a ventriculus (glandular region) and either the pharynx or the intestine or both may be provided with one or more caeca (Fig. 160). This group of nematodes inhabits aquatic or fish-eating vertebrates and in at least some species an intermediate host, usually a fish, is involved in the life cycle. Among the genera of this family may be mentioned

Anisakis, in the stomach and intestine of seals, dolphins, and other marine mammals, with a ventriculus but no caeca; *Raphidascaris*, in fishes, with a small ventriculus and a ventricular caecum; *Angusticaecum*, in amphibians and reptiles, without ventriculus but with a long intestinal caecum; *Porrocaecum*, in fishes, birds, and marine mammals, with a ventriculus and forwardly directed intestinal caecum; *Contracaecum*, in

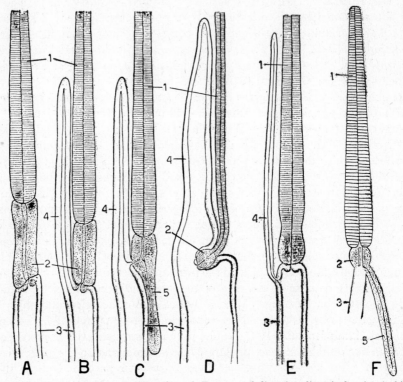

Fig. 160.—Ascaroidea (continued). *A–F*, types of digestive diverticula of anisakine ascaroids. *A. Anisakis. B. Porrocaecum. C. Contracaecum. D. Dujardinia. E. Angusticaecum.* (*A–E, after Baylis, 1920.*) *F. Raphidascaris (after Yamiguti, 1935).* 1, muscular part of pharynx; 2, ventriculus; 3, intestine; 4, intestinal caecum; 5, pharyngeal caecum.

fishes and fish-eating birds and mammals, with a reduced ventriculus and both a ventricular and an intestinal caecum; *Dujardinia*, in fishes, crocodiles, and dugongs, without ventriculus but with a small muscular end bulb and a large forward intestinal caecum; and *Multicaecum*, in crocodiles (Fig. 161*B*), with several ventricular caeca and also an intestinal caecum.

The life cycle is best known for *Contracaecum*, several species of which have been investigated (Wülker, 1929; Kahl, 1936; Thomas, 1937a; Markowski, 1937). The eggs, laid in an early state, are passed in the host feces into water where they develop wholly or partly to an infective

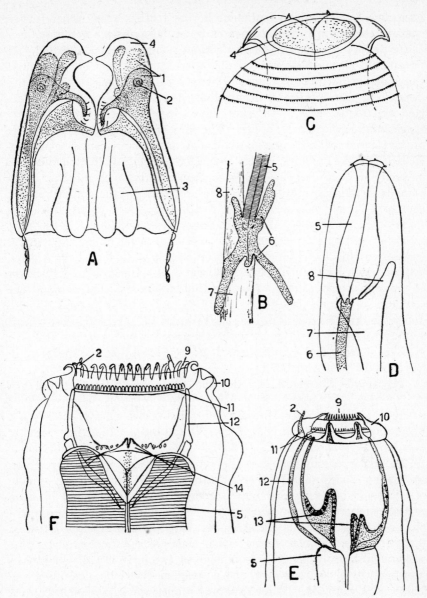

FIG. 161.—Ascaroidea (concluded), Strongyloidea. *A. Heterocheilus (after Draschke,* 1884). *B. Multicaecum, digestive diverticula (after Baylis,* 1923). *C. Goezia,* anterior end. *D. Goezia,* anterior part of digestive tract. (*C, D, after Maplestone,* 1930.) *E.* Anterior end of *Strongylus equinus (after Theiler,* 1923). *F.* Anterior end of *Cylicostomum (after Boulenger,* 1920). 1, lip pulp; 2, papilla; 3, cuticular collar; 4, lips; 5, pharynx; 6, ventricular caeca; 7, intestine; 8, intestinal caecum; 9, outer leaf crown; 10, mouth collar; 11, inner lead crown; 12, buccal capsule; 13, teeth; 14, dorsal cone.

juvenile provided with a cuticular boring tooth. This, either free or while in the egg membranes, is eaten by an intermediate host, usually a fish; a variety of invertebrates as medusae, *Sagitta*, copepods, amphipods, or cephalopods may also serve. The juveniles usually penetrate through the intestine of the intermediate host into body spaces where they develop further. Infected intermediate hosts may be eaten by fishes that apparently serve as transport hosts, in which penetration to body spaces and reencystment occur. The idea of some workers that there are two intermediate hosts—a planktonic invertebrate and a plankton-feeding fish—is probably erroneous. Development of the nematode to maturity with loss of the boring tooth occurs only after fish or other animals containing encysted juveniles are eaten by the definitive host, usually a large predaceous fish or a fish-eating bird or mammal. In *Raphidascaris* (Thomas, 1937b), the eggs, after developing in water to second-stage juveniles, are infective to small fishes in which they encyst in the liver and mesenteries; the cycle is completed when such infected fish are eaten by the definitive host, the pike. Encapsulated juveniles of a marine species of *Porrocaecum*, with adults in seals and walruses, are common in marine fishes (Baylis, 1916), and similar juveniles found under the skin of moles and shrews (Schwartz, 1925) probably have birds of prey as final hosts. Juvenile *Multicaecum* encysted in the stomach muscles of frogs and salamanders developed toward sexual maturity in the alligator (Walton, 1937).

The family Goeziidae includes the single genus *Goezia*, in fishes, characterized by spiny cuticular rings, posteriorly directed ventricular caecum, and anteriorly directed intestinal caecum (Fig. 161*C*, *D*). According to Freitas and Lent (1946), *Diaptomus* serves as intermediate host for *G. spinulosa*.

26. Order Strongyloidea.—The strongyloid or bursate nematodes are distinguished from all other nematodes by the presence in the male of a conspicuous expanded bursa (greatly reduced, however, in some genera) supported by muscular rays, hence differing from the diocto-phymoid bursa which is muscular but without rays and the bursa of rhabditoids and similar forms which consists of cuticular alae. The strongyloid bursa typically is composed of two large lateral lobes, each supported by six muscle rays, and a small median lobe containing one main ray (Fig. 162*A*). These rays may branch and subdivide in various ways and the pattern so formed is of great importance in taxonomic diagnoses. The strongyloids lack conspicuous bulging lips such as characterize the ascaroid nematodes, the pharynx is clavate or cylindrical without definite bulbs or glandular specializations, and the digestive tract lacks caeca. The excretory system is H-shaped with two renette cells (Fig. 116*C*). The female system is generally didelphic with opposed

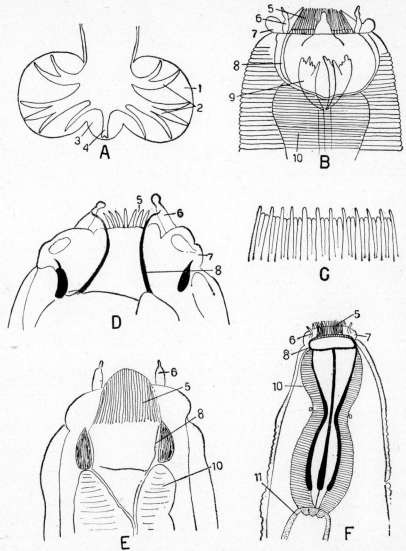

FIG. 162.—Strongyloidea (continued). *A.* Scheme of the strongyloid bursa. *B. Triodontophorus* (*after Boulenger*, 1916). *C.* Part of the leaf crown of *Equinurbia*. *D. Quilonia. E. Murshidia,* lateral view. (*C–E, after Lane,* 1914.) *F. Khalilia* (*after Khalil,* 1922a). 1, lateral lobe of bursa; 2, lateral rays; 3, dorsal lobe of bursa; 4, dorsal ray; 5, outer leaf crown; 6, papillae; 7, collar; 8, buccal capsule; 9, teeth; 10, pharynx; 11, intestine.

uteri and with highly developed muscular ovejectors (Fig. 121*F, H*). The strongyloids are obligatory parasites of the digestive tract, sometimes other systems, of vertebrates, especially mammals. The life cycle is direct, usually including two free-living juvenile stages. The strongyloids are among the most injurious helminth parasites of man and domestic animals, whence several species have been the object of intense investigation. The order is divisible into three groups on the basis of pharyngeal structure: the strongyloids proper, the metastrongyloids, and the trichostrongyloids.

The strongyloids proper usually lack typical lips and are provided with a cuticularized buccal capsule and a typical strongyloid bursa. In the family Strongylidae, lips appear to be absent but the mouth is encircled by an upstanding mouth collar (Fig. 161*E, F*) that seems to represent the lips, at least in part, for it is often subdivided into lobes and bears conspicuous papillae as well as the amphids. Characteristic of the family is the fringe of cuticular teeth, the *corona radiata* or *external leaf crown*, at the entrance to the buccal capsule; in many species a similar *internal* leaf crown occurs within the buccal capsule (Fig. 161*E, F*). In some genera there is a longitudinal thickening, the *dorsal gutter*, or a prominent projection, the *dorsal cone*, in the roof of the buccal capsule; these contain the termination of the duct of the dorsal pharyngeal gland (Fig. 161*F*). The strongyles, also called sclerostomes, include the most characteristic nematodes of the colon and caecum of horses and other equines (Looss, 1901; Boulenger, 1916, 1920, 1921; Yorke and Macfie, 1918–1920; Ihle, 1922; Foster, 1936). Some genera which are common in horses throughout the world are *Strongylus* (= *Sclerostomum*) with internal leaf crown reduced or absent (Fig. 161*E*) and with or without teeth in the depths of the globular buccal capsule; *Triodontophorus* with two well-developed leaf crowns and three large buccal teeth (Fig. 162*B*); *Cyathostomum* (= *Trichonema* and includes *Cylicostomum, Cylicostephanus, Cylicocercus, Cylicocyclus, Cylicodontophorus*, all often raised to generic rank) with two leaf crowns and cylindrical buccal capsule devoid of teeth (Fig. 161*F*); *Poteriostomum* (Fig. 97*A*), differing from *Cyathostomum* in the pattern of the bursal rays and the shape of the elements of the internal leaf crown; and *Gyalocephalus* with two leaf crowns, short buccal capsule, and anterior pharyngeal expansion containing three large teeth. A number of strongylids are parasitic in the intestine of elephants, including besides species of *Strongylus*, members of the genera *Decrusia* with two ventrolateral teeth in the buccal capsule; *Equinurbia* with alternating long and short elements of the external leaf crown (Fig. 162*C*); *Murshidia* with elements of the external leaf crown increasing in length laterally (Fig. 162*E*); *Quilonia* (Fig. 162*D*) with only a few teeth in the single leaf crown; and *Khalilia* (= *Amira*) with two leaf crowns, very short buccal capsule, and hourglass pharynx (Fig. 162*F*). Species of *Quilonia, Murshidia*, and *Khalilia* also parasitize rhinoceroses and these animals further harbor *Kiluluma* (Thapar, 1921) with external leaf crown of six leaves and mouth collar of six lobes, each bearing a papilla. Other strongylids occur in various mammals, as rodents, pigs, and marsupials, and members of the family are also found in ratite birds (ostrich, *Rhea*) and even in reptiles.

The genus *Oesophagostomum* (Fig. 163*A–C*) and the related genera *Ternidens* and *Chabertia* (Fig. 163*D*), all parasites of the mammalian intestine, differ from other strongylids in the presence of a pronounced transverse groove on the ventral surface of the cervical region. In *Bosicola*, in ruminants, this groove completely encircles the cervical region (Fig. 164*A*). The cuticle anterior to the cervical groove is inflated in *Oesophagostomum* and *Bosicola* producing the so-called cervical vesicle (Figs. 163*A*, 164*A*). The oesophagostomes or nodular worms are common and important parasites of pigs, ruminants, and primates, damaging the intestinal wall by the swellings or nodules evoked by the juvenile stages (Goodey, 1924a). *Ternidens* (so called because of the three teeth in the depths of the buccal capsule) *deminutus* parasitizes the intestine of man in southern Africa (Sandground, 1931).

The life cycle of the Strongylidae is known in a general way but exact details in particular cases are often obscure or disputed. The eggs passed to the exterior in early stages in the host feces develop and hatch in moist feces or contaminated soil to rhabdiform juveniles (Fig. 164*D*) that molt twice and become strongyliform third-stage infective worms (Fig. 164*E*) ensheathed in the cuticle of the second molt. These are rather resistant to temperature extremes and to drying; under favorable conditions (coolness, moisture, diffuse light) they mount on vegetation and await ingestion by a suitable herbivorous mammal. Their history after ingestion varies from simple passage to the intestine where they remain throughout life to extensive migrations in the host body before the final sojourn in the intestine. The three common species of horse strongyles, *Strongylus vulgaris, equinus*, and *edentatus*, differ surprisingly in their life cycles, although in fact exact, complete information is not available for any of them. *S. vulgaris* juveniles after reaching the intestine penetrate through the intestinal wall into the circulatory system and are believed to undergo extensive migrations, involving the liver and the lungs, eventually lodging mainly in the anterior mesenteric artery where they evoke aneurisms and thromboses. Here they undergo two more molts and are then carried in the arteries to the colon or caecum in the wall of which they remain embedded for some time before finally passing into the lumen. Juveniles of *S. equinus* also migrate to various abdominal organs but finally come to rest in nodules in the wall of the

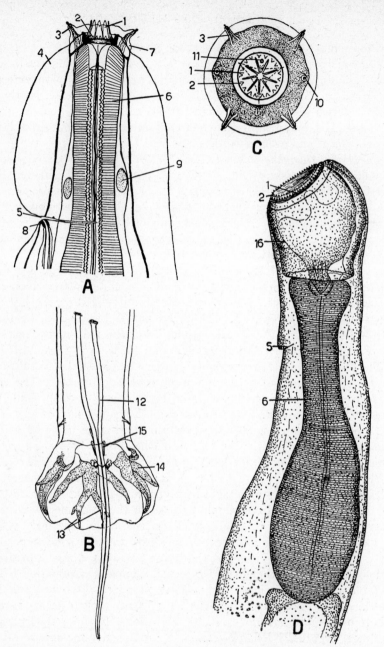

Fig. 163.—Strongyloidea, Strongylidae. A. Anterior end of *Oesophagostomum dentatum*. B. Bursa of the same. C. *En face* view of anterior tip of the same. (*A–C, after Goodey*, 1924b.) D. *Chabertia ovina* (*after Ransom*, 1911). 1, outer leaf crown; 2, inner leaf crown; 3, papillae of external circlet; 4, cervical vesicle; 5, groove; 6, pharynx; 7, mouth collar; 8, excretory pore; 9, nuclei of amphidial glands; 10, amphids; 11, opening of dorsal pharyngeal gland; 12, spicules; 13, dorsal bursal rays; 14, lateral bursal rays; 15, gubernaculum; 16, buccal capsule.

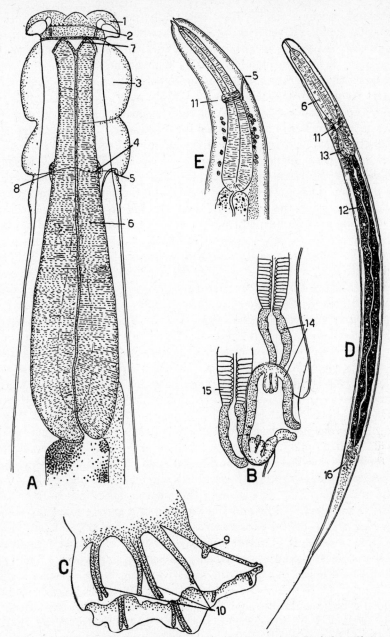

FIG. 164.—Strongyloidea, Strongylidae. *A.* Anterior end of *Bosicola radiatum.* *B.* Ovejectors of same. *C.* Male bursa of same. *D.* First-stage rhabdiform juvenile of same. *E.* Third-stage strongyliform juvenile of the same. (*All after Anantaraman, 1942.*) 1, mouth collar; 2, inner leaf crown; 3, cervical vesicle; 4, groove; 5, excretory pore; 6, pharynx; 7, buccal capsule; 8, amphidial glands; 9, dorsal bursal ray; 10, lateral rays; 11, nerve ring; 12, intestine; 13, end bulb; 14, ovejectors; 15, uteri; 16, anus.

colon and caecum whence they eventually penetrate into the lumen (Thwaite, 1928). *S. edentatus* juveniles, however, seem to omit extensive migrations, remaining in the intestinal wall under the peritoneum for some time, then migrating along the roots of the mesenteries to the colon and caecum where they dwell in nodules before passing into the lumen. Wetzel (1938) and Wetzel and Enigk (1938b) assert that horse strongyles never wander anterior to the diaphragm although passage through the lungs as in *Ascaris* has been claimed for *S. vulgaris*. Valuable studies of the anatomy and differentiation of the infective juveniles of horse strongyles have been made by Lucker (1936a, 1938a). *Triodontophorus tenuicollis* in the horse apparently develops directly in the colonic and caecal lumen without occupying nodules in the intestinal wall during juvenile stages and the same is claimed for *Chabertia ovina* in sheep and other ruminants. Juvenile members of the genus *Oesophagostomum* usually enter the intestinal mucosa after being swallowed by the host and dwell there for some time in inflamed or liquefied swellings or nodules, finally exiting into the intestine after the fourth molt. The best investigated species are *O. quadrispiculatum* (= *longicaudum*) and *O. dentatum* in pigs (Spindler, 1933; Goodey, 1924b, 1926; Schwartz, 1931), and *O. columbianum* in sheep (Veglia, 1924, 1928). The *Cyathostomum* group of horse nematodes, called small strongyles, also pass their third and fourth juvenile phases in intestinal nodules. The cycle of *Bosicola radiatum*, a common nodular worm of cattle, is similar to that of *Oesophagostomum;* the third- and fourth-stage juveniles (Fig. 164D, E) inhabit nodules in the colonic wall and after the fourth molt emerge into the lumen to complete development to sexual maturity (Anantaraman, 1942).

In the Syngamidae there is an expanded somewhat hexagonal buccal capsule with strongly cuticularized walls and small teeth in its depths and the bursa is reduced with short broad rays. The principal genera are *Syngamus* in the respiratory tract of birds and mammals and *Stephanurus* in the ureters of pigs. *Syngamus* with numerous species is characterized by the lack of leaf crowns and the presence of a groove marking off the beginning of the buccal capsule as a thickened ring (Fig. 165B). The best known species is *S. trachea*, causing a respiratory disease termed the gapes in domestic poultry, and hence called the gapeworm. The eggs pass up the trachea and down the digestive tract, being evacuated with the feces. Development to the third-stage infective juvenile occurs inside the egg membranes and such free or ovic juveniles are infective when swallowed by appropriate birds (Ortlepp, 1923a; Wehr, 1937). Usually, however, the juveniles are eaten by transport hosts in which they live for some time without undergoing further development. Various invertebrates may serve as transport hosts, as earthworms, slugs, snails, flies and other insects, and centipedes (Clapham, 1934, 1938, 1939;

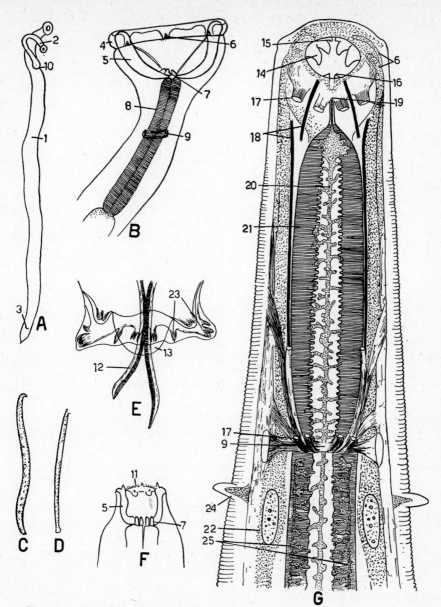

Fig. 165.—Strongyloidea, Syngamidae, Ancylostomidae. *A. Syngamus trachea* in copulation (*after Chapin, 1925*). *B.* Anterior end of *S. trachea* (*after Yorke and Maplestone, 1926, courtesy the Blakiston Co.*). *C. Stephanurus dentatus*, female. *D. S. dentatus*, male. *E. S. dentatus*, bursa. *F.* Anterior end of *S. dentatus*. (*C–F, after Taylor, 1899.*) *G.* Anterior part of female hookworm, *Ancylostoma duodenale* (*after Looss, 1905*). 1, female; 2, male; 3, anus; 4, buccal ring; 5, buccal capsule; 6, papillae of outer circlet; 7, teeth; 8, pharynx; 9, nerve ring; 10, vulva; 11, outer leaf crown; 12, spicules; 13, dorsal bursa lobe; 14, teeth of cutting plates; 15, medial tooth; 16, lancets; 17, muscles of buccal capsule; 18, papillary nerves; 19, opening of dorsal pharyngeal gland; 20, dorsal pharyngeal gland; 21, pharynx; 22, amphidial glands; 23, bursal rays; 24, cervical papillae; 25, ventral pharyngeal glands.

Ryzhikov, 1941; Taylor, 1935); in such hosts the juveniles penetrate the gut wall into body spaces where they become encapsulated and remain viable for long periods.   After direct ingestion or ingestion by way of a transport host, the infective juveniles reach the lungs of the definitive bird host, presumably by way of the circulatory system (Clapham, 1939), and develop to maturity.   Young sexual adults copulate early and remain in permanent copulation (Fig. 165*A*).

Stephanurus (Fig. 165*C–F*) lacks the thickened rim of the buccal capsule and is provided with an external leaf crown of many very small elements; the vulva is near the anus whereas that of *Syngamus* is anterior. There is but one species, *Steph. dentatus*, the swine kidney worm (anatomy in Daubney, 1923; life-cycle studies by Schwartz and Price, 1929, 1931, 1932, and Ross and Kauzal, 1932).   The eggs passed in the urine develop outside into juveniles that molt twice and become third-stage infective juveniles which may live several months under favorable conditions. Pigs become infected either by swallowing such juveniles or by the penetration of the latter through damaged areas of skin.   The worms reach the liver by way of the portal system and remain there for some time, causing serious lesions.   From the liver they may migrate to almost any abdominal organs and tissues and they also may pass to the lungs by way of blood vessels.   Eventually they proceed to the perirenal tissues from which they enter the renal system where final maturity is attained.

The Ancylostomidae or hookworms are distinguished from other strongyloids by the presence at the entrance to the large buccal capsule of two ventrolateral cutting plates provided or not with teeth; small sharp teeth (lancets) are often present in the depths of the buccal cavity (Fig. 165*G*).   Lips and leaf crowns are wanting but a dorsal gutter is often present and in several genera forms a projecting conical eminence, the dorsal cone, on which the gland duct opens.   The anterior end is frequently curved dorsally, presumably to permit a better grip of the cutting plates on the intestinal wall.   The hookworms are parasites of the intestine of mammals where they cling to the wall by pinching a bit of the latter into the buccal cavity with the aid of the cutting plates.   As they feed primarily on blood, they are extremely injurious to their hosts. The principal genera are *Ancylostoma*[1] in which the edge of each cutting plate is formed into one to three teeth, and *Necator, Gaigeria, Uncinaria,* and *Bunostomum* which lack such teeth.   In *Necator* (Fig. 167*A, B*) there is a dorsal cone and two pairs of lancets in the base of the buccal capsule; *Gaigeria* with a dorsal cone and a pair of ventrolateral lancets is characterized by the bursa, of which the dorsal lobe is much larger than the lateral

---

[1] The original and therefore correct spelling was *Agchylostoma* but the spelling *Ancylostoma* was validated by a ruling of the International Commission on Zoological Nomenclature; other spellings are also extant in the literature.

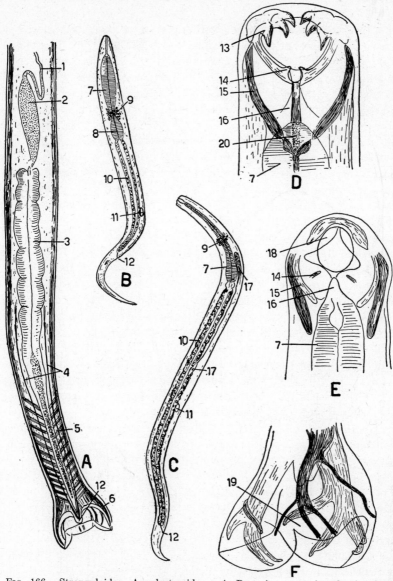

FIG. 166.—Strongyloidea, Ancylostomidae. *A*. Posterior part of male *Ancylostoma duodenale* (*after Looss*, 1905c). *B*. First-stage rhabdiform juvenile of *A. duodenale*. *C*. Third-stage infective strongyliform juvenile of *A. duodenale*. (*B, C, after Looss*, 1911.) *D*. Anterior end of dog hookworm, *Ancylostoma caninum* (*after Lane*, 1916). *E*. Anterior end of sheep hookworm, *Bunostomum trigonocephalum*. *F*. Bursa of same. (*E, F, after Lane*, 1917.)   1, sperm duct; 2, seminal vesicle; 3, ejaculatory duct with glandular walls; 4, spicules; 5, copulatory muscles; 6, bursa; 7, pharynx; 8, end bulb of pharynx; 9, nerve ring; 10, intestine; 11, primordium of reproductive system; 12, anus; 13, cutting plate with three hooks; 14, lancets; 15, buccal capsule; 16, dorsal cone; 17, renette system; 18, cutting plates; 19, dorsal bursal lobe with asymmetrical rays; 20, dorsal pharyngeal gland.

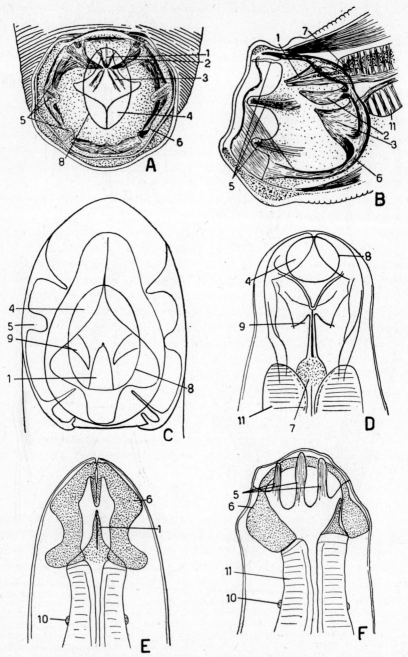

FIG. 167.—Strongyloidea, Ancylostomidae, Diaphanocephalidae. *A. Necator ameri-canus*, view of anterior tip. *B.* Same, from side. (*A, B, after Looss*, 1905c.) *C.* Anterior end of *Gaigeria pachycelis* (*after Cameron*, 1924). *D.* Anterior end of *Uncinaria steno-*

lobes (Fig. 167*C*); *Uncinaria* (Fig. 167*D*) also has a pair of ventrolateral lancets but the dorsal cone is absent and the dorsal bursa lobe is small as usual; *Bunostomum* with a strong dorsal cone and one or two pairs of lancets is distinguished by the asymmetrical dorsal lobe of the bursa (Fig. 166*E, F*).

The human hookworms, *Ancylostoma duodenale* and *Necator americanus*, are the most injurious parasites of man, producing devastating effects on entire populations, and as such have evoked an immense literature, dealing mainly with the geographical distribution of the worms, their pathological effects on the host, and the means of eradicating the worms (books by Chandler, 1929; Lane, 1932). *A. duodenale* (Figs. 165*G*, 166*A*) was discovered in an autopsy of an Italian peasant woman by Dubini in 1838 and has since been found to occur in man and other mammals in western Europe, mainly in mines, and in tropical and subtropical areas of Asia, Africa, various Pacific islands, and South America. Wide attention was first directed to the parasite in 1880 by the disability resulting from its presence in laborers working on the Saint Gotthard tunnel through the Swiss Alps, and subsequently these workmen spread the worm throughout mines in western Europe. The fact that infection occurs usually by skin penetration was discovered by Looss in 1898, who accidentally spilled water containing infective juveniles on his hand, and later (1905a) Looss traced the wanderings of the juveniles through the human body. This author (1905c, 1911) also published an exhaustive treatise on the anatomy and development of *A. duodenale*. Other important species of *Ancylostoma*, sometimes occurring in man, are *A. caninum* (Fig. 166*D*) and *A. braziliense*, widely distributed in dogs, cats, and other carnivores in tropical and subtropical regions. In these species three obvious teeth are borne on each of the cutting plates whereas in *A. duodenale*, the medial tooth is greatly reduced so that only two pairs of teeth seem to be present (Fig. 165*G*).

Necator americanus (Fig. 167*A, B*) was first described by Stiles (1902); it is prevalent in tropical and subtropical countries including the southeastern United States, where extensive campaigns against it have been conducted by the Rockefeller Institute, and the West Indies. Related hookworms of economic importance are *Gaigeria pachyscelis* (Fig. 167*C*) in sheep and goats (Cameron, 1924; Ortlepp, 1937), *Uncinaria stenocephala* (Fig. 167*D*) in dogs, wolves, and foxes, and *Bunostomum* (= *Monodontus*, *Bustomum*) *trigonocephalum* (Fig. 166*E, F*) and *phlebotomum* in cattle,

---

cephala (after Baylis, 1933). (*A* and *B* are oriented dorsal side up, *C* and *D* are ventral side up.) *E. Kalicephalus,* dorsal view. *F.* Same, lateral view. (*E, F, after Ortlepp,* 1923b.) 1, dorsal cone; 2, lateral teeth; 3, ventral teeth; 4, cutting plates; 5, papillae of outer circlet; 6, buccal capsule; 7, dorsal pharyngeal gland; 8, mouth opening; 9, teeth; 10, nuclei of amphidial glands; 11, pharynx.

sheep, and other ruminants (Ransom, 1911; Cameron, 1923b, 1927a; Schwartz, 1925; Hall, 1946; Sprent, 1946a).

The life cycle is much the same for all members of the Ancylostomidae. The eggs are passed to the exterior in host feces in early cleavage stages as they require oxygen for their further development. Under warm, moist conditions in feces and contaminated soil they develop rapidly, hatch, and pass through two rhabdiform stages, during which they feed mainly on bacteria (Fig. 166*B*). They then molt to a third-stage, infective, strongyliform juvenile (Fig. 166*C*) that remains ensheathed in the cuticle of the second molt and is resistant to external conditions. In moist conditions these mount on objects by way of water films and await an opportunity to penetrate into a suitable host. Hookworm juveniles typically penetrate through the skin, leaving their sheaths behind. They enter the lymphatic system by which they are carried to the heart and eventually the lungs, thence passing up the trachea and down the digestive tract to the intestine, where they grow rapidly and pass the last two molts to the adult condition. Most hookworms are also infective by way of the mouth and in such cases they may proceed directly along the digestive tract to the intestine, omitting the passage through the lungs (Fülleborn, 1926, for *Uncinaria;* Foster and Cross, 1934, for *Ancylostoma caninum*). Although hookworms in general may infect either through the skin or by mouth, one route or the other appears to be obligatory in some species or genera; thus *Gaigeria pachyscelis* cannot infect by way of the mouth (Ortlepp, 1925) and *Bunostomum* juveniles are incapable of skin penetration (Schwartz, 1925). It is perhaps to be expected that the hookworms of herbivorous mammals are usually ingested during grazing.

The small family Diaphanocephalidae is characterized by the laterally compressed, bivalved buccal capsule of which each half bears on the inner surface one or two transverse ridges and on the outer surface three strands leading to the sensory papillae. This family, of which the chief genera are *Diaphanocephalus* and *Kalicephalus*, is parasitic in the intestine of reptiles (Fig. 167*E*, *F*).

The trichostrongyloids, regarded by the Chitwoods as a separate order Trichostrongyloidea, are small slender worms without leaf crowns or cutting plates and with the buccal capsule rudimentary or wanting. The bursa is well developed except that the dorsal lobe is small or wanting and a telamon is often present in the male apparatus. Two families are usually recognized—Trichostrongylidae with double female tracts and Heligmosomidae with a single female system. These families include a number of common parasites of the digestive tract of vertebrates. The family Trichostrongylidae was monographed by Travassos (1921) but generic changes were subsequently made. The more prominent genera are: *Trichostrongylus* (Fig. 168*E*, *F*), in birds and mammals, with a small

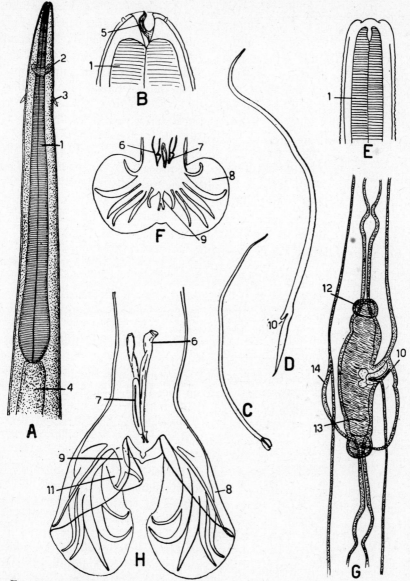

Fig. 168.—Strongyloidea, Trichostrongylidae. *A*. Anterior part of *Haemonchus contortus*. *B*. Head end of *H. contortus*, showing tooth. *C. H. contortus*, male, five times natural size. *D. H. contortus*, female, times 5. *E*. Anterior part of *Trichostrongylus*. *F*. Bursa of *Trichostrongylus* (*after Court*, 1945). *G. Ostertagia ostertagia*, ovejector. *H. Haemonchus contortus*, bursa. (*A, C, D, G, H, after Ransom*, 1911; *B, E, from Yorke and Maplestone, The nematode parasites of vertebrates, courtesy the Blakiston Co.*) 1, pharynx; 2, nerve ring; 3, cervical papillae; 4, intestine; 5, tooth; 6, spicules; 7, gubernaculum; 8, lateral bursal lobe; 9, dorsal ray; 10, vulva; 11, asymmetrical dorsal lobe; 12, sphincter; 13, ovejector; 14, cuticular swelling at vulva.

head, three small lips, no cervical papillae, short spicules, a gubernaculum, and without or with a very slight dorsal bursa lobe; *Haemonchus* (Fig. 168*A–D*, *H*), in ruminants, with prominent cervical papillae, a dorsal buccal tooth, and an asymmetrical dorsal bursa lobe; *Ostertagia* (Figs. 168*G*, 169*A*), in mammals, mostly ruminants, with cervical papillae and an accessory dorsal membrane between the lateral bursal lobes in addition to the small dorsal lobe; *Oswaldocruzia* (Fig. 169*B*, *C*), in amphibians and reptiles, with inflated, cross-striated anterior end, without a gubernaculum, and with spicules subdivided distally into a number of processes; *Ornithostrongylus* (Fig. 169*D*, *E*), in birds, also with inflated head but distal spicule ends subdivided into three processes; *Nematodirus* (Figs. 169*F*, *G*, 170*A*, *C*), in mammals, with longitudinally ridged body very attenuated anteriorly, and filiform spicules simple at their tips; and *Cooperia*, in mammals, with cross-striated, slightly inflated head, longitudinal ridges, and short spicules with simple tips (Fig. 170*B*).

Several species of *Trichostrongylus*, hair-like worms under 8 mm. in length, are common and widespread parasites of the true stomach (abomasum) and small intestine of sheep, goats, and other ruminants (Mönnig, 1926; Nagaty, 1932), sometimes occurring in man. *Haemonchus contortus*, the stomach worm, is an injurious cosmopolitan parasite of the abomasum of cattle, sheep, goats, deer, and other ruminants, attacking the mucous membrane by means of its tooth (Ransom, 1906; Veglia, 1915).   *Ostertagia* is represented by several species in the abomasum, less often also the intestine, of various ruminants; the most common species are *O. circumcincta* prevalent in sheep (Threlkeld, 1934) and *O. ostertagi* chiefly in cattle (Threlkeld, 1946), both forming small nodules in the stomach wall.   *Ornithostrongylus quadriradiatus* has attracted attention in recent years as a serious parasite of pigeons (Cuvillier, 1937) in which it dwells chiefly in the duodenum embedded in the mucosa. *Nematodirus filicollis* is a cosmopolitan parasite of the small intestine of domestic ruminants and other herbivorous mammals (Boulenger, 1915). *Cooperia* is represented by several species of economic importance as attacking cattle, sheep, and goats; the most common of these, *C. curticei*, has been studied by Andrews (1939).

In the family Heligmosomidae mention may be made of the genera *Heligmosomum*, in rodents and marsupials, with longitudinal alae, inflated cephalic end, and long slender spicules; *Nippostrongylus* (Fig. 170*D*, *E*), in rats, with inflated head, asymmetrical bursa and filiform spicules; *Ollulanus*, in cats, with coiled anterior end, short spicules, unlobed bursa, and three-pronged tail end in females (Figs. 170*F*, 171*A*); and *Longistriata*, in mice, rats, and other rodents, with coiled body, transversely striated inflated anterior end, longitudinal body striations, and filiform spicules (Dikmans, 1935, Fig. 171*B*, *C*).

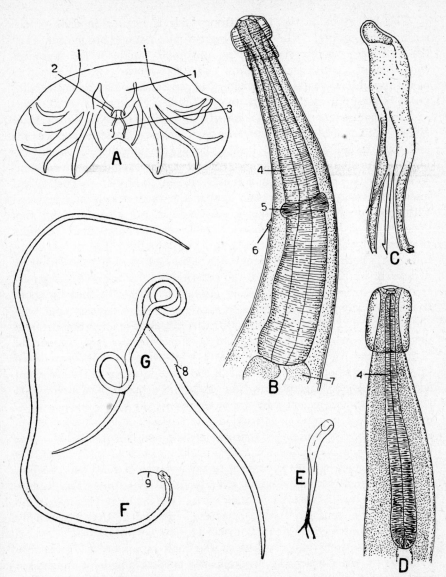

Fig. 169.—Strongyloidea, Trichostrongylidae. *A*. Bursa of *Ostertagia circumcincta*. *B*. Anterior part of *Oswaldocruzia* (after *Travassos*, 1921). *C*. Spicule of *Oswaldocruzia* (after *Morishita*, 1926). *D*. Anterior part of *Ornithostrongylus quadriradiatus*. *E*. Spicule of same. (*D*, *E*, after *Cuvillier*, 1937). *F*, *G*. *Nematodirus filicollis*, times 15. *F*. Male. *G*. Female. (*A*, *F*, *G*, after *Ransom*, 1911.) 1, accessory bursal membrane; 2, supporting rays of same; 3, dorsal rays; 4, pharynx; 5, nerve ring; 6, cervical papilla; 7, intestine; 8, vulva; 9, protruded spicule.

The life cycle of the trichostrongyloids is similar to that of the strongyloids proper. The eggs in segmentation stages are evacuated in the host feces wherein they develop and hatch rapidly under favorable conditions of warmth and moisture. The rhabditiform young (Fig. 172*A*) pass through two molts during their free existence. One molt was supposed to be suppressed in *Nippostrongylus muris* (Yokogawa, 1920, 1922) and in *Longistriata musculi* (Schwartz and Alicata, 1936) but Lucker (1936b) demonstrated its occurrence in *N. muris*. In some species, the first two stages are passed inside the egg membranes (*Nematodirus filicollis*, Ransom, 1911, Boulenger, 1915; *Oswaldocruzia filiformis = Strongylus auricularis*, Maupas and Seurat, 1913). Third-stage ensheathed infective strongyloid young then appear and these are usually ingested with food by the hosts, although some species can also infect by skin penetration as *Nippostrongylus muris* and *Longistriata musculi*. Species that infect by the oral route mostly proceed directly to the stomach and intestine where frequently some time is passed in the walls either in nodules or by the embedding of the anterior end. Following skin penetration there is usually a juvenile migration similar to that of hookworms, by way of blood vessels to the lungs, where development continues, then up the trachea, and down the digestive tract. Sojourn and development in the lungs appear to be obligatory for *Nipp. muris* for Schwartz and Alicata (1934b) found that infective juveniles introduced into the mouths of white rats died in the large intestine if they did not succeed in penetrating the intestinal walls and attaining the lungs. On the other hand, *Long. musculi* when penetrating by the skin appears to omit the usual migration and enters the stomach and intestine by an unknown route within a few hours (Schwartz and Alicata, 1935). The life cycle of the cat stomach worm, *Ollulanus tricuspis*, differs from that of other trichostrongyles according to the account of Cameron (1927b). This exceedingly small worm (1 mm. long) is viviparous (Fig. 171*A*), giving birth to third-stage juveniles that are believed to develop no further in the same cat but to be ejected in vomitus that is eaten by another cat in which they attain maturity.

The metastrongyloids, raised to the rank of an order Metastrongyloidea by the Chitwoods, resemble the trichostrongyloids in general appearance and in the absence or rudimentation of the buccal capsule, but inhabit the respiratory or circulatory system and usually require an intermediate host. The bursa exhibits more or less reduction with eventual disappearance in some genera; the vulva lies near the anus. There are two families, the Metastrongylidae in ungulates, carnivores, rodents, and primates, and the Pseudaliidae, sometimes reduced to a subfamily Pseudaliinae, in the lungs of dolphins and porpoises. The meta-

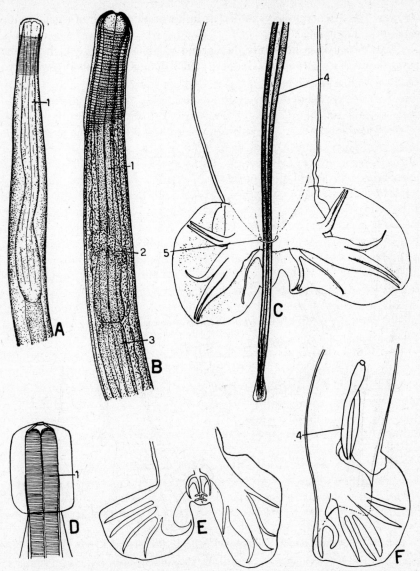

Fig. 170.—Strongyloidea, Trichostrongylidae (concluded), Heligmosomidae. *A*. Anterior part of *Nematodirus filicollis*. *B*. Anterior part of *Cooperia curticei*. *C*. Bursa of *N. filicollis*. (*A, B, C, after Ransom, 1911*.)   *D*. Anterior end of *Nippostrongylus muris*. *E*. Bursa of *N. muris*. (*D, E, after Yokogawa, 1920*.)   *F*. Bursa of *Ollulanus tricuspis* (*after Cameron, 1923a*).   1, pharynx; 2, nerve ring; 3, intestine; 4, spicules; 5, anus.

strongyloids are commonly known as lungworms and are of considerable economic importance.

The Metastrongylidae include a group of genera among which may be mentioned: *Metastrongylus* (Gedoelst, 1923; Dougherty, 1944b), with two

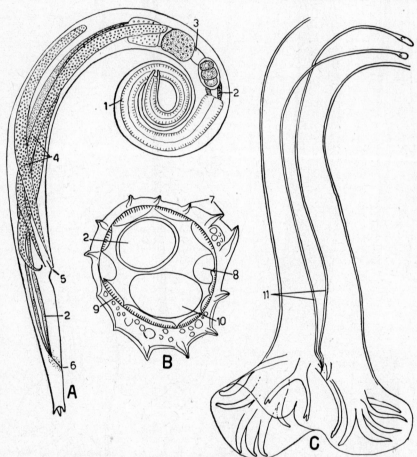

Fig. 171.—Strongyloidea, Heligmosomidae. *A. Ollulanus tricuspis*, female (*after Cameron*, 1923a), with three young worms inside. *B. Longistriata*, transverse section (*after Yamaguti*, 1935). *C.* Posterior end of male *Longistriata* (*after Chandler*, 1932a). 1, pharynx; 2, intestine; 3, uterus with developing eggs; 4, young worms; 5, vulva; 6, anus; 7, longitudinal ridges; 8, lateral chords; 9, muscles; 10, uterus; 11, spicules.

lateral trilobed lips, small bursa with short thick rays, long slender spicules with hooked tips, and swollen vulvar region (Fig. 172*B, C, D*); *Protostrongylus* (= *Synthetocaulus*, Cameron, 1926b, 1927d; Dougherty and Goble, 1946), with short spicules, small bursa with partially fused rays, and bow-shaped cuticular support at the base of the bursa (Fig. 172*F*); *Varestrongylus*, with four lip-like structures around the mouth, small

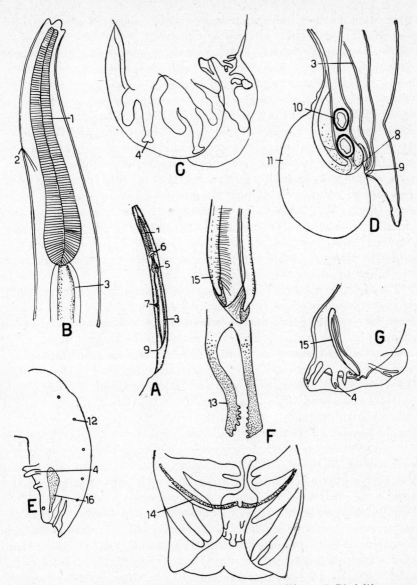

Fig. 172.—Strongyloidea, Heligmosomidae, Metastrongylidae. *A.* Rhabdiform young of *Longistriata* (*after Schwartz and Alicata*, 1935). *B.* Anterior part of *Metastrongylus* (*after Gedoelst*, 1923). *C.* Bursa of *Metastrongylus*. *D.* Vulvar region of female *Metastrongylus*. (*C, D, after Dougherty*, 1944b.) *E.* Bursa of *Muellerius* (*after Cameron*, 1927). *F.* Posterior end of male *Protostrongylus* (*after Cameron*, 1927d). *G.* Bursa of *Aelurostrongylus* (*after Dougherty*, 1946). 1, pharynx; 2, excretory pore; 3, intestine; 4, bursal rays; 5, pharynx bulb; 6, nerve ring; 7, primordium of reproductive system; 8, vulva; 9, anus; 10, eggs; 11, swelling at vulva; 12, genital papillae; 13, gubernaculum; 14, bow-shaped support in bursa; 15, spicules; 16, telamon.

bursa, stout spicules, and gubernaculum and telamon; *Muellerius* (Cameron, 1927d), with bursa reduced to finger-like projections (Fig. 172*E*); *Aelurostrongylus* (Dougherty, 1946), with short spicules and much reduced bursa (Fig. 172*G*); *Angiostrongylus* (= *Haemostrongylus*), with fairly developed bursa, long spicules with simple tips, and no gubernaculum; *Filaroides* (= *Oslerus*, Dougherty, 1943) with the bursa reduced to papillae that retain the ray pattern (Fig. 173*B*); *Metathelazia* (= *Osleroides*), with similar papillae devoid of a pattern (Fig. 173*F, G*); *Dictyocaulus* (Dougherty, 1946), with four lip-like structures around the mouth, cuticularized ring in the shallow buccal capsule, short bursa, and short, stout, simple spicules with a gubernaculum (Fig. 173*A*); and *Crenosoma* (Dougherty, 1945), with crenulated annules on the anterior part of the body (Fig. 173*C*). *Filaroides*, *Metathelazia*, and related forms were formerly considered to be spiruroids (Dougherty, 1943) and this same author regards *Dictyocaulus*, *Crenosoma*, and relatives as trichostrongylids (Dougherty, 1945); but objections to these rearrangements have been raised by others (e.g., by Gerichter, 1949).

The life cycle is known for a number of Metastrongylidae and typically involves an intermediate host, usually an earthworm or snail. *Metastrongylus elongatus*, *salmi*, and *pudendotectus* (= *brevivaginatus*) infest the lungs of pigs; the first and third are common in the United States. The thick-shelled eggs passed in the host feces contain fully developed first-stage juveniles but normally do not hatch until ingested by earthworms (the Hobmaiers, 1929a; Schwartz and Alicata, 1934a; Alicata, 1934; Schwartz and Porter, 1938). The young worms then penetrate into the wall of the anterior part of the earthworm's digestive tract, later often into the hearts and the dorsal blood vessel, and there undergo two molts, becoming third-stage infective juveniles. When infected earthworms are devoured by pigs, the young nematodes penetrate the intestinal wall into the lymphatic system from which they reach the veins and so the heart, to be carried to the lungs via the pulmonary vessels. Infective juveniles may remain alive in earthworms as long as 4 years. These pig lungworms are not only injurious in themselves but work further damage as carriers of the virus of swine influenza (Shope, 1939, 1941). Most other Metastrongylidae utilize slugs or other terrestrial snails as intermediate hosts. In such case the eggs hatch either before or slightly after leaving the host body and such first-stage juveniles may live for a time outdoors but cannot develop further until they find a suitable snail whereupon they penetrate the mucous glands of the foot, eventually reaching the foot musculature. Here they pass two molts and reach an infective stage that attains maturity when such infected snails are eaten by the appropriate host. This type of cycle obtains for *Varestrongylus pneumonicus*, a lungworm of sheep and goats (Bhalero, 1945); *Aeluro-*

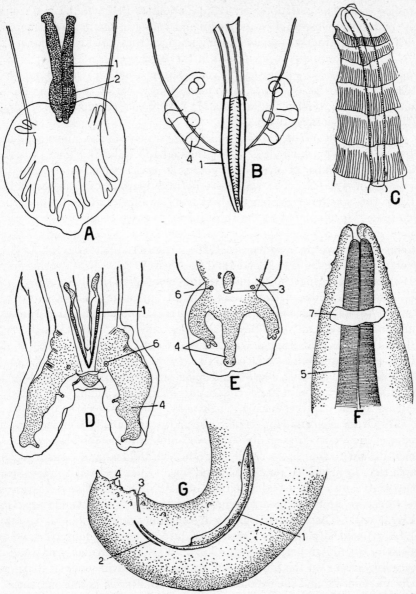

Fig. 173.—Strongyloidea, Metastrongylidae. *A*. Bursa of *Dictyocaulus arnfeldi*. *B*. Bursa of *Filaroides*. (*A, B, after Cameron, 1927d*.) *C. Crenosoma* (*after Dougherty, 1945*). *D*. Bursa of *Pseudalius*. *E*. Bursa of *Stenurus*. (*D, E, after Baylis and Daubney, 1925*.) *F*. Anterior end of *Metathelazia*. *G*. Male tail of *Metathelazia*. (*F, G, after Skinker, 1931*.) 1, spicules; 2, gubernaculum; 3, anus; 4, reduced bursal rays; 5, pharynx; 6, genital papillae; 7, nerve ring.

strongylus abstrusus (Hobmaier, 1935; Gerichter, 1949), found mature in the pulmonary vessels of cats, as eggs and young in the lungs (Cameron, 1928) and apparently capable of using mice as transport hosts (Cameron, 1927c); *Aelurostrongylus falciformis* in the badger (Wetzel, 1937); *Protostrongylus rufescens*, a lungworm of goats, sheep, and deer (the Hobmaiers, 1930b); *Muellerius capillaris*, a common lungworm of sheep (the Hobmaiers, 1929b, 1930a; Pavlov, 1937); *Crenosoma* (Petrov, 1942); and others (see Gerichter, 1949).

The life cycle of *Dictyocaulus* lacks an intermediate host and resembles that of the trichostrongyles. The principal species of this genus are *D. filaria* in the lungs of sheep and goats, *D. viviparus* in cattle, and *D. arnfieldi* in equines. The young are born viviparously in the host lung, or else the eggs hatch within the host body or shortly after reaching the exterior. Development to the third infective stage occurs outdoors and such juveniles are directly infective to the hosts, which usually ingest them while grazing (Cameron, 1926c; Kauzal, 1933; Pavlov, 1935; Wetzel and Enigk, 1938b; Porter and Cauthen, 1942). Earthworms may also serve as transport hosts but are not essential to the life cycle.

The Pseudaliidae with a much reduced bursa are limited, so far as known, to the lungs and circulatory system of dolphins and porpoises (articles on the family by Baylis and Daubney, 1925; and Dougherty, 1943, 1944a). The principal genera are *Pseudalius* (Fig. 173D) with short spicules and bursa reduced to two lateral projections each with one thick ray; *Stenurus* with short broad spicules and small bursa (Fig. 173E) provided with five rays; and *Halocercus* with long spicules and greatly reduced bursa with very short, thick rays. The life cycle is unknown.

27. Order Spiruroidea.—The Spiruroidea are mostly slender nematodes of moderate size usually with two unlobed or trilobed lateral lips,[1] sometimes with four or six small lips, often with dorsal and ventral interlabia that form shields over the lateral lips. The head sense organs are represented by an inner labial circlet of six reduced papillae, sometimes very obscure, and an external circlet of four double or eight single papillae (Fig. 174B). There is a cuticularized, sometimes toothed, buccal capsule and a cylindrical pharynx differentiated into an anterior muscular and a posterior glandular portion (Fig. 175B). Various cuticular ornamentations may occur on the anterior end or along the entire body. Renette cells are wanting and the excretory canals lack anterior extensions, therefore forming a U-pattern. In females, the vulva is generally situated near the body middle and seldom anteriorly placed; an ovejector is typically present. In males, a bursa is wanting although caudal alae

---

[1] Regarded by the Chitwoods as not true lips but pseudolabia on evidence said to be presented by Chitwood and Wehr (1934); examination of this article fails to reveal any such evidence.

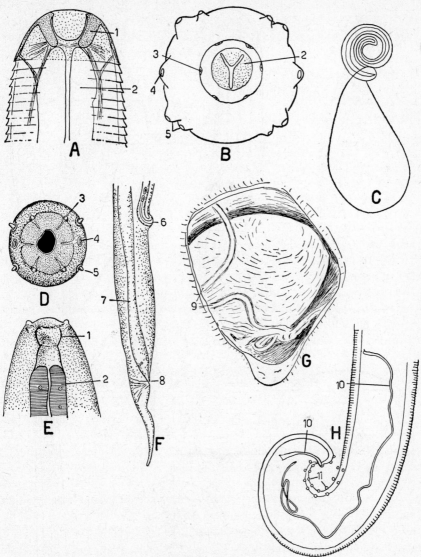

Fig. 174.—Spiruroidea, Thelaziidae. *A. Thelazia callipaeda*, anterior end. *B. Thelazia*, *en face* view (*after Herde*, 1942). *C.* Juvenile *T. callipaeda*, with float. *D. Oxyspirura mansoni*, *en face* view. *E. O. mansoni*, anterior end. *F. O. mansoni*, posterior end of female. (*D, E, F, after Ransom*, 1904a.) *G.* Eye of a pheasant infected with *Oxyspirura* (*after McClure*, 1949). *H.* Posterior end of male *Thelazia callipaeda*. (*A, C, H, after Faust*, 1928b.) 1, buccal capsule; 2, pharynx; 3, labial papillae; 4, amphids; 5, outer circlet of papillae; 6, vulva; **7**, intestine; 8, anus; 9, worms in eye; 10, spicules; 11, genital papillae.

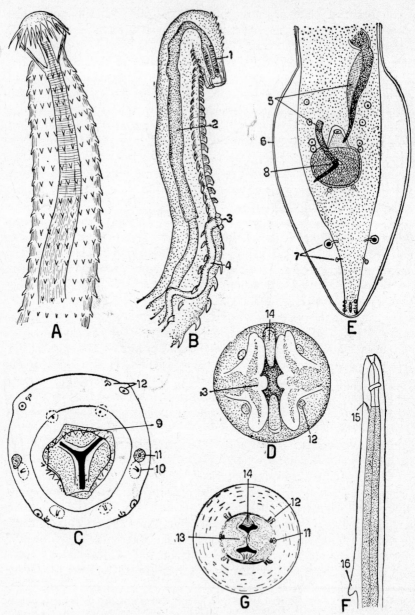

FIG. 175.—Spiruroidea, Thelaziidae, Spiruridae. *A. Echinonema (after Linstow*, 1898).
B. Rictularia (after Hall, 1916). *C. Rictularia, en face* view (*after Tiner*, 1948a). *D.
Spirura, en face* view (*after Draschke*, 1883). *E. Spirura rytipleurites*, male tail (*after
Seurat*, 1915). *F. Spirura rytipleurites*, anterior region (*after Seurat*, 1916). *G. Habronema
muscae, en face* view (*after Chitwood and Wehr*, 1934). 1, muscular part of pharynx; 2,
glandular part of pharynx; 3, vulva; 4, vagina; 5, spicules; 6, caudal alae; 7, genital papillae;
8, anus; 9, teeth; 10, labial papillae; 11, amphids; 12, outer circlet of papillae; 13, lips;
14, shields or interlabia; 15, excretory pore; 16, boss.

provided with papillae are often present, the tail is spirally coiled in a number of genera, and the two spicules are nearly always very unequal in length and dissimilar in shape (Fig. 176*B*). The Spiruroidea are obligatory parasites of the digestive tract, respiratory system, and eyes and nasal cavities and sinuses of vertebrates. The life cycle in known cases is complicated, involving an intermediate arthropod host, sometimes two intermediate hosts. The thick-shelled eggs contain a fully developed juvenile when laid but this hatches only after ingestion by the intermediate host; some spiruroids are viviparous. The classification of the Spiruroidea was revised by Chitwood and Wehr (1934) but as their scheme does not appear to have received wide acceptance it is only partially followed here. The systematic position of many genera remains doubtful.

The Thelaziidae, regarded by Chitwood and Wehr as the most primitive spiruroid family, have an elongated oval or hexagonal mouth with small or obscure lips, eight more or less single or four double papillae in the external circlet (Fig. 174*B*, *D*), and a well-cuticularized buccal capsule, usually unarmed but sometimes with teeth or other projections. *Thelazia*, with coarse annules (Fig. 174*A–C*, *H*), hexagonal rim of the buccal capsule, anterior vulva, blunt tail, and numerous genital papillae but no caudal alae, is parasitic on the eye and in the lacrymal ducts of mammals and under the nictitating membrane of birds. *Oxyspirura* (Fig. 174*D–G*) with pointed tail and more posterior vulva also dwells under the nictitating membrane of birds (Fig. 174*G*). *Ascarophis*, referred to this family by Baylis (1933) is found in the digestive tract of the cod and other fishes. A group of four genera superficially characterized by a spiny cuticle, often regarded as a family or subfamily Rictulariidae or -inae, are provisionally placed in the Thelaziidae by Chitwood and Wehr. The main genus *Rictularia*, in the small intestine of mammals, has two ventral longitudinal rows of comb-like spines, the mouth opening is bordered by small teeth, and the buccal capsule contains teeth and spines (Dollfus and Desportes, 1945, Fig. 175*B*, *C*). In *Rictularoides*, in the small intestine of rodents, there are three longitudinal rows of large hook-like spines. *Pneumonema* in reptilian lungs is characterized by two longitudinal rows of large thorns on each side, and in *Echinonema*, in the small intestine of a marsupial, the spines are arranged in circles decreasing in size posteriorly (Fig. 175*A*).

The members of the genera *Thelazia* and *Oxyspirura* are known as eye worms and are of some importance as parasites of domestic animals, and occasionally of man. They dwell on the surface of the eye (Fig. 174*G*) in the inner corner and may at times wander over other areas of the eye. Of the many species of *Thelazia*, the more common are *T. rhodesi* in cattle, *T. lacrymalis* in horses, *T. leesei* in camels, *T. erschowi* in pigs,

T. callipaeda in dogs, rabbits, and man in China (Faust, 1927a, 1928b; Hsue, 1933a), and *T. californiensis* in dogs, deer, cat, sheep, bear, and rarely man in California (Kofoid, Williams, and Veale, 1937; Herman, 1944). The life cycle of *Thelazia* is unknown but the eggs hatch in the conjunctival fluid to juveniles that are not directly infective to the definitive host and whose manner of leaving the host is unknown (Faust, 1928b; Krastin and Tvashkin, 1946). Transmission by an intermediate insect host is presumed. In the Chinese human eye worm, *T. callipaeda*, the egg membranes swell to form a float (Fig. 174C) for the juveniles, preventing their immersion in the conjunctival fluid (Faust, 1928b). The life cycle of the poultry eye worm, *Oxyspirura mansoni* (= *parvovum*. Fig. 174D–G), has been elucidated by Fielding (1926–1928) and Sanders, (1928). The eggs pass into the digestive tract of the fowl by way of the nasolacrymal duct and are voided in the feces where they are eaten by cockroaches in which they hatch to juveniles that become encapsulated on the outer surface of the digestive tract. While so encapsulated they develop to third-stage infective worms that pass into the roach's haemocoel. When infected roaches are eaten by poultry, the young nematodes escape in the host's crop and reach the eyes in as little as 13 minutes, by passing up into the nasopharynx and then through the nasolacrymal ducts.

In the Spiruridae, there are four double papillae in the external circlet and two simple or trilobed lateral lips (considered by Chitwood and Wehr to be pseudolabia formed by the eversion of the distal part of the buccal capsule), often accompanied by intervening dorsal and ventral projections regarded as interlabia by Chitwood and Wehr, usually called head shields by others (Fig. 175D, G). The distinctions between the Spiruridae and the Thelaziidae seem to be very vague as the distribution of the genera between them varies greatly in different accounts. *Spirura* in the stomach of insectivores, carnivores, and rodents, with principal species *S. talpae* in moles and *S. rytipleurites* (= *gastrophila*) in carnivores differs from other spiruroids in the presence of a ventral boss near the anterior end used as a holdfast (Fig. 175F); pronounced caudal alae are present in males (Fig. 175E), and the usual unequal spicules. In *Habronema*, with principal species *H. muscae* (Figs. 175G, 176A, B) and *H. microstoma* in the stomach of equines, there are simple or trilobed lateral lips, dorsal and ventral shields, usually one or two cervical alae, and caudal alae (Fig. 176B) in males. *Seurocyrnea* (= *Cyrnea*) in the proventriculus of birds, differs in the notched interlabia and the absence of cervical alae (Fig. 177E, F). In *Draschia*, with one species *D. megastoma* in the stomach wall of equines, the simple interlabia overlap the unlobed lateral lips as shields, and lateral alae are present. The next five genera to be mentioned are placed in the Thelaziidae by

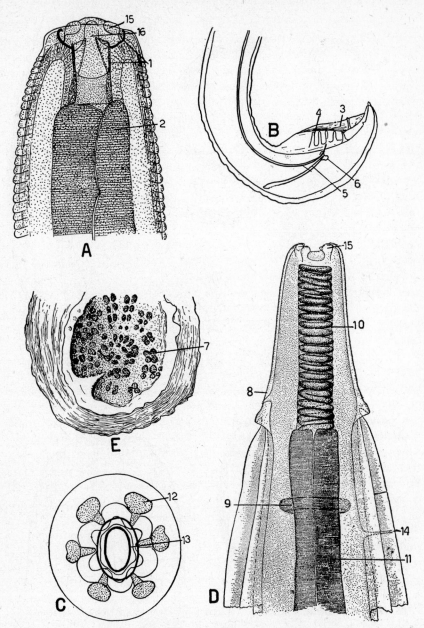

Fig. 176.—Spiruroidea, Spiruridae. *A. Habronema muscae*, anterior region (*after Ransom*, 1913). *B. H. muscae*, posterior end of male (*after Theiler*, 1923). *C. Spirocerca lupi*, en face view (*from Yorke and Maplestone, The nematode parasites of vertebrates, courtesy the Blakiston Co.*). *D. Physocephalus sexalatus*, anterior region (*after Foster*, 1912). *E.* Cut stomach of a pig, showing lesions caused by *Simondsia* (*after Cobbold*, 1883). 1, buccal capsule; 2, pharynx; 3, caudal alae; 4, genital papillae; 5, spicules; 6, anus; 7, depressions occupied by the parasites; 8, cervical alae; 9, nerve ring; 10, buccal capsule; 11, pharynx; 12, masses attached to papillae; 13, mouth; 14, cervical papilla; 15, lip; 16, shield.

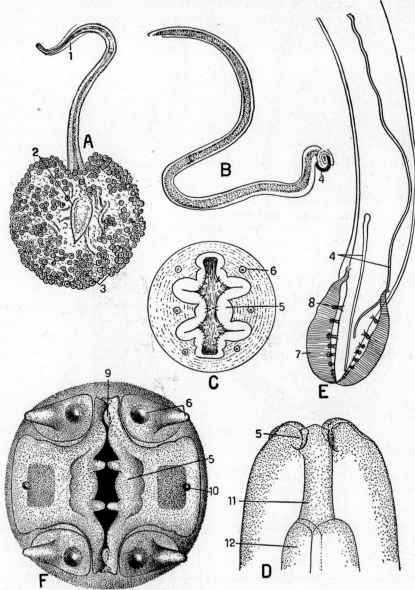

FIG. 177.—Spiruroidea, Spiruridae. *A. Simondsia*, female. *B. Simondsia*, male. (*A*, *B*, *after Cobbold*, 1883.) *C. Protospirura*, en face view (*after Linstow*, 1889). *D. Protospirura*, side view of anterior end (*after Hall*, 1916). *E. Seurocyrnea*, male tail (*after Yamaguti*, 1935). *F. Seurocyrnea*, en face view (*after Cram*, 1931). 1, cervical alae; 2, tail; 3, lobes of uterus with eggs; 4, spicule; 5, lips; 6, papillae; 7, caudal alae; 8, genital papillae; 9, interlabia; 10, amphids; 11, buccal capsule; 12, pharynx.

Chitwood and Wehr. *Spirocerca* (= *Spiroptera*), without lips but with six masses ending in papillae (Fig. 176*C*) within the hexagonal mouth opening and with narrow caudal alae, is represented by one species, *S. lupi* (= *sanguinolenta*), inhabiting tumors of the stomach and esophagus of the dog, fox, and other carnivorous mammals. In *Physocephalus* with principal species *P. sexalatus* (Fig. 176*D*) in the stomach of pigs and related mammals, there are two lateral trilobed lips each bearing three labial papillae, a long buccal capsule with circular thickenings in its walls, three cervical alae, and in the male a curved tail with caudal alae. The similar *Ascarops* (= *Arduenna*) with *A. strongylina* in the stomach of pigs, differs in having a tooth on the inner surface of each lip, only one cervical ala (left), and spiral buccal thickenings (Fig. 178*A*). The related *Simondsia paradoxa* is peculiar in that the female, which lives in cavities in the pig stomach (Fig. 176*E*) with her anterior end protruding, bears posteriorly a large protuberance containing the ovaries and the uteri distended with eggs (Cobbold, 1883; Piana, 1897, Fig. 177*A*, *B*). *Gongylonema*, with a number of species in the esophagus and stomach of various birds and mammals, is distinguished by the numerous cuticular warts or plaques on the anterior part of the body (Fig. 101*B*).

The related genera *Protospirura*, *Hartertia*, and *Spiroxys*, often considered to belong to the Gnathostomidae, are best placed in the Spiruridae (Hedrick, 1935). They have massive trilobed lateral lips provided with teeth on their inner surfaces (Fig. 177*C*) and bearing the papillae of the external circlet; in *Spiroxys* (Fig. 178*B*) and more so in *Hartertia* (Fig. 178*E*) the cuticle of the inner surface of each lip is thrown into folds tending to interlock with those of the opposite lip. *Protospirura* with principal species *P. muris* in the stomach of rats and mice and *P. muricola* in the digestive tract and nasopharynx of rodents is distinguished by the elongated buccal capsule (Fig. 177*D*). *Spiroxys* in turtles and snakes with *S. contortus* as the most common species has nearly equal spicules whereas the spicules are very unequal in *Hartertia* (Fig. 178*F*), parasitizing birds.

The peculiarities of *Tetrameres* and *Hedruris* often lead to their being placed in separate families of the Spiruroidea, the Tetrameridae and the Hedruridae. *Tetrameres* is notable for a pronounced sexual dimorphism; the males are filiform (Fig. 179*A*) and usually provided with four longitudinal rows of spines, whereas the females without spines are greatly distended into a stout spindle shape (Fig. 179*B*). The numerous species of this genus inhabit the proventriculus of birds with the males free in the lumen and the stout reddish females partly embedded in the gastric glands. *Hedruris*, in the stomach and buccal cavity of amphibians and turtles, has large lateral lips and conspicuous dorsal and ventral shields

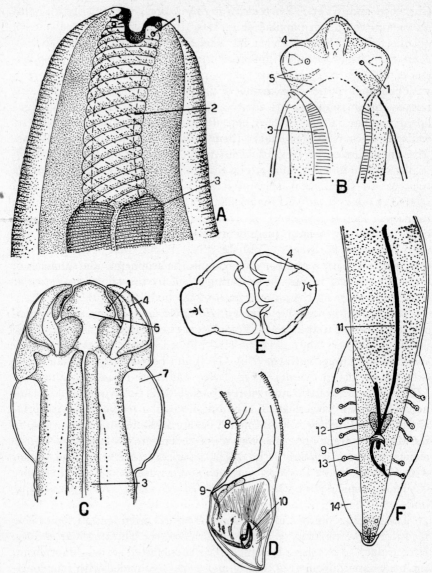

Fig. 178.—Spiruroidea, Spiruridae. A. Anterior part of *Ascarops strongylina* (*after Foster*, 1912). B. *Spiroxys contortus*, side view, anterior end (*after Hedrick*, 1935b). C. *Hedruris*, anterior end, dorsal view (*after Morishita*, 1926). D. *Hedruris*, posterior end (*after Yamaguti*, 1935). E. *Hartertia, en face* view (*after Cram*, 1927). F. *Hartertia*, male tail (*after Seurat*, 1915). 1, papillae; 2, buccal capsule; 3, pharynx; 4, lateral lip; 5, cuticularized support in lip; 6, shield; 7, cervical inflation; 8, vulva; 9, anus; 10, hook; 11, spicules; 12, gubernaculum; 13, genital papillae; 14, caudal alae.

(Fig. 178*C*); the posterior end of the female is invaginated to form a hold-fast containing a large hook (Fig. 178*D*).

The spiruroids parasitizing the digestive tract and swim bladder of fishes, usually distributed among the Thelaziidae and Spiruridae, are assembled by Skrjabin (1946) into a family Rhabdochonidae. The principal genera here are: *Rhabdochona* (Fig. 179*D, E*) with 10 or 12 buccal ridges terminating anteriorly in teeth; *Cystidicola* with small lips, no interlabia, a cylindrical cuticularized buccal capsule, and numerous double preanal papillae; *Metabronema* (= *Cystidicoloides*) with strongly cuticularized head and longitudinal alae; and *Spinitectus*, with the rear edges of the annules serrated into spines (Fig. 179*C*).

Two small genera, *Desmidocerca* and *Desmidocercella*, found in the air sacs of aquatic birds, regarded as Spiruridae by some, are placed in a special family Desmidocercidae by Chitwood and Wehr, although they later transferred them to the Filarioidea. They lack lips, interlabia, cephalic ornamentations, and caudal alae.

The life cycles, so far as known, follow a similar course throughout these families. The eggs, usually fully developed, reach the exterior in the host's feces but do not hatch until swallowed by an appropriate intermediate host in which the rhabdiform juveniles emerge and penetrate into the haemocoel or various tissues, there developing to the third infective stage which is not ensheathed and not rhabdiform. These infective juveniles become encapsulated by the host's tissues and continue their development only when the infected intermediate host is devoured by the definitive host; but can reencyst in transport hosts. *Spirura talpae* in the stomach of moles (Seurat, 1911) and *S. rytipleurites* (= *gastrophila*) in the hedgehog, fox, and cat (Seurat, 1913a; Stefanski, 1934) employ cockroaches as intermediate hosts and the second species has been recorded as using lizards for transport hosts. Grasshoppers and cockroaches serve as intermediate hosts for *Seurocyrnea colini*, parasitic in the proventriculus of quail (Cram, 1931, 1933b); the cycle here differs slightly from that of other spirurids in that the third-stage juveniles are free in the insect host, not encysted. Coprophagous beetles act as intermediate hosts for *Spirocerca lupi* (Seurat, 1912) but the carnivorous definitive host usually becomes infected by eating transport hosts as toads, reptiles, birds, and small mammals (Faust, 1927b, 1928a). The life cycle of this worm is complicated by a migration, for the ingested juveniles pass through the host stomach wall into the arteries of the digestive tract whence they reach the aorta, in the wall of which they dwell for a time in nodules before finally migrating to the esophageal wall (Hu and Hoeppli, 1936). The typical spirurid cycle obtains for *Ascarops strongylina* in which beetles, especially dung beetles, serve as intermediate hosts and various terrestrial vertebrates may act as transport hosts (Alicata, 1935). Simi-

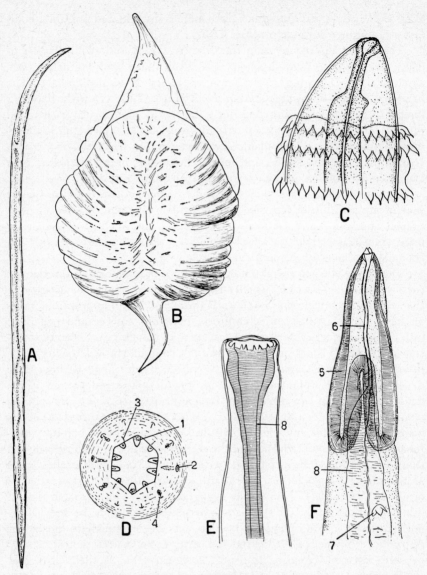

Fig. 179.—Spiruroidea, Tetrameres, Rhabdochonidae, Acuariidae. A. *Tetrameres*, male. B. *Tetrameres*, female. (*A, B, after Cram*, 1931.) C. *Spinitectus* (*after Morishita*, 1926). D. *Rhabdochona*, en face view (*after Chitwood and Wehr*, 1934). E. *Rhabdochona*, anterior end (*after Yamaguti*, 1935). F. *Synhimantus* (*after Skrjabin*, 1917), with cordons. 1, teeth in buccal capsule; 2, amphids; 3, labial papillae; 4, papillae of outer circlet; 5, cordons; 6, buccal capsule; 7, cervical papilla; 8, pharynx.

larly in another swine stomach worm, *Physocephalus sexalatus*, dung and other beetles act as intermediate hosts and small vertebrates as transport hosts (Seurat, 1913b; Alicata, 1935). *Gongylonema pulchrum* (= *scutatum*), parasitic in the esophagus, tongue, and oral cavity of ruminants, pigs, and other mammals, is normally transmitted by dung and other beetles, although cockroaches have been used in experimental studies (Ransom and Hall, 1915; Baylis, Sheather, and Andrews, 1926; Alicata, 1935). After ingestion of the intermediate host, the young worms emerge in the stomach of the definitive host and travel in the esophageal wall, under the mucous membrane, to their final sites. *Gongylonema ingluvicola* in the crop of chickens and other gallinaceous birds is naturally transmitted by dung beetles but will also develop in cockroaches (Cram, 1935), and *G. neoplasticum* in rats and other rodents can use cockroaches, mealworms, and earwigs as intermediate hosts (Bacigalupo, 1933, 1934). *Protospirura muris* is also transmitted by mealworms (Seurat, 1916d) and *P. muricola* by cockroaches (Foster and Johnson, 1938). *Hartertia gallinarum* in fowls employs termites as intermediate hosts (Theiler, 1918). The life cycle of *Spiroxys contortus* found threaded in the stomach wall of turtles differs from the foregoing in that aquatic intermediate hosts are employed (Hedrick, 1935b). The eggs are laid in water in early stages and develop and hatch to an ensheathed worm that sticks to objects and by its lashing attracts *Cyclops*. After ingestion by *Cyclops*, the young worms penetrate into the haemocoel by means of a cuticular tooth, and grow to the third infective stage. Although this is directly infective to turtles, transport hosts such as fish, tadpoles, and dragonfly nymphs are usually employed. Grasshoppers serve as intermediate hosts for *Tetrameres americana* in the proventriculus of chickens (Cram, 1929, 1931, 1937a) and for *T. pattersoni* in quail (Cram, 1933a); but *T. fissispina* and *T. crami* that normally parasitize ducks and other anseriform birds are transmitted by aquatic crustaceans as amphipods (Linstow, 1894; Swales, 1936). According to a brief note by Leuckart (1876), isopods are the intermediate hosts of *Hedruris androphora*, a parasite of *Triton* and other salamanders, and Moniez (1889) suspected but did not prove that amphipods act as intermediate hosts for *H. orestiae* in the intestine of fish. *Rhabdochona* was observed by Gustafson (1942) to develop in mayfly nymphs. In short, insects, usually beetles or orthopterans, act as intermediate hosts for spirurids inhabiting vertebrates with terrestrial habits, and aquatic crustaceans such as *Cyclops*, *Daphnia*, amphipods, and isopods serve when the definitive hosts are of aquatic nature or frequent aquatic habitats.

A variant in the direction of the filarioid life cycle occurs in the spirurids of horses, *Habronema muscae*, *H. microstomum*, and *Draschia megastoma* (Ransom, 1913; Johnston and Bancroft, 1920; Roubaud and Descazeaux, 1921, 1922; Skvortsov, 1937). The eggs or juveniles in horse feces are ingested by muscid and sarcophagid fly maggots that feed in manure. In these maggots the young worms develop in the fat body or Malpighian tubules to the third infective stage. After the maggots have metamorphosed to adult flies, the young nematodes migrate to the fly's proboscis through which they pass onto the horse as the flies are feeding on moist surfaces as the mouth, nostrils, or skin wounds. If they escape into the mouth, they are swallowed and so attain the horse's stomach, their definitive habitat; but if they find themselves on some other part of the horse's body, they are unable to reach the stomach and perish. *Habronemas* of carnivorous birds and mammals probably reach their definitive hosts by way of transport hosts.

The family Acuariidae is characterized by the cordons or other cuticular ornamentations on the anterior end; the males are furnished with caudal alae, usually four pairs of preanal papillae, and a variable number of postanal papillae. The family is parasitic in the esophagus, stomach, and gizzard of birds, free or embedded in the wall. A revision of the family was made by Skrjabin in 1941 but his arrangement differs from that of Chitwood and Wehr chiefly in the separation of certain genera to make two additional families. In *Acuaria* (Fig. 180*A*) and *Cheilospirura* there are four straight longitudinal cordons but the former has nearly equal and the latter very unequal spicules. The cordons are recurrent at their posterior ends in *Dispharynx* (Fig. 97*D*) and these recurrent parts are confluent to make short, forwardly directed loops in *Synhimantus* (Fig. 179*F*). In *Echinuria* and *Chevreuxia* the cordons fuse in pairs at their posterior ends so that two long loops are present (Fig. 102*C*); *Chevreuxia* is distinguished by the bell-like cuticular fold over the cervical papillae (Fig. 104*A*) and *Echinuria* has four longitudinal rows of spines. The cordons of *Seuratia* form four short scallops with raised posterior spiny edges (Fig. 98*A*); and in this genus there is on each side in the cervical region a large trident hook followed by smaller cuticular spines. The anterior end of *Ancyracanthus* is oddly ornamented with four feathery projections (Fig. 98*E*).

Schistorophus and related genera are separated by Skrjabin into a family Schistorophidae. This group of genera has numerous preanal papillae and the cuticular ornamentations consist of or spring from a hood-like cuticular expansion on the anterior extremity encircling the mouth. In *Viguiera* the cuticular hood has the form of a simple circular disk; in *Schistorophus* it sends out two straight dorsal and ventral projections (Fig. 181*C*); in *Serticeps* (Fig. 98*C*, *D*) it forms a number of irregular processes; and in *Torquatella* there are two circles of rounded projections, one behind the other.

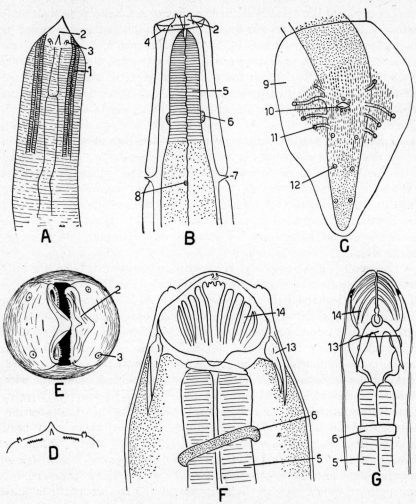

Fig. 180.—Spiruroidea, Acuariidae, Physalopteridae, Camallanidae. *A. Acuaria* (*after Gendre*, 1912). *B. Physaloptera*, anterior end. *C. Physaloptera*, male tail. *D. Physaloptera*, inner surface of lip, showing teeth. (*B, C, D, after Ortlepp*, 1922.) *E. Abbreviata, en face* view (*after Chitwood and Wehr*, 1934). *F. Camallanus*, anterior end, lateral view (*after Baylis and Daubney*, 1922). *G. Camallanus*, dorsal view (*after Törnquist*, 1931). 1, cordon; 2, lips; 3, papillae; 4, collar; 5, pharynx; 6, nerve ring; 7, cervical papillae; 8, excretory pore; 9, caudal alae; 10, anus; 11, pedunculated papillae; 12, other genital papillae; 13, trident support of buccal capsule; 14, shell-shaped half of buccal capsule.

Histiocephalus and *Parabronema* constitute the family Histiocephalidae, according to Skrjabin. In these two genera there are again four pairs of preanal papillae but the cervical region bears a thick cuticular ring which in *Histiocephalus* is longitudinally ribbed (Fig. 97*F, G*) and in *Parabronema* is formed into six scallops (Fig. 97*B, C*).

The acuariid life cycle is similar to that of the Spiruridae. *Acuaria anthuris*, the gizzard worm of crows, employs grasshoppers and crickets as intermediate hosts (Cram, 1934). Grasshoppers also serve as intermediate hosts for the gizzard worms, *Cheilospirura hamulosa* in poultry (Cram, 1931; Cuvillier, 1934) and *C. spinosa* in grouse and quail (Cram, 1931). The eggs ingested by grasshoppers hatch in the latter's intestine and the juveniles develop in the grasshopper's tissues to the third infective stage which encysts. After ingestion of infected grasshoppers by the appropriate bird hosts, the parasites reach the adult condition in which they reside in burrows in the gizzard. *Dispharynx spiralis*, found in the proventriculus of various domestic and game birds is transmitted by sowbugs (Cram, 1931) and *D. nasuta* by flies and sowbugs (Piana, 1896). (According to Goble and Kutz, 1945, *D. spiralis* and *D. nasuta* are identical.) *Daphnia* acts as intermediate host for *Echinuria uncinata*, in the stomach of ducks and other aquatic birds (Hamann, 1893; Romanova, 1947).

The family Gnathostomidae is here limited to spiruroids with a head bulb, i.e., an inflated region behind the lips caused by the presence within of four cavities, the ballonets, each of which is continuous with an elongated cervical sac hanging free in the pseudocoel (Figs. 98*B*, 99*A*, *B*). The two large lateral trilobed lips (Fig. 100*A*) are subdivided on their inner surfaces into interlocking cuticular ridges. In males there are caudal alae supported by pedunculated papillae. In *Gnathostoma*, parasitic in the stomach wall of carnivores, the head bulb is covered with transverse rows of spines (Fig. 99*A*), and body spines are also present, diminishing posteriorly. *Echinocephalus* (Fig. 100*A*), in the intestine, usually the spiral valve, of elasmobranch fishes, also has a spiny head bulb but lacks body spines. In *Tanqua* (Figs. 98*B*, 99*B*), found in the stomach of lizards and snakes of aquatic habits, the head bulb is transversely ridged and shows externally two or four swellings containing the ballonets. The life cycle of *Gnathostoma spinigerum*, occupying nodules in the stomach or esophagus of cats, dogs, mink, and other carnivores, has been studied by several workers (Chandler, 1925; Prommas and Daengsvang, 1933, 1936, 1937; Yoshida, 1934; Africa, Refuerzo, and Garcia, 1936; Refuerzo and Garcia, 1938). The eggs laid in early stages develop in water and hatch to spineless sheathed juveniles that develop further only when ingested by copepods, in whose haemocoel they grow to a stage having a spiny cuticle and a head bulb armed with four rows of spines. Infected *Cyclops* are apparently not infective to the definitive host but the juveniles will grow without developing additional rows of spines on the head bulb (adults have 8 to 11 rows) in fish, frogs, snakes, and probably other vertebrates. Such second intermediate hosts are infective when ingested by the definitive host but the young worms seem to burrow and feed actively in the liver before settling down in nodules of the stomach or esophagus. *G. spinigerum* is the only spiruroid known to require two intermediate hosts. *Echinocephalus* juveniles have been found encysted in the pearl oyster but the details of the cycle are not known.

In the Physalopteridae there are two large but simple lips provided on their inner surfaces with one or more teeth; behind the lips the cuticle forms a forwardly projecting circular collar (Fig. 180*B*). Males have well-developed caudal alae, supported by pedunculated papillae (Fig. 180*C*) and often confluent across the ventral surface in front of the anus. Four, eight, or more uteri may be present in members of this family. The genera are distinguished primarily by the number and arrangement of teeth on the lips. The main genus *Physaloptera* (Fig. 180*B–D*), with over 40 species in the stomach and, less often, other parts of the digestive tract of frogs, lizards, snakes, alligators, birds, and mammals, has been extensively treated by Morgan (1941–1946). In some species a backwardly directed circular fold of cuticle occurs near the posterior end (Fig. 104*D*). The related genus *Abbreviata* (Fig. 180*E*) occurs in the digestive tract of frogs, toads, lizards, snakes, turtles, and a few mammals (Morgan, 1945b). *Skrjabinoptera* in the stomach of reptiles is best known by *S. phyrnosoma* in horned lizards in the southwestern United States (Morgan, 1942). In *Proleptus* in the stomach and intestine of elasmobranch fishes, the anterior end is retractile into a conspicuous cuticular collar and the caudal alae are not fused anteriorly (Fig. 97*E*).

The life cycle of the Physalopteridae is not completely known. Eggs of *Physaloptera*, ingested by cockroaches, will hatch therein and develop to third-stage infective juveniles (Alicata, 1937; Hobmaier, 1941) but these are not infective to laboratory mammals, an indication that a second intermediate host may be necessary for the life cycle. *Physaloptera* juveniles have also been found in an earwig (Basir, 1948) and encysted in the muscles of grouse (Boughton, 1937). Shore crabs, hermit crabs, and other crustaceans act as intermediate hosts for *Proleptus* (Lloyd, 1928).

The family Camallanidae (treated by Baylis, 1923, and Törnquist, 1931) lacks lips and the dorsoventrally elongated mouth leads into a capacious cuticularized buccal capsule; the females are viviparous with two opposed uteri but only one ovary as the posterior uterus is blind. The family parasitizes the digestive tract of cold-blooded vertebrates, especially fishes. The main genus *Camallanus* is distinguished by the division of the buccal capsule into two ridged lateral halves, resembling scallop shells (Fig. 180*F, G*); middorsally and mid-ventrally there is a trident backward projection from the buccal capsule used for attachment of the muscles operating the halves of the capsule. In *Procamallanus*

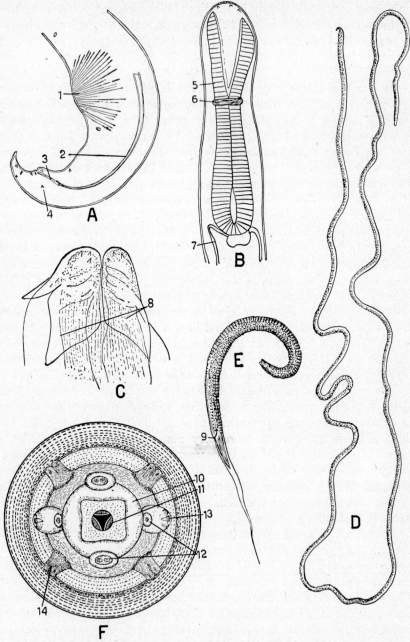

Fig. 181.—Spiruroidea (concluded), Dracunculoidea. *A. Cucullanus*, male tail (*after Yamaguti*, 1935).   *B. Cucullanus*, anterior end (*after Törnquist*, 1931).   *C. Schistorophus* (*after Skrjabin*, 1915).   *D. Dracunculus medinensis*, female.   *E. D. medinensis*, juvenile. (*D, E, after Leuckart*, 1876.)   *F. En face* view of female *D. medinensis* (*after Moorthy*,

the wall of the buccal capsule forms a continuous cup, smooth or with spiral thickenings, and tridents are lacking. The juvenile camallanids leave the mother nematode in the host's body and pass out into water in the latter's feces. For their further development they require to be eaten by a copepod (*Cyclops, Diaptomus*) within whose haemocoel they develop further (Li, 1935; Pereira *et al.*, 1936; Moorthy, 1938a). Ingestion of infected copepods by small fish usually precedes ingestion by the definitive host but it is not clear whether the small fish are necessary second intermediate hosts or merely transport hosts.

The Cucullanidae (discussed by Barreto, 1922; Baylis, 1923; and Törnquist, 1931) have two large lateral lips bounding the slit-like mouth and the large, noncuticularized buccal capsule is typically embraced by the expanded anterior part of the pharynx (Fig. 181*B*). The pharynx differs from that of other spiruroids in being muscular throughout, lacking a glandular portion. An intestinal caecum occurs in some genera. The females are oviparous with two opposed uteri. In males a preanal sucker similar to that of the Kathlaniidae is typically present (Fig. 181*A*). The principal genus *Cucullanus*, found in the intestine of fishes, and sometimes other cold-blooded vertebrates, lacks a caecum but is provided with a preanal sucker. There appear to be no accounts of the life history of members of this family.

28. Order Dracunculoidea.—The members of this order are filiform worms without definite lips or cuticularized buccal capsule; there are six conspicuous labial papillae and an external circlet of eight separate or four double papillae. The pharynx is divisible into an anterior narrow muscular portion and a posterior broader glandular portion except in *Philometra*. In females the vulva is near the middle of the body or some distance behind it but usually atrophies or degenerates as maturity is attained. The female reproductive system is didelphic with directly opposed uteri. Viviparity obtains in the order. In males there are equal filiform spicules and a gubernaculum. The dracunculoids are parasitic in the connective tissue or the coelom and its membranes of vertebrates. The life cycle involves an intermediate host, typically a copepod. The dracunculoid worms are usually considered to belong to the Filarioidea and are then arranged into one family Dracunculidae or two families, Dracunculidae and Philometridae. The author here follows the Chitwoods in removing these nematodes from the Filarioidea. There are three main genera—*Dracunculus, Philometra,* and *Micropleura*.

The genus *Dracunculus* is best known by the species *D. medinensis*,

---

1937). 1, preanal sucker; 2, spicule; 3, gubernaculum; 4, genital papillae; 5, pharynx; 6, nerve ring; 7, intestine; 8, cuticular wings; 9, anus; 10, cuticular ring; 11, pharynx seen through mouth; 12, papillae of internal circlet; 13, amphids; 14, papillae of external circlet.

the guinea worm (Fig. 181*D*), perhaps the most spectacular of human helminth parasites; other species occur in snakes and turtles. The guinea worms inhabit the deeper subcutaneous tissues of man and other mammals in tropical countries, especially India and adjacent areas and Africa. The anterior end in both sexes has a thickened cuticular ring encircling the mouth and bears six labial papillae and four double papillae of the external circlet (Figs. 181*F*, 182*A*). The females attain a length of 3 or even 4 feet and when mature contain little more than the two uteri, forming a continuous tube stuffed with young; anus, vulva, and intestine degenerate. The males were practically unknown until Moorthy and Sweet (1936) obtained them experimentally in dogs; Moorthy (1937) gave a further description of both sexes. The males are very much smaller than the females (up to 4 cm. or $1\frac{1}{2}$ inches in length) with a conical pointed tail bearing 10 pairs of genital papillae (Fig. 182*B*). The tail of the female ends in four spine-like projections when young, a single projection when mature. Copulation apparently occurs while both sexes are young and the males then seem to disappear. The mature female when ready to give birth to her young migrates to the more superficial layers of the skin in those parts of the body that most frequently make contact with cold water, namely, the limbs, and, by the exudation of a toxic substance from her anterior end, evokes a small blister under the epidermis. This blister then breaks, exposing an ulcerous area about the size of a dime with a central hole underlain by the worm's head. When such an ulcer is doused with water, the female contracts convulsively, a loop of ruptured uterus is forced through a cuticular rupture near the anterior end, and a cloud of juveniles is emitted into the water. After having discharged all her young, the female guinea worm shrivels and dies. The young worms are 0.6 mm. long with a long filamentous tail (Fig. 181*E*). They swim about for several days and develop further only when ingested by *Cyclops*, within which they reach the third infective stage in about 3 weeks (Fig. 182*C*). Infection of the definitive host results from drinking infected *Cyclops* in the drinking water. The infection is perpetuated by infected natives wading bare-legged into sources of drinking water, thus releasing juveniles into the water while at the same time filling their containers with water containing infected *Cyclops*. The exact route followed by the young worms after attaining the definitive host has not been ascertained but the worms soon reach the deeper subcutaneous tissues; development of the female to the gravid stage requires about a year.

A *Dracunculus* very similar to the guinea worm has been reported in the United States in a variety of mammals (raccoon, fox, mink, muskrat, skunk, weasel, dog) by several workers (Chitwood, 1933; Chandler, 1942; Dikmans, 1948). Although some of these authors incline to the

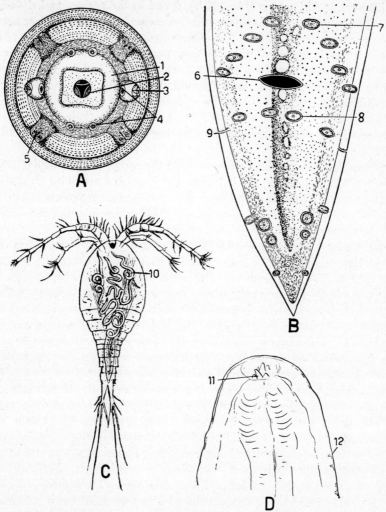

Fig. 182.—Dracunculoidea. *A. En face* view of male *D. medinensis.* *B.* Tail of male
D. medinensis. (*A, B, after Moorthy,* 1937.) *C. Cyclops* containing young *D. medinensis*
(*after Fedchenko,* 1870). *D. Philometra* (*after Thomas,* 1929). 1, cuticular ring; 2, pharynx
seen through mouth; 3, amphids; 4, papillae of internal circlet; 5, papillae of external circlet;
6, anus; 7, preanal genital papillae; 8, postanal papillae; 9, phasmids; 10, young worms;
11, lips; 12, cuticular bosses.

view that the worm in question is identical with *D. medinensis,* it seems
improbable that this can be the case.

A cycle similar to that of the guinea worm has been described by
Brackett (1938) for *D. ophidensis* in garter snakes. Here again *Cyclops*
serves as the necessary intermediate host but probably transport hosts,
such as tadpoles, are utilized.

The genus *Philometra* (Fig. 182*D*), found in the coelom and tissues of fish, differs from *Dracunculus* in the absence of the thickened cuticular ring on the anterior end, in the enlargement of the anterior part of the pharynx, and in the more posterior position of the vulva. As in *Dracunculus* the females are very much longer than the males and anus and vagina atrophy with the onset of sexual maturity. So far as known *Philometra* also employs *Cyclops* as an intermediate host; the ripe females leave the fish host and rupture in water releasing their young which require ingestion by *Cyclops* for their further development (Thomas, 1929; Furuyama, 1934).

Micropleura resembles *Dracunculus* in the morphology of the pharynx and the central position of the vulva but lacks the cuticular thickening on the anterior end; the posterior end of the mature female is bluntly rounded with a pair of large papillae. The genus inhabits the coelom and its membranes in crocodilian reptiles.

29. Order Filarioidea.—The Filarioidea are filiform worms of moderate to large size with the males considerably smaller than the females. Lips and buccal capsule are absent or but slightly developed and the pharynx usually consists of an anterior muscular and a posterior glandular portion (Fig. 184*B*). In females, which are oviparous or viviparous, the vulva is placed anteriorly, in the pharyngeal region, and remains functional. The male spicules are usually unequal and dissimilar as in the Spiruroidea (Fig. 183*D*). The order differs from the Spiruroidea chiefly in the life cycle, which involves transmission of the young by a bloodsucking insect. The filarioids are parasites of the circulatory system, coelomic cavities, and muscular and connective tissues of vertebrates.

The order was revised by Wehr (1935) and the Chitwoods who recognize four families: Filariidae, Dipetalonematidae, Stephanofilariidae, and Desmidocercidae; the last was previously placed by the same authors in the Spiruroidea where it was already considered. Skrjabin and Schikhobalova (1936) recognized but one family, Filariidae, divided into six subfamilies but subsequently (1945a) they raised two of these to family rank and made some other rearrangements. The Filarioidea are therefore regarded as comprising three families: Filariidae, Aproctidae, and Setariidae.

In the Filariidae, the anterior end lacks ornamentations or special peculiarities and the male spicules are unequal in size and dissimilar in shape. In the genus *Filaria*, found in the subcutaneous tissues of carnivores and rodents, there are four small lips and lateral alae along the entire body; in females, the vulva is near the mouth (Fig. 183*B*) and the anus and terminal part of the intestine are atrophied; in males the broad caudal alae meet behind the tail tip. *Parafilaria*, with principal species *multipapillosa*, dwelling in nodules under the skin in equines in

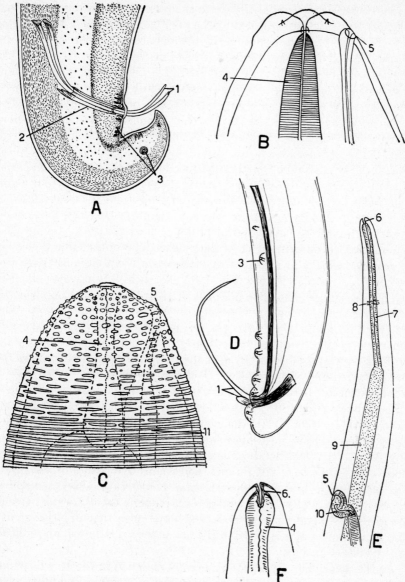

Fig. 183.—Dracunculoidea (concluded), Filarioidea. *A*. Tail of male *Dracunculus* (*after Moorthy*, 1937). *B*. Anterior end of *Filaria martis*. *C*. Anterior end of *Parafilaria multipapillosa*. (*B, C, from Yorke and Maplestone, 1926, The nematode parasites of vertebrates, courtesy the Blakiston Co.*) *D*. Posterior end of *Parafilaria* (*after Railliet, 1893*). *E*. Anterior part of *Litomosoides carinii*. *F*. Head of *L. carinii.* (*E, F, after Chandler, 1931.*) 1, spicules; 2, gubernaculum; 3, genital papillae; 4, pharynx; 5, vulva; 6, buccal capsule; 7, muscular part of pharynx; 8, nerve ring; 9, glandular part of pharynx; 10, ovejector; 11, uterus.

oriental countries, is similar to *Filaria* as regards vulvar position and anal degeneration; it is distinguished by the papillate condition of the anterior end (Fig. 183*C*). *Diplotriaena*, in the connective tissue of birds, is peculiar in having a cuticularized trident structure on each side of the anterior end of the pharynx (Fig. 184*A*). The foregoing genera are oviparous and according to Wehr (1935) produce short, stout, first-stage juveniles with a spiny anterior end. In the remaining filariids to be mentioned, the females are viviparous, producing slender, nonspiny young. The vulva is situated at the pharynx middle in *Wuchereria* (Fig. 184*B*), *Acanthocheilonema*, and *Mansonella*, shortly anterior to or behind the posterior end of the pharynx in the others. *Acanthocheilonema*, in the coelomic membranes and connective tissues of various mammals, has a pair of lateral conical cuticular projections near the tail tip in both sexes. *Mansonella*, in the coelomic membranes of man, is characterized by a pair of fleshy lateral projections on the tail. In the next four genera, the differentiation of the pharynx into muscular and glandular regions is slight or absent. In *Litomosa* in the abdominal cavity of bats and *Litomosoides* in rats (Fig. 183*E, F*), there is a narrow cuticularized buccal capsule; the male tail of the former lacks alae or papillae and *Litomosoides* has a long ovejector with a bulbous enlargement (Fig. 183*E*). The males of *Wuchereria* are provided with caudal alae and numerous genital papillae (Fig. 184*C, D*) and in females there is a pyriform ovejector (Fig. 184*B*) near the vulva; this genus parasitizes the connective tissues of mammals. *Onchocera*, with a number of species in the connective tissues and blood vessels of man and various mammals, is very filiform (Fig. 186*B*) with a thickened cuticle marked by transverse striations (Fig. 186*C*). In the next three genera, the pharynx again shows differentiation into muscular and glandular regions. *Dirofilaria* (Fig. 185*A, B*) with smooth cuticle and caudal alae occurs in the heart, blood vessels, coelomic membranes, and connective tissues of mammals. *Loa*, with cuticle ornamented with small bosses (Fig. 186*A*), except at the extremities, and without caudal alae, inhabits the connective tissues and coelomic membranes of man and other primates. *Foleyella* with lateral and caudal alae is found in the subcutaneous tissues of amphibians and reptiles (Fig. 185*C, D*).

In the Setariidae, the male spicules are unlike as in the Filariidae but the anterior end is provided with a variety of cuticularized structures. *Setaria*, found in the abdominal cavity of mammals, chiefly ungulates, is characterized by a projecting cuticularized circumoral ring notched into two or four divisions (Fig. 186*F*). In *Dipetalonema*, in the coelomic membranes and connective tissues of various mammals, there is a rectangular cuticular shield on the anterior tip around the mouth (Fig. 186*E*) and a pair of lateral conical projections near the tail end in both sexes

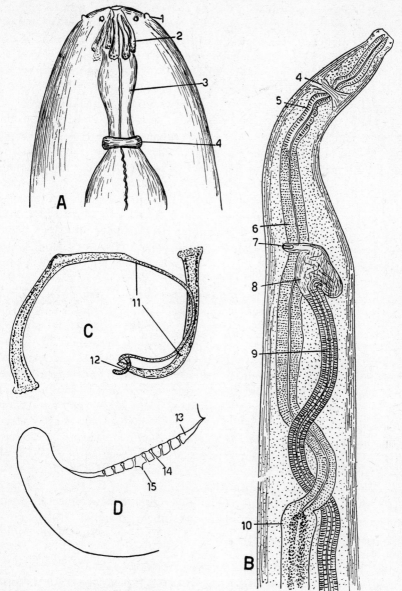

Fig. 184.—Filarioidea (continued). *A. Diplotriaena (after Skrjabin,* 1917). *B.* Anterior part of female *Wuchereria bancrofti (after Vogel,* 1928a). *C.* Spicules of male *W. bancrofti. D.* Male tail of *W. bancrofti. (C, D, after Maplestone,* 1929.) 1, papillae; 2, tridents; 3, pharynx; 4, nerve ring; 5, muscular part of pharynx; 6, glandular part of pharynx; 7, vulva; 8, ovejector; 9, vagina; 10, intestine; 11, spicules; 12, gubernaculum; 13, caudal ala; 14, genital papillae; 15, anus.

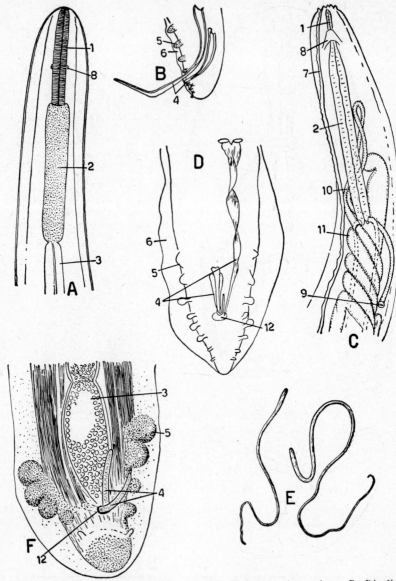

Fig. 185.—Filarioidea (continued). *A. Dirofilaria*, anterior region. *B. Dirofilaria* male tail. (*A, B, after Canavan, 1929.*) *C. Foleyella*, anterior region. *D. Foleyella*, posterior end of male. (*C, D, after Walton, 1929.*) *E. Loa loa*, male and female, magnified twice. *F.* Male tail of *Loa loa*. (*E, F, after Looss, 1904.*) 1, muscular part of pharynx; 2, glandular part of pharynx; 3, intestine; 4, spicules; 5, genital papillae; 6, caudal ala; 7, longitudinal ala; 8, nerve ring; 9, vulva; 10, vagina; 11, uterus; 12, anus.

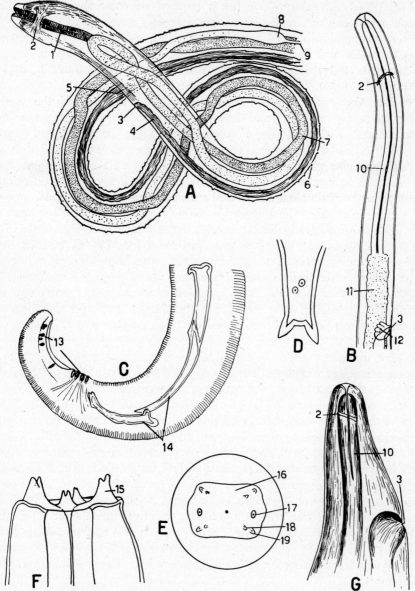

Fig. 186.—Filarioidea (continued). *A. Loa loa*, anterior end of female (*after Looss*, 1904). *B. Onchocerca volvulus*, anterior end of female (*after Brumpt, 1919, slightly altered*). *C. Onchocerca volvulus*, male tail (*after Strong et al., 1934*). *D. Dipetalonema*, male tail. *E. Dipetalonema*, en face view. (*D, E, after Highby, 1943a.*) *F. Setaria*, anterior end (*after Boulenger, 1920*). *G. Aprocta*, anterior end of female (*after Skrjabin, 1917*). 1, muscular part of pharynx; 2, nerve ring; 3, vulva; 4, vagina; 5, union of the two vaginae; 6, cuticular bosses; 7, uterus; 8, seminal receptacle; 9, oviduct; 10, pharynx; 11, intestine; 12, rosette around vulva; 13, genital papillae; 14, spicules; 15, projections of circumoral ring; 16, cuticular shield; 17, amphids; 18, labial papillae; 19, outer papillae.

(Fig. 186D). *Stephanofilaria* has a toothed cuticular ring around the mouth and one or two girdles of spines shortly posterior to this. This genus causes skin lesions in cattle, buffaloes, and goats in the Netherlands Indies and the United States (Ihle and Ihle-Landenberg, 1933; Chitwood, 1934; Dikmans, 1934; Bubberman and Kraneveld, 1934; Kraneveld, 1935).

The Aproctidae are characterized by the similarity of the male spicules in size and shape and the lack of head ornamentations. *Aprocta* (Fig. 186G), with a number of species parasitizing the orbital and nasal cavities of birds, is oviparous without lips or buccal capsule and with a short muscular pharynx lacking glandular differentiation. *Tetracheilonema* with four prominent lips and the usual pharyngeal differentiation occurs in the abdominal cavity and subcutaneous tissues of birds.

The life cycle of the Filarioidea differs from that of all other nematodes in requiring transmission through the skin by way of a bloodsucking intermediate host. This fact was discovered by Manson in 1878 for *Wuchereria bancrofti* and was a discovery of prime importance since it was the first proof of transmission of a human blood parasite by an insect. The majority of the Filarioidea are viviparous (probably really ovoviviparous), releasing their young into the tissues of the definitive host; some, however, lay thick-shelled eggs containing a young worm that soon hatches *in situ*. The young filarioids, known as *microfilariae*, are born in a very immature state, being in fact embryos rather than juveniles. Some are naked whereas others are enclosed in a sheath; it is not settled whether this sheath is a shed cuticle or a persistent inner lipoid ("vitelline") egg membrane. The microfilariae when not shed directly into the circulatory system soon reach this and circulate in the blood stream, showing active movements. They are microscopic, being generally about 0.2 to 0.3 mm. in length, and microscopic examination of drawn blood for microfilariae constitutes the stock procedure for the detection of filarioid infections. As diagnosis of the filarioid involved depends upon the specific characters of the microfilariae, great attention has been directed to the shape and structure of the latter, usually studied after staining. The body of a microfilaria (Fig. 187A) consists of a surface covering of flattened epidermal cells and an inner cytoplasmic column containing nuclei and representing the future digestive tract. The spacing of certain landmarks on this column is of diagnostic importance. These landmarks from the anterior end posteriorly are: a dash at the anterior end, probably representing the future mouth but thought by some to be a stylet, a clear band representing the nerve ring, the excretory pore or a "V-spot" representing this pore, a renette cell shortly behind this, a darkly staining "inner mass" somewhat behind this, farther back about four spaced large cells, all thought by some to be genital cells, three regarded by others as contributing to the digestive tract, and, finally, the anus or a "tail spot" indicating the future location of the anus.

The details of the life cycle are best known for *Wuchereria bancrofti*, a parasite of the human lymphatic system in tropical and subtropical countries. The adults appear as white threads to 10 cm. long that give off microfilariae into the lymphatic system whence they reach the blood vessels. The accumulation of living and dead worms eventually blocks the lymphatic system, resulting in various pathological conditions, of which the most spectacular is an immense swelling of the legs and other parts termed elephantiasis. The microfilariae develop no further and eventually die unless ingested by certain species of mosquitoes while sucking blood from an infected human. In the mosquito's stomach, the microfilariae lose their sheaths, penetrate the stomach wall, and migrate to the thoracic muscles, where they alter first to a plump "sausage" shape (Fig. 187*C*), later to a more elongated (Fig. 187*D*), and finally to a long slender form (Fig. 187*E*). During this period they have passed two molts and reached the third infective stage (Abe, 1937). They then migrate into the mosquito's labium and as the latter is piercing the warm-blooded definitive host, they are stimulated by the warmth to exit through the labium (not part of the piercing apparatus) onto the skin of the victim. They probably penetrate through the wound made by the mosquito. The course of the young worms after entering the definitive host is not known.

Similar cycles obtain for other filarioids as far as investigated. *Acanthocheilonema perstans* inhabits the coelomic membranes and perirenal tissues of man in Africa and South America; its unsheathed microfilariae are transmitted by nocturnal biting midges of the family Chironomidae in which they follow the same development as do *Wuchereria* microfilariae in mosquitoes (Sharp, 1928). Transmission by the tick *Ornithodorus* has also been claimed (Welman, 1907). *Acanth. grassi* in the coelomic membranes, subcutaneous tissues, and muscles of dogs uses the dog tick *Rhipicephalus* as intermediate host; the microfilariae of this species do not circulate in the blood but occur in the lymph whence they are sucked in by the tick (Noe, 1908). *Acanth. reconditum*, found in various organs of the dog, has the usual life cycle; the microfilariae circulate in the blood whence they are ingested by mosquitoes of the genus *Culex* (Rao, 1923). This species was claimed by Grassi and Calandruccio (1890) to be transmitted by dog fleas and the dog tick but these claims have not been substantiated. *Dipetalonema arbuta* in the coelomic cavities of the porcupine employs mosquitoes of the genus *Aedes* as intermediate hosts (Highby, 1943a). *Setaria cervi* (= *labiatopapillosa*), infesting the abdominal cavity and also the eyes of cattle and other ruminants, is transmitted by the stable fly *Stomoxys* (Noe, 1903). *Mansonella ozzardi*, a human parasite

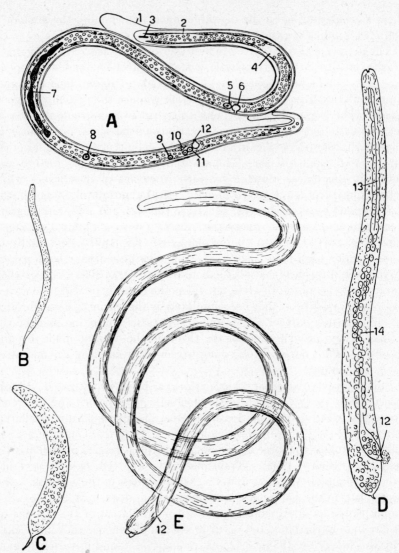

Fig. 187.—Filarioidea (concluded). *A.* Microfilaria of *Wuchereria bancrofti* (*after Fülleborn*, 1913). *B.* Youngest stage of microfilaria of *W. bancrofti* in mosquito. *C.* Later sausage stage. *D.* Still later stage. *E.* Final infective stage in mosquito. (*B–E, after Manson*, 1884, *to scale.*) 1, sheath; 2, epidermis; 3, stylet; 4, nerve ring; 5, renette cell; 6, excretory pore and bladder; 7, interior mass; 8–11, the four large cells; 12, anus; 13, pharynx; 14, intestine.

of the mesenteries in the West Indies, Mexico, Panama, and parts of South America, was found by Buckley (1934) to use sand midges (*Culicoides furens*) as intermediate hosts. *Litomosoides carinii*, a filariid worm of the pleural cavity of the cotton rat (Chandler, 1931), has become prominent in recent years as a parasitic nematode practical for laboratory study. The parasite is also infective to white rats and is transmitted by the rat mite *Liponyssus bacoti* which can be maintained in laboratory cultures (Bertram, Unsworth, and Gordon, 1946). The ensheathed microfilariae circulate in the rat's blood and after being taken into the rat mite develop in the haemocoel to the infective stage in 15 to 20 days (Williams and Brown, 1946; Bertram, 1947; Cross and Scott, 1947; Williams, 1948). They then seem to pass through the mite and through the skin of the rat, as the mite is engaged in biting the rat. The genus *Onchocerca* is represented by several species in horses, cattle, and related mammals, and by *O. volvulus* (= *caecutiens*) in man. This genus lives in the subcutaneous and connective tissues of the host where its secretions evoke inflammatory processes resulting in the formation of dense fibrous nodules and tumors which contain the adult worms coiled into inextricable tangles, mingled with numerous microfilariae. As the adult females are thread-like and may reach a length of 75 cm. in some species, extraction of them entire from the nodules is extremely difficult. The human species is found in central Africa, where the nodules occur chiefly on the lower parts of the body, and in a strip on the western slopes of the coastal ranges in Guatemala and southwestern Mexico, where most of the lesions occur on the head. A study of the parasite in Guatemala was published by Strong, Sandground, Bequaert, and Ochoa in 1934. The microfilariae do not circulate in the blood but travel under the skin and show a considerable tendency in long-standing cases to enter the eye where they evoke various disturbances of vision, eventuating in blindness. *Onchocerca* of man is transmitted by black flies of the genus *Simulium*, which have aquatic larvae, inhabiting swift water as of mountain streams. While the fly is biting the human host, microfilariae seem to be attracted to the site by the fly's salivary secretions, for a greater number of microfilariae is subsequently found in the fly than can be accounted for by their distribution in the skin at the site of the bite. *Onchocerca reticulata* (= *cervicalis*), found in the cervical ligament and the suspensory ligament of the fetlock of horses, is transmitted by the chironomid midge *Culicoides*. The principal species of *Dirofilaria* is *D. immitis*, the dog heart worm, inhabiting the right ventricle and base of the pulmonary artery of dogs. The unsheathed microfilariae circulate in the peripheral blood and complete their development in mosquitoes (Noe, 1901), dog fleas (Breinl, 1921; Summers, 1940), and probably also in ticks (Savani, 1933). Highby (1943b) has described the transmission of

Dirofilaria scapiceps in snowshoe hares by mosquitoes of the genus *Aedes*, having experimentally completed the cycle in domestic rabbits. The genus *Foleyella*, parasitic in frogs, toads, and lizards, also utilizes mosquitoes as intermediate hosts (Causey, 1939; Kotcher, 1941; Witenberg and Gerichter, 1944). The sheathed microfilariae circulate in the peripheral blood in large numbers, being easily seen in the stretched webs of the feet, and after being taken into the mosquito, develop in the haemocoel or muscles to the third infective stage in about 2 weeks. *Loa loa*, the African eye worm (Fig. 185*E*), is a human parasite in equatorial Africa and the West Indies (anatomy in Looss, 1904). The adults, to 7 cm. in length, inhabit the subcutaneous tissues where they creep about, being especially prone to enter the eye. Transmission takes place by way of tabanid flies of the genus *Chrysops* (Leiper, 1913b; Connal and Connal, 1922).

It is a striking peculiarity of the microfilariae of some species (e.g., *Wuchereria bancrofti*, *Dirofilaria immitis*, *Loa loa*) that their appearance in the peripheral blood vessels is periodic, showing a diurnal rhythm. The microfilariae of the first two species are found in the peripheral blood only at night or during sleep, those of *L. loa* during the day. Although various theories have been advanced to account for this phenomenon, no entirely satisfactory explanation has been established.

30. Order Trichuroidea or Trichinelloidea.—The outstanding feature of this order is the embedding of the slender, delicate, nonmuscular pharynx in the stichosome ("cell body"), a structure consisting of one or two longitudinal rows of large cells, the stichocytes, that apparently represent pharyngeal gland cells (Chitwood, 1930, 1935). The anterior part of the body containing the pharynx is generally more slender than the posterior part, markedly so in the genus *Trichuris* (Fig. 188*A*, *B*). The mouth is simple, without lips (Fig. 188*D*); the arrangement of the head papillae is not well known. In the genera *Trichuris* and *Capillaria* one or more bacillary bands are present anteriorly; these are longitudinal tracts of minute projections that constitute the outlets of subcuticular glands (Fig. 189). The female reproductive system is single, long and tubular, with a variously placed vulva (Fig. 188*A*). Most species are oviparous, laying unsegmented eggs enclosed in an oval shell with an opercular plug at each end (Fig. 122*G*). Males either lack a copulatory apparatus altogether or are provided with an eversible spicule sheath, hence a cirrus, armed or not with one spicule (Fig. 188*C*, *E*). The trichuroids usually parasitize the digestive tract of birds and mammals but also occur in other vertebrates and in other sites. The life cycle is typically simple without the intervention of an intermediate host; the juveniles are provided with a buccal stylet, whence a relationship of the Trichuroidea with the Dorylaimoidea is presumable (Fülleborn, 1923).

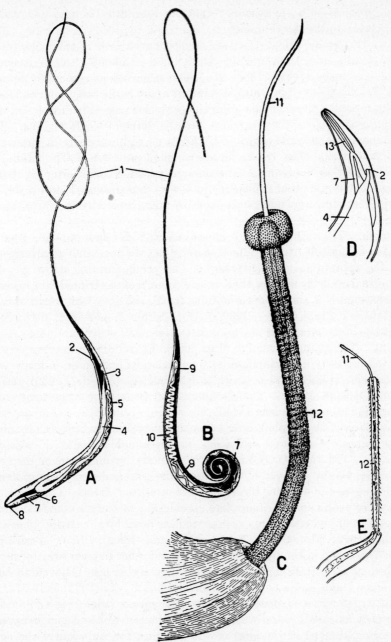

Fig. 188.—Trichuroidea. *A. Trichuris ovis,* female. *B. Trichuris ovis,* male. *C.* Cirrus and spicule of *T. ovis,* everted. (*A–C, after Ransom,* 1911.) *D.* Anterior end of *Capillaria. E.* Everted cirrus of *Capillaria.* (*D, E, after Madsen,* 1945.) 1, anterior whip-like region; 2, vulva; 3, vagina; 4, uterus; 5, oviduct; 6, ovary; 7, intestine; 8, anus; 9, testis; 10, sperm duct; 11, spicule; 12, cirrus; 13, pharynx.

The presence of a stichosome recalls the mermithoids, also believed to be related to the dorylaimoids.

In the family Trichuridae, the stichosome consists of one longitudinal row of cells (Fig. 189), and the cirrus, lined or not with spines, is armed with one spicule (Fig. 188C, E). The principal genera are *Trichuris* (= *Trichocephalus*), in which the anterior part of the body is much longer and markedly more slender than the posterior part (Fig. 188A, B), and *Capillaria* (Fig. 93C) with only slightly different body regions. The members of the genus *Trichuris*, known as whipworms from the whip-like body shape (Fig. 188A, B), are common parasites of the intestine of man and other mammals. The human species, *T. trichiura* (Fig. 93D), also occurring in other primates and in pigs, is a cosmopolitan inhabitant of the caecum, appendix, and colon of man, especially in warm, moist climates. The slender anterior region is usually buried in the host's mucosa. The eggs are laid uncleaved and develop outside, best in moist, heavy soils, to the infective stage but do not hatch until ingested by the appropriate definitive host. The young worms burrow into the intestinal wall for a time, then emerge, and seek their final site, usually the caecum. A similar cycle obtains for *T. vulpis*, a whipworm of dogs and other canines (Miller, 1939, 1947), and for *T. ovis* (Fig. 188A–C), a cosmopolitan parasite of sheep, goats, cattle, and other ruminants (Deo, 1946). The genus *Capillaria* (Fig. 188D, E) contains numerous species parasitic chiefly in birds, especially gallinaceous and anserine birds, and in mammals; species also occur in salamanders (Mueller, 1932) and in fishes (Heinze, 1933). The *Capillarias* of birds have been treated by Cram (1936) and Madsen (1945); they reside primarily in the crop and other parts of the esophagus and may seriously damage birds of economic importance. *Capillaria columbae*, an intestinal parasite of pigeons, chickens, and turkeys, is transmitted directly by ingestion of the ovic juveniles (Wehr, 1939). *C. contorta*, in the crop and esophagus of many gallinaceous and anserine birds, is also transmitted directly (Cram, 1936); but *C. annulata* and *C. caudinflata*, in chickens and other domestic birds, seem to require earthworms as intermediate hosts (Wehr, 1936; Allen and Wehr, 1942; Morehouse, 1944; Wehr and Allen, 1945). *Capillaria hepatica*, found in the liver of rats, mice, and other rodents, was formerly placed in a separate genus *Hepaticola*, because it was believed to lack bacillary bands and a copulatory spicule; but Baylis (1931) showed that both structures are present and hence the species belongs in *Capillaria*. Livers of rodents infected with *C. hepatica* present yellowish spots caused by accumulations of the eggs of the parasite; but apparently the eggs do not escape to the exterior by way of the host's digestive tract. Eggs taken directly from infected livers are not directly infective to appropriate hosts and in cultures they develop very slowly, requiring 5 to 6 months to reach the embryo stage. According to the work of Shorb (1931) the eggs await ingestion of infected hosts by a carnivorous bird or mammal through whose intestine the eggs pass; after such passage the eggs develop readily at warm temperatures and are then infective. After ingestion by the definitive host, the juveniles penetrate the caecum and enter the portal circulation by which they are carried to the liver (Fülleborn, 1924; Luttermoser, 1938). Juveniles injected into the spleen or lungs, or under

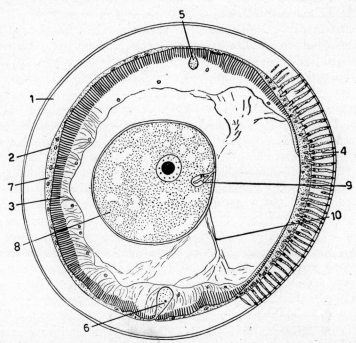

Fig. 189.—Trichuroidea (continued). Section through the pharyngeal region of *Trichuris* (*after Rauther*, 1918). 1, cuticle; 2, epidermis; 3, muscle layer; 4, bacillary band; 5, dorsal chord; 6, ventral chord; 7, lateral chord; 8, cell of stichosome; 9, pharynx; 10, tissue in pseudocoel.

the skin also eventually reach the liver (Vogel, 1930). *C. aerophila,* inhabiting the air passages of the fox, dog, cat, and other carnivores, has a simple life history (Christenson, 1938); the eggs, coughed out directly or swallowed and emitted in the feces, develop in 35 to 50 days to an infective stage. The life cycle of *C. plica,* in the urinary bladder of dogs, foxes, and other carnivores was investigated by Petrov and Borovkova (1942); a sojourn in an intermediate host appears obligatory.

The family Trichosomoididae, regarded by some as a subfamily under Trichuridae, contains the single species *Trichosomoides crassicauda,* parasitic in the urinary bladder and other parts of the urinary tract of

domestic rats.   The diminutive males of this species lack a copulatory
apparatus altogether and retain the stylet and other juvenile characteristics; they reside in the uterus and vagina (Fig. 190E) of the female
where they were formerly mistaken for embryos (history in Linstow,
1874).   The eggs emitted in the host urine are fully developed and are
infective to other rats; they hatch in the rat stomach and the juveniles
penetrate the stomach wall into the blood system where they are carried
to various organs; but only those that reach the urinary tract develop
normally (Thomas, 1924).

   In the family Trichinellidae, the males also lack spicule and cirrus
(Fig. 190C) but are not parasitic in the female, although somewhat smaller
than the latter.   The pharyngeal region is only slightly more slender
than the body remainder and contains one row of stichocytes (Fig.
190A, B).   The females are ovoviviparous with the vulva in the middle
of the pharyngeal region (Fig. 190A).   The family contains only one
species, *Trichinella* (= *Trichina*) *spiralis*, the trichina worm, one of the
most studied human helminths.   The life cycle of the trichina worm
differs from that of any other nematode and therefore sets this species
apart.   The adult worms inhabit the small intestine of man and numerous
other mammals, including nearly all domestic and laboratory mammals.
The males (Fig. 190B) die soon after breeding and the impregnated
females (Fig. 190A) bore through the crypts of Lieberkühn into the
lymphatic spaces where they release their young, probably about 1500
per female, and then perish.   The juveniles, 0.1 mm. long when born,
migrate by way of the lymph and blood vessels throughout the body,
eventually entering every organ and tissue but maturing to the infective
stage only in the voluntary musculature.   They enter the muscle cells
and grow to a length of 1 mm., being then fourth-stage juveniles showing
some sexual differentiation.   In this stage they coil up into a quiescent
condition (Fig. 190D) and the host animal forms a cyst around them
that eventually calcifies.   Unless the host containing such encapsulated
juvenile trichinas is eaten by a suitable host, the young worms degenerate
and die in time.   When so eaten, the juveniles undergo a final molt to
sexually mature worms in the host intestine in 2 or 3 days and the adult
females, after reaching the lymphatic spaces of the intestine, release
hordes of young whose migrations through the body evoked serious ill-
ness and even death.   Human infection usually results from eating
insufficiently cooked pork or pork products, especially sausage.   Investigations of recent years indicate that pigs usually obtain their infection
through being fed garbage containing pork scraps.   In recent years,
numerous autopsy examinations of human diaphragms for encysted
trichinae have shown that trichinosis is far more prevalent in the United
States than formerly supposed, averaging 16 per cent (Wright, Kerr, and

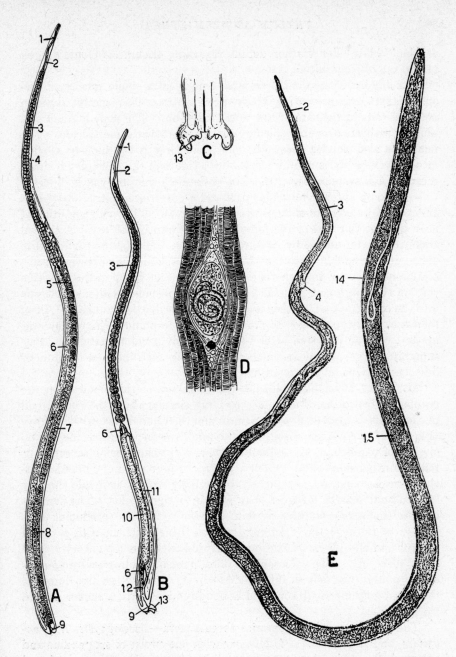

Fig. 190.—Trichuroidea (continued). *A. Trichinella spiralis*, female. *B. Trichinella*, male. *C. Trichinella*, male tail. *D. Trichinella* juvenile encapsulated in host muscle. (*A–D, after Leuckart*, 1876.) *E. Trichosomoides crassicauda*, female with male in uterus (*after Hall*, 1916). 1, nerve ring; 2, free part of pharynx; 3, stichosome along rest of pharynx; 4, vulva; 5, uterus with young; 6, intestine; 7, oviduct; 8, ovary; 9, anus; 10, testis; 11, sperm duct; 12, union of sperm duct with intestine; 13, papillae on male tail; 14, male; 15, uterus.

Jacobs, 1943). For further details regarding trichinosis Gould's book (1945) may be consulted.

The family Cystoopsidae likewise comprises a single species, *Cystoopsis acipenseri*, presenting many peculiarites. This species lives in pairs in cysts in the skin of the Volga sturgeon. The male is small and slender with an eversible spicule sheath armed with one spicule. The female is also slender anteriorly but posteriorly is enormously swollen into a globular mass containing the intestine and the coils of the single reproductive system (Fig. 191). In both sexes the pharynx is differentiated into an anterior muscular part and a posterior slender tube that is embraced by two rows of stichocytes (Fig. 192*A*). The vulva is situated near the anterior end of the female but apparently the eggs, of typical trichuroid form, escape by rupture of the cyst wall, followed by rupture of the uterine coils. According to the work of Janicki and Rasin (1930), amphipods serve as intermediate hosts. The eggs hatch in the digestive tract of the amphipod, and the young worms provided with a stylet bore into the haemocoel where they undergo considerable development. They then seek the appendages or muscles of the amphipod where they curl up and become encysted after the manner of trichina juveniles. Presumably sturgeons become infected by eating such infected amphipods but observations on this point are wanting.

31. Order Dioctophymoidea.—The members of this small order are entoparasitic worms of moderate to large size in which the caudal end of the male is provided with a muscular bell-like bursa without rays (Fig. 192*E*). Lips are absent but the mouth is encircled by one or two circlets of papillae, 6, 12, or 18 in number. The elongated pharynx lacks bulbous expansions (Fig. 192*D*). There are four rows of somato-intestinal muscles that are so attached to the body wall as to divide the four longitudinal muscle fields of that wall into eight fields. The females have a single reproductive system and are oviparous, producing eggs similar to those of the Trichuroidea, oval, thick-shelled, with a pitted surface and end plugs. Males are provided with one copulatory spicule (Fig. 192*C*, *E*). The Dioctophymoidea parasitize birds and mammals and probably use fish as intermediate hosts. There are two families, the Dioctophymidae without and Soboliphymidae with a sucker around the mouth.

The Dioctophymidae comprise three genera—*Dioctophyme*, *Eustrongylides*, and *Hystrichis*. *Dioctophyme* with one circlet of six papillae and anteriorly located vulva is represented by one species, *D. renale*, found in the abdominal cavity and kidney, sometimes other organs, of various mammals, especially the dog and other carnivores (Fig. 192*B*). Although called the kidney worm, the parasite appears to be more often found in the abdominal cavity of dogs than in the kidney (Brown, Sheldon, and Taylor,

1940) and probably invades the kidney from the abdominal cavity. Curiously, the worm is nearly always found in the right kidney. Eventually the entire kidney tissue may be destroyed by the worms so that the greatly enlarged kidney consists merely of a connective tissue capsule enclosing a coiled mass of worms (Fig. 192*B*). The female kidney worm, blood-red in color, is one of the largest known nematodes, reaching a length of 1 m. The smaller males do not exceed 45 cm. in length (Fig.

Fig. 191.—Trichuroidea (continued). Female *Cystoopsis* dissected from cyst (*after Janicki and Rasin*, 1930). 1, anterior end; 2, body; 3, coils of viscera in body.

192*C*). The life cycle was imperfectly known until recently when it was described by Woodhead (1945). The uncleaved eggs voided in the urine develop slowly outdoors, requiring about 6 months to develop to an infective juvenile stage. Branchiobdellid worms constitute the first intermediate host; these are peculiar oligochaetes that are epizoic on crayfish. The young worm hatches in the digestive tract of the branchiobdellids and penetrates into the coelom where it occupies various organs and tissues, finally encysting. Fish constitute the second intermediate host, devouring the branchiobdellids directly or with the castoff crayfish exoskeleton. Within the fish, the juvenile kidney worm migrates to the mesenteries where it again encysts but continues to grow and develop an

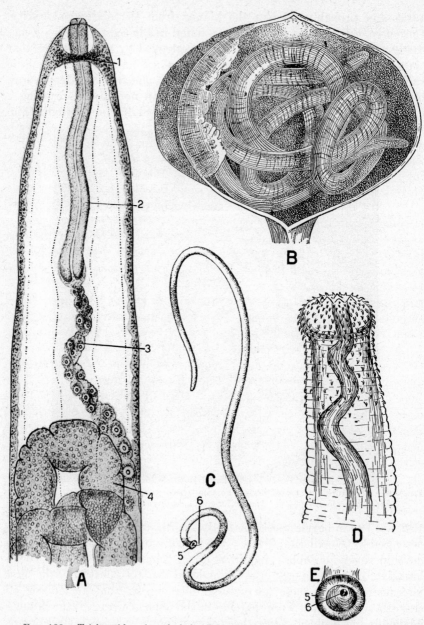

FIG. 192.—Trichuroidea (concluded), Dioctophymoidea. *A.* Anterior end of male *Cystoopsis* (*after Janicki and Rasin,* 1930). *B. Dioctophyme renale* coiled in host kidney. *C. D. renale,* male. (*C, D, after Railliet,* 1893.) *D. Hystrichus,* anterior end. *E. Hystrichus,* male bursa. (*D, E, after Jägerskiöld,* 1909.) 1, nerve ring; 2, free part of pharynx; 3, stichosome; 4, coils of testis; 5, bursa; 6, spicule.

adult type of head, being then infective when infected fish are devoured by the definitive host. The entire cycle requires about 2 years. Evidence that fish are involved in the life cycle was previously presented by Ciurea (1921) and Law and Kennedy (1932). *Eustrongylides* (Fig. 193*C, D*) with 12 or 18 papillae in two circlets and vulva near the anus inhabits the proventriculus of various aquatic birds (Jägerskiöld, 1909; Cram, 1927). In this genus also fish are implicated in the life cycle for juvenile *Eustrongylides* have frequently been found in *Fundulus* enclosed in fibrous capsules attached to the mesenteries (Chapin, 1926; Brand, 1938; Cullinan, 1945). The genus *Hystrichis* (Jägerskiöld, 1909) differs from other dioctophymids in the presence of spines anteriorly (Fig. 192*D*) or over the entire body; there are six small papillae in one circle on the head and the vulva is close to the anus. The species of *Hystrichis* also inhabit the proventriculus of aquatic birds.

The family Soboliphymidae contains one genus, *Soboliphyme* with principal species *baturini*, found in the digestive tract of sables, foxes, and the domestic cat in Kamchatka and Siberia (Petrov, 1930) and the wolverine in North America (Price, 1930). The genus is small, to 20 mm., and is distinguished from all other nematodes by the presence of a large oral sucker similar to the oral sucker of digenetic trematodes (Fig. 193*A, B*). The females are oviparous with the vulva near the anus.

32. Ecology and Physiology.—As already intimated, the free-living nematodes occur in almost every conceivable habitat from arid deserts to the bottoms of lakes and rivers and from hot springs to polar seas (Cobb, 1914a). Marine nematodes are found in any sample of bottom muck in the littoral zones and also descend to great depths in the ocean. However, very little exact information is available about the ecology of marine nematodes. They have been studied chiefly along the north coasts of Europe and in dredgings of marine expeditions and these publications are mostly of a taxonomic nature. Stekhoven in an ecological study of Zuider Sea nematodes (1931, 1935) limited himself chiefly to salinity relations; most species were found to endure a wide range of salinity but an optimal salinity exists for each species, so that the dominant species in different localities vary with salinity. However, other factors are important in the distribution of marine nematodes, especially the amount of food present and this in turn is related to the characteristics of the bottom. A mucky bottom rich in diatoms, algae, and organic detritus supports a vast nematode population of which some counts are available. Stekhoven found 4,420,000 nematodes per square meter of surface muck off the Dutch Coast. Bougis (1946) got up to 456 nematodes in the top 4 cm. of 4.5 sq. cm. areas at a depth of 30 m. in the French Mediterranean. In 1 cc. of mud at Teneriffe Allgen (1933) counted 45 nematodes belonging to 19 species. Microletzky (1922) found 1074 nematodes belonging to 20 genera and 36 species in 6.7 cc. of bottom material on the Italian Coast at Rovigno. Sandy beaches are usually poor in nematodes because of a lack of food in such situations, but Cobb (1917, 1929b) reported 527,000,000 per acre in the top 3 inches of lower beach sand on the Massachusetts Coast and believes there are thousands

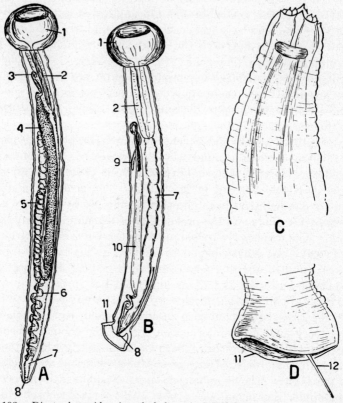

Fig. 193.—Dioctophymoidea (concluded). *A. Soboliphyme,* female. *B. Soboliphyme,* male. (*A, B, after Petrov,* 1930.) *C. Eustrongylides ignotus,* anterior end. *D. E. ignotus,* male bursa. (*C, D, after Jägerskiöld,* 1909.) 1, oral sucker; 2, pharynx; 3, vulva; 4, uterus; 5, oviduct; 6, ovary; 7, intestine; 8, anus; 9, testis; 10, seminal vesicle; 11, bursa; 12, spicule.

of millions per acre in mucky ocean bottoms. In general it appears that nematodes are the most abundant of all the small Metazoa found in the bottom muck of oceans.

The marine nematode species appear to have a wide distribution and are not known to be limited to specific environments or regions. Nematodes have repeatedly been dredged in arctic and antarctic seas but offer no peculiarities, belonging to common genera and species. Although the temperature of polar waters is near or below the freezing point of fresh water, nematodes may occur in great abundance in polar seas; thus Cobb (1914c) records hundreds of nematodes in a thimbleful of dredged bottom material in the antarctic. There are no genuine pelagic marine nematodes. Micoletzky (1922) found three species on floating *Sargassum* from the Sargasso Sea but all have a wide distribution elsewhere. However, the *Sargassum* specimens were more transparent, more delicate, less cuticularized, and smaller than specimens of the same species from coastal waters.

Very little has been done on the marine nematodes of American coasts. In 1936, B. G. Chitwood published a couple of papers on nematodes from the Carolina Coast and Allgen in 1947 reported on a nematode collection from the coasts of Panama and California. This collection contained 100 species, 51 of which were already known from a wide variety of other localities.

The fresh-water and terrestrial nematodes are also abundant throughout the earth and occupy a wide variety of habitats. Most of them are cosmopolitan or at least have a wide range of distribution, as nematodes because of their small size are easily spread around by winds, by animals, and on plant shipments. A few species, however, appear limited to very peculiar habitats as *Turbatrix silusiae* in the felt mats under beer mugs in Silesian Germany (de Man, 1914), *Aphelenchus nivalis* on a snow field in Spitsbergen (Auriviellius, 1883), and *Anguillula* (?) *nepenthicola* in the pitchers of the pitcher plant *Nepenthes* in the Netherlands East Indies (Micoletzky and Menzel, 1929).

Not much ecological information is available about the fresh-water nematodes. They occur everywhere in both standing and running waters but are most abundant in the littoral zone of lakes. Most genera and many species of fresh-water nematodes are cosmopolitan or at least have a wide distribution, being readily spread about by animals. Ecological studies are limited to the central European area (Hofmänner, 1913; Hofmänner and Menzel, 1915; Micoletzky, 1914, 1925a). The first two authors studied the nematodes of Lake Geneva and other Swiss lakes. They found a total of 43 species belonging to 19 genera and divided these into three ecological groups: littoral forms found among plant growth on muddy bottom; forms from deeper waters (to 310 m.); and cosmopolites occurring at any depth and common to many lakes. The majority of species belong in the first category but a few species preferring deeper waters were encountered. Micoletzky (1914) also studied the aquatic nematodes of Switzerland and obtained a total of 55 species from several lakes, mostly widely distributed forms. Three habitats in shallow lakes were recognized: stony bottom, mucky bottom, and bottom with plant growth. The second has the greatest number of species but the first the most individuals; thus, 5000 nematodes may occur in the surface accumulations on a stone the size of the hand.   Pasture puddles also harbor a rich nematode fauna; such puddles are subject to much seasonal change, enduring great fluctuations of temperature in summer, when the nematode population is rich in individuals, and being flooded with melting snow in spring, when a different nematode fauna, abundant in species but poor in individuals, obtains.   Micoletzky also found nematodes in mountain streams, mostly in mosses, and even two species in tumbling torrents. In such habitats nematodes make extensive use of the caudal glands for clinging to objects.

An extensive study of the nematodes of Danish lakes and moors was made by Micoletzky (1925a), who found a total of 73 species in bodies of fresh water and 87 species in water-saturated areas.   In the lakes, the following types of habitat or biotopes were recognized: sandy bottom with some detritus, stony bottom covered with algal growth, stony bottom with incrustations of blue-green algae, mucky bottom, and areas of emergent vegetation such as sedges and reeds.   In each biotope a more or less characteristic assemblage of nematode species was found, of which certain ones dominated in numbers.   The type of food available in the different biotopes appeared to be the chief factor determining the species found, but the oxygen supply was also of importance.   Sandy bottom was dominated by species of *Trilobus*, *Chromadora*, and *Monhystera* and algal growth on stones by the same *Chromadora* species.   The *Chromadora* species are algal feeders that also require a high oxygen content of the water and soon die when brought into aquaria.   The zone of emergent vegetation, characterized by a high oxygen content due to wave action and a rich algal growth between the plant stems, was occupied mainly by algal and detritus eaters, again with *Chromadora* species dominant. Mucky bottom, more to the interior of the lakes, had a poor nematode fauna, with *Trilobus* and *Theristus* species as the leading forms.   Several other aquatic biotopes were also studied.   Moor lakes were found to have a much poorer nematode fauna than ordinary lakes and ponds also showed a reduced nematode fauna with *Plectus tenuis* as a common species, accompanied by other feeders on plant detritus and algae.   Small pools either in or apart from moors contained relatively few nematodes. *Plectus cirratus* probably transported thither by mosquitoes was found in water-containing cavities in trees.   Treeless water-soaked areas such as swampy meadows and mossy moors were found to harbor a fair nematode fauna consisting of species characteristic of such habitats intermingled with terrestrial species; fresh-water species were mostly wanting.   *Bunonema* and *Criconema* (Fig. 101*A*, *C*) were typical inhabitants of mossy moors.

There are a number of reports of the nematode fauna of hot and mineral springs, where nematodes live at temperatures of 35 to 53°C., often in the presence of various minerals. Most of the nematodes of such habitats are cosmopolites, hence adapted to a wide range of conditions, and it has been noted that they rather resemble the nematodes of brackish waters, no doubt because most thermal waters are high in salt

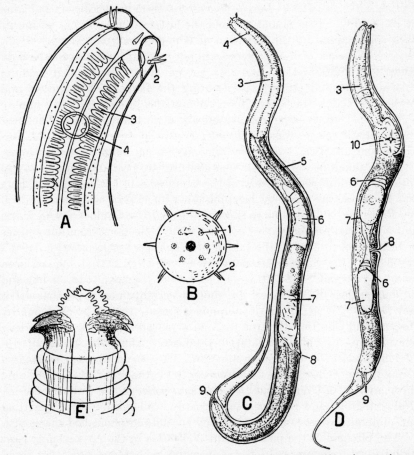

FIG. 194.—Some common terrestrial nematodes. *A. Monhystera filiformis,* anterior end (*after de Coninck, 1940*). *B. Monhystera filiformis, en face* view. *C. M. filiformis,* entire worm. *D. Diploscapter coronata,* entire worm. (*B–D, after Hoeppli and Chu, 1932*). *E.* Anterior end of *Diploscapter coronata* (*after Steiner, 1921*). 1, inner labial papillae; 2, outer circlet of bristles; 3, pharynx; 4, amphid; 5, intestine; 6, ovary; 7, uterus; 8, vulva; 9, anus; 10, pharyngeal bulb.

content. Among the cosmopolitan species frequently found in hot springs may be mentioned *Mononchus brachyuris, M. macrostoma, Monhystera filiformis* (Fig. 194*A–C*), *Plectus parvus, Trilobus allophysis, Aphelenchoides parietinus, Chromogaster gracilis,* and *Diploscapter coronatus.* The last is a curious-looking nematode (Fig. 194*D, E*) with a wide distribution in soil, especially around diseased plant roots, and in sewage beds, and has even been found in the human digestive tract (Chandler, 1938). Besides cosmopolites, thermal waters contain nematodes apparently limited to this habitat. Thus Linstow (1901) described *Chromadora salinarum* from Nauheim springs at 31.6°C. and 2.18 per cent salinity; also (1901) *Dorylaimus atratus* from hot springs near Padua at 40 to 45°C. Issel (1906) refound the latter at 46 to 47°C., noting its dark color caused by the ingestion of blue-green algae. Menzel (1925) reported a species of *Adoncholaimus* in hot mineral springs in the Netherlands East Indies at 45°C. and 2.67 per cent salt content, mostly sodium chloride. Hoeppli (1926), investigating the fauna of hot springs and geysers in Yellowstone Park, found nematodes in only 9 of 39 samples, only three of which came from waters above air temperature. The most characteristic species was *Dorylaimus thermae* in waters up to 53°C., but of the other 10 species two, *Microlaimoides setosus* and *Chromadora nanna*, although taken in water at air temperature, are probably limited to hot springs. An interesting study of the nematodes of hot springs in China and Formosa was made by Hoeppli and Chu (1932), who listed several species as probably limited to thermal waters. De Coninck (1940) found four cosmopolitan nematodes in 5 out of 46 collections from hot springs in Iceland; of interest is the taking of *Monhystera filiformis* (Fig. 194*C*) at 53.5°C., the highest temperature at which nematodes have been found. Pax and Soos (1943) reported that the nematodes of hot and sulphur springs in Germany are mostly cosmopolites with *Mononchus* and *Dorylaimus* as the most common genera. It was pointed out by Hoeppli and Chu that the true thermal nematodes show close taxonomic relationship in widely separated localities. Thus one notes *Microlaimoides setosus* in the Yellowstone and *M. lingi* in China; *Chromadora nanna* in the Yellowstone, *C. salinarum* in Germany, and closely related chromadorids in China; and *Dorylaimus thermae* in the Yellowstone, *D. atratus* in Italy, and *D. couteri* in Germany. The nematodes of thermal and mineral waters do not present any special morphological characters.

The pitchers of the pitcher plant *Nepenthes* in the Netherlands East Indies furnish an unusual habitat in which nematodes and other small animals occur (Menzel, 1923, 1929; Micoletzky and Menzel, 1929). These pitchers act as a trap for insects which die in the acid fluid therein. The pitchers lying on the ground were found to contain ordinary nematodes of the genera *Plectus, Dorylaimus, Rhabditis,* and *Diplogaster* but in aerial pitchers only one species, *Anguillula nepenthicola,* not found elsewhere, occurred; as many as 200 specimens might be taken in one pitcher. The nematode was always associated with the remains of dipterous insects which probably serve as the means of transport of the nematodes into the pitchers. It seems likely that nematodes occur in other water-holding devices of tropical plants.

Cobb (1918) reported hundreds to thousands of millions of nematodes, often of one or a few species, mostly carnivorous types, in the top inches of sand of sand filter beds employed for water purification. Peters (1920) investigated sewage-disposal beds of London where the sewage percolates over stones and found in the bacterial films on the stones scavenger types of nematodes such as *Diploscapter coronatus* (Fig. 194*D*) and species of *Diplogaster, Dorylaimus,* and *Rhabditis.*

The available material indicates that the nematode fauna of fresh waters consists chiefly of widely distributed species. Some of these can live in almost any kind of habitat but the majority are somewhat limited to a certain constellation of environmental conditions.

No sharp distinction can be drawn between the fresh-water and terrestrial nematodes since the latter probably for the most part really dwell in the water films between soil particles. Extremely dry and extremely wet soils are generally poor in nematodes which are best developed in soils with 10 to 70 per cent moisture. All observers agree that the soil nematodes are most numerous around the roots of plants and therefore their distribution in the soil is not uniform. Nematodes also occur chiefly in the top few inches of the soil and fall off rapidly in numbers at greater depths. The nematode population of the soil is highest in fertilized agricultural lands where the count may run to fantastic figures. Thus Brown (1931) reported two to six billion nematodes per acre in the top 3 inches of farm soils in North China that had been fertilized with animal and human feces. In undisturbed soils covered with grass and sod or not grown to crops the counts ran from seven to nine hundred millions. Cobb (1914a) gave a figure of three billion nematodes per acre in low-lying alluvial soil in the United States and Micoletzky (1921) confirmed this count for Austria. Thorne (1927) studying the soil nematodes of sugar beet fields in Utah and Idaho found eight hundred million to over a billion per acre, belonging to about 35 species (apart from billions of the sugar-beet nematode). The figures of Steiner and Heinly (1922) for various parts of the United States are somewhat lower—one to six hundred millions per acre in the top 6 inches of soil—and still lower counts obtain for English farm lands. According to Steiner and Heinly, nematodes may be found in the soil to a depth of 25 feet.

The outstanding work on the free-living terrestrial nematodes is that of Micoletzky (1921), whose studies were made in Austria and adjacent regions, and supplement and extend the earlier work of de Man (1884) for the Netherlands. The areas studied by these two authors were thus very different ecologically, the one consisting of a variety of alpine and subalpine habitats, the other composed of nonforested lowlands, mostly of a marshy or sandy nature. Some species of nematodes were common to the two regions, although often differing in abundance, but for the most part the species encountered in the two countries differed. Thus the indications are that some nematode species can live in a wide range of terrestrial habitats but others are somewhat limited to certain ecological surroundings. Of 127 species and 25 varieties collected by Micoletzky, 8 species and 3 subspecies were encountered in all the habitats studied and 11 others occurred in more than one type of habitat. Micoletzky recognized the following ecological subdivisions of the area studied: marshes and bogs saturated with acid water, fields and meadows, forest floor, moss-covered ground, and sandy ground. The first habitat contained chiefly fresh-water nematodes and there appear to be a few species limited to moors poor in or devoid of calcium. Fields and meadows yield the most abundant nematode fauna and present a variety of local conditions that affect the nematode distribution. The forest floor was found to be poor in nematodes but a number of species occur in mosses. In the sandy areas of the Netherlands, de Man recorded a number of characteristic species.

There have been a number of studies of the nematode fauna of mosses, lichens, and other cushion plants in various parts of the world, probably because such materials are easily collected and preserved (Steiner, 1916, for points in the antarctic; Menzel, 1920, for Spitsbergen; Heinis, 1920, for the Swiss Alps; Micoletzky, 1925, for Sumatra, Trinidad, and East Africa; Heinis, 1928, for the island of Krakatao in the Sunda Straits; Burkholder, 1928, for the Alps; Allgen, 1929, for Tasmania, New Zealand, and other Pacific Islands; Rahm, 1937, for China). Mosses and other cushion plants harbor a characteristic fauna of protozoans, rotifers, tardigrades, and nematodes; these are capable of enduring extremes of cold, heat, and desiccation, passing under such conditions into a dormant state and reviving when better conditions obtain (further later). The nematodes of such habitats are much the same throughout the world, being species of *Mononchus, Dorylaimus, Plectus, Monhystera, Cephalobus, Trilobus, Tripyla, Tylenchus, Aphelenchus*, and other tylenchoids. Micoletzky (1925) states that the nematodes of tropical mosses are somewhat more characteristic than those of mosses from temperate and polar zones.

In a study of the soil nematodes in the foothills of the Alps to 2000 m., Burkhalter (1928) found an abundance of individuals but a paucity of species, all of types capable of enduring extreme conditions. The abundance of nematode individuals was positively related to moisture and the presence of plant roots; altitude and type of substratum were of little or no consequence except that the number of species declined with increasing altitude. The nematode population declined in winter and increased in summer with a maximum in September and October.

The reason for the aggregation of soil nematodes around the roots of plants seems to be that most of these feed on dead, decaying, or diseased plant material. Marcinowsky in studies of such nematodes (1906, 1909) terms them semiparasitic, but saprophagous is a more correct appellation. Lands grown to cereal crops were found very rich in such saprophagous nematodes of the genera *Cephalobus, Rhabditis,* and *Plectus.* Around the roots of a 10 cm. high wheat seedling 95 nematodes belonging to 13 species were counted. Such nematodes were also found to aggregate in germinating seeds; as many as 75 worms belonging to several species might be found in one germinating wheat seed. The saprophagous nematodes often accompany true phyoparasitic nematodes, attacking diseased plant tissues caused by the activities of the latter. Soil nematodes also, of course, include predaceous types.

The terrestrial nematodes may ascend on vegetation by swimming upward after rains and then establishing themselves in damp sites as crevices of bark or leaf axils. Greater heights are attained by the use of insect or other animal transports, either occasionally or regularly. Cobb (1914a) noted that saprophagous nematodes feeding on diseased apples on the ground had been carried to similar apples on the tree by wasps and other insects; a single apple contained 90,000 nematodes of several different species. Nematodes are also abundant in the exudations ("slime flux") from the wounds of trees, in fungus growths and galls on trees, and in the galleries made by bark beetles and other borers. In short, they will occur wherever decaying vegetable or animal food is available.

In general it appears that the terrestrial nematodes, like the aquatic ones, are classifiable into three ecological categories: cosmopolitan species that can live under almost any conditions, widely distributed species that are somewhat limited to particular combinations of environmental conditions, and sharply local species that are found only in very special, often peculiar, situations. Moisture, the presence of plant roots, and the presence of decaying plant and animal material are the chief factors favoring the occurrence of free-living soil nematodes. The texture of the soil is of some importance as the nematode population is generally higher in lighter than in heavy soils (Thorne, 1927). The pH of the soil appears to be of little consequence.

In a general consideration of the free-living nematodes, Steiner (1917) remarks that they show no particular morphological adaptations to aquatic or terrestrial life. The marine forms tend to be more bristly and more given to cuticular ornamentations than fresh-water or terrestrial species; but extreme cuticular ornamentations may occur in terrestrial nematodes as witness the scales of *Criconema* (Fig. 101*C*), the warts of *Bunonema* (Fig. 101*A*), and the head excrescences of *Wilsonema* (Fig. 96*B, C*), *Acrobeles* (Fig. 96*E–G*), and related types. The marine nematodes usually have their excretory apparatus in the form of ventral glands rather than excretory canals, are more generally provided with caudal glands than are fresh-water or terrestrial nematodes, and commonly lack caudal alae or a bursa.   But it appears that these are primitive rather than adaptive characters.   As already noted, the fresh-water and terrestrial nematodes are closely affiliated.   According to Steiner more than half the fresh-water species of Europe also occur in the soil and there are very few nematodes strictly limited to fresh water; but no case is known of a marine species that also inhabits fresh water or soil, or vice versa.   Both marine and fresh-water species spread into brackish waters but seem never to cross the line into the other habitat.   Apparently the terrestrial nematodes have arisen directly from the marine ones and then have spread into fresh-water habitats.

Some terrestrial nematodes, especially those of mosses, lichens, and alpine plants, can endure great extremes of temperature and desiccation. *Plectus* in the desiccated state was found by Rahm (1921, 1922, 1926, 1928, 1937) to recover after exposure to liquid air ($-190°$C.) for 125 hours, liquid hydrogen ($-253°$C.) for 26 hours, and liquid helium ($-270°$C.) for $7\frac{3}{4}$ hours.   Although the vinegar eel in general is poorly resistant to freezing and desiccation, this nematode was alive after solidification in liquid air for 1 minute (Luyet and Hartung, 1941) if subjected to some preliminary desiccation; but the worms died in a few hours after revival whereas moss nematodes recover completely from freezing.   Rapid drying of moss nematodes on a slide is fatal but when dried naturally in moss cushions or similar plants they survive for months and years.   Menzel (1920) reported that Spitsbergen mosses kept dry for 2 years, yielded on wetting live specimens of *Plectus*, *Dorylaimus*, and *Cephalobus*.   Dried and hard frozen mosses and rosette plants and frozen soil from the Alps yield lively nematodes on wetting or thawing (Heinis, 1920; Burkhalter, 1920).   Live nematodes were obtained on wetting a sample of moss kept dried in a herbarium for $4\frac{1}{2}$ years.   The longest records for endurance of desiccation concern the phytoparasitic nematodes (further below).

Very little work has been done on the action of other factors on free-living nematodes.   Stephenson (1942, 1944) worked on the osmotic relations of *Rhabditis terrestris*, obtained from rotting earthworms, and found an osmotic pressure equivalent to 1.8 per cent sodium chloride satisfactory for culture of the worm.   The worm swells in distilled water but soon regulates by losing water, mainly through the anus.   In hypertonic media it loses water but recovers by emitting osmotically active substances.   Osmotic regulation appears to be controlled primarily by the epidermis, not by the cuticle.   Imperviousness of the body wall to vital dyes was noted by Honda (1924) for *Rh. elegans;* neutral red and methylene blue were effective only by way of the mouth. This species also proved highly resistant to other chemicals. Several studies have been made on the resistance of the vinegar eel to various factors (Henneberg, 1900; Peters, 1928; Belehradek and Schwarz, 1928; Belehradek and Necasova, 1929; Stoklasa, 1933). This nematode can endure a concentration of acetic acid of 13.5 per cent (vinegar generally contains less than 10 per cent) but flourishes only at concentrations of 6 per cent or less with a pH of 2.7. A pH of 1.4 is fatal to the worm as is also a concentration of hydrochloric acid of only 0.4 per cent. The vinegar eel is also very resistant to alkalies, enduring these to a pH of 11.5, and in general is far more resistant than other small fresh-water invertebrates to acids, especially organic acids of the formic acid series, and to salts, and toxic substances, being able to live for a few hours in mercuric chloride fixatives that are usually instantly fatal. Free-living nematodes in general show very little resistance to heat, cold, and drying except those that naturally live in habitats subject to such extremes (see above).

A few references are available on the responses of free-living nematodes to isolated factors. Clapham (1931), working with *Dorylaimus* and *Rhabditis* species from sewage beds, was unable to obtain any very definite responses to temperature, light, or chemicals diffusing from the end of a capillary tube placed in their culture. A positive response to agar in the tube was noted. A similar indifference to various chemicals placed in a small depression in the agar culture was noted by Taniguchi (1933) for *Rh. filiformis*, except that dilute acids were attractive to the worms.

Because of their stiff cuticle and lack of circular muscles, the nematodes possess poor powers of locomotion. In an article on the locomotion of nematodes Stauffer (1924) recognizes six types of progression. Swimming is accomplished by serpentine undulations in the dorsoventral plane; it is employed by relatively few nematodes, chiefly algal inhabitants, and is kept up only for short distances and at slight speed. The other types of locomotion involve progression on a substratum on which purchase is obtained by bristles, body rings, other cuticular excrescences, or adhesive secretions. Gliding, very characteristic of algal inhabitants, is accomplished by the same succession of serpentine waves as characterize swimming. Crawling consists of alternate lengthening and shortening of the body which is held straight during elongation but exhibits two types as regards the shortened phase. In the one type, the body is thrown into sinuous curves during shortening while in the other it remains straight (Fig. 195G–K). The latter type resembles earthworm progression and is associated with strong annulation since a grip on the substratum by the annule edge is necessary for this kind of progression. The last two types of locomotion involve the use of stilt bristles assisted

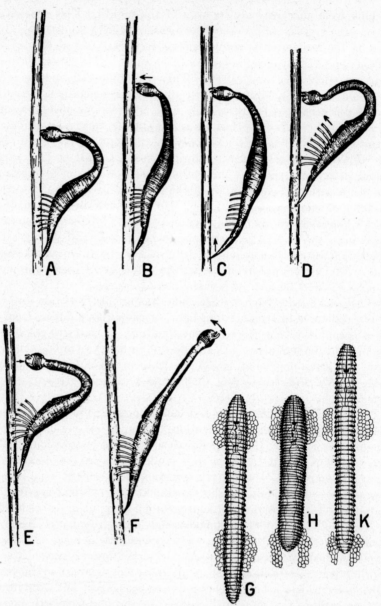

Fig. 195.—Locomotion of nematodes.　*A–F*. Locomotion of a draconematid.　*A*. With stilt bristles fastened, head detaches.　*B*. Head reaches forward and attaches.　*C*. Stilt bristles detach.　*D*. Posterior end is brought forward.　*E*. Stilt bristles attach.　*F*. Head again reaches forward.　*G–K*. Earthworm type of locomotion, *Hoplolaimus*.　*G*. Anterior end gets purchase by means of annules.　*H*. Body contracts, bringing posterior end forward.　*K*. Posterior end gets purchase, anterior part stretches forward.　(*All after Stauffer*, 1924.)

by the adhesive secretion emitted from the bristle tips. The Desmoscolecidae (Fig. 100*D*) walk upon their bristles much after the manner of ordinary lepidopterous larvae, with contraction waves progressing from the rear end forward; the thick body rings remain unaltered but the depressed rings can be shortened. The Draconematidae (Fig. 138*A*) loop along in a leech-like manner, attaching first the head bristles, then moving up the rear part of the body, then attaching body stilt bristles, and so on (Fig. 195*A–F*). The Epsilonematidae lack adhesive bristles on the anterior end and therefore loop by alternate attachment of the body stilt bristles and the tail tip supplied by the caudal adhesive glands. It is to be noted, finally, that all locomotory movements of nematodes take place in the dorsoventral plane.

Many of the microscopic nematodes employ what may be called thrashing movements that seem to serve no locomotory function. The animal lies upon its side and alternately brings the body ends together and straightens itself, or curves in the opposite direction. According to Stauffer this thrashing about serves the function of investigating the environment.

As regards food habits, the free-living nematodes are saprophagous, herbivorous, or carnivorous. The saprophagous forms feed on detritus and dead and decaying plant and animal material; here perhaps may be included those that eat the accompaniments of decay as bacteria, yeasts, fungal filaments, etc. The vinegar eel, for instance, seems to eat primarily the bacteria, yeasts, and molds present in old-fashioned processes of making vinegar. The herbivorous nematodes are those that feed on green plants, chiefly diatoms and algae. Diatoms appear to constitute the main food item of many marine nematodes and green and blue-green algae are devoured by numerous fresh-water forms. From such feeders on live vegetation is but a short step to phytoparasitism by way of soil nematodes that pierce the roots of plants and suck their juices. Carnivorous or predaceous nematodes occur in every type of habitat but are especially abundant in the soil where Cobb (1917) reported 30,000,000 mononchs per acre in the top 6 inches of soil in arable land in New Jersey and Thorne (1927) estimated up to 300,000,000 mononchs per acre in sugar beet fields in Utah and Idaho. The predaceous nematodes eat primarily rotifers, tardigrades, small annelids, and other nematodes (Menzel, 1920a). *Oncholaimus dujardinii* was described by Stekhoven (1933) as thrusting its head down the digestive tract of bryozoans and sucking in the intestinal cells. Predaceous nematodes are usually either provided with buccal teeth, as the oncholaims, mononchs, and other enoploids, or with a buccal spear as the tylenchoids, or with an odontostyle, as dorylaims. The feeding behavior of the enoploid type has been described for *Monochus papillatus* by Steiner and Heinly (1922). This

mononch eats primarily other nematodes.   The lips attach firmly to the
victim, a hole is made in the latter by the mononch's dorsal tooth, and
the mononch then sucks out the fluid contents of the prey by vigorous
sucking movements of the pharynx.   Prey may also be swallowed whole.
A graphic account of the feeding process in dorylaims has been given by
Linford (1937).   After contact, the lips of the dorylaim are firmly
applied to the prey, the stylet is thrust out repeatedly until the prey is
penetrated, and then, with the stylet held protruded into the prey, the

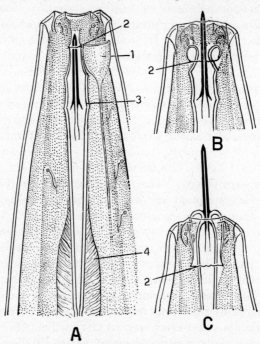

Fig. 196.—Dorylaim *Nygolaimus* using its spear (*after Thorne*, 1930).   *A.* Spear in
place.   *B.* Spear partly extruded.   *C.* Spear fully extruded; note eversion of buccal capsule
cephalad to spear ring.   1, amphid; 2, guide ring; 3, buccal capsule; 4, pharynx.

contents of the latter are drawn in through the stylet by rhythmic sucking actions of the pharynx.   Periods of suction alternate with periods of
rest until finally the prey is reduced to an empty shell.   In the dorylaim
Nygolaimus (Fig. 196) (Thorne, 1930), the tooth lacks an opening; it
is driven into the prey (chiefly oligochaetes) by a forward thrust of the
pharynx (Fig. 196*A–C*) and is then withdrawn, so that the contents of
the prey are sucked directly into the pharynx.   However, most dorylaims
suck plant juices.   Tylenchoids are mostly phytoparasites but some are
predaceous as *Aphelenchoides tenuicaudatus* observed feeding on nematodes by Linford (1937).   The feeding process is similar to that of other
hollow-stylet nematodes but of interest here is the fact that the secretion

of the dorsal pharyngeal gland was seen ejected into the pharynx and then passed through the stylet into the prey. This secretion or saliva appears both to paralyze the prey and to initiate digestion of its organs, causing these to break down into an emulsion. Cases were observed in which the prey was abandoned after being pierced by the stylet; nevertheless such victims showed paralysis and inner disintegration. Tylenchoids may also feed on fungus hyphae which are pierced and sucked in the same manner as animal prey (Christie and Arndt, 1936). Predaceous nematodes in general can feed only when in contact with a solid substratum on which they obtain purchase while thrusting out the spear.

Observers are agreed that nematodes seem unable to detect prey at even very short distances and recognize food organisms only after making contact with them by way of the lips which evidently act as their chief chemotactic organs. However, there seem to be no experiments in which damaged prey giving off juices was employed except those of Buerkel (1900) who noted an accumulation of *Oncholaimus vulgaris* on pieces of mussel and concluded the worms must have been oriented by perception at a distance. No participation of the amphids in food finding has been noticed.

The free-living nematodes, especially saprophagous rhabditoids, are readily cultivable on almost any kind of organic material undergoing putrefaction. Such cultures also furnish data on fertility and longevity. Maupas (1900) cultivated 18 species of rhabditoids, some for many generations, on depression slides but gave little information as to culture composition. The species studied were either parthenogenetic females or protandrous hermaphrodites that continued to lay unfertilized eggs after using up their stock of spermatozoa. Some of the data obtained may be quoted. *Rhabditis elegans*, a common species, lays fertile eggs to the number of about 240 for about 3 days, then may lay infertile eggs, with a total longevity from egg to death of 10 to 12 days; but life may be shortened to 7 days if eggs hatch in the uterus and the young devour the infertile eggs and eventually the mother's viscera. In *Diplogaster robustus*, the eggs hatch in 12 hours, development to sexual maturity requires 3 days, fertile eggs to the number of 140 to 230 are laid for 3 days, infertile eggs for 6 to 8 days longer, and the total life duration is about 16 days. A longer life span is shown by *Cephalobus dubius*, in which the development of the eggs requires 3 days, growth to sexual maturity 10 to 11 days, production of fertile eggs continues for 2 months to a total of about 415, production of sterile eggs for another month, and death ensues after an age of 5 months.

Metcalf (1902) cultured *Rhabditis brevispina* on agar containing plant juices. Potts (1910) reported that large numbers of soil nematodes can be obtained by placing scraps of raw meat on samples of rich soil; he found that hermaphrodites such as species of *Rhabditis* and *Diplogaster* usually lay 200 to 250 fertile eggs whereas bisexual species generally produce 700 to 800 fertilized eggs. Welch and Wehrle (1918) cultivated the parthenogenetic *Cephalobus dubius* and the bisexual *Pristionchus* (= *Diplogaster*) *aerivora* on triturated eggs, ovaries, or tissues of grass-hoppers and other insects, and also on diluted egg yolk; the former lived about 30 to 50 days, producing up to 285 eggs, and the latter (see also Merrill and Ford, 1916) about 18 days, producing 55 eggs and requiring frequent copulations. Honda (1925), using a medium of peptone, beef extract, salt, and water, obtained better survival of *P. aerivora*, to 54 days, with a production of 465 to 731 eggs. The vinegar eel was cultured by Peters (1925) on putrefying fruits and vegetables, also on gelatin or egg white in vinegar. Zimmerman (1921) and Guyénot and Zimmermann (1921) found that it will not grow in bacteria-free vinegar, as it requires live or dead bacteria as food, but would thrive and reproduce in a sterile medium containing 2 per cent peptone, 0.5 per cent common salt, 0.5 per cent lecithin, and yeast autolysate. Chandler (1924) publicized the method of culturing soil nematodes on nutrient agar (agar containing beef extract, peptones, and often also other nutrients) and this method has since been generally employed for rhabditoids (Dotterweich, 1938; Dougherty and Calhoun, 1948). Stephenson (1942) reared *Rhabditis terrestris* successfully on agar mixed with earth-worm broth; but found that actually the nematodes ate bacteria and the cysts of a small flagellate growing in the culture. Dougherty and Calhoun (1948) give a valuable review of previous experiences in culti-vating rhabditoid soil nematodes. By adding peanut butter, inulin, pieces of raw liver, pieces of mushrooms, or earthworm fragments to topsoil, they obtained an abundamce of soil nematodes from which *Rhabditis pellio* was selected and cultured in a bacteria-free medium composed of nutrient agar, homogenized liver, and raw liver extract; but growth was poorer than in bacteria-containing media and a weakening of the strain soon became apparent.

Somewhat more difficulty was experienced by Glaser and associates in growing *Neoplectana glaseri* in artificial media. This work, summar-ized in Glaser (1940) and Glaser, McCoy, and Girth (1940), is always quoted in the literature as a case of the successful culture of a parasitic nematode through its entire cycle. But *N. glaseri* cannot be regarded as a parasitic nematode and its culture is similar to that of other rhab-ditoids. The culture medium consists of a dextrose-veal-agar combina-tion to which living yeast is added. The females are ovoviviparous, producing about 15 young, and 5 to 7 days elapse between successive generations. Eventually, however, the strain weakens on the medium cited and females cease producing eggs; but rejuvenation of the cultures can be accomplished by sprinkling on them dried powdered beef ovary or beetle grubs or by passages through live insect larvae. Better results have been attained in bacteria-free cultures (Glaser, 1940b), consisting of agar slants on which are placed pieces of animal tissue, as mouse embryos, beef kidney, rabbit ovary, or rabbit kidney. *N. glaseri* is obviously a saprophagous nematode, requiring decomposing animal flesh. *N. chresima*, another facultative insect parasite, has been similarly cultured successfully in sterile media consisting of rabbit kidney, beef liver, or beef kidney on a salt-agar base (Glaser, McCoy, and Girth, 1942). This species is also ovoviviparous, producing 250 to 400 young.

Predacious nematodes may be cultivated by feeding them rhabditoids grown on nutrient agar. Steiner and Heinly (1922) thus reared *Mononchus papillatus*, which lived up to 18 weeks, producing a maximum of 41 eggs, and might eat in its life over 1000 *Rhabditis*.

Culture methods seem to affect the relative sizes and proportions of parts of nematodes. Clapham (1930) found that *Rhabditis succaris* became much larger on nutrient agar than when grown on the sewage-bed material of its natural habitat. Ludwig (1938) noted much variation in *Rh. teres* grown in nutrient agar when different substances were added to this medium, notably an increase in spicule length in the presence of plant juices.

A large literature exists on the phytoparasitic nematodes but this concerns chiefly economic aspects (see Goodey, 1934c; Filipjev and Stekhoven, 1941). The tylenchids are notoriously resistant to desiccation, at least in some stages. Dry wheat galls yield on soaking thousands of first-stage juveniles of *Anguina tritici;* 27 years' survival of this nematode in dry galls is reported in the literature but Goodey (1923) found no more than 9 years' survival. *Ditylenchus dipsaci* survives 4 to 9 years in the desiccated state, depending on the plant material involved (Corder, 1933; McBeth, 1937; Goodey, 1936). *Pratylenchus pratensis* dried in fig roots were all alive after 11 years (Corder, 1923). The record survival seems to be that of adult *Tylenchus polyhypnus*, which revived after 39 years' dessication in a rye leaf (Steiner and Albin, 1946). The dry cysts of *Heterodera* remain viable for years although the number of healthy eggs therein decreases steadily with time (Franklin, 1938); cysts of the potato eelworm 8 years old were still capable of producing heavy infections of potato plants. Appropriate stages of phytoparasites endure winter cold in soil or plant material but no tests seem to have been made of their resistance to extreme cold.

The infective stages of phytoparasitic nematodes are not only resistant to cold and desiccation but also to starvation. As these nematodes feed only on plant juices, the infective stages take no food until they find an appropriate food plant. The infective stages contain a large store of reserve food that gradually disappears if they fail to find a food plant so that they become more and more transparent. *Heterodera* juveniles can live free in soil over a year without food (Nebel, 1926; Franklin, 1937), other tylenchids for weeks at least (Stewart, 1921; Hodson, 1926).

Very few attempts have been made to cultivate the phytoparasitic nematodes on artificial media. Christie and Crossman (1936) grew the strawberry eelworm, *Aphelenchoides fragariae*, on agar containing corn meal extract, malt extract, sugar, and salts, and implanted with a suitable fungus on the hyphae of which the worms fed. Berliner and Busch (1914) cultivated the sugar-beet nematode on agar strewn with germinating seeds whose roots were penetrated by the nematode. These do not constitute successful culture on artificial media as in both cases the worms fed on live plants, but they facilitate observation of the worms' habits. The phytoparasitic nematodes are usually reared for experimental purposes in pots of soil in which an appropriate food plant is growing. As these worms feed only on plant juices, the active part of their life outdoors in temperate zones is limited to the growing season, at the end of which they must produce a stage capable of extended dormancy under severe conditions. This stage usually consists of the third-stage juveniles or in *Heteroderas* of the cysts containing eggs or first-stage juveniles; but sometimes adult stages survive through the winter. With the advent of favorable conditions of moisture and temperature in spring, these dormant stages resume activity, seek out and penetrate new plants, grow to maturity, and breed, often producing several generations during the growing season. The time passed in any of the active stages depends primarily on temperature; thus Goodey (1932) reported that in England the root gall *Heterodera* requires 20 days to reach maturity after root penetration, lays eggs for 10 to 12 days longer, and produces a new crop of first-stage juveniles 64 days after the original penetration, whereas in the warmer climate of California, the cycle from juvenile to juvenile may be reduced to 26 days (Tyler, 1944). According to Voss (1930), the chrysanthemum eelworm may produce 10 generations annually; the cycle from egg to egg requires but 14 days under optimum conditions.

It is generally reported that light soils containing sand are more favorable for the propagation of the phytoparasitic nematodes than heavy soils which probably impede their migrations to new plants. Soil acidity seems not to be of much significance. Heavy infections with root-gall nematode were found by Godfrey and Hagan (1933) in soils ranging from pH 4.1 to 8.1 whereas the sugar-beet nematode is favored by acidity in some localities and in certain kinds of soils (Peters, 1926; Smith, 1929) but not in others.

It seems to have been first noticed by Stewart (1921) that plant exudations are attractive to tylenchids, and the experiments of Baunacke

(1922) proved that *Heterodera* juveniles can find host plants at considerable distances. They traveled 2.4 m. to host plants in 8 to 9 days and ascended vertical shafts of soil at the top of which beet seedlings had been planted, traveling upward 1 m. in 2 weeks. Rensch (1925) found that juveniles of the sugar-beet nematode would gather around a bit of cotton soaked in beet-root water (water poured through a pot containing a growing beet plant). Direct observations on tylenchid juveniles traveling toward and attaching to roots of various plants, even some that are not their normal hosts, were made by Linford (1939) who also noted an attractive effect of plant wounds. Not only are *Heterodera* juveniles attracted by the roots of plants, but the emergence of young from *Heterodera* cysts is enormously stimulated by placing the cysts in root water, especially root water of their host plants, as compared with tap water (Baunacke, 1922; Rensch, 1925; Schmidt, 1930; Triffitt, 1930). According to Rensch, a similar effect is obtained with organic acids, as citric acid. According to Triffitt, the cysts of the potato eelworm are dormant in winter and will not hatch at that time even when exposed to proper temperature and moisture and the root excretions of potato plants. Voss (1930) was unable to find any attractive effect of chrysanthemum roots or leaves or root water on juveniles of the chrysanthemum eelworm.

In addition to the positive response of tylenchid juveniles to root excretions and other plant exudations, some other taxes have been noted. The juveniles of the chrysanthemum eelworm are definitely negative to water currents, ascending on plant stems during rains (Voss, 1930); this response is irrespective of gravity. Oxygen appears to be necessary for all stages of phytoparasites; a positive reaction to air bubbles in an agar culture was noted by Rensch (1925). Plant tissue that has become diseased through nematode activity appears to be toxic or repellent to such nematodes so that they tend to leave it in spring if they have wintered in it (Voss, 1930; Hastings and Newton, 1934).

The feeding habits of the phytoparasitic tylenchids are identical with those of free-living spear-bearing predaceous nematodes. The parasite pierces the plant cell with its spear and sucks out the contents by means of vigorous action of the pharynx (Linford, 1937). There appears to be a general impression that the parasites do not employ the spear to penetrate into roots in the first place but rather enter through weak places. Root parasites are classifiable into three categories (Goodey, 1943): the parasite remains outside the root with only the stylet embedded; the parasite buries its head in the root with most of the body outside; and finally the parasite enters the root completely, usually evoking a swelling or gall. The leafy parts of plants appear to be penetrated by way of the stomata.

The infestations of plants with nematodes are often prodigious and inevitably lead to the death of the plant.   Steiner (1926) reported 50,000 to 60,000 *Ditylenchus dipsaci* in one small leaf of a Chinese primrose.   A single cowpea plant had 4000 egg masses of *Heterodera marioni*, each containing 500 to 1000 eggs (Godfrey, 1931).   One chrysanthemum leaf may harbor over 1000 *Aphelenchoides ritzemabosi* (Goffert, 1928).   In sugar-beet fields in the western United States, Thorne (1927) estimated up to 35 billion *Heterodera schachtii* per acre.

In regard to the zooparasitic nematodes the discussion at this point will be limited to the ecological relations of the free-living stages.   It is usual for nematodes inhabiting the digestive tract to pass their eggs to the exterior in the host feces and development then ensues to the infective juvenile stage that may or may not lead a free existence. In general it may be said that the eggs of nematodes of the digestive tract do not develop far within the host body because of a lack of oxygen in the digestive contents and in some cases probably because of the high temperature of warm-blooded hosts.   Data on the conditions necessary for development and survival of the young worms in nature are available only for the nematodes of man and domestic animals.

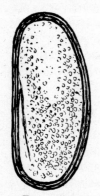

Fig. 197.— Tadpole stage of *Enterobius vermicularis* (after Zawadowsky and Schalinov*, 1903).

Among oxyuroids, studies are available on the human pinworm, *Enterobius vermicularis* (life history, page 313).   According to Zawadowsky and Schalimov (1929b), pinworm eggs can develop only to the "tadpole" stage (Fig. 197) inside the host intestine and require oxygen to reach the infective stage although they are not killed by short exposure to oxygen-free conditions.   A ripening of the lipoid membrane is also prerequisite to completion of development.   Eggs in stages prior to the tadpole stage when removed from females and placed in suitable conditions *in vitro* fail to develop further.   In such stages, the lipoid membrane is permeable to water, salts, and various substances and fails to protect the embryo sufficiently.   At the tadpole stage, the membrane alters so as to become impervious and development to the infective stage will then be completed in highly toxic media as 4 per cent formalin, saturated mercuric chloride, saturated copper sulphate, 2 per cent carbolic acid, and 5 per cent lysol.   Ovic juveniles also survive hydrocyanic gas fumigation (Nolan and Jones, 1942).   Moisture and temperature play an important role in the development and survival of pinworm eggs.   Under optimum conditions of high humidity and warm temperatures (to 36°C.), the juvenile stage may be reached in 6 hours; survival is best in cool moist conditions.   Temperatures of −8 to −12°C. are fatal in a few days but excellent survival was noted after 18 days at 3 to 5°C. (Jones and Jacobs, 1941). Dry conditions, especially in combination with warm temperatures, are rapidly fatal to ovic juveniles and in fact these seem to lack good resistance to external agents and require to be rapidly ingested by new hosts.

In ascaroids, as in oxyuroids, the free stages are passed inside the egg membranes and hatching of juveniles occurs only after ingestion by the appropriate host. Many studies have been made on the conditions for development and survival of the eggs and juveniles of human, pig, and horse ascarids. Ascarid eggs are usually in the uncleaved state or in early cleavage when ejected in the host feces. Failure to develop in the host intestine is attributable to the lack of oxygen and also, in the case of human, pig, and cattle ascarids, to the high temperature (38°C.); but according to Martin (1913), the eggs of horse and dog ascarids develop rapidly at 38°C., reaching the infective stage in 2 days. For other ascarids, temperatures of 30 to 35°C. are favorable and infective juveniles are produced as early as 10 days, but mostly in 2 to 3 weeks (Wharton, 1915; Martin, 1926; the Caldwells, 1928; Alicata, 1934). The juveniles are not infective until they have undergone one molt. Ascarid eggs have very high viability and if kept wet and cool may remain capable of developing to infective juveniles for 4 or 5 years (Davaine, 1858, 1863; Fülleborn, 1922; Martin, 1926). At room temperature, survival may be limited to about 2 years (Martin, 1926). Exposure to the summer sun, even in feces, is generally fatal because of the high temperatures reached (Brown, 1928b; the Caldwells, 1928; Owen, 1928; Otto, 1929) but less pervious soils may offer some protection (Brown, 1927). Summer shade temperatures are usually well endured. Ascarid eggs survive in high percentage under winter conditions in nature involving repeated freezings and thawings (Martin, 1922; Owen, 1928; Brown, 1928b; the Caldwells, 1928). Uncleaved eggs or early cleavage stages kept up to 40 days at temperatures below 0°F. (to −16°F.) developed normally to active juveniles, and ovic juveniles were alive after 10 days at −2 to −17°F. (Cram, 1924); but the longer exposures resulted in diminished vitality.

Moisture is necessary for the development of ascarid eggs and desiccation inhibits development but the eggs are not necessarily killed and may resume development with the advent of moisture. Drying of eggs in an incubator (37°C.) is fatal (Ransom and Foster, 1920; the Caldwells, 1928) and so is exposure in dry soils to the summer sun but the effect is probably one of temperature rather than of desiccation. In experiments with eggs exposed on glass slides to air at room temperature, Otto (1929) found that the dog ascarid requires 77 per cent humidity in order to complete development, the pig ascarid about 80 per cent, and the horse ascarid 40 to 50 per cent. Wharton (1915) found that pig ascarid eggs dried on glass plates for 2 to 3 weeks at room temperature remained viable and continued development when moistened. The most striking experiment on desiccation is that of Martin (1926) who kept thoroughly dried female pig ascarids at −5 to 10°C. and found that the eggs removed from such females after 25 months would develop fully. The moisture requirements of ascarid eggs under natural conditions in soil and feces are probably slight and desiccation is well endured unless temperatures are too high.

Oxygen is necessary for the development of ascarid eggs and development ceases in the absence of oxygen but is resumed on access to oxygen, even after a lapse of 3 months (Hallez, 1885). According to Kosmin (1928), horse ascarid eggs develop at the normal rate in an atmosphere containing half the usual oxygen, but are slowed in pressures lower than this.

Ascarid eggs are notoriously resistant to chemicals and will continue to develop in solutions fatal to most animal protoplasm (Galli-Valerio, 1915; Yoshida, 1920; Zawadowsky, 1927). According to Yoshida, they are killed by 0.5 per cent carbolic acid, 10 per cent sulphuric acid, 20 per cent hydrochloric acid, 10 per cent glacial acetic acid, and 15 per cent formalin but can continue to develop in 0.3 per cent carbolic acid, 9 per cent sulphuric acid, 14 per cent hydrochloric acid, 8 per cent glacial acetic acid, and 12 per cent formalin. They also develop normally in saturated mercuric chloride, saturated copper sulphate and copper acetate, normal sodium hydroxide, and half-normal ammonium hydroxide. It is in fact customary to culture the eggs in 2 per cent formalin or 10 per cent potassium bichromate as a means of inhibiting bacterial fouling. Cram (1924) reported 5 per cent carbolic acid and 3 per cent cresol as satisfactory chemicals for killing the eggs. It is usually believed that the resistance of ascarid eggs to chemicals results from the imperviousness of the shell but this appears to be erroneous. According to the experiments of Zawadowsky (1929) and Zawadowsky and Sidorov (1928), it is the lipoid membrane that is impervious to almost all substances except lipoid-soluble ones. This view is borne out by the observations of Ransom and Foster (1920) with antiformin (patent preparation containing 5.3 per cent chlorine and 7.5 per cent sodium hydroxide). This mixture dissolves all the membranes except the lipoid one and the embryo remains alive as long as this membrane is intact but instantly dies if the membrane is ruptured.

Ascaris eggs also show remarkable resistance to some other factors. Whereas cleavage of most eggs is inhibited at 300 to 400 atmospheres pressure, *Ascaris* eggs continued to cleave up to 800 atmospheres pressure (Pease and Marsland, 1939). Eggs would develop after centrifugalization at 150,000 times gravity for 4½ days, 300,000 times gravity for

10 hours, and 400,000 times gravity for 1 hour (Beams and King, 1936, 1940).

Eggs of chicken ascarids (species of *Ascaridia*) seem somewhat less resistant than those of mammalian ascarids (Hartman, 1923; Ackert and Cauthen, 1931). Exposure to the summer sun on or in the soil surface is fatal in a short time but in shaded places or under at least 2 inches of soil survival is good, increasing with increasing depth of soil. Burial under at least 2 inches of soil is necessary for survival over winter. *Ascaridia* eggs appear to have higher moisture requirements than eggs of mammalian ascarids (McRae, 1935b).

Ascarid eggs normally hatch in the intestine of the definitive host, releasing the contained juveniles, but surprising difficulty is encountered in attempts to hatch the eggs of human and pig ascarids artificially (McRae, 1935a; Fenwick, 1939a). Usually no result is obtained by exposure to mammalian temperature, artificial gastric juice, hydrochloric acid, sodium bicarbonate, alterations of pH and osmotic pressure, alkalies, trypsin, pancreatin, bile, or pepsin in hydrochloric acid followed by trysin and pancreatin. As hatching occurs on injection into the blood stream (Ransom and Foster, 1919), the action of digestive fluids and enzymes appears unnecessary. Hatching may be obtained *in vitro* by methods of mechanically abrading the egg membranes (McRae, 1935a; Fenwick, 1939a) or by exposure to sodium hypochlorite in alkaline medium (Fenwick, 1939; Pitts, 1947) but these methods do not explain the normal hatching.

In strongyloids, the eggs are also passed to the exterior in early stages but usually hatch in contaminated soil so that both eggs and juveniles are exposed to climatic factors. Much study has been devoted to the role of these factors in the life cycle of the hookworms of man and domestic animals. Development will be complete between 8 and 37°C. (Stiles, 1921; McCoy, 1930) but is very slow at the lower temperatures, finding its optimum from 25 to 30°C. Continued temperatures of 37 to 40°C. are fatal to eggs and free juveniles although both may survive exposure to 40 to 50°C. for a few minutes. Under optimum conditions, embryonic development may be completed in 1 to 2 days but in nature frequently requires several days to a few weeks. Rise of temperature, up to 35°C., greatly augments juvenile activity (Payne, 1923; Lane, 1933). Low temperatures and freezing are highly detrimental to the free stages of hookworms, whence their general limitation to the warmer parts of the earth. Loss of the sheath greatly reduces resistance.

Moisture is a necessity for the free stages of hookworms and hence hookworm infection is low or absent in dry regions and areas of scanty rainfall (Chandler, 1926–1928); excessive moisture is also unfavorable and juveniles cannot survive in soils subject to flooding. As shown by

Payne (1923), the juveniles live in the capillary water films between soil particles and ascend and descend in the soil in correlation with the movement of soil water; this is a definite reaction, not a passive conveyance by the water. Soils that appear very dry may still have sufficient water films to keep the juveniles alive (Lane, 1933).

Hookworm eggs will not develop in the absence of oxygen but dog hookworm eggs remained viable and resumed development after 9 days without oxygen (McCoy, 1930); they would complete development in water containing 0.4 cc. of oxygen per liter (air saturation about 6 cc. per liter). Development was retarded at still lower oxygen contents but oxygen could be utilized at very small tensions. Juveniles lived for days at tensions below 1 cc. per liter. Oxygen tensions above air saturation proved harmful to developing eggs.

The natural acidity of human feces (pH 4.8 to 5.0) is inimical to the development of human hookworm eggs and hence it is customary in artificial cultures to mix infected feces with charcoal, wood ashes, etc., to reduce the acidity. Dog hookworm eggs, however, developed well from pH 4.6 to 9.4 (McCoy, 1930), although a reaction of pH 6 to 7 was most favorable.

Numerous studies have been made on the behavior and survival of hookworm eggs and juveniles in naturally deposited feces on soil or in experiments simulating such deposition (Ackert, 1923; Payne, 1923a; Augustine, 1922, 1923, 1926; Augustine and Smilie, 1926; Mhoskar, 1924; Chandler, 1926–1928). Juveniles remain where hatched and do not migrate horizontally but may be transported by animals. Eggs may pass unharmed through dogs, rats, chickens, and similar animals. Feces are seldom left unmolested but soon become infested with dung beetles, fly larvae, etc., and the disturbance thus created is generally favorable to hookworm development and survival as it aerates the mass and reduces acidity by mixing the feces with the soil; but Ackert (1923) reported the presence of fly larvae inhibitory to hookworm development. Under favorable conditions of moisture and temperature, juveniles are found in or on the surface of the soil but retreat downward in hot dry conditions. Because of these vertical migrations with conditions, juvenile survival is greatly dependent on soil texture; light and sandy soils favor survival whereas heavy and impervious clay soils are usually devoid of hookworm infestation. Burying infested feces is futile since eggs hatch under such conditions and juveniles migrate to the surface from at least 36 inches (Payne, 1922, 1923a) in soils of loose texture; but in pure clay juveniles failed to reach the surface from depths greater than 6 inches. Because of the susceptibility of juveniles to desiccation and high temperatures, they survive best in shaded areas or in areas covered with grass and low vegetation. However, even under the most favorable conditions, survival in tropical climates is relatively brief. Augustine (1923), working in Puerto Rico, reports survival of 5 days in direct sunlight, 3 weeks at 35°C., 6 weeks in light shade, and 8 weeks in deep shade. Similarly in India, Mhoskar (1924) found most juveniles dead by the eighth week although some might survive to 14 weeks. In laboratory cultures at moderate temperatures, human hookworm juveniles have lived 18 months in water (Nicoll, 1917; Ackert, 1924) but are not infective at the end of this period; Svensson (1925) kept juveniles of the dog hookworm over 15 weeks in a refrigerator.

It was shown by McCoy (1929) that first- and second-stage hookworm juveniles feed on certain kinds of bacteria; they will not grow on yeast, dead bacteria, sterile feces, or proteins. Third-stage infective juveniles do not feed but subsist on their reserves, which visibly diminish as time passes (Rogers, 1939). Any factor that stimulates activity, as rise of temperature, moisture changes leading to vertical migrations, and contact with objects, increases the consumption of the food reserves and hence shortens the life of the infective stage. Infective juveniles become incapable of penetrating the definitive host long before they perish from starvation. Tests of infectivity are usually made by applying the young worms to a piece of shaved mouse skin stretched over a cork ring and floated in saline.

The behavior of infective hookworm juveniles is keyed to the necessity of finding a suitable host as rapidly as possible. The most striking feature of this behavior is the tendency to vertical migration when moisture conditions permit (Payne, 1922, 1923), and in soils of suitable texture. The worms not only ascend to the soil surface, but mount on objects. Rise of temperature, mechanical agitation, and contact with objects increase juvenile activity. The young worms appear to be highly thigmotactic, remaining in angles and corners. They tend to orient themselves at right angles to objects, apparently a boring reaction. Wakeshima (1933) found that infective young of the dog hookworm would enter the interstices of blotting paper or cracks in the culture substratum or gather under a supported cover glass. They would aggregate in that part of an agar substratum that had been impregnated with tissue extract, bile, or dog blood and reacted positively to dog blood in various dilutions down to 10 per cent. A positive reaction to light was also observed. Ancylostome juveniles are positively thermotactic, gathering around a heated object (Khalil, 1922b; Fülleborn, 1924; Wakeshima, 1933).

Juvenile stages of *Bunostomum trigonocephalum*, a common hookworm of ruminant mammals, were cultivated by Cameron (1923) in sheep feces; the infective stage lived for several months in plain water. Infective juveniles showed greatest activity at 35 to 40°C. and were unable to withstand even brief freezing or desiccation. The climbing habit so characteristic of other hookworm juveniles seems to be lacking in this species. The juveniles were very positive to warmth, collecting around a heated object, and very positive to light, assembling on the lighted side of the culture vessel.

Conditions for the survival of eggs and juveniles of horse strongyles have been studied by Ober-Blöbaum (1932), Enigk (1934), and Lucker (1935, 1936c, 1938b, 1941). Under optimum conditions, eggs may hatch in 30 hours but the infective stage is not reached until 5 to 8 days. Unprotected eggs retained ability to develop after an exposure of 45 days to $-8°$C., eggs protected in feces, after 55 days. Many eggs in feces developed after 65 days' drying in an incubator at $30°$C. and some developed after 30 minutes' exposure to full sun. First- and second-stage juveniles were found by Enigk poorly resistant to drying, cold, submergence under water, and chemical disinfectants, but third-stage infective juveniles lived 6 to 8 months in water, 16 months in feces subjected to summer and winter conditions, and $4\frac{1}{2}$ years dried on glass. Similar high resistance of infective juveniles was reported by Ober-Blöbaum for *Cyathostomum* and *Strongylus edentatus;* some survived continuous freezing of $4\frac{1}{2}$ months' duration, $8\frac{1}{2}$ months at -6 to $-12°$C., $8\frac{1}{2}$ months in tap water, and 9 months when dried on glass and kept either at -6 to $-12°$C. or at room temperature. Less resistance was noted for *Str. vulgaris* juveniles. Lucker, however, reported no survival of free stages of horse strongyles in feces spread out on soils over summer in Maryland. Oxygen is essential for development and survival but eggs may endure anaerobic conditions for over a month. Eggs buried up to $10\frac{1}{2}$ inches hatched, and in light moist soils juveniles would reach the surface, in a minimum time of 6 days from $3\frac{1}{2}$ inches depth; but were practically unable to migrate vertically in clay soils. In small bottles of soil, infective juveniles of horse strongyles lived 3 months at $31°$F., 4 months at $26°$F., and over a year at 3 and $-5°$F. Juveniles evidence a strong tendency to vertical migration, ascending on grass blades after dews and rains and climbing the moist walls of containers.

The eggs of the pig nodular worm, *Oesophagostomum dentatum*, cultivated on moist soil, yield infective juveniles in 5 to 7 days. Neither eggs nor juveniles seem very resistant. Eggs protected in feces survived continuous freezing at -1 to $-9°$C. for 72 to 75 hours; they died in 24 hours when spread out thinly on glass at 20 to $30°$C. and in 47 hours when kept in feces at 41 to $44°$C. Infective juveniles might survive continuous freezing at -5 to $-10°$C. for about 4 days, drying on glass at 20 to $30°$C. for 25 days, and outdoor conditions for 9 months on bare soil, 14 months in heavy grass. Juveniles hatched from eggs buried at various depths reach the surface in sandy clay soil and like other strongyloid young migrate vertically in the soil in correlations with moisture conditions (data from Spindler, 1936a). Much less resistance is shown by the free stages of the sheep nodular worm, *Oes. columbianum*, which are unable to endure the summers on pastures in Maryland (Kates, 1943) or Kentucky (Doll and Hull, 1948) or the winters in Canada (Swales, 1940).

The free stages of the swine kidney worm, *Stephanurus dentatus*, studied by Spindler (1931, 1934) in Georgia, cannot survive freezing or exposure to the sun even in moist soil, and are short-lived in wet and muddy soils or in dry soils whether shaded or sunny. Hence they remain alive only in moist protected spots in summer. Juveniles migrate but little in the soil but will ascend wet grass blades and moist walls of containers; they are somewhat negative to light, hence move out of sunlit areas, and quite positive to warmth, migrating to warm objects.

Many studies are available on the ecology of the free stages of the trichostrongyles of ruminants, especially sheep, including such genera as *Trichostrongylus, Haemonchus, Ostertagia, Cooperia,* and *Nematodirus.* Several investigations concern the twisted stomach worm, *Haemonchus contortus* (Bozevitch, 1930; Swales, 1940; Rogers, 1940a; Sarles, 1943; Kates, 1943; Dinaburg, 1944; Shorb, 1944; Wetzel, 1945). At 68 to 95°F., the eggs hatch in 24 hours and the infective stage is reached in 4 to 5 days. There is general agreement that the free stages of this worm cannot endure freezing, desiccation, or high summer temperatures. Consequently there is no survival on pastures in the winter in Canada or the northern United States, as far south as Maryland. In western Australia, however, Rogers found that *H. contortus* infective juveniles are most active in relatively dry, warm conditions and then ascend higher on grass blades than do other trichostrongyles. In regard to other sheep trichostrongyles, several workers report failure of survival of the free stages either over winter in the north or over summer in the south (Swales, 1940; Shorb, 1942; Doll and Hull, 1948; Seghetti, 1948); others found winter survival in Maryland (Griffiths, 1937; Dikmans and Andrews, 1933b) and New York State (Baker, 1939). Baker's results indicate survival of free stages of sheep trichostrongyles for over 21 months on open pastures, and of cattle trichostrongyles for at least 9 months. Laurans (1946) also reported good resistance of juveniles of sheep trichostrongyles.

More exact studies of the conditions for survival of the free stages have been made for *Trichostrongylus* by Mönnig (1930) in South Africa and Stewart and Douglas (1938) in California. At 37 to 38°C., eggs may hatch but the juveniles die rapidly. Exposure to -6°C. is fatal to the eggs. Eggs submersed under water do not hatch but may remain viable up to 20 days at moderate temperatures. Eggs not fully developed cannot resist desiccation but after the completion of development they are highly resistant to desiccation, surviving in dust-dry feces 6 to 15 months.

Preinfective juvenile stages, however, cannot withstand drying but infective juveniles exhibit good resistance to external factors. They lived over 104 days at 38°C. in low humidity but not more than a day in dry feces; from 2 to 7 months submersed under water; from 16 to 50 days dried on glass slides at room temperature and up to $8\frac{1}{2}$ months at lower temperature and in moist atmosphere; but showed little endurance to temperatures below freezing. They survive several months in moist soil but in nature probably live mainly in the vegetation rather than in the soil.

Probably the infective juveniles of all ruminant trichostrongyles have the habit of ascending grass blades since in this situation they are more likely to be ingested by grazing animals. The study of Rogers (1940) indicates that this behavior is favored by dim light and moderate wetness of the grass, and inhibited by strong light, too much water on the grass, or an actual layer of water on the soil.

In a study of a rabbit trichostrongyle (*Tr. retortaeformis*), Crofton (1948) concluded that egg development is governed primarily by temperature, juvenile survival by humidity. Eggs survived winter cold but suspended development below 50°F. Dry conditions did not prevent development and hatching but were fatal to juveniles; the latter survive long periods (20 weeks) of exposure to cold weather. The behavior of juveniles appeared to be directed primarily by a humidity gradient along the stems of low vegetation, secondarily by a seeking of regions of dim illumination.

As the metastrongyles of lungworms inhabit the respiratory or circulatory system, they are plentifully supplied with oxygen and consequently their eggs develop completely before leaving the host body or hatch in the host lungs or blood vessels or in the maternal uterus. Studies of the free-living infective stage of the ovine lungworm, *Dictyocaulus filaria*, indicate no great resistance to external conditions (Pavlov, 1935; Wetzel, 1945), and juveniles of the bovine lungworm, *D. viviparus*, survived only a week on well-drained pastures (Porter, 1942). Another ovine lungworm, *Muellerius capillaris*, leads a free existence only as first-stage juveniles, since entry into a molluscan intermediate host is prerequisite to further development. The free juveniles show considerable resistance to climatic conditions (Morgan, 1929; Williams, 1942), enduring desiccation on glass for a week, freezing, and heating to 50°C. for 15 minutes; they lived up to 3 months in slightly contaminated water. No definite reactions to light or heat were observed.

Spiruroids in general lack active free stages and no data have been found concerning the ecology of the eggs. According to Torres (1925), *Habronema muscae* juveniles will exit from the fly proboscis into defibrinated horse blood but not into human, rabbit, or guinea pig blood, nor into milk or sugar solution.   A positive response to the blood of the specific host is indicated.

Filarioids altogether lack free-living stages but probably can exist for long periods as microfilariae in the blood of their host; thus microfilariae of *Dirofilaria immitis* persist for 2 to 3 years in the circulation of the dog (Fülleborn, 1912; Underwood and Harwood, 1939).   Some observations are available on the behavior of microfilariae.   They swim actively in the blood stream and are not merely carried along; should they get into a vessel too small for them, they back out (Augustine, Field, and Drinker, 1936).   Infective *Wuchereria* juveniles in the mosquito are thrown into activity by warmth and movements of the mosquito's mouth parts and are caused thereby to move toward the tip of the labium (Gailiard, 1941; Menon and Ramamurti, 1941); these stimuli seem to be the chief factors inducing the exit of the worms from the mosquito.   Exit has been observed from mosquitoes sucking up warm saline or warm host serum *in vitro* (Highby, 1943; Menon and Ramamurti, 1941; Pratt and Newton, 1946).

In those trichuroids that inhabit the digestive tract, the eggs are passed in the feces in an uncleaved state and develop outdoors to an infective stage, but hatch only after ingestion by a suitable host.   Whipworm eggs have much higher moisture requirements than ascarid eggs and are very susceptible to desiccation and high temperatures.   Eggs of the dog whipworm (*Trichuris vulpis*) develop in air only at humidities above 76 per cent and are killed at 37°C. (Onorato, 1932) but in water proceed to the infective stage in 12 to 15 days at 37°C., 16 days at 30°C., and 35 days at 22°C. (Spindler, 1929).   Centrifuging the eggs or culturing them in dilute saline or a combination of both treatments greatly shortens the developmental period (to a minimum of 9 days compared with 19 days in water, Miller, 1939b).   This author surmises that the salts of the soil may play some role in the development of whipworm eggs.   Fully developed dog whipworm eggs hatched after exposure of 20 hours to artificial gastric juice followed by 2 hours in artificial pancreatic juice (Miller, 1939b), whereas after ingestion by the dog they hatch in the duodenum in 30 minutes.   Human whipworm eggs (*T. trichiura*) also have high moisture requirements and therefore the incidence of this parasite is greatest in regions of heavy rainfall (Spindler, 1929).   At 30°C., the eggs die in air of less than 77 per cent humidity and survive outdoors only on damp, shaded soil (Brown, 1927) but have been kept alive in water as long as 5 years according to Davaine (1863).   Development to the infective stage is slow, requiring 3 to 5 weeks (Brown, 1927).

The life cycle of the trichina worm does not include any free-living stages but encapsulated young can be obtained for experimentation by digesting trichinous flesh with artificial gastric juice.   The acid in the juice weakens the calcareous capsules and the activated young then quickly escape from the capsules (Van Somersen, 1937). Such free young worms may live for a long time in 0.6 per cent sodium chloride; they are killed in a short time by exposure to 53°C. and in 1½ hours at 50°C. (Ransom and Schwartz, 1919) but a few may stand short plunges into 55 or 60°C. (Otto and Abrams, 1938). Trichinous meat that has been heated to 130 to 140°F. should therefore lose its infectivity. Extreme cold (0°F.) is destructive to the decapsulated young but temperatures of 11 and 15°F. were withstood 6 days (Ransom, 1914). Clearly ordinary refrigeration of meat (40°F.) does not protect against trichina infection.

The free-living preinfective young of zooparasitic nematodes presumably all feed on bacteria; the infective young do not feed until taken into an appropriate host and hence neither grow nor develop further outdoors, subsisting on their food reserves. Several attempts have been made to induce the further development of immature stages of parasitic nematodes by growing them in nutrient cultures. Lapage (1935) attempted this with infective juveniles of sheep trichostrongyles, using sera, blood, blood products, chicken extract, cultured chick tissues, starches, sugars, amino acids, fragments and extracts of sheep digestive tract, liver extracts, plant extracts, yeast extract, and various kinds of balanced salt solutions. The most successful medium consisted of balanced salts (Peter's) plus sheep serum; in this the worms lived up to 41 days and showed some progress toward the fourth stage. Enigk (1938) attempted to culture immature stages of *Graphidium strigosum*, a trichostrongyle of the rabbit stomach; third-stage juveniles were caused to exsheath in acid-pepsin medium and fourth-stage young were obtained from the rabbit stomach. The culture medium consisted of a salt solution containing various carbohydrates and proteins, including rabbit serum. Third-stage young lived up to 5 weeks in such media at pH 3 to 4 but gave equally good survival in 0.2 per cent hydrochloric acid; fourth-stage young survived 18 to 21 days at pH 4 to 5.5; but in neither case was there any growth or development. Glaser and Stoll (1938) and Stoll (1940) obtained fourth-stage *Haemonchus contortus* by cultivating third-stage juveniles (artificially deprived of their sheaths) in balanced salt media (Ringer's or Tyrode's) plus aqueous liver extract, ground yeast, sheep blood, and sheep kidney. Incubation at mammalian temperature is necessary and reduction of oxygen and dilution of salt media below the osmotic pressure of mammalian fluids favored growth but pH appeared unimportant. Despite the development obtained, it was evident that the young worms were still relying on their food reserves. Young *Ascaridia* removed from chickens survived for 2 weeks and showed considerable growth when implanted in incubating hen's eggs or kept at 106 to 108°F. on dextrose–corn meal–agar plates with added starch and dextrose or salt and xdetrose (Ackert, Todd, and Tanner, 1938). Brand and Simpson (1944) maintained young *Eustrongylides ignotus* removed from fish tissues about 7 months at 37°C. and over 30 months at 20°C. in a peptone (or proteose-peptone)–salt-glucose medium; one worm underwent the final molt into an adult with external male characters but undeveloped reproductive system. Hoeppli, Feng, and Chu (1938) attempted to culture young pig ascaris removed from the liver in diluted mammalian serum, liver extract, chick tissue culture, or serum plus liver debris; the worms survived up to a week, mostly only 2 or 3 days, but showed no growth or development. The same authors kept third-stage juveniles of *Spirocerca sanguinolenta* removed from the hedgehog alive in Ringer's 11 weeks in a refrigerator and 6 weeks at 37°C.; addition of mammalian serum, peptone, or chick embryo juice gave poorer survival than the salt medium alone. Decapsulated *Trichinella spiralis* juveniles seem favorable material for experiments on artificial culture as they are already in the fourth stage and need undergo only one molt to assume the mature condition. McCoy (1936), however, failed to provoke any development by culturing them in a suspension of minced chick embryos in Tyrode's solution. Following injection into the amniotic sac (but not other parts) of developing chick embryos, a few worms developed to sexual maturity. Good success with production of many mature females containing young resulted from injection of trichina juveniles into the amniotic sacs of rat embryos *in situ* in the maternal uterus or even into the pregnant uterus. The young worms died if the rat embryos died or if injected into a nonpregnant uterus; neither would they develop *in vitro* in sterile amniotic fluid. It is impossible to understand the claims of Weller (1934), also using a chicken medium (plasma, serum, embryonic tissue, embryonic extract, salts), that some decapsulated trichina juveniles underwent two molts and showed some sexual differentiation, for these worms are already in the fourth stage and already show some sexual differentiation. Levin (1940) kept decapsulated young trichina alive 4 months at 5°C. in Tyrode's medium; survival was limited to 11 days at 38°C.

Numerous attempts have been made to maintain and induce further development of microfilariae outside the host body. Fülleborn (1912) kept microfilariae of *W. bancrofti* alive in coagulated human blood for 6 or 7 weeks at 4°C. and those of *Acanthocheilonema perstans* similarly for 4 or 5 weeks. Menon and Ramamurti (1940) obtained survival of *W. bancrofti* microfilariae up to 40 or 50 days at 10°C. in 0.85 per cent sodium chloride; various other media tried, including blood and plasma, proved less favorable. Although many of the microfilariae lost their sheaths, there was no definite growth or development. Coutelen (1929), however, claimed considerable increase in size and some internal changes in *W.*

bancrofti microfilariae cultivated 32 days in unheated human serum at room temperature. Nagano (1923) failed to obtain any growth or development of *Dirofilaria immitis* microfilariae in dextrose-blood medium in either low or warm temperatures, and Hoeppli, Feng, and Chu (1938) also failed to obtain any growth during 10 days' survival in blood; Joyeaux and Sautet (1937) noted 60 per cent increase in length during 12 days' cultivation in dog blood or serum but did not consider this alteration to represent normal growth. Frog microfilariae (*Icosiella neglecta*) survived 12 to 15 days at 18°C. in hypotonic Ponselle's medium without growth (Coutelen, 1928). Later stages of *W. bancrofti* removed from the mosquito are short-lived *in vitro*, surviving 37 to 58 hours in physiological saline (Abe, 1937), and a maximum of 4 to 6 hours in tap water, egg albumen, or starch (Menon and Iyer, 1933); but in closed vessels under aseptic conditions might live over a week in blood or egg yolk (Menon and Ramamurti, 1941).

It may be concluded that no obligatory zooparasitic nematode has been reared to functional sexual maturity in artificial media but in a few cases some growth and development have been induced.

For the investigation of physiological processes in zooparasitic nematodes, it is essential to devise a medium in which the worms will remain in a healthy, normal condition for at least a few days. Most workers have kept their worms in a solution of 1 per cent or less of sodium chloride despite the well-known fact that sodium chloride alone is generally unfavorable to animal tissues and much inferior to balanced salt solutions as a medium. Balanced salt media generally consist of sodium, potassium, and calcium chloride, also usually magnesium chloride or sulphate, plus often some phosphate and bicarbonate, sometimes with glucose added as a nutrient. The proportions of the salts vary slightly in the formulas most often employed: Ringer's, Locke's, and Tyrode's. Some more recent formulas are given by Hobson (1948) who also finds 30 per cent sea water a favorable medium for ascarids; sea water contains more magnesium relative to the other salts than do most artificial salt media. What are essentially Tyrode's proportions (0.8 per cent sodium chloride, 0.02 per cent each of potassium and calcium chlorides, and 0.01 per cent of magnesium chloride or sulphate) have been used by several recent workers (Fenwick, 1939b; Stoll, 1940; Baldwin, 1943; Rogers, 1945). (Tyrode's formula also contains 0.005 per cent monosodium phosphate, 0.01 per cent sodium bicarbonate, and 0.1 per cent glucose.)

Adult parasitic nematodes removed from their hosts usually survive in fair condition in such media, with or without the addition of nutrients, long enough for experimental purposes. Hall (1917) kept *Ascaris lumbricoides* alive 24 to 26 days in alkaline sodium chloride (Kronecker's solution). Davey (1938) reported that *Ostertagia circumcincta* from sheep would not live more than 1 day in 0.9 per cent sodium chloride; addition of calcium prolonged life to 3 days and addition of potassium (making a simple Ringer's solution) gave 4 to 12 days' survival. Inclusion of phosphate, bicarbonate, or magnesium in the medium did not lengthen the survival time. Varying the sodium chloride content from 0.15 to 1.2 per cent did not affect survival time. Baldwin (1943) using the Tyrode salt proportions kept *A. lumbricoides* alive 10 to 11 days but admitted that the worms were not in good condition after the first few days. Later Baldwin and Moyle (1947) were able to keep the worms in better condition by increasing the potassium content relative to the other salts but obtained no longer survival. Apparently the best medium so far used for keeping *A. lumbricoides* alive in healthy condition is the 30 per cent natural or artificial sea water employed by Hobson and associates (Hobson, 1948); worms survived up to 28 days. The survival *in vitro* of juvenile parasitic nematodes was considered above. Although nematodes from warm-blooded hosts survive longer at lowered temperatures, it would seem desirable to keep them at the body temperature of the host if wanted in good condition for physiological experiments; but this encourages the growth of bacteria and these are detrimental to nematodes. Bacteriological sterility is probably a necessity for the best culture of parasitic nematodes *in vitro*.

Both the total concentration and the relative proportions of the various salts in the foregoing media are based on the composition of vertebrate body fluids, in which the total salt content is equivalent to a 0.7 to 0.9 per cent solution of sodium chloride. But it is highly probable that such a concentration is hypertonic to nematode body fluids and the ion proportions also may not be suitable for nematode tissues. In the thought, therefore, of finding a better culture medium for parasitic nematodes, some workers have utilized the pseudocoel fluid of ascarids as a basis. In the pseudocoel fluid of the horse ascaris, Flury (1912) reported a sodium chloride content of 0.36 per cent and Duval and Courtois (1928), of 0.26 to 0.34 per cent. A still lower figure, 0.12 per cent, was obtained by Schopfer (1932). According to the findings of Rogers (1945) and Hobson and associates (1948), the sodium chloride content of the pseudocoel fluid of the pig ascaris is a little higher than that of the horse ascaris but in any case is considerably less than that of vertebrate body fluids. These workers also call attention to the higher concentration of potassium and magnesium in ascarid body fluids than in vertebrate fluids. Acting on the findings of Rogers, Baldwin and Moyle (1947) made up a salt medium in which to keep pig ascaris that imitated the salt composition of the pseudocoel fluid, consisting of 0.38 per cent sodium chloride, 0.07 per cent potassium chloride, 0.06 per cent calcium chloride, and 0.05 per cent magnesium chloride, plus phosphate

buffer and alkali to bring the pH to 6.7.   Although the worms kept well
in this, they survived no longer than in salt media used by others.   Surprisingly enough, this medium proved unfavorable for ascaris muscle
strips, and further modification was necessary, especially a reduction of
potassium relative to sodium.   One must admit that the problem of
finding a suitable medium for maintaining parasitic nematodes *in vitro*
has not yet been satisfactorily solved.

The pseudocoel fluid is generally found to be hypotonic to the intestinal contents of the host.   This situation would seem to keep the worms
plump and distended.   Schopfer (1924, 1926, 1932) has shown that,
when horse ascarids are placed in a hypotonic medium, they increase in
weight with accompanying dilution of the pseudocoel fluid; when placed
in hypertonic media, the worms decrease in weight with concomitant
concentration of the pseudocoel fluid.   The body wall is therefore pervious to water in both directions (ligatured ends prevented intake through
the body apertures).   The experiments of Pannikar and Sproston (1941)
with a large turtle ascaroid, *Angusticaecum*, indicate permeability to
sodium chloride.   Although this worm lost and gained salts in relation
to the salts of the medium, it could remain hypertonic to tap water.
Hobson and associates (Hobson, 1948) also found that pig ascaris would
take chloride into the pseudocoel fluid when kept in 30 per cent sea water
(equivalent to about 1 per cent salt solution) but not to equality with
that of the external medium.   Apparently parasitic nematodes are poi-
kilosmotic, that is, vary the concentration of their internal medium with
that of the external one, although exercising some control over the
passage of substances through the body wall.   They are apparently
little affected by considerable alteration of osmotic conditions and survive quite well in media that are certainly hypertonic.

Available data indicate a wide tolerance of parasitic nematodes to
alterations of hydrogen-ion concentration, although some correlation
with the pH of their natural habitat is evident.   Davey (1938) working
with sheep trichostrongyles found that *Haemonchus contortus* would
tolerate a pH range of 3.2 to 9.0 and did not survive better in strongly
acid media although the sheep stomach, its natural environment, is
highly acid (about 3.8).   Trichostrongyles from the sheep intestine
proved somewhat more sensitive to acid; species of *Trichostrongylus*
endured a pH range of 3.4 to 9.0, and species of *Nematodirus* and *Cooperia*
a range of 4.0 to 4.4 to 8.5 to 9.0.   High acidities, of 3.2 to 3.8, were
clearly deleterious to the two last genera, which therefore cannot survive
conditions in the sheep stomach (abomasum).   The horse strongyle,
Str. vulgaris, is damaged by acidities greater than pH 5.5 and survives
best in media at 6.5 to 8.5, corresponding to the reaction of its normal
environment (Whitlock, Link, and Leasure, 1939).   Some relation

between acidity and the distribution of nematodes along the digestive tract is indicated. Parasitic juvenile stages of sheep trichostrongyles in Lapage's experiments (1935) tolerated a pH range of 3.4 to 9.6, and Stoll (1940) reared *Haemonchus contortus* juveniles in media varying from pH 5.0 to 8.6, finding highly acid media not advantageous. Greater dependence on acidity is recorded by Enigk (1938) for the rabbit trichostrongyle, of which the third-stage juvenile requires a highly acid medium (pH 3 to 4) for good survival whereas less acidity is more favorable for later stages.

Chemical analyses have been made of a few nematodes, chiefly ascarids, most completely by Flury (1912) for the pig ascaris. He found 85 per cent water, 8.1 per cent proteins, 1.63 per cent fats, 3.65 per cent glycogen, and 0.7 per cent ash (salts), reckoned as percentages of the fresh weight. Smorodinzev and Bebeschin (1936) obtained the following analysis for the same species: 80.5 per cent water, 9.5 per cent proteins, 1.4 per cent fats, 8.67 per cent glycogen in females, 6.13 per cent in males, and 0.79 per cent ash, good agreement with Flury's figures, except for the higher glycogen content. Considerable differences between human and pig *A. lumbricoides* were reported by Clavers and Mallol (1945) whose results were: 78.25 per cent water, 10.23 per cent proteins, 5.36 per cent fats, and 3.68 per cent ash for the human variety, and 85.8 per cent water, 9.75 per cent proteins, 1.75 per cent fats, and 2.38 per cent ash for the pig form, again good agreement with Flury's figures except for the higher ash. Other data on the pig ascaris are those of Weinland (1901a) who reported 5.1 to 7.1 per cent of glycogen and 1.5 per cent of fats, and of Schulte (1916) who found 79.12 per cent of water and 6.0 to 7.4 per cent of glycogen. Toryu, using the horse ascaris, obtained 75 to 81 per cent of water, mostly about 80 per cent, and 2.4 to 4.7 per cent of glycogen in females, 2.4 to 3.5 per cent in males. Brand (1938) analyzed juvenile *Eustrongylides ignotus*, finding 75 per cent water, 1.1 per cent fats, 6.9 per cent glycogen, and 1.1 per cent ash. As shown above, intestinal nematodes live in a hypertonic medium and are permeable to water and salts; presumably the foregoing variations in water and salt content result from varying conditions present in the host intestine at the time of removal of the worms for analysis. The proteins of the pig ascaris were hydrolyzed by Flury (1912) and Yoshimura (1930) and found to yield the usual assortment of amino acids. Further examination of the fatty substances of the pig ascaris (Flury, 1912) gave: 30.9 per cent of saturated fatty acids, 34.1 per cent of unsaturated fatty acids, 24.7 per cent of ascaryl alcohol, 2.4 per cent of glycerin, and 6.6 per cent lecithin. The fatty acids found include butyric, formic, proprionic, acrylic, valerianic, stearic, and palmitic. About one-fourth of the fatty substances (non-saponifiable material) was found to consist of a higher alcohol, named ascaryl alcohol by Flury.   To this he gave the formula $C_{32}H_{64}O_4$ but a later investigation by Schulz and Becker (1933) indicated the formula $C_{33}H_{68}O_4$.   Their other figures for the fatty substances of horse and pig ascarids agreed well with Flury's findings: 65 per cent total fatty acids, 26 per cent unsaponifiable material (presumably ascaryl alcohol), and 8.8 per cent glycerin.   For the ether-soluble substances of pig ascaris, Brand and Winkeljohn (1945) obtained the following analysis: 12.8 per cent phospholipids, 50.4 per cent fatty acids (including stearic, oleic, and palmitic acids), and 15.6 per cent unsaponifiable material (mostly cholesterol and ascaryl alcohol).   As in other parasitic worms, the glycogen content of zooparasitic nematodes is high; further figures on this item for the pig ascaris are: 5.1 to 7.1 per cent (Weinland, 1901a); 5.29 to 7.18 per cent (Brand, 1934); 5.29 per cent in females and 5.77 per cent in males (Brand, 1937); and 3.55 to 6.67 per cent in females and 3.78 to 6.74 per cent in males (Ro, 1939).   There appears to be no consistent difference between the sexes of the pig ascaris as to glycogen content.   Other glycogen figures are: 4.4 to 5.5 per cent in *Toxocara mystax* (Weinland, 1901a; Smorodinzev and Bebeschin, 1938); 3.5 per cent in *Strongylus vulgaris* and 2.2 per cent in a horse filarioid (Toryu, 1933); 4.63 per cent in female and 3.60 per cent in male *Ascaridia galli* (Reid, 1944); and 1.5 per cent in *Ancylostoma caninum* (Brand and Otto, 1938).   The ash was analyzed by Flury for the pig ascaris and found to consist of chlorides, phosphates, sulphates, and silicates of sodium, potassium, calcium, magnesium, aluminum, and iron.   Rogers (1940b) reported zinc, copper, silver, and iron in the intestine of *Strongylus*.

The pseudocoel fluid, also called perienteric fluid, of pig and horse ascarids has been examined by several workers.   Marcet (1865) recorded that of the horse ascaris as containing 91.7 per cent water, 5.3 per cent proteins, 0.51 per cent fats, and phosphorus and potassium.   Flury's (1912) analysis of the same species gave 95 per cent water, 0.92 per cent ash (0.36 per cent sodium chloride), 4.1 per cent proteins (including albumins, globulins, and peptones), and 0.36 per cent of alcohol-soluble substances (including soaps and fatty acids).   Fauré-Fremiet (1913) noted the presence of neutral fats, phospholipids, and glucose in the pseudocoel fluid of the horse ascaris.   For the same fluid, Schopfer (1925, 1926, 1927) found a salt concentration equal to 0.1 to 0.12 per cent sodium chloride while Duval and Courtois (1928) gave a higher value, 0.26 to 0.34 per cent.   The latter authors also noted the presence of amino acids (0.06%) in the pseudocoel fluid.   Using the pig ascaris, Rogers (1945) found the pseudocoel fluid to be composed of 93.36 per cent water and 6.64 per cent solids; the latter include glucose, proteins, non-protein nitrogenous substances, sodium, chloride, and phosphate.

Other noteworthy constituents of nematodes are vitamins and haemoglobin. Ascorbic acid (vitamin C) occurs in both the intestinal wall and the pseudocoel fluid of ascarids (Rogers, 1945; Smyth, Bingley, and Hill, 1945) and vitamins of the B complex were found in the pig ascaris and *Nippostrongylus muris* in amounts comparable with those in vertebrate tissues (Chance and Dirnhuber, 1949). A good many zooparasitic nematodes have a slight or pronounced reddish tint caused by the presence of haemoglobin. Although some nematodes do suck the host blood, the haemoglobin is of intrinsic origin in at least some cases. Thus Keilin (1925) remarked that the pig ascaris has two kinds of haemoglobin, one in the body wall and the other in the pseudocoel fluid. This finding was confirmed by Davenport (1945, 1949) who showed that the spectra of these two haemoglobins differ decidedly from the spectrum of the host haemoglobin and that pig ascarid haemoglobins are therefore distinct compounds. A similar type of haemoglobin was found by Davenport (1945, 1949) in the pseudocoel fluid of a horse *Strongylus*. According to Davey (1938) sheep trichostrongyles generally contain haemoglobin, not of host origin, and so does *Nippostrongylus muris* (Davenport, 1949). Juvenile *Eustr. ignotus* have a red pseudocoel fluid containing haemoglobin, said by Brand (1937) to give a spectrum identical with that of the host haemoglobin; but it is difficult to suppose that host haemoglobin could pass unaltered through the intestinal wall into the pseudocoel. The haemoglobin of the horse ascaris is definitely identical with that of the horse (Hurlaux, 1947).

Other details of the chemical composition of zooparasitic nematodes are given in Hobson's review (1948) and by Brand and Jahn in *An Introduction to Nematology*, Section II, Chap. XI. The chemical composition of the cuticle and the egg membranes was considered with those topics.

Not much information is available concerning the actual food of the zooparasitic nematodes. The subject is well reviewed by Ackert and Whitlock in *An Introduction to Nematology*, Section II, Chap. X. Presumably in those nematodes that lie free in the digestive lumen, as most ascaroids and oxyuroids, the food consists primarily of the intestinal contents. Archer and Peterson (1930) administered a barium meal to persons infected with ascaris and demonstrated ingestion of barium by the worms. Li (1933) fed recognizable material as charcoal, blood cells, or starch grains, often mixed with beef, to dogs and cats infected with ascarids and recovered some worms that had definitely ingested these materials. Similar experiments on chickens infected with *Ascaridia* resulted in the ingestion of large amounts of charcoal or starch by the worms. Ackert, Whitlock, and Freeman (1940) agree that the chicken *Ascaridia* feeds on the contents of the host intestine. Some workers have maintained that ascaroids ingest blood, at least to some extent. Liévre (1934) and Rogers (1940a) examined spectroscopically the intestinal contents of ascaroids and found little or no haemoglobin in human, pig, and horse ascarids, but some in dog and cat ascarids. Oxyuroids also probably subsist mainly on the contents of the host's digestive tract. Rogers (1940a) found no evidence of blood ingestion in *Oxyuris equi* and Hsu and Li (1940) concluded that *Heterakis gallinae* eats the host's food. However, fourth-stage juveniles of *Oxyuris equi* (Wetzel, 1930) and *Dermatoxys veligera* (Wetzel, 1931) grasp a plug of host tissue in their buccal capsules and ingest tissue exudate and disintegrating tissues. The buccal equipment of these juveniles is lacking in the adult and presumably the absence of a well-developed buccal capsule in many adult ascaroids and oxyuroids prevents them from directly attacking the host's tissue. According to Hoeppli (1927) some of the smaller ascaroids such as species of *Contracaecum*, *Porrocaecum*, and *Anisakis* have been found with their anterior ends buried in the host mucosa but evidence of an actual dissolution of host tissue was inconclusive. Although the human pinworm may invade the mucosa, there is no evidence that it feeds there.

Spiruroids are usually firmly attached to the wall of the digestive tract by their well-developed buccal capsule or else live embedded in nodules in the wall. The presumption is that they cause inflammatory and necrotic changes in the surrounding tissues and then ingest tissue exudate and disintegrated tissues. This has been shown to be the case for species of *Physaloptera*, *Tanqua*, *Gongylonema*, and *Spirocerca* (Hoeppli, 1927, 1928, 1929; Feng, 1931; Hsu, 1939). Pieces of digestive wall with attached or embedded worms were sectioned; areas of tissue dissolution and inflammatory changes were found around the worms and tissue fragments were seen inside them. Similarly *Camallanus intermedius* feeds on mucosa and tissue exudate (Hsu and Li, 1940). Stekhoven (1932) investigated the feeding habits of *Proleptus obtusus*, which lives attached to the intestinal epithelium of elasmobranchs at the beginning of the spiral valve. This worm uses its cuticular collar to form a suction cup by which it adheres firmly to the host mucosa. Its pharyngeal glands open on the teeth in the buccal capsule and the digestive fluid they emit disintegrates the host tissue which is thereupon swallowed. In general, the spiruroids here mentioned alter the host tissue around their heads by giving off enzymatic fluids, presumably secreted by the pharyngeal glands.

The strongyloids proper feed on blood and tissues. Rogers (1940) demonstrated blood spectroscopically in the intestinal contents of *Strongylus vulgaris*, *Str. edentatus*, and *Syngamus trachea*. According to Hoeppli (1927), *Str. vulgaris* grasps a plug of host tissue and ingests blood and tissue fragments. *Chabertia ovina* draws mucosa into its buccal capsule and ingests tissue fragments (Wetzel, 1931); evidence of ingestion also of blood by this species was presented by Kauzal (1931). The

Ancylostomidae are probably all habitual bloodsuckers. The blood-sucking activities of the dog hookworm, *Ancylostoma caninum*, were observed directly in opened loops of dog intestine under anesthesia by Wells (1931) and Nishi (1933). The worm attached by its buccal capsule sucks blood continuously through a sucking action of the pharynx, which may occur 120 to 250 times per minute. The intestine is also active but at a slower rate. Some blood spills out of the mouth, and this added to the amount swallowed by the worm brings the amount of blood lost by the dog per worm in 24 hours to a considerable figure—0.36 with a maximum of 0.7 cc., according to Nishi, 0.84 cc. in very vigorous worms, according to Wells. Both observers agree that the blood remains in the worm only a few minutes at most and is ejected through the anus frequently. This fact led Wells to conclude that the corpuscles are not digested and only the fluid part of the blood is absorbed; he thought perhaps the main purpose of the rapid bloodsucking is to furnish the worm with a supply of oxygen. However, Hsu (1939) found plain evidence of corpuscle digestion in dog hookworms removed with an attached piece of dog intestine and fixed immediately. The sections showed disintegrating corpuscles, also some host tissue fragments, in the worms' intestine, and numerous granules giving a test for iron in their intestinal epithelium. Ingestion of blood by the swine hookworm, *Necator suillus*, was noted by Ackert and Payne (1933). The human hookworm, *Ancylostoma duodenale*, swallows both blood and mucosa, after they have been partially digested in the buccal capsule by pharyngeal secretions, according to Hoeppli (1930); but Doubrow and Rousset (1930) in a histological examination of this worm saw no signs of host tissue, only blood cells, in the worm's digestive tract.

Although often regarded as blood feeders, the metastrongyloids and trichostrongyloids probably eat primarily the fluids and tissues of their hosts. Porter (1936) found the intestinal contents of swine lungworms to be identical with the inflammatory exudate in which they live and which they evoke. According to Enigk (1938), the rabbit trichostrongyle, *Graphidium strigosum*, does not attach to the host's stomach wall and consequently presumably ingests the fluid in the stomach. When rabbits were fed charcoal, carmine, and trypan blue, these substances were recovered in considerable amounts in the worms. Fallis (1938) was unable to demonstrate the presence of blood cells in the intestine of sheep trichostrongyles and Davey (1938) working with the same worms was unable to decide what they ate. The assumption of Martin and Ross (1934) that *Haemonchus contortus* feeds on blood would seem to be unwarranted. The red color of many of these nematodes results from haemoglobin of intrinsic origin and is not evidence of blood ingestion.

Little information was found concerning the food of filarioids.

According to Hsu (1939) *Dirofilaria immitis* from the dog heart eats blood exclusively and *Diplotriaena tricuspis* from the thoracic cavity of crows ingests the inflammatory exudate that its presence evokes, consisting chiefly of white blood cells with some red cells and pleural serosa. Granules giving an iron test occur throughout the intestine of this worm but chiefly anteriorly.

The structural peculiarities of the Trichuroidea, the slenderized anterior region, the capillary pharynx embedded in the trichosome, and the bacillary bands, complicate the question of the nature of their food. It appears that *Trichuris* species bury the filiform anterior region in the host mucosa at least part of the time. Several workers agree that the host tissue is altered around the worm (Christoffersen, 1914; Hoeppli, 1927, 1933; Müller, 1929). Müller believed the secretions of the bacillary bands dissolved the host cells and the nutrition so produced was taken into the worm by osmosis. However, Li (1933) and the Chitwoods (1937) have shown that *Trichuris* possesses a stylet and the latter find the pharynx well-muscled anteriorly and provided with muscle fibers even throughout the portion embedded in the stichosome. Hence there is no reason to doubt that *Trichuris* takes in food by mouth like other nematodes. Probably the food consists primarily of more or less liquefied tissues. The Chitwoods (1937) also found red blood corpuscles in the worm's digestive tract. Similar conditions obtain in *Trichinella* which has a stylet and a sufficiently muscularized pharynx to permit sucking (Chitwood, 1930; Van Someren, 1939). Heller (1933) found that the fourth-stage juveniles decapsulated in the host stomach would not grow unless permitted contact with the host mucosa and that later they penetrate into the host tissue; these observations indicate ingestion of host tissue. Van Someren (1939) observed the feeding of adult *Trichinella;* rapid pulsations of the buccal capsule indicated thrusting movements of the stylet into host tissues and pseudobulb contractions at the rate of about one per second were presumptive of food sucking. Only fluid material was ingested and added neutral red was taken into the digestive tract.

Summarizing the foregoing evidence, one may say that all adult zooparasitic nematodes have a functional digestive tract and ingest food by way of the mouth. The food may consist of the material in the lumen of the host's digestive tract or of tissue exudate and disintegrated tissues or exclusively or chiefly of blood.

The question whether zooparasitic nematodes also absorb nutrients through the body wall cannot be answered decisively on present evidence. Data on the culture of juvenile nematodes in nutrient media have already been reviewed, and it was shown that such culture usually fails and only a little growth has been obtained in the best cases; even then the ingestion of the nutrients by mouth was not excluded. Similarly adult nematodes generally survive as well or better in salt media than in media containing nutrients in addition. In Davey's (1938) experiments, sheep trichostrongyles were not benefited by abomasal fluid, serum, blood digest, or defibrinated blood, but Enigk (1938), using the rabbit trichostrongyle, noted a slight favorable effect of adding glucose and albumin or rabbit serum to the medium; added fibrin and starch grains were ingested.

Not much information is available concerning the actual processes of digestion in parasitic nematodes. The enzymes present have been studied by several workers but the earlier investigators often employed extracts of entire worms and did not exclude bacterial contamination. Abderhalden (1911) and Abderhalden and Heise (1909) found evidence of a proteolytic enzyme in the intestine of the dog ascarid. Schimmelpfenning (1903), using whole horse ascaris, reported a diastatic enzyme and trypsin-like and pepsin-like proteolytic enzymes. Flury (1912) found that the defatted intestinal wall of pig and horse ascarids would hydrolyze starch, glycogen, fats, and proteins, although its fibrin-digesting power was poor. Rabbit trichostrongyles *in vitro* ingested starch grains and rabbit fibrin added to the medium and evidence was seen of digestion of these substances in the worm's intestine, an indication of the presence of proteolytic and amylolytic enzymes (Enigk, 1938). The best available experiments are those of Rogers (1940b, 1941), using glycerin suspensions of the intestine of *Strongylus edentatus* and *Ascaris lumbricoides* (pig). Both worms contain an amylase that hydrolyzes soluble starch, best at pH 8.0 in *Strongylus*, at pH 9.4 in *Ascaris*, hence not identical in the two worms. In *Strongylus* the amylase is most abundant in the anterior part of the intestine. The intestinal suspension of both worms is able to hydrolyze olive oil and ethyl butyrate, thus containing a lipase and an esterase; it also digests gelatin, blood albumin, and casein, and breaks down haemoglobin. The protease appeared to be trypsin-like, although reacting best in a slightly acid medium, pH 6.2. In general the digestive power of *Strongylus* was found much greater than that of *Ascaris* and this fact was taken by Rogers to indicate that *Ascaris* subsists mainly on partially digested food.

Although Hoeppli and associates, as already cited, have repeatedly maintained that many parasitic nematodes predigest the tissues around their heads by pouring out enzymatic secretions of the pharyngeal glands, Hoeppli and Feng (1931) were unable to demonstrate any tissue-dissolving action of pharynx emulsions of *Spirocerca* and *Physaloptera* injected into and under the skin of small laboratory mammals. Chitwood (1938) obtained evidence of the presence of a proteolytic enzyme in suspensions of the pharynx of pig ascaris.

It is presumable that the intestinal wall is the site of absorption of the products of digestion and possibly even carries on intracellular digestion. As noted above, granules giving a test for iron have been demonstrated in the intestinal epithelium of several bloodsucking nematodes. Hirsch and Bretschneider (1937) found that starved pig ascaris would take in an iron-sugar compound and iron could be demonstrated in the intestinal epithelium 10 minutes later. After feeding of infected rabbits with charcoal, particles of charcoal were thickly present in the intestinal epithelium, especially posteriorly, of the rabbit trichostrongyle (Enigk, 1938). Indicative of glucose absorption by the intestinal epithelium is the presence therein of phosphatases (Pennoit de Cooman, 1947; Rogers, 1947).

As already intimated, excess food is stored as glycogen and fats. The distribution of the glycogen has been studied histologically in adult ascarids by Kemnitz (1912), Toryu (1933), and Hirsch and Bretschneider (1937) and in ascarids and several other nematodes by Busch (1905). The glycogen occurs in the epidermis including the chords, the non-contractile parts of the body-wall musculature, the intestinal epithelium (Fig. 198) and the ovaries, especially the later stages of the ovogonia. The greater part of the glycogen is concentrated in the muscles and the female reproductive system. Little or no glycogen appears to be present in the free-living juvenile stages of parasitic nematodes (Giovannola, 1936) which instead are usually abundantly supplied with fat reserves (Payne, 1923a; Giovannola, 1936; Rogers, 1939), localized mainly in the wall and lumen of the intestine. The fat reserves are utilized during the interval between attainment of the infective stage and entry into the definitive host as no food is taken in the infective stage. Following entry into the definitive host, fat and glycogen are again accumulated, chiefly in the intestine and pseudocoel (Giovannola, 1936). The fat content of adult zooparasitic nematodes is rather low, around 1 to 2 per cent as itemized above; in pig ascaris, the fat is localized in the body wall and reproductive organs, according to Flury (1912), chiefly in the epidermis, especially the chords, according to Kemnitz (1912); in the horse ascaris, in the intestinal epithelium and pseudocoel (Fauré-Fremiet, 1913); in the epidermis and body-wall musculature in both pig and horse ascaris (Mueller, 1929); and almost entirely in the bursal rays in the dog hookworm (Giovannola, 1936). According to Giovannola, glycogen serves primarily as a source of energy and hence is accumulated prior to periods of rapid and intense development during which it is metabolized; whereas fat constitutes a food reserve and is stored as a provision against periods of starvation. However, in adult ascarids kept *in vitro* or otherwise starved, the glycogen reserves are definitely utilized for they decline in quantity progressively with time (Schulte, 1916; Toryu, 1935; Hirsch

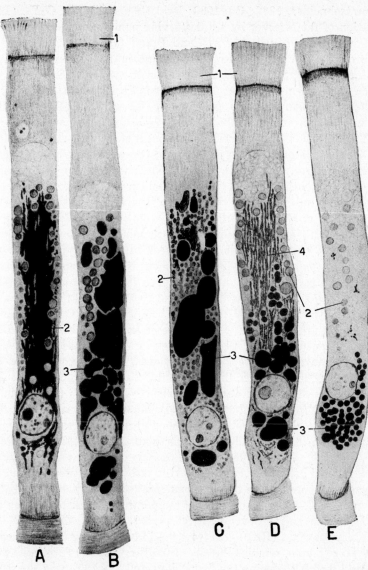

Fig. 198.—Intestinal cells of *Ascaris*. *A*. Stained to show glycogen (black). *B*. Stained to show fat (black). *C*. After 1-day starvation, fat black, glycogen gray. *D*. Same, after 3-day starvation. *E*. Same after 6-day starvation, showing depletion of food reserves. 1, rod border; 2, glycogen; 3, fat; 4, mitochondria. (*All after Hirsch and Bretschneider, 1937a.*)

and Bretschneider, 1937; Ro, 1939; Reid, 1945a, Fig. 198*C–E*). Little utilization of fat reserves by adult starving nematodes was reported by Weinland (1901), Mueller (1929), and Brand (1934, 1941); but Hirsch and Bretschneider (1937a) found a decline in the fat content of the intestinal epithelium of ascaris during starvation (Fig. 198*C–E*).

The metabolism of various stages of zooparasitic nematodes has been the object of many studies (reviews by Laser, 1944; Hobson, 1948; Bueding, 1949; Brand and Jahn in *An Introduction to Nematology*, Section II, Chap. XI); but all such work probably suffers from lack of knowledge of an ideal medium in which to maintain the worms during the experiments. As already stated, the eggs of these worms require oxygen for their development and hence their metabolism is of the ordinary aerobic or oxybiotic type. Although the eggs of zooparasitic nematodes typically contain stores of glycogen and fat, these are utilized in large part for the formation of the egg membranes; what remains is presumably oxidized as a source of energy. Some figures are available for the total oxygen consumed by one egg during its development from the one-celled stage to the motile stage: 0.0025 cu. mm. of oxygen for the pig ascaris (Brown, 1928a); 0.00278 for the dog hookworm (McCoy, 1930); 0.0027 for the human *Trichuris* (Nolf, 1932); and 0.0041 for the pig ascaris (Huff, 1936). These figures are consistent except those of Huff who also reported that the oxygen consumption of pig ascaris eggs was enormously increased, to 0.023, by removal of the protein membranes. It is not clear what purpose this excessive oxygen intake would serve. Rogers (1948) gave figures for the developing eggs of *Haemonchus contortus* (and remarked that those of *Nippostrongylus muris* had similar values) but stated them in terms not directly comparable with the foregoing results. The utilization of oxygen in cubic millimeters per hour per milligram dry weight was 9.7 for the early morula, 10.7 for the late blastula, and 12.6 for the fully developed juvenile. Brown and Huff also noted progressive increase of oxygen consumption as development proceeds. Although the rate of development is accelerated by rise of temperature, the total oxygen consumed for the entire developmental period remains the same. The respiratory quotient (R.Q.) rose from 0.8 to 0.98 during development in Huff's experiments, remained at about 0.6 throughout in Rogers's work, and was 1.0 to 0.91 during the first 8 days, fell to 0.73 during the second week, and rose slightly to 0.80 during the third week in Nolf's investigations. These figures indicate that the energy for embryonic development is obtained chiefly from the oxidation of fat but in some species carbohydrate (presumably glycogen) is oxidized, especially in early stages. As Rogers (1948) has shown that the oxygen consumption of developing strongyloid eggs is strongly inhibited by cyanide, the respiratory mechanism at this time is evidently of the ordinary aerobic type.

The few data available on the free-living juveniles of parasitic nematodes are to the same effect. McCoy (1930), studying dog hookworm juveniles found the oxygen consumption to increase with temperature, ranging from 0.00169 cu. mm. at 17°C. to 0.0196 at 42°C., per worm per 24 hours; at 37°C. the value was 0.47 cu. mm. of oxygen consumed per thousand worms per hour. Rogers (1948) reported for fresh infective juveniles of *Nippostrongylus muris* an oxygen consumption of 18.4 cu. mm. per milligram dry weight per hour with a decline to 9.2 cu. mm. 12 days later. The figures for *Haemonchus contortus* were said to be somewhat lower but for both species the R.Q. was 0.7. This value indicates fat utilization, something already known from direct observation of a decline of fat reserves during starvation of these juveniles. The marked inhibitory action of cyanide on the oxygen consumption of these forms again suggests that the oxidation is of the ordinary aerobic type.

Some work has been done on parasitic juveniles, artificially removed from the egg membranes or the host. Pig ascaris juveniles, artificially hatched, were found (Fenwick, 1938) to show three respiratory phases: a preliminary phase of very low oxygen consumption, lasting half an hour; a phase of very high oxygen consumption, lasting an hour and giving a figure of 9.3 cu. mm. consumed per 1000 worms per hour; and a final enduring phase of constant oxygen consumption at a rate of 0.9 cu. mm. per 1000 worms per hour. The author attributed the second phase to an oxygen debt acquired while enclosed in the egg membranes where an inadequate oxygen supply would compel the use of anaerobic processes. Excess oxygen is therefore consumed after release from such conditions to complete the imperfect oxidations occurring while enclosed in the egg membranes. Decapsulated *Trichinella spiralis* juveniles consumed 2.24 cu. mm. of oxygen per milligram of dry weight per hour in Tyrode's medium, 1.78 in Tyrode's without bicarbonate, and 1.70 in sodium chloride alone (Stannard, McCoy, and Latchford, 1938). These figures were recalculated by Brand and Jahn to give values of 1.12, 0.88, and 0.85 cu. mm. per 1000 juveniles per hour, figures comparable with those of other workers. According to Stanford, McCoy, and Latchford, 1000 *Trichinella* juveniles yield 0.35 mg. of dry weight or about 3000 are required to furnish 1 mg. of dry weight. Dry weight may be regarded as constituting about 20 per cent of the wet weight. According to the same authors, *Trichinella* juveniles can live a week or more without oxygen, so that they are capable of anaerobic respiration, but in the presence of oxygen, their respiration is of the aerobic type, being strongly inhibited by cyanide. Alterations of the oxygen tension from 1 to 100 per cent were without effect on the rate of oxygen consumption. The respiratory quotient was 1.13 or 1.17, an indication of the utilization of carbohydrates. The oxygen consumption and R.Q. were unaffected by the addition of glucose, glycogen, serum, or other nutritive media so that evidently *Trichinella* juveniles are unable to utilize nutrients in the medium. Much work has been done by Brand and associates (Brand, 1938, 1941, 1943, 1945, 1947; Brand and Simpson, 1943, 1945) on fourth-stage *Eustrongylides ignotus*, found encapsulated in fish. The oxygen consumption of fresh worms was 0.148 to 0.166 cu. mm. per milligram of wet weight per hour at 37°C.; 0.065 to 0.095 at 24 to 25°C. After the worms had been kept *in vitro* for 3 to 5 weeks, the oxygen consumption at 37°C. was 0.079 to 0.108, and after 3 to 8 months *in vitro*, it was 0.038 to 0.059 at 20°C. The oxygen consumption was not affected by alterations of pH between 3.4 and 8.3 but showed some variation with alterations of the ion content of the medium. Evidence was obtained of some utilization of glucose and xylose added to the medium but other nutrients supplied were not metabolized. An R.Q. of 1 and the progressive depletion of the glycogen reserves of the worms during starvation indicate carbohydrate utilization as the chief source of energy. These worms are killed in 17 days by a complete lack of oxygen but can live for a long time in low oxygen conditions. As glycogen is consumed three times as fast in anaerobic as in aerobic conditions, it is evident that the worms are capable of carrying on anaerobic oxidation of glycogen. Under such circumstances, however, they accumulate an oxygen debt so that a high oxygen consumption obtains at first when they are returned to aerobic conditions. In aerobic conditions, the respiration is greatly inhibited by cyanide and is accelerated by typical respiratory stimulants as dinitrophenol and paraphenylenediamin. The sum total of the evidence indicates that *Eustrongylides* juveniles ordinarily respire by the usual aerobic method, employing the cytochrome oxidase mechanism, but are capable of anaerobic fermentation during which they accumulate an oxygen debt.

It is to be noted regarding these three juvenile parasites (*Ascaris, Trichinella, Eustrongylides*) that they normally live embedded in the host's tissues where there is a plentiful supply of oxygen. The indications are that they usually respire by the ordinary aerobic method, utilizing glycogen as a source of energy, but when circumstances necessitate can metabolize glycogen anaerobically, accumulating an oxygen debt.

Data on the respiratory metabolism of adult zooparasitic nematodes concern chiefly the large ascarids of the pig and horse. The work centers around the question whether these worms are obligatory anaerobes or not. This question was brought into prominence by Weinland (1901b) who found that pig ascaris use up their glycogen as they starve *in vitro* and in an oxygen-free atmosphere produce carbon dioxide and fatty acids. He therefore reached the conclusion that this worm respires by the anaerobic method, also called fermentation or glycolysis, in which energy is obtained by the breakdown of glycogen, and that it is an obligatory anaerobe, which not only does not require free oxygen but is harmed by it. However, Slater (1925) showed that the pig ascaris is stupefied by continuous exposure to an oxygen-free atmosphere and regains activity on the admission of oxygen. Further, Adam (1932) proved by direct measurements that the pig ascaris consumes oxygen when this is available and this result has since been generally verified (Harwood and Brown, 1934; Krüger, 1936; Brand, 1938; Laser, 1944). Davey (1938) found that several species of sheep trichostrongyles are killed in 24 to 48 hours by lack of oxygen and irreparably damaged in 7 to 24 hours, whereas they would live 4 to 12 days with access to air; change of medium to remove metabolic products did not improve the survival under anaerobic conditions. Later Rogers (1948) indicated a relatively high rate of oxygen consumption of trichostrongyles. The horse ascaris appears to utilize oxygen less than other zooparasitic nematodes tested for according to Toryu (1936) it survives better without than with oxygen but even this species consumes oxygen when available.

The role of oxygen in the metabolism of intestinal nematodes is naturally correlated with the matter of the amount of oxygen present in the intestinal contents. Data on this question have been furnished by Tappeiner (1883), Long and Fenger (1917), Brand and Weise (1932), and Toryu (1934). The general findings are to the effect that the intestinal contents of domestic mammals (horse, cattle, sheep, goat, pig, rabbit) usually contain only very small or undetectable amounts of free oxygen, but considerable may be present at times, especially in the pig intestine. It is clear that some oxygen is available at least at times to intestinal nematodes. Presumably those worms that lie loose in the intestine, as the larger ascarids, would have the poorest available oxygen supply while those that live in contact with the mucosa or partly or wholly buried in it would have access to better supplies.

Quantitative data on the oxygen consumption of intestinal nematodes, chiefly pig ascaris, have been published by several workers. The following figures on the pig ascaris are stated in terms of cubic millimeters of oxygen consumed per gram of fresh weight per hour: 30 to 45 for females and 50 to 70 for males (Harwood and Brown, 1934); 40 to 120 for pieces from the anterior end and 172 for a suspension pressed through gauze (Harnisch, 1933); 42 to 99, with an average of 60 (Brand, 1934); 156 (Krüger, 1936); and 80 (Laser, 1944). These results are in fair agreement. Toryu, using the horse ascaris, reported 100 for males, 38 for small females, and 12 for large females. Rogers (1948) gave the following figures, expressed in terms of cubic millimeters of oxygen consumed per milligram of dry weight per hour: 2.5 for *Ascaridia galli*, 5.1 for *Nematodirus*, 6.8 for *Nippostrongylus muris*, and 12.6 for *Neoaplectana glaseri*. When expressed in the same terms as above (on the basis that the dry weight is 20 per cent of the wet weight) these figures are very much higher than those for ascarids. Harwood and Brown stated that the oxygen consumption of the dog hookworm is at least ten times that of the pig ascaris but gave no exact figures.

Available figures indicate that male ascarids consume oxygen at a higher rate than females (Adam, 1932; Harwood and Brown, 1934; Toryu, 1934); this is probably correlated with both their smaller size and their greater activity. A higher rate of oxygen consumption per unit weight obtains for smaller as compared with larger members of the same species (Adam, 1932; Krüger, 1936, 1937) and possibly their very small size accounts partly for the high rate of oxygen consumption of the worms used by Rogers (1948). The oxygen consumption of different parts of pig ascaris was studied by some workers and although Harnisch (1935) claimed the highest rate of oxygen consumption for the intestine, it is more probable that most of the oxygen is consumed by the body wall as found by Adam (1932) and Krüger (1936).

There is general agreement that in the ascarids the oxygen consumption is highly dependent on the oxygen tension (percentage of oxygen present) and rises and falls with the latter (Harnisch, 1933; Krüger, 1936, 1937; Brand, 1938; Laser, 1944). This means that at the very low oxygen tensions prevailing in the host intestine, the worms could take in very little oxygen. However, it should be recalled that the ascarids contain haemoglobin which in the pig ascaris has a very high affinity for oxygen (Davenport, 1945) and may therefore be of service in the utilization of oxygen at low tensions. Toryu (1934) reported that the horse ascaris continues to take in oxygen at very low tensions. Rogers (1948) found no effect of increased oxygen tension above that of air (which is 20 per cent) on the oxygen intake of the small worms with which he worked.

There seems to be no unanimity of opinion as to whether or not an oxygen debt is accumulated during a sojourn in anaerobic conditions. If the metabolism of parasitic nematodes were strictly anaerobic, one would not expect the occurrence of an oxygen debt. Krüger (1936) reported absence of an oxygen debt but Laser (1944) found that pig ascaris, after a sojourn of 17 to 20 hours in oxygen-free conditions, use during the first 2 hours after return to air 60 to 100 per cent more oxygen than worms given access to air throughout. This is again evidence that the pig ascaris requires a certain amount of oxygen. However, the anaerobic splitting of glycogen continues in aerobic conditions but is less than under anaerobic conditions. Brand (1934) found a glycogen consumption of 1.39 g. per 100 g. of fresh ascaris per day under anaerobic circumstances and 1.18 in the presence of oxygen.

The respiratory quotient of course can be determined only for aerobic respiration. For the pig ascaris an R.Q. of 0.9 to 1.1 was found by Krüger (1937) and 1.1 to 1.2 by Laser (1944), figures indicative of carbohydrate utilization. Rogers (1948) obtained a similar value (0.96) for *Ascardia galli* but only about 0.6 to 0.7 for *Nematodirus, Nippostrongylus,* and *Neoaplectana.* Possibly there is some fat metabolism in the last three worms. As already noted, *Neoaplectana* cannot be regarded as a parasitic nematode.

The totality of the evidence indicates that the zooparasitic nematodes are facultative but not obligatory anaerobes. They obtain their energy chiefly by the anaerobic splitting of glycogen but all of them utilize and probably require free oxygen, to different extents. The large ascarids have the lowest oxygen requirements and are the best adapted to live in low oxygen environments whereas the small trichostrongyles studied by Davey and Rogers seem to require considerable amounts of oxygen. High oxygen requirements probably obtain for the hookworms and other bloodsucking nematodes.

It is usual at present to test the nature of the respiratory mechanism of animals by measuring the oxygen consumption in the presence of cyanide or similar respiratory depressants. Cyanide interferes with the mechanism of ordinary aerobic respiration (cytochrome oxidase system) and reversibly lowers the rate of oxygen consumption by 90 per cent or more. Harnisch (1935) reported that cyanide was without effect on the oxygen uptake of pig ascaris, Laser (1944) obtained the same result with whole pig ascaris or muscle pulp, and Hurlaux (1947) failed to find any action of cyanide on the respiration of tissues of the horse ascaris. These results indicate that the oxidative processes in horse and pig ascarids proceed by some other mechanism than the cytochrome oxidase system. Herrick and Thede (1945) indicate that the pig ascaris lacks cytochrome oxidase and a similar lack is reported for the horse ascaris by Hurlaux (1947). On the other hand, Rogers (1948) noted around 40 to 60 per cent depression of the oxygen intake by cyanide in *Ascaridia, Nematodirus,* and *Nippostrongylus,* and deduced that the cytochrome system must be present and operative in these worms. It is again evident that results obtained with pig and horse ascarids cannot be applied indiscriminately to other zooparasitic nematodes and that the oxygen relations differ somewhat in different species. Interestingly enough, cyanide depresses the oxygen consumption of *Neoaplectana glaseri,* essentially a free-living aerobic worm, by 96 per cent, an indication that this worm respires in the ordinary fashion.

In an elaborate study of the four giant pseudocoelocytes of the horse ascaris, Hurlaux (1947) has assigned an important oxidative function to these cells. He finds that they contain an assortment of oxidizing enzymes (phenolases, dopa-oxidases, peroxidases, phosphatases) as well as food supplies (glycogen, lipoids, glutathion).   The haemoglobin present in the pseudocoel, hence bathing these cells, is considered essential in carrying to them the minimum amount of oxygen needed for their chemical activities.

Evidence has already been given of the uptake of nutrients from the medium by nematodes under culture, in a few instances.   A little additional evidence has been obtained in metabolic studies.   Hoffman (1934), using the pig ascaris, determined a decline in the sugars glucose, fructose, and galactose added to the medium, and a corresponding increase in heat production by the worms.   The mean values obtained for the utilization of sugars by 100 g. of worms per hour were: 0.061 g. glucose, 0.055 g. fructose, and 0.080 g. galactose.   Krüger (1936) noted an increase in the carbon dioxide output in the presence of glucose, in the pig ascaris.

As already intimated, the end products of anaerobic respiration by parasitic nematodes are carbon dioxide and fatty and other organic acids. There is now no doubt that the acids are normal metabolic products of the worms although this was questioned earlier.   Weinland (1901) determined that valerianic acid is the chief fatty acid produced by the pig ascaris and this has since been verified.   Schimmelpfennig (1903) claimed that in addition to this acid a whole series of fatty acids—butyric, formic, acetic, caproic, and proprionic—is produced by the horse ascaris. For the pig ascaris Flury (1912) reported valerianic, butyric, formic, proprionic, and acrylic acids.   Fischer (1924) identified lactic and phosphoric acids in the medium in which horse ascaris was kept.   Brand (1934) in one of the best studies that have been made of the metabolism of the pig ascaris summarized his findings as follows: in the absence of oxygen, 100 g. of worms in 24 hours consume 1.39 g. of glycogen and 0.18 g. of protein and produce 0.71 g. of carbon dioxide, 0.22 g. of valerianic acid, 0.02 g. of lactic acid, and 0.02 g. of soluble nitrogenous metabolites; and in the presence of oxygen there is consumed 1.18 g. of glycogen and 0.17 g. of protein, with the production of 0.84 g. of carbon dioxide, 0.16 g. of valerianic acid, 0.01 g. of lactic acid, and 0.02 g. of nitrogenous metabolites.   Adam (1932) had previously identified lactic acid in the end products of the pig ascaris.   Waechter (1934) confirmed the finding that valerianic acid is the chief metabolic product of the pig ascaris. Krüger (1936, 1937), identified valerianic, caproic, and lactic acids as the main fatty acids excreted by pig ascaris, and Toryu (1935, 1936) found valerianic, proprionic, and lactic acids to be excreted by the horse ascaris. Oesterlin (1937) again identified valerianic acid as the chief fatty acid produced by the pig ascaris and also found formic and acetic acids, and traces of higher fatty acids.   It therefore appears established that valerianic acid is the main end product of carbohydrate metabolism in the horse and pig ascarids and that several other fatty acids are also produced in small quantities. These acids are given off in both aerobic and anaerobic metabolism.

Hardly anything is known of the nitrogenous end products of nematodes. That such are produced was shown for the pig ascaris by Weinland (1901, 1904), Flury (1912), and Brand (1934). Brand made no attempt to identify the nitrogenous products but Weinland and Flury indicate that ammonia and ammoniated compounds are concerned. Flury determined the absence of urea, uric acid, and creatinine. Hurlaux (1947) reported the presence of urea, but no uric acid, in the giant pseudo-coelocytes, muscles, and pseudocoel fluid of the horse ascaris.

Evidence for the excretory role of the renette-canal system is very scanty. Cobb (1890) reported a positive test for urea in the lateral canals of *Enterobius vermicularis*. Mueller (1929) found no evidence in ascarids of the passage into the lateral canals of ammonia-carmine and urea injected into the pseudocoel although the urea was excreted. He showed that preparations of the body wall of ascarids, set up as dialyzer tubes, passed urea and aniline dyes through from the inside to the outside, but not glucose. He concluded that excretion in ascarids probably takes place through the body wall rather than through the canal system although he observed fluid exuded from the excretory pore. Chitwood (1930), using *Rhabditis*, disagreed with Mueller's results and observed that, after the worms were stained with neutral red, droplets containing the dye were emitted from the excretory pore. In unstained specimens clear transparent droplets were seen exuding from the excretory pore. In the pig ascaris Chitwood (1938) obtained a positive test for urea in fluid collected at the excretory pore with a capillary pipette but felt this might have come from the host rather than from the metabolic processes of the worm. Working with a variety of free-living nematodes, Stefanski (1917) found that dyes are taken in through the body wall or by the mouth and are excreted by the digestive tract and in some cases by gland cells acting as athrocytes.

33. Host-parasite Relations; Immune Reactions.—The parasitic nematodes, like other helminths, show a wide range of host specificity, from those that can develop in a variety of hosts to those limited to a single host. As examples of nematodes with a low degree of host specificity may be mentioned the guinea worm, which can develop in man, horse, ox, sheep, goat, dog, wolf, fox, cheetah, jackal, and presumably other carnivores; and the trichina worm, able to use as hosts man, other primates, pig, rats, mice, rabbit, guinea pig, ox, sheep, goat, horse, dog, cat, fox, and apparently almost any mammal. Some nematodes are limited to closely related hosts, as *Ascaridia galli*, occurring in gallinaceous and anseriform birds; *Parascaris equorum*, found only in equines (horse, mule, donkey, zebra); *Neoascaris vitulorum*, only in bovines; and

Toxocara mystax, only in felines.   *Wuchereria bancrofti* is usually mentioned as an example of a nematode that will mature in only one host, man.

Little is known of the factors that enter into susceptibility or resistance of hosts to helminth infections.   Domestication seems to render animals peculiarly susceptible to invasion by a large assortment of parasites.   Each of the common domestic animals harbors or can harbor a long list of nematode parasites.   Thus the dog is host to *Thelazia callipaeda* in the eye; *Oslerus osleri* and *Capillaria aerophila* in the respiratory passages; *Haemostrongylus vasorum* and *Dirofilaria immitis* in the heart and pulmonary arteries; *Gnathostoma spinigerum* and *Spirocerca vulpi* in the esophagus and stomach; *Physaloptera felidis, rara,* and *praeputialis, Spirura rytipleurites,* and *Spirocerca vulpi* in the stomach; *Toxocara canis, Toxascaris leonina, Ancylostoma caninum* and *braziliense, Uncinaria stenocephala,* and *Rictularia cahirensis* in the small intestine; *Trichuris vulpis* in the large intestine; *Capillaria plica* in the bladder; *Dioctophyme renale* in the kidneys; *Dipetalonema dracunculoides, Acanthocheilonema reconditum* and *grassii* in the coelomic spaces and linings; and *Dracunculus medinensis* in the connective tissues; and a number of others may be found in this animal.   The domestic cat is similarly parasitized and the larger grazing mammals as the horse, ox, sheep, and goat harbor an even greater number of nematode species.   The list for the sheep includes *Dictyocaulus filaria, Protostrongylus rufescens, ocreatus,* and *unciphorus, Muellerius capillaris,* and *Neostrongylus linearis* in the air passages and lungs; *Gongylonema pulchrum* in the esophagus; *Haemonchus contortus, Gongylonema verrucosum,* and *Ostertagia ostertagi, circumcincta, marshalli, trifurcata,* and *occidentalis* in the stomach (abomasum), usually extending into the duodenum; *Bunostomum trigonocephalum, Gaigeria pachyscelis, Cooperia curticei* and *oncophora, Nematodirus filicollis* and *spathiger, Strongyloides papillosus, Trichostrongylus colubriformis, vitrinus, probolurus, extenuatus,* and *capricola,* and *Capillaria longipes* and *brevipes* in the small intestine; and *Trichuris ovis, Chabertia ovina,* and *Oesophagostomum columbianum* and *venulosum* in the large intestine; plus a number of other more casual inhabitants.   Domestic birds also, as the hen, duck, pigeon, and turkey, harbor a considerable assortment of parasitic nematodes.   Contrasting strongly with this parasitization of domestic birds and mammals by numerous species is the state of affairs with regard to related wild species which generally are infested with only a few species of nematodes.

In several cases, host age has been established as a factor in resistance to nematode infestation, in that young animals as a rule are more susceptible to invasion than older ones (review in Ackert, 1942).   Looss (1911) noted some development to maturity of the human hookworm,

Ancyl. duodenale, in young dogs whereas previous workers had failed to infect adult dogs. In a study of pig infestation with pig ascaris by means of slaughterhouse examinations, Ransom and Foster (1920) reported that 50 per cent of pigs less than 5 months old were infected whereas pigs 18 months old were only 33 per cent infected. Age resistance is well established for the fowl ascarid, *Ascaridia galli* (Herrick, 1926; Ackert, Porter, and Beach, 1935). Not only does resistance of chickens to infestation with this worm increase with age but the worms in a given time grow ten times as much in 5-day-old chicks as in chickens 103 days old. Ransom (1921), examining market chickens, found no infestations with *Syngamus trachea* in chickens 6 months or more of age and on feeding ovic juveniles obtained a take of 87 per cent in chicks 1 to 4 weeks old and a decline to 29 per cent take in older chickens. Age resistance of dogs to the dog hookworm, *Ancyl. caninum*, was reported by Herrick (1928), Scott (1928), and Sarles (1929c). The proportion of administered juveniles that reach maturity declines greatly with increasing age of the dog host and the worms take longer to reach maturity in older dogs. A similar age resistance was found for cats against *Ancyl. caninum* by Scott and for both dogs and cats against *Ancyl. braziliense* by Sarles (1929c, d); with the latter species, a take of 32 per cent for kittens and 44 per cent for young dogs was contrasted with 4 per cent and 5.5 per cent, respectively, for adult cats and dogs. Infection of laboratory rats with *Nippostrongylus muris* is more successful with young than with old rats (Africa, 1931). Age resistance of rats to *Heterakis spumosa* was noted by Winfield (1933), and to *Capillaria hepatica* by Luttermoser (1938). In a study of age resistance of rats to *Trichinella spiralis* juveniles administered by mouth, Nolf and Zaiman (1941) reported that rats 5 weeks of age were more susceptible than rats 3 to 12 months old, but suckling rats proved more resistant than any others, an indication that some factor in the milk may be inimical to the parasite. It is well known that there is a much higher incidence of common human nematodes, as ascaris, pinworms, and hookworms, in children than in adults but it is not clear that this is a true age resistance; more probably the unhygienic habits of children expose them more frequently to intake of infective stages.

Various theories have been advanced to explain age resistance to helminths. Sandground (1929) strongly took the position that age resistance is in reality the expression of an incompatability between the parasite and the host, or, in other words, it is shown against parasites developing in other than the original or normal host. Distinctions between species presumably accentuate as animals age and hence young animals are more alike than adults and more open to infection by foreign parasites which cannot maintain themselves when adult differences have matured fully. There is undoubtedly much to be said for this point of view. Evidence for the action of other factors has, however, been brought forward in some cases. In regard to *Ascaridia galli*, it has been shown (Ackert, 1942) that the duodenal mucus of the chicken is inimical to the worm and that the number of goblet cells secreting the mucus increases greatly as chickens age. Sarles (1929c) indicated that juveniles of the dog hookworm readily penetrate the skin of young dogs but are unable to pass through the thicker and tougher skin of older dogs; however, this cannot be the whole explanation of the age resistance of dogs to this worm since oral infection with juveniles also fails with old dogs although very successful with young ones. A general age resistance of dogs to helminthic infections was noted by Hinman and Baker (1936) and is probably indicative of some inimical intestinal condition that accentuates with age.

In recent years, evidence has accumulated that the resistance and susceptibility of hosts to helminthic invasion may be considerably affected by dietary factors. This aspect of the host-resistance problem was initiated by the work of Ackert and associates on *Ascaridia galli* (Ackert, Fisher, and Zimmerman, 1927; Ackert, McIlvaine, and Crawford, 1931; Ackert and Beach, 1933). When ovic juveniles of this worm were fed to growing chickens, more and longer worms developed in chickens on a diet deficient in vitamin A than in control chickens. A similar result was obtained with diets deficient in vitamins of the B complex (Zimmerman, Vincent, and Ackert, 1926). Addition of skim milk and meat meal to standard feeds of mixed grains also increased the resistance of chickens to *Ascaridia* and stunted the growth of the worms (Ackert and Beach, 1933). In another fowl ascaroid, *Heterakis gallinae*, Clapham (1933, 1934) failed to note any effect on susceptibility to the worm by a diet deficient in vitamin A but did find that an otherwise good diet deficient in minerals, especially calcium and phosphorus, greatly favored retention of the worms without affecting their size. Lack of vitamin A did not affect pig ascariasis but did accelerate the growth and favor the retention of horse ascaris in rats (Clapham, 1934), increase the take of dog ascaris in dogs (Wright, 1935b), and lower the resistance of rats to *Strongyloides* (Lawler, 1941). The resistance of dogs to dog hookworm is greatly lowered when they are put on a diet deficient in vitamins, proteins, and minerals and under such circumstances the worms develop faster and lay an increased number of eggs (Foster and Cort, 1932, 1935). The resistance of rats to *Nippostrongylus muris* is lowered by diets deficient in iron, proteins, or vitamins of the B group (Porter, 1935; Watt, 1944; Donaldson and Otto, 1946). Lambs fed on a deficient diet picked up over three times as many stomach trichostrongyles when put out to graze on infected pastures as did well-fed lambs (Fraser and Robertson, 1933). A lack of vitamin A in the diet greatly reduces the resistance of young rats to infection with *Trichinella spiralis* (McCoy, 1934a) but a deficiency of vitamin E was inimical to the migration of the juveniles into the muscles (Zaiman, 1940). In general, therefore, a poor nutritional condition of the host favors infection with nematodes. But, as might be expected, a point is reached that is detrimental to the worms. Thus Reid (1945b) has found that complete starvation of chickens rapidly leads to the expulsion of *Ascaridia*, apparently through depletion of the glycogen reserves of the worms.

A number of instances show that genetic factors are involved in resistance-susceptibility relations between nematode parasites and plant and animal hosts. It has already been noted that phytoparasitic nematodes may develop strains adapted to one plant species and refractory to other species subject to attack by other strains of the same nematode. Similar conditions obtain with zooparasitic nematodes. In a study of speciation in the genus *Strongyloides*, Sandground (1925, 1928) pointed out that, although the so-called species of this genus show considerable host specificity, there is very little morphological difference between them. *Str. stercoralis* of man will infect dogs but dogs display great individual differences with regard to this worm; in some individuals the infection will endure for many weeks whereas in others it soon disappears. Infection can also be established in cats, either by way of dogs or directly from man but is of short duration in this host. After passage through dogs, the worm remains infective to man but may take poorly. As already noted, *Ascaris lumbricoides* exists as pig and human strains, neither of which will infect the other host; but according to Hiraishi (1926) pigs can be made susceptible to human ascaris by lowering their resistance through a diet deficient in vitamin A. Strains of white leghorn chickens relatively resistant and susceptible to *Ascaridia galli* can be established by selection (Ackert, Pratt, and Freeman, 1936). Some breeds of chickens, those of heavier type, as Rhode Island reds and Plymouth Rocks, are naturally somewhat less susceptible to *Ascaridia* than lighter breeds as white leghorns, buff orpingtons, and white minorcas; two genetically different strains of white minorcas were also found to exhibit differential susceptibility to this nematode (Ackert and associates, 1935). Negroes are much less susceptible than whites to the pinworm (Cram, 1940, negroes around 15 per cent infected, whites 40 per cent) and to the hookworm (Smillie and Augustine, 1925; Keller, Leathers, and Knox, 1937). The dog hookworm, *Ancyl. caninum*, exists as cat and dog strains, morphologically indistinguishable (Scott, 1929; McCoy, 1931b). When juveniles of the dog strain are administered to dogs, 45 to 66 per cent develop whereas when administered to cats less than 5 per cent reach maturity. The cat strain is 27 per cent infective to cats but not more than 1 per cent infective to dogs. The egg production of both the dog strain and the cat strain in cats is greatly reduced as compared with that of both strains in dogs. Each strain takes poorly in the other host and lasts but a short time. Apparently there are ovine and bovine strains of *Haemonchus contortus;* Ross (1931) reported that lambs are readily infected with either the bovine or the ovine strain but calves are highly resistant to the ovine strain. Different breeds of sheep differ considerably as to susceptibility to *Ostertagia circumcincta* but even within the same breed marked variations of susceptibility occur (Stewart, Miller, and Douglas, 1937) and these appear to be primarily of a genetic nature (Gregory, Miller, and Stewart, 1940). Chicken and starling strains of *Syngamus trachea* have been studied by Taylor (1928) who noted morphological identity but found that the starling strain takes poorly in chicks and grows more slowly than the chicken strain in chicks. After passing one generation in chickens, the starling strain gave a higher take in chicks. According to Lewis (1928), *Syngamus trachea* exhibits morphological differences in different hosts. Evidence of the existence of strains of *Nippostrongylus muris* with different egg-producing capacities was published by Graham and Porter (1934).

As a result of a previous or of repeated infections, hosts may become refractory or immune to additional infections. The human pinworm will take in dogs and cats but in some individual dogs, the infection soon disappears or decreases in intensity and such dogs cannot be reinfected; cats soon lose their worms spontaneously and thereafter are absolutely refractory to this worm (Sandground, 1927, 1928). An infection of rats with *Strongyloides ratti* that runs its course and disappears confers an almost absolute protection against further infection and a similar resistance results from repeated inoculations with small doses of living or heat-killed juveniles (Sheldon, 1937, 1939). Cats harboring natural infections of *Toxocara mystax* prove very resistant to superimposed infection with this nematode (Sarles, 1933; Sarles and Stoll, 1935). Guinea pigs are killed by the administration of 30 to 50 ovic juveniles of pig ascaris per gram of weight but after repeated sublethal doses become resistant to the dose that was previously lethal (Kerr, 1938). As the juveniles of ascaroids migrate through the body before settling down in the intestine, it is understandable that they would evoke the formation of immune bodies inimical to their continuance in the host; in fact, it is rather surprising that many hosts fail to become refractory to repeated infections with ascaroid nematodes. Several cases of acquired resistance to strongyloid nematodes have been reported. Domestic fowls show increased resistance to a second infection with *Syngamus trachea* (Olivier, 1944). Acquired resistance of dogs to *Ancyl. caninum* is generally admitted although Foster (1935) obtained somewhat uncertain results on this point. Sarles (1929b) found that dog hookworms are rapidly lost by most dogs and these then become completely or partly refractory to a second infection. McCoy (1931a) also reported that, after evacuation of large numbers of hookworms by infected dogs, these would quickly expel worms acquired by a subsequent infection. Otto (1941, 1948) showed that a high degree of immunity of dogs to dog hookworm can be conferred by graded administration of juveniles by mouth or subcutaneous injection and that dogs recovered from a heavy infestation are highly refractory to reinfection. There appears to be no refractoriness developed to human hookworms by repeated infections. Calves, after successive infections with hookworm (*Bunostomum phlebotomum*) and nodular worm (*Oesoph. radiatum*), may suddenly eliminate most of the worms and are then resistant to further infection for at least some months (Mayhew, 1940). Similar experiences have been reported for several trichostrongyles of cattle, sheep, and other mammals. Infection of calves with *Haemonchus contortus* may be followed by sudden self-cure and complete or partial resistance to reinfection (Stoll, 1929; Mayhew, 1940). Lambs infected with *Nematodirus* eventually lose their infection and then become immune to further infection (Tetley, 1935). Taylor (1934) indicates that lambs early subject to light infections with various trichostrongyles develop resistance to later infestations that would be fatal to previously uninfected lambs of the same age. This resistance particularly concerned *H. contortus* and *Nematodirus filicollis*. Repeated daily doses of infective juveniles over a long period confers resistance on lambs to superinfection with *Cooperia curticei* (Andrews, 1938). The development of this resistance was accompanied by a visible reaction of the intestinal mucosa which formed nodules around the young worms, ordinarily not enclosed in nodules. After repeated doses of juveniles of *Trich. calcaratus* by mouth or skin, rabbits become refractory and expel the mature worms already present (Sarles, 1932). Sheep eventually throw off infection with the metastrongyle *Dictyocaulus filaria* (Kauzal, 1933). A number of studies concern *Nippostrongylus muris* in rats. Wild rats constitute the natural hosts of this worm but laboratory rats are readily infected with it; however, the worms are generally expelled after a few weeks and rats that have experienced one infection become refractory to superinfection, to a degree dependent on the severity of the original infection (Africa, 1931; Schwartz, Alicata, and Lucker, 1931; Graham, 1933, 1934; Chandler, 1932b, 1935, 1936; Spindler, 1936b). The presence of some of the original lot of worms retards the growth and development of superimposed worms and reduces the egg production of the latter. Such stunted worms will resume growth and produce eggs at the normal rate if they are transferred to rats not previously infected (Chandler, 1936a). Similar findings obtain for infection of rats with *Trichinella spiralis* as first noticed by Ducas (1921). After repeated doses of trichina juveniles rats manifest no symptoms to

doses that are fatal to previously uninfected rats; the later juveniles
fail to mature and eventually all administered juveniles are evacuated
alive and unaltered (McCoy, 1931, 1940). Guinea pigs also become
resistant to lethal doses of trichina juveniles after experiencing a heavy
infection and later administered juveniles fail to develop to maturity
and are evacuated (Roth, 1939). After a heavy infection with *Capillaria
hepatica*, rats acquire considerable immunity to a second infection
(Luttermoser, 1938).

Presumably the development of a resistance or immunity to superinfection with nematode parasites depends on the formation of immune
bodies as a result of invasion of the host tissues by the parasites. The
presence of such immune bodies has been demonstrated in some of the
cases cited above. Thus the plasma of rats rendered immune to *Strongyloides ratti* by a previous infection confers some protection against this
worm on rats that have not experienced a prior infection (Lawler, 1940).
Serum from dogs resistant to *Ancyl. caninum* failed to give any protection
to puppies against this worm but the infectivity of juvenile worms was
decreased by short exposure to such serum; longer exposures evoked
deposits around the young worms and eventually damaged and killed
them (Otto, 1940). In *Nippostrongylus muris*, serum from immune rats
confers temporary protection on rats not previously infected (Chandler,
1935, 1938; Sarles and Taliaferro, 1936; Sarles, 1939). Passage of the
juveniles of this worm through the skin and lungs and invasion of the
intestinal mucosa by them evokes severe inflammatory reactions in these
tissues in previously infected rats but only a mild response in rats not
previously infected (Chandler, 1936; Taliaferro and Sarles, 1939); the
injection of dead worms is ineffective. Apparently, then, the immune
response of rats to *N. muris* is limited to the tissues invaded and results
from the activities of the worms, not from their proteins. Resistance of
rats and mice to superinfection with *Trichinella spiralis* also depends on
the formation of immune bodies, and serum of immune rats (Culbertson,
1942) or of infected rabbits (Culbertson and Kaplan, 1938) confers some
resistance on previously uninfected rats or mice, primarily by preventing
juveniles from attaining maturity on reaching the intestine. If *Trichinella* juveniles are exposed to X-radiation before administration to rats,
they fail to mature or to produce eggs so that there is no migration into
the muscles; such rats, however, develop the same resistance to superinfection as those infected with undamaged worms so that here, too, the
intestine is the site of the immune reactions (Levin and Evans, 1942).
Trichina juveniles incubated for 18 hours in the serum of infected rabbits
are less infective to rats than those similarly treated with the serum of
uninfected rabbits (Mauss, 1940b). Offspring of trichinous rats, rabbits,
and hamsters are less susceptible to trichina than offspring of uninfected

animals (Mauss, 1940a), and according to the experiments of Culbertson (1943), the resistance is transmitted by way of the milk. The presence of immune bodies in the serum of infected hosts may be demonstrated by the ability of such serum to evoke precipitates around the worms involved. Thus the serum of trichinous humans produces precipitates around the anterior end of trichina juveniles (Roth, 1945). The serum of lambs infected with gastrointestinal nematodes will cause precipitates at the body openings of juveniles of the same parasites (Hawkins and Cole, 1945) and the serum of rabbits harboring pig ascaris produces precipitates in ascaris juveniles that may be fatal (Oliver-Gonzalez, 1943). Deposits form around the eggs of *Trichosomoides crassicauda* when they are exposed to the serum of rats harboring this worm (Smith, 1948).

As the presence of nematodes may evoke the formation of immune bodies inimical to the worms, it is not surprising that attempts have been made to immunize animals artificially against nematodes by the injection of antigens prepared from the worms. Such experiments, however, usually fail to give any protection. Thus injection of extracts of dried and powdered trichina juveniles or of rabbit antiserum fails to give rats any protection against infection with trichina according to Lucker (1933) and Bachman and Gonzalez (1936), although McCoy (1933) claimed some protection by intraperitoneal injections of live, heat-killed, or dried and pulverized juveniles; the last method was the least effective. The serum of rabbits infected with trichina contains immune bodies and when injected into mice will give the latter some protection against the worm (Culbertson and Kaplan, 1938). Feeding of dead trichina juveniles is ineffective in evoking immune bodies (Averá and others, 1946) as might be expected since immune bodies arise only in case of tissue invasion by helminths or their products.

Numerous attempts have been made to utilize immune reactions, such as the formation of skin wheals or the production of precipitins, for the diagnosis of the presence of nematode parasites. Such tests would be especially useful in diagnosing infection with nematodes that do not pass eggs into the feces, as the trichina worm. It is usual to employ as antigen acid, alkaline, or neutral saline extracts of dried and powdered worms. It was shown by Hektoen (1928) that when such extracts are suitably injected into rabbits, immune bodies are evoked and the serum of such rabbits will give a precipitin test with the extract of the worm employed. Hektoen produced such antisera for *Ascaris lumbricoides*, *Stephanurus dentatus*, and *Gongylonema scutatum* and tested them against 12 different nematode antigens, including those of these three species, by means of the precipitin reaction. He found high specificity in that a precipitate was produced only between homologous serum and antigen except that ascaris antiserum would give precipitates with other ascaroids. Canning

(1929) separated the different organs of ascaris and used them separately as antigens, finding considerable specificity, best shown by the cuticle. It further appears that nematodes (ascaris, trichina) contain a polysaccharide, presumably glycogen, that has antigenic powers (Campbell, 1936; Melcher and Campbell, 1942; Oliver-Gonzalez, 1946).

A considerable literature exists on the practical application of immune reactions to the diagnosis of the presence of nematode parasites but only a few citations will be given. The usual procedure is to prepare an antigen in the form of a saline extract of dried and powdered worms, to apply this to the skin, either by the scratch method or, preferably, by intradermal injection, and to await the appearance of a wheal. The size of the wheal and the presence or absence of projections ("pseudopods") are considered of importance. In general, skin tests have proved unsatisfactory and unreliable for diagnosing the presence of nematode parasites, and the results vary in the hands of different workers. Thus Coventry and Taliaferro (1928), using the scratch method, applied ascaris antigen to the skin of a considerable number of Honduras natives (130) and found that the majority would give a positive skin reaction whether or not they were infected with ascaris; nor was there any correlation with the presence of other helminths. Precipitin tests also showed no correlation with the presence of ascaris. Brunner (1928), using intradermal injection of ascaris antigen, obtained a positive skin reaction in all cases that harbored nematodes, but nematodes other than ascaris gave a positive response and positive response was also manifested by persons whose stools were negative for nematode eggs. Coventry (1929) reported positive skin reactions of variable intensity following intradermal injection of ascaris antigen into rabbits and guinea pigs that had been infected with ascaris or injected intraperitoneally with an acid suspension of dried and powdered ascaris. Reactions might continue to be given long after the animals had lost their worms and no correlation could be found between the intensity of the skin reaction and the presence of precipitins in the serum. More reliable results are reported for filarioids, which apparently possess a common antigen so that antigens made from various species (*Dirofilaria immitis*, *Wuchereria bancrofti*, and *Litomosoides carinii*) are usable (Warren, 1947). Antigen prepared from *Dirofilaria immitis* gives a high percentage of positive reaction when applied to the skin of persons with *W. bancrofti* (Zarrow and Tifkin, 1946; Wharton, 1947; Taliaferro and Hoffman, 1930), and no reaction to the presence of other helminths. Antigen prepared from *Onchocerca volvulus* evoked a positive skin response to this worm in 96 per cent of infected persons and gave complement fixation test in all cases (Bozicevich and others, 1947). Most of the work concerns the trichina worm since diagnosis of the presence of this worm by other means is difficult; but here again results are uncertain and unreliable. Frisch, Whims, and Oppenheim obtain a positive skin response in only 50 per cent of 200 persons that had eaten trichinous meat and found great variability as a result of different methods of preparation of the antigen. Spindler and Cross (1939) and Spindler, Cross, and Avery (1941) tried variously prepared trichina antigens but found that none were reliable when applied to swine in slaughterhouses and positive skin reactions might be obtained from swine not infected with trichina. In the total series of tests conducted on swine, clear-cut positive reactions were obtained in only 43 per cent of infected animals, but one type of antigen employed, containing particulate material of trichina juveniles, evoked a positive response in 71 per cent of infected pigs. Apparently improvement in the method of preparing antigens is necessary before immunological tests for the presence of nematode worms achieve reliability.

As is usual in parasitic infections, the number of nematodes per host may reach prodigious numbers. Heavy infections with ascaris in man may total one to five thousand worms and over 500 worms may be present in heavy infections with human hookworms. In examinations of human diaphragms for encysted trichinae, nearly 1000 worms per gram of muscle were found in one case (Hall and Collins, 1937) but of course their distribution throughout the diaphragm may not have been uniform. A maximum of 845 *Trichuris* in a dog was reported by Miller (1939). The nodules produced by *Onchocerca* may contain over 100 worms and a person may be afflicted with 25 to 100 nodules. In an investigation of chicken helminths in Tennessee, Todd (1946) recorded a maximum of 1981 *Heterakis gallinae* and 66 *Ascaridia galli*. Trichostrongyles are often present in enormous numbers in domestic mammals; thus Shorb (1942) reported 20,000 *Haemonchus contortus*, 6400 *Ostertagia circumcincta*, 5585 *Cooperia curticei*, and 7800 *Trich. vitrinus* in individual sheep; Andrews (1937) found 25,000 *Cooperia curticei* in one lamb; and Tetley (1935) remarks that lambs may have up to 5000 *Nematodirus*.

There are some indications that crowding of a host with one species adversely affects the worms. In *Ascaridia galli*, the percentage of worms gaining a foothold tends to increase as the number of ovic juveniles fed is decreased and the worms also grow to a larger size when fewer are present (Ackert, Graham, Nolf, and Porter, 1931). The daily egg production of the human *Necator* declines as the number of worms harbored increases (Hill, 1926) and the same is true of *Ancyl. caninum* (Sarles, 1929a).

As may be expected, the egg production of parasitic nematodes vastly exceeds that of free-living species. Typically the egg production increases daily during early sexual maturity, reaches a maximum figure at which it remains fairly constant for some time, and then declines to a low figure during the remaining life of the worm. As already indicated egg production is affected by the nutritional state, age, and genetic constitution of the host. The following figures assume a normal condition of the worms. *Ascaris lumbricoides* (human) probably has an egg production of over 200,000 daily (Brown and Cort, 1927) and one female probably contains a total of 27,000,000 eggs (Cram, 1925). *Parascaris equorum* was estimated by Pick (1947) to produce 60,000,000 eggs annually, or about 170,000 daily. Counts of the total egg content of *Enterobius vermicularis* gave values of 5000 to 17,000 eggs (Reardon, 1938). Counts for the human hookworm (*Necator americanus*) are given as 6000 to 11,000 daily by Stoll (1923), 8000 to 10,000 by Soper (1927). *Ancylostoma duodenale* produces about twice this number daily, 22,000 to 24,000 (Soper, 1927). The dog hookworm, *Ancyl. caninum* has an egg production of 7700 to 28,400 daily, or an average of 16,000 (McCoy, 1931). The other dog hookworm, *Ancyl. braziliense*, is less productive, with 4000 eggs daily (McCoy, 1931). The dog whipworm (*Trichuris vulpis*) averages about 3000 eggs daily and a similar figure obtains for the human whipworm (*T. trichiura*, Miller, 1939). *Haemonchus contortus* produces 5000 to 6000 eggs daily (Martin and Ross, 1934).

Data on the longevity of common zooparasitic nematodes have been assembled by Taylor (1933) and Sandground (1936), where exact references will be found. Probably the nematodes of wild animals are relatively short-lived but the larger species in man and domestic animals may last for years. Some of the available figures are: *Ancylostoma duodenale*, 5 to 7 years, maximum, 16 years; *Ancyl. caninum*, 6 months to 2 years; *Necator americanus*, 12 to 20 years; *Loa loa*, 12 to 15 years; *Acanthocheilonema perstans*, $3\frac{1}{2}$ years; *Dioctophyme renalis*, over 2 years; *Haemonchus contortus*, more than 1 year (Mayhew, 1942); and a species of *Trichostrongylus* with which Sandground infected himself was still present and producing eggs after 8 years. Microfilariae persist for many years in the circulation; thus there are records of 15 years for the microfilariae of *Loa loa*, 17 years for those of *Wuchereria bancrofti*, and 7 years for those of *Dirofilaria immitis*. Other common human nematodes have briefer existences; *Ascaris lumbricoides* probably lasts less than a year, *Enterobius vermicularis* is thought to live but a couple of months, and *Trichinella spiralis* is very short-lived as an adult, only a week or two, although the encapsulated juveniles retain their viability for several years.

The question why parasitic worms are not digested in the digestive tract of their hosts has always interested helminthologists and is discussed by Hobson (1948) where references will be found. There are probably three factors involved: the fact that intact live animals are not affected by the ordinary proteolytic enzymes of animals, such as pepsin and trypsin (Northrop, 1926); the protection afforded by the cuticle;

and the production by the worms of antienzymes that null the action of proteolytic enzymes. This last factor is probably the most important. It is interesting to note that helminths cannot withstand proteolytic enzymes of plant origin.

Probably the most interesting relations of nematodes and their hosts are the induction of galls by phytoparasitic nematodes and the alterations produced in ants by infestation with mermithoids. The structure of plant galls evoked by nematodes has been described by several authors,

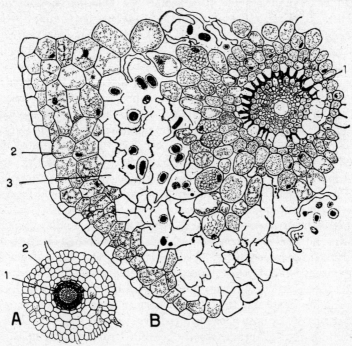

Fig. 199.—Grass root with gall of *Heterodera marioni* (*after Goodey*, 1932). *A*, Normal root. *B*, Section through the gall, to scale. 1, vascular bundle; 2, green tissue of leaf; 3, spaces occupied by nematode.

especially Goodey. These galls are characterized in general by an increase in the size and in the number of cells. In a simple type of root gall formed by *Heterodera marioni* on grass roots (Goodey, 1932), the cortical tissue between the surface epidermis and the central vascular bundle is increased from the normal 4 or 5 rows to 10 to 12 rows and the cells are also greatly enlarged and filled with granular protoplasm (Fig. 199). Spaces in the cortical tissue due to cell breakdown are occupied by the worms. More elaborate changes caused by the root gall nematode were described by Christie (1936) who noted that the hypertrophied cortical cells might fuse to form giant multinucleate cells, three to six per gall, filled with a dense cytoplasm.   The simpler types of gall formed on grass blades by species of *Tylenchus* (Goodey, 1933, 1934a) consist essentially of an increase in the size and number of the mesophyll cells (green tissue of the leaf), with the formation of spaces occupied by the worm. In a more complicated gall evoked on grass blades by *Tylenchus cecidoplastes* (Goodey, 1934b), the central cavity occupied by the worm is surrounded by two or three layers of enlarged nutritive cells without chlorophyll; outside these is a zone three to six cells deep of sclerenchyme (lignified cells) and outside these come the enlarged mesophyll cells (Fig. 200).   The structure of this gall is said to be similar to that of insect galls and apparently nematode galls like those of insects are caused by substances emitted from the worm that stimulate growth but inhibit mitosis and differentiation.

Although ants altered by the presence of mermithids had been noted prior to this date, it was Wheeler (1901) who discovered the causal relation of the mermithid to such alterations.   In 1928, Wheeler published a review of the subject with a complete bibliography, and made some additional remarks in 1937.   Gösswald (1930) listed over 20 species of ants that he had found parasitized with mermithids but most of the accounts concern species of *Lasius* and *Pheidole*.   Any of the castes of ants may be altered by mermithid parasites and the alterations in general represent a mixture of the characters of the various castes.   Mermithized female ants are called *mermithogynes;* workers, *mermithergates;* soldiers, *mermithostratiotes;* and males, *mermithaners*.   The outstanding feature of all mermithized ants is the greatly swollen abdomen, and this may constitute the only alteration but other changes are often evident.   Mermithogynes of *Lasius* (described by Crawley and Baylis, 1921; Gösswald, 1929, 1938) have a smaller head and thorax than normal females, small wings that may be reduced to stumps, and reduced ovaries, and the fat body is more or less eliminated.   Mermithergates combine features of females, workers, and soldiers; the form and size of the head are similar to those of workers, the thorax and pedicel resemble those of soldiers, and ocelli may be present as in females.   Mermithostratiotes of *Pheidole* were treated at some length by Vandel (1930).   They are about the same size as normal soldiers but the head and mandibles are reduced, showing gradations between those of normal soldiers and those of normal workers, and the thorax is altered in the female direction.   Other female characters are increased hairiness and the presence of one ocellus in some specimens. Mermithized males were unknown until 1930 when Gösswald found them in *Lasius* (1930, 1938).   These may not differ from normal males except for the distended abdomen but may also present shortened wings. Mermithized ants generally lack normal behavior but are always exceedingly hungry because of depletion of their food stores by the parasite.

34. Relationships.—The nematodes possess an array of characters that seem to set them off from other groups of invertebrates, so that their systematic position has always been somewhat uncertain. However, increased knowledge in recent years of the free-living members has somewhat lessened this gap, and close inspection reveals many features in common with the other groups here allied with the nematodes to form

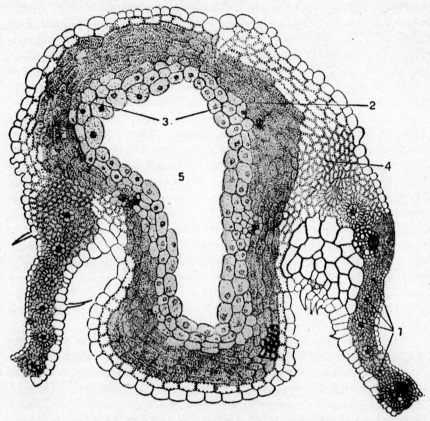

Fig. 200.—Gall formed by *Tylenchus cecidoplastes* in grass leaf (*after Goodey*, 1934). 1, vascular bundles; 2, sclerenchyme; 3, nutritive cells; 4, mesophyll cells; 5, cavity occupied by worm.

the Aschelminthes. The general grade of nematode structure is clearly pseudocoelomate. The radial symmetry of the anterior end is more or less in evidence in all Aschelminthes but is especially developed in the nematodes, kinorhynchs, and priapulids. The propensity toward cuticular specializations in the form of spines, bristles, scales, and so on is also noticeable throughout the Aschelminthes but is most pronounced in gastrotrichs, kinorhynchs, priapulids, and nematodes. Superficial segmentation is common to rotifers, kinorhynchs, priapulids, nematodes, and the gordioid larva. The process of molting the cuticle occurs in kinorhynchs, nematodes, and priapulids. The epidermal chords so characteristic of nematodes also occur in kinorhynchs, priapulids, and nematomorphs, and possibly derive from the epidermal cushions of rotifers; lateral epidermal thickenings are also seen in the macrodasyoid gastrotrichs. An absence of definite circular and longitudinal muscle layers in the body wall with an emphasis on longitudinal fibers is general throughout the Aschelminthes except Priapulida and the histological structure of the muscles is strikingly similar in nematodes and nematomorphs. The characteristics of the nematode pharynx are also seen in gastrotrichs and to a less extent in kinorhynchs and priapulids. The structure of the gonad shows great similarity between nematodes and kinorhynchs and the development of the gonads and their continuity with their ducts are strikingly similar between nematodes and priapulids. Copulatory spicules are found in kinorhynchs as well as in nematodes. Caudal adhesive glands of very similar appearance and relations occur in rotifers, gastrotrichs, free-living nematodes, and the priapulid larva, and the adhesive tube on which they open in many nematodes very likely corresponds to the adhesive tubes of gastrotrichs, kinorhynchs, and the *Halicryptus* larva. A circumenteric nerve ring giving off a main ventral cord is common to kinorhynchs, priapulids, and nematodes. The eyes found in some free-living nematodes are similar to rotifer eyes and the amphids of nematodes may correspond to the lateral head organs of gastrotrichs. The absence of protonephridia in nematodes is certainly a stumbling block in relating this group to other Protostomia but ventral glands that suggest the renette cells of nematodes occur in marine gastrotrichs.

The foregoing considerations seem to indicate that the nematodes find their nearest relatives among the kinorhynchs and priapulids.

Concerning relationships within the nematode class itself, there can be no doubt that all nematodes derive from marine free-living forebears. Relationships among the marine orders have been discussed by Stekhoven and de Coninck (1933) and de Coninck (1942). These authors are agreed that the spiral type of amphid is the most primitive and other forms of amphid are easily derivable from it. Hence the Chromadoroidea presumably represent the most primitive existing nematodes and from them the other orders originate in a polyphyletic fashion. One line of evolution leads to the groups with cyathiform amphids, namely, the Enoploidea, culminating in the oncholaims on the one hand, and the Dorylaimoidea on the other hand. The Mermithoidea are obviously derivable from the Dorylaimoidea and the possession of a buccal stylet indicates relationship of the Trichuroidea with the Dorylaimoidea. Probably the Dioctophymoidea are also an offshoot of this line of evolution. The marine orders Araeolamoidea and Desmoscolecoidea have amphids that are obvious variations of the spiral type and hence no doubt are descended from the Chromadoroidea. The circular amphid of the Monhysteroidea also appears to be a variant of the spiral type.

The terrestrial and fresh-water nematodes appear to have come from marine ancestors; de Coninck links the Rhabditoidea culminating in the tylenchids with the Chromadoroidea. The great similarity of the pharynx in the two groups makes probable the derivation of the Oxyuroidea from the Rhabditoidea. The Rhabdiasoidea are also related to the Rhabditoidea, as shown by their general structure and the occurrence of rhabdiform young. The occurrence of rhabdiform young in the Strongyloidea would also seem to link this group to the Rhabditoidea. The difficulty encountered in allocating families between the Oxyuroidea and Ascaroidea is indicative of a relationship of the latter to the former. There would seem to be no doubt of an affinity between the Spiruroidea and the Filarioidea because of an approach to the filarioid type of life cycle in certain spiruroids (e.g., *Habronema*, page 362), but the derivation of the Spiruroidea is uncertain. Similarity of life cycle may indicate relationship of the Dracunculoidea with the Spiruroidea.

IX. CLASS NEMATOMORPHA

1. Historical. The gordian worms were noticed during the fourteenth and fifteenth centuries and from this period also dates the myth that they are transformed horsehairs. The name *Gordius* originated with Linnaeus who listed this worm under his Vermes Intestina in a mixture of various kinds of worms. For many years thereafter the gordian worms were confused with nematodes, especially filarioids, until studies on the anatomy by Charvet (1834), Siebold (1838), Berthold (1843), and Dujardin (1842) led Siebold to separate them from nematodes in 1843 under the name Gordiacea. However, Siebold also included *Mermis* in this group and it remained for Vejdovsky (1886) to separate the gordiaceans altogether from the nematodes under the name Nematomorpha which is here adopted as the most suitable name for the group. Although zoologists have long recognized the many differences between the gordian worms and the nematodes, they have continued the practice of allocating the two groups to the same phylum. The author has been led by certain lines of evidence to include the Nematomorpha under the Aschelminthes. As in the case of other classes of Aschelminthes the elevation of the group to the rank of a separate phylum is proposed as an alternative to the course here adopted. The fact that juvenile gordians are parasitic in insects was discovered by Dufour in 1828. The characteristic larvae were seen by Grube (1849) but first adequately described by Meissner in 1856. During the latter part of the nineteenth century, main contributions to the knowledge of the Nematomorpha were made by Grenacher (1868), Villot (1874, 1881, 1887), Vejdovsky (1886, 1888, 1894), Camerano (1888, 1897), Bürger (1891), and Ward (1892). The more valuable later contributions are those of Montgomery (1903, 1904), Mühldorf (1914), and May (1919). The available information on the group to 1930 was summarized by Rauther in the *Handbuch der Zoologie*.

2. Definition.—The Nematomorpha are Aschelminthes of very filiform shape, free-living as adults, parasitic in arthropods as juveniles, without lateral chords or excretory system, with a digestive tube more or less degenerate at one or both ends, and with a cloaca in both sexes.

3. External Characters.—The nematomorph body (Fig. 201*A*) is excessively slender and elongated, whence the common name of hairworms, and often reaches a length of $\frac{1}{2}$ to 1 m. or more with a diameter of less than 1 mm. to 2 or 3 mm. As in nematodes, the males are shorter than the females except in *Nectonema* where the males are larger. The body is generally of about uniform diameter throughout with rounded ends (Fig. 201*C, F*) but in the genus *Chordodes* tapers markedly anteriorly (Fig. 201*B*). The coloration varies from yellowish or buff to dark brown except for the anterior tip or *calotte* which is usually white, usually bounded posteriorly by a dark ring (Fig. 201*C*). The mouth is situated terminally or ventrally in the calotte. The posterior end is rounded (Fig. 201*E*) or is lobulated into two or three caudal lobes (Fig. 201*D, G–J*) in relation to genus and sex. The anus or, more accurately, cloacal aperture, is situated terminally or ventrally at the posterior end and is anterior to the caudal lobes when present. As in nematodes the posterior part of males may be coiled or ventrally curved. In the genus *Chordodes*, a longitudinal mid-ventral groove marks the position of the ventral chord.

The cuticle clothing the body is rather thick in most nematomorphs and is of rough texture in the family Chordodidae, which includes most members of the group. This roughness is attributable to the *areoles*, which are closely contiguous rounded or polygonal areas in the cuticle (Fig. 202). The areoles often project above the surface as papillae which may be topped by one or more bristles (Fig. 202*A, B*) or perforated by a pore (Fig. 202*D*). The interareolar furrows between the areoles may bear bristles or warts or the pores of canals running in the cuticle. Tracts of bristles or thorns, sometimes altered into adhesive warts, are often present on the cloacal region of males (Fig. 201*G, J*). In the genus *Gordius*, males are characterized by a crescentic cuticular fold behind the cloacal aperture (Fig. 201*D*). *Nectonema* has a double row of natatory bristles along the middorsal and mid-ventral lines except at the body ends (Fig. 206*A*) but these appear laterally located because of a body torsion.

4. Internal Anatomy.—The body wall as in other Aschelminthes consists of cuticle, epidermis, and muscle layer. The cuticle, much thicker in the gordioids than in *Nectonema*, consists of an outer homogeneous and an inner fibrous layer (Fig. 202*G*). The homogeneous layer is thin except in forms provided with areoles, the presence of which greatly increases the thickness of this layer. The areoles, of unknown nature and function, appear as condensations in the homogeneous layer (Fig. 202*G*). The fibrous layer is of lamellate construction (Fig. 202*G*), consisting in gordiods of a number (up to 45) of fibrous strata. In *Nectonema* a zone

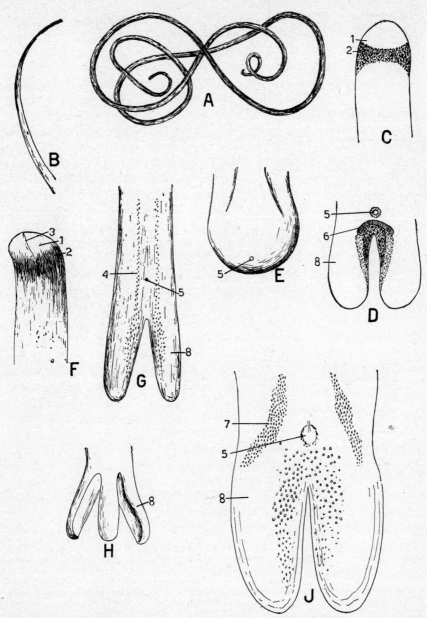

Fig. 201.—Nematomorpha. *A*. A gordian worm (*after Janda*, 1893). *B*. Anterior end of *Chordodes* (*after Römer*, 1896). *C*. Anterior end of *Gordius*. *D*. Posterior end of male *Gordius*. (*C, D, after Heinze*, 1937.) *E*. Posterior end of female *Gordius*. *F*. Anterior end of *Paragordius*. *G*. Posterior end of male *Paragordius*. (*F, G, after May*, 1919.) *H*. Posterior end of female *Paragordius* (*after Montgomery*, 1898). *J*. Posterior end of male *Gordionus* (*after Heinze*, 1937). 1, calotte; 2, pigment ring; 3, pharynx; 4, tracts of thorns; 5, anus; 6, postanal crescent; 7, preanal tracts of thorns; 8, caudal lobes.

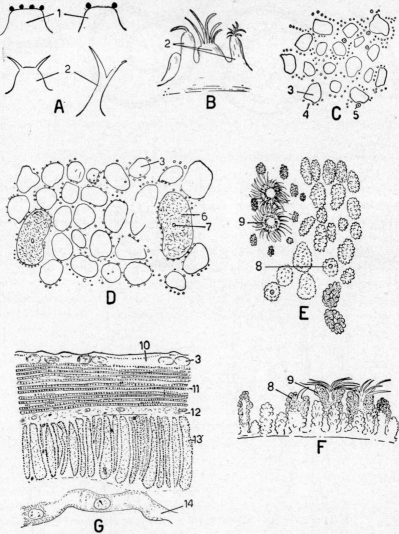

Fig. 202.—Nematomorpha, cuticle. *A, B.* Various types of areoles, schematic (*after Müller,* 1927). *C.* Areoles of *Gordionus,* surface view. *D.* Areoles of *Parachordodes.* (*C, D, after Heinze,* 1937.) *E.* Areoles of *Chordodes,* surface view. *F.* Areoles of *Chordodes,* side view. (*E, F, after Camerano,* 1897.) *G.* Section through the body wall of *Paragordius* (*after Montgomery,* 1903). 1, type of areole topped with granules; 2, types topped with bristles; 3, areoles; 4, interareolar papillae; 5, interareolar bristle; 6, large areole with central pore; 7, pore; 8, areole with single bristle; 9, areole with numerous bristles; 10, homogeneous layer of cuticle; 11, fibrillar layer of cuticle; 12, epidermis; 13, muscle layer; 14, mesenchyme.

of dark granules lies between cuticle and epidermis. The epidermis is a one-layered epithelium varying from a low cuboidal to a columnar shape. In the gordioids it forms only one chord, the ventral one, whereas in *Nectonema* there are conspicuous dorsal and ventral chords (Fig. 204*B*). A dorsal epidermal thickening is present in *Paragordius* (Fig. 203*B*) but this is not a true chord as it does not interrupt the musculature. The body-wall musculature consists, as in nematodes, of longitudinal fibers only and these in *Nectonema* are histologically identical with the coelomyarian type of muscle cell of nematodes (Fig. 203*A*); but in the gordioids the contractile fibrils completely encircle the protoplasmic part of the cell (Fig. 202*G*).

Only in *Nectonema* is there a complete pseudocoel extending the body length between body wall and digestive tube (Fig. 204*B*); a septum at the level of the brain separates off a small anterior part of the pseudocoel from the remainder (Fig. 203*D*). In adult gordioids the pseudocoel is more or less filled with mesenchyme cells and tissue so that only limited spaces remain. Typically the digestive tube is surrounded by a space throughout its course (Fig. 203*B*) and the gonads also lie in spaces bounded by mesenchyme (Fig. 205*D*). The arrangement of the mesenchyme is such as often to produce partitions resembling mesenteries (Fig. 205*D*).

The digestive tract is more or less degenerate in all nematomorphs, not only in adults but also in juvenile stages, so that the ingestion of food at any time appears improbable. A patent mouth is often wanting. The anterior part of the digestive tract, presumably representing a pharynx, is a solid cord of cells in most gordioids but in *Paragordius* this becomes patent late in development and a pharynx provided with an end bulb results (Fig. 203*C*). The intestine or midgut in gordioids is a simple epithelial tube lying free in the pseudocoel (Fig. 205*D*). According to May (1919) the midgut greatly resembles histologically the Malpighian tubules of insects and hence probably serves an excretory function. Toward its posterior end, the intestine receives the genital ducts and thereafter forms a cloaca lined with cuticle and hence of proctodaeal nature. The digestive tract of *Nectonema* differs considerably from that of gordioids and presents many resemblances to that of mermithoid and trichuroid nematodes. The minute mouth leads into a slender cuticularized tube more or less accompanied by cellular material (Fig. 203*D*) and this enters the intestine which consists of two or four rows of cells or of long syncytia (Fig. 204*C*). Posteriorly the nectonematoid intestine dwindles away without reaching the cloaca which is present to serve sexual functions.

The nervous system is very similar to that of echinoderids and priapulids, being closely related to the epidermis and consisting of a cir-

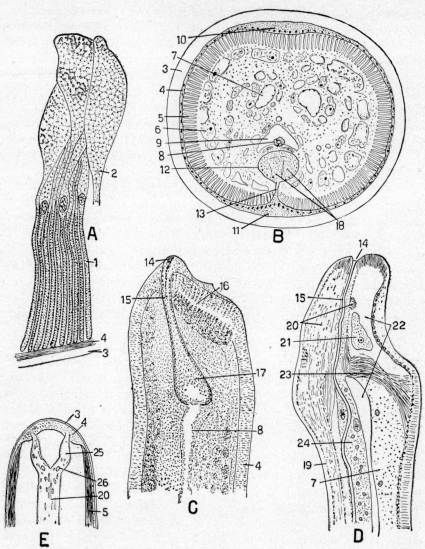

Fig. 203.—Nematomorpha, muscles, digestive, nervous systems. *A.* Muscle cells of *Nectonema*, to show nematode resemblance (*after Rauther*, 1914). *B.* Section through *Paragordius*. *C.* Longitudinal section through the anterior end of *Paragordius* (*after May*, 1919). *D.* Longitudinal section through the anterior end of *Nectonema* (*after Bürger*, 1891). *E.* Dorsal view of the brain of *Paragordius*. (*B, E, after Montgomery*, 1903.) 1, fibrillar part of muscle cell; 2, cytoplasmic part of muscle cell; 3, cuticle; 4, epidermis; 5, muscle layer; 6, mesenchyme; 7, testes; 8, intestine; 9, pseudocoel around intestine; 10, dorsal thickening; 11, ventral chord; 12, nerve cord; 13, lamella connecting nerve cord with ventral chord; 14, mouth; 15, pharynx; 16, eye; 17, pharyngeal bulb; 18, nerve tracts; 19, pigment layer; 20, brain; 21, giant nerve cell; 22, pseudocoel; 23, septum; 24, syncytium accompanying pharynx; 25, cephalic nerves; 26, dorsal nerves.

cumenteric cerebral mass lying in the head calotte (Fig. 204*A, E*) and a mid-ventral cord. The ventral cord originates in the epidermis and remains in this position in the ventral chord throughout life in *Nectonema* (Fig. 204*B*) but in gordioids later moves inward and remains connected with the ventral chord by a strand, the nervous lamella (Fig. 203*B*). The ventral cord is subdivided by glial partitions into three tracts (Fig. 203*B*) and where it passes into the brain there occur a variable number of giant nerve cells (Fig. 204*A*), presumably cells with very long processes in the cord tracts, acting to coordinate long stretches of the worm. At its posterior end the ventral cord may present a thickening called the cloacal ganglion (Fig. 205*B*) but this hardly merits the name of ganglion since it contains no additional nerve cells. Little has been seen of the peripheral nervous system. In *Paragordius*, Montgomery (1903) found that the two lateral tracts of the cord continue forward from the brain as cephalic nerves into the calotte epidermis (Fig. 203*E*) and each of these gives off two ventral nerves into the ventral epidermis of the calotte. From the cerebral mass arises a pair of dorsal nerves into the so-called eye (Fig. 204*E*). In *Paragordius* females, a pair of anterior and a pair of posterior cloacal nerves supplying the cloaca spring from the cloacal ganglion and in males this ganglion gives off some small genital fibers into the sperm ducts and then bifurcates into the caudal lobes (Fig. 205*B*).

Little definite can be said about the sensory equipment of the nematomorphs. The epidermis, especially that of the calotte, contains the usual bipolar sensory nerve cells, presumably tangoreceptors (Fig. 204*D*) and similar cells synapsing with a nerve fiber in the epidermis were also seen by Montgomery (1903) in *Paragordius* (Fig. 204*D*). Presumably the various bristles, spines, and warts of the cuticle may have sensory functions and those of the rear end of males may play a sensory role in copulation. A large sac situated in the calotte of *Paragordius* is considered to be an eye by Montgomery (1903). The slender and attenuated epidermal cells of the tip of the calotte form the anterior wall of this sac which is elsewhere bordered by a capsule of altered mesenchyme (Fig. 204*E*). The sac contains a coagulated fluid and a number of small fusiform cells regarded as retinal cells by Montgomery and is heavily innervated by way of the two dorsal nerves mentioned above. In favor of the photic nature of this structure is the transparency of the calotte epidermis concerned and the presence of a dark pigment ring just behind the sac. A similar organ does not appear to have been seen in any other nematomorph.

The sexes are separate in all nematomorphs and the gonads consists of a pair of cylindrical bodies running the body length in both sexes throughout the Gordioidea. Whereas a thin flat epithelial boundary of the gonads is reported by some authors, others state that the cylinders of sex

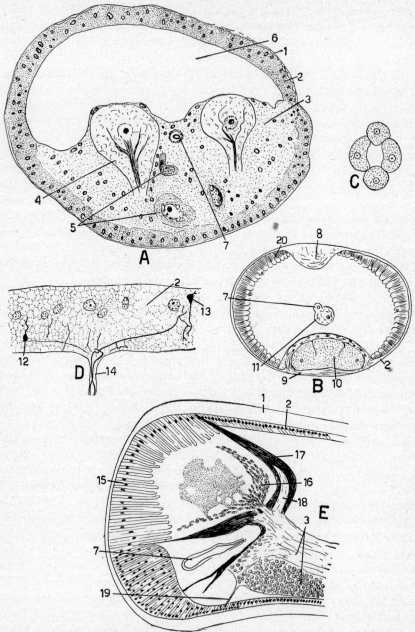

Fig. 204.—Nematomorpha, nervous system, digestive system. *A.* Section through the brain of *Nectonema* (*after Feyel*, 1936). *B.* Section through the pharyngeal region of *Nectonema.* *C.* Section of intestine of *Nectonema.* (*B, C, after Bürger*, 1891.) *D.* Epidermis of *Paragordius*, with sensory nerve cells. *E.* Section of the anterior end of *Paragordius*, showing eye. (*D, E, after Montgomery*, 1903.) 1, cuticle; 2, epidermis; 3, brain; 4, giant nerve

cells are confined only by mesenchymal tissues (Fig. 205D). In males each gonad continues posteriorly and enters the cloaca separately from its fellow by way of a short sperm duct (Fig. 205B); the posterior part of the testis cylinder is sometimes considered to be a seminal vesicle. Copulatory spicules are wanting throughout the Nematomorpha but in *Gordius* and *Paragordius* the cloaca bears spines or bristles. This suggests that it may act as a cirrus but there are no observations to this effect. The spermatozoa are simple elongated bodies (Fig. 205F). Early stages of the ovaries are similar to the testes and indistinguishable from them but later each ovary puts out a large number (up to three or four thousand) of lateral diverticula that lie in mesenchymal spaces (Fig. 205D). According to some authors the eggs ripened in these diverticula reenter the main ovarian tube (now called uterus) but May (1919) states that in the two species he studied such eggs pass backward in the mesenchymal spaces and reenter the uterus only near the cloaca. Caudally the uteri narrow to oviducts that open separately into a common chamber or antrum lined with glandular epithelium. From this an elongated sac, the seminal receptacle, extends anteriorly beneath the intestine (Fig. 205C). The antrum continues into the cloaca, distinguished by its cuticular lining; this is usually short but is very elongated in *Paragordius* (Fig. 205C).

The reproductive system of the Nectonematoidea is imperfectly known because of a lack of good sexually mature specimens. The best account is that of Feyel (1936) who worked with parasitic juveniles. There is a single testis suspended from the dorsal epidermal chord (Fig. 205A) and posteriorly becoming a tube opening to the exterior (Fig. 205E). There appears to be no definite ovary but the ovocytes, at first attached by strands to the epidermis, later become free and fill the pseudocoel. The eggs are emitted to the exterior by way of a short genital tube at the rear end of the worm which presumably represents the remains of a cloaca.

The sex cells apparently originate from mesenchyme cells, although this seems to have been definitely established only for *Nectonema* (Feyel, 1936).

5. Breeding Habits.—After completing their development almost to sexual maturity, the gordioids emerge from their insect hosts, apparently while the latter are in the vicinity of water. Emergence in most species occurs in spring and early summer and copulation and egg laying ensue immediately. *Gordius robustus* studied by May (1919) leaves the grasshopper host in September and October but does not breed until the follow-

---

cells; 5, ordinary nerve cells; 6, pseudocoel; 7, pharynx; 8, dorsal chord; 9, ventral chord; 10, nerve cord; 11, syncytium accompanying pharynx; 12, sensory nerve cell; 13, sensory nerve cell with synapse; 14, lamella to nerve cord; 15, altered epidermis of eye; 16, presumed retinal cells; 17, capsule of eye; 18, dorsal nerve; 19, ventral nerve; 20, muscle layer.

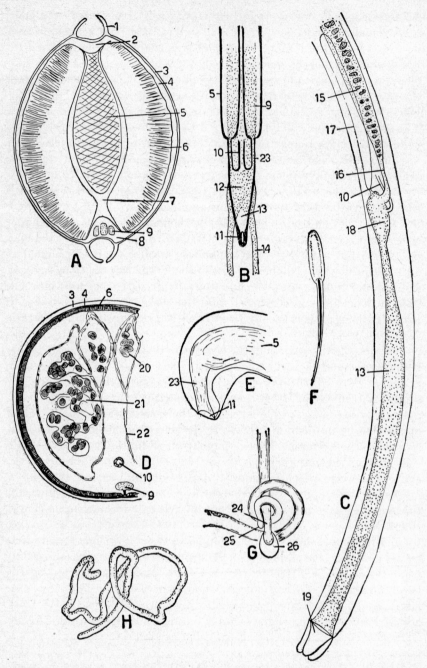

FIG. 205.—Nematomorpha, reproductive system. *A.* Section through male *Nectonema*. *B.* Scheme of the male system of *Paragordius*. *C.* Scheme of the female system of *Para-*

ing spring. The adult gordioids seek the borders of streams and lakes and the males may swim by body undulations. At the right season both sexes may be found in numbers in favorable localities. Copulation (Fig. 205*G*) occurs by the spiral coiling of the rear end of the male body around the rear end of the female; after attaining the right position the male deposits a drop of sperm in the vicinity of the female anus (Fig. 205*G*). The sperm then migrate into the seminal receptacle. The eggs are laid in water in long strings (Fig. 205*H*) formed by a secretion presumably coming from the glandular antrum. Egg strings are usually easily found in the vicinity of the adults during the proper season.

6. Order Gordioidea.—The Nematomorpha are divisible into two orders, Gordioidea and Nectonematoidea. The Gordioidea include all the fresh-water and terrestrial forms and are distinguished by the presence of only the ventral epidermal chord, the filling of the pseudocoel with mesenchyme, the paired gonads, and the putting out of lateral diverticula by the ovaries. There are two families of Gordioidea, the Chordodidae with conspicuous cuticular areoles, and the Gordiidae without areoles or with inconspicuous ones. In the former family the shape and arrangement of the areoles constitutes a main taxonomic character for generic distinctions. The generic arrangement of the Gordioidea has been considered in recent years by Müller (1927), Heinze (1934, 1935, 1937), and Carvalho (1942). The principal genera of the Chordodidae are *Chordodes, Paragordius, Parachordodes,* and *Gordionus; Chordodes* has been split into three genera by Carvalho and *Parachordodes* into a number of genera by Müller and Heinze. In *Chordodes,* the posterior end is unlobed in both sexes; in this genus there is a mid-ventral groove along the body length. In *Paragordius,* the female posterior end is trilobed (Fig. 201*H*), that of the male deeply bilobed and covered with little spines or bristles (Fig. 201*G*). The posterior end of the male is also bilobed and provided with bristles tracts in *Parachordodes* and related genera (Fig. 201*J*) but the lobes are shorter and broader than in *Paragordius;* the posterior end of the female is unlobed in this group of genera. The genus *Gordionus* differs from *Parachordodes* in the less prominent areoles and in the frequent occurrence of adhesive warts in place of some of the thorns of the cloacal region. The Gordiidae comprise the single genus *Gordius* in which the female caudal end is unlobed while that of the male is strongly

---

gordius. D. Section through female *Paragordius.* (*B, C, D, after Montgomery,* 1903.) *E.* Posterior end of male *Nectonema.* (*A, E, after Feyel,* 1936.) *F.* Nematomorph sperm (*after Mühldorf,* 1914). *G.* Gordian worms in copulation. *H.* Egg string of a gordian worm. (*G, H, after Müller,* 1927.) 1, natatory bristles; 2, dorsal chord; 3, cuticle; 4, epidermis; 5, testis; 6, muscle layer; 7, pseudocoel; 8, ventral chord; 9, nerve cord; 10, intestine; 11, anus; 12, cloacal ganglion; 13, cloaca; 14, caudal nerves into caudal lobes; 15, ovary; 16, oviduct; 17, seminal receptacle; 18, glandular part of cloaca; 19, caudal lobes; 20, uterus (main ovarian tube); 21, ovarian diverticula; 22, mesenchymal partitions; 23, sperm duct; 24, rear end of female; 25, rear end of male; 26, drop of sperm.

bilobed with a postanal crescentic fold and without preanal bristle tracts (Fig. 201*D, E*).

7. Order Nectonematoidea.—This order consists of the single genus *Nectonema*, a marine pelagic nematomorph, reported by Verrill in 1879 as having been seen several times swimming at the surface in Vineyard Sound, off the coast of Massachusetts. Since then *Nectonema* has been taken in various coastal waters—Gulf of Naples, Netherlands Indies, Spitsbergen, Norwegian Coast. *Nectonema* differs from the gordioids in having both dorsal and ventral chords, in the presence of natatory bristles, in the inclusion of the ventral nerve cord in the epidermis, in the open pseudocoel, and in the single gonad. The worm is around 200 mm. long and usually of a pale translucent appearance. Most of the specimens found probably belong to the original species, *N. agile* (Fig. 206*A*), although other species have been named (listed by Feyel, 1936).

8. Embryonic Development.—The best studies of the embryology are those of Montgomery (1904) for *Paragordius* and Mühldorf (1914) for *Gordius*. Differences in the accounts of these two authors may result from their having used different genera. The egg undergoes equal holoblastic cleavage into three- and four-cell stages; the latter is usually symmetrical but may assume the rhomboidal shape characteristic of nematodes. In *Paragordius* there is produced a coeloblastula from which a typical gastrula arises by embolic invagination; after the archenteron has formed the blastocoel fills up with mesenchyme originating around the base of the archenteron and hence of purely entomesodermal nature (Fig. 206*C*). In *Gordius*, according to Mühldorf, the blastula fills with mesenchyme of ectomesodermal nature (Fig. 206*B*) and following the embolic gastrulation, there occur entomesodermal additions to the mesenchyme. The end result is the same in that the blastocoel of the typical archenteral gastrula becomes filled with loose mesenchyme. Through the thickening of the ectoderm of the future anterior end of the embryo (Fig. 206*D*), the latter becomes divisible into two regions, an anterior presoma, and a posterior trunk, and these by the fusion of the ectodermal thickening at its inner end with the surface ectoderm become completely separated by a septum, seen to be of ectodermal nature (Fig. 206*E, F*). In the presoma an invagination occurs, cuticularized spines appear, and it is soon evident that the presoma consists chiefly of an evaginable proboscis armed with spines (Fig. 206*E–G*). The proboscis armature consists of three long stylets held together in front when the proboscis is protruded (Fig. 207*C*) and of three circlets of spines around the sides of the proboscis, composed of three, four or six, and seven spines, respectively, and differing somewhat in arrangement in different genera (Fig. 207*B, C*). Retractor muscles for the proboscis soon develop from the mesenchyme of the presoma. In the trunk the anterior part of the archenteron, immediately

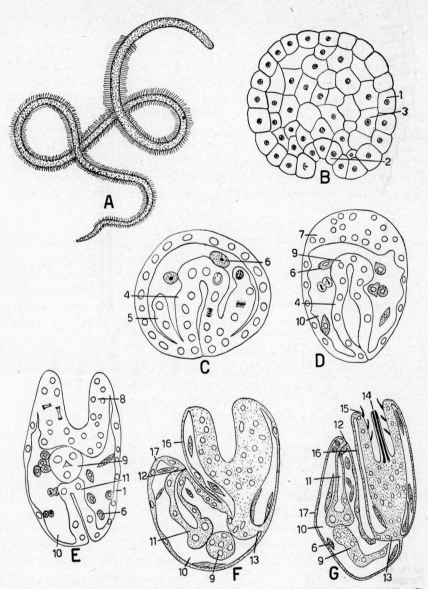

FIG. 206.—Nectonema, embryology. *A. Nectonema agile (after Fewkes,* 1883). *B.* Early gastrulation of *Gordius (after Mühldorf,* 1914). *C.* Gastrulation of *Paragordius. D–G.* Further stages of *Paragordius,* showing formation of the proboscis and the entodermal gland. *(C–G, after Montgomery,* 1904.) 1, ectoderm; 2, entoderm; 3, ectomesoderm; 4, archenteron; 5, entomesoderm; 6, mesenchyme; 7, thickening to form presoma; 8, presomal primordium invaginating; 9, gland; 10, pseudocoel; 11, intestine; 12, anus; 13, septum; 14, proboscis stylets; 15, proboscis spines; 16, presoma; 17, trunk.

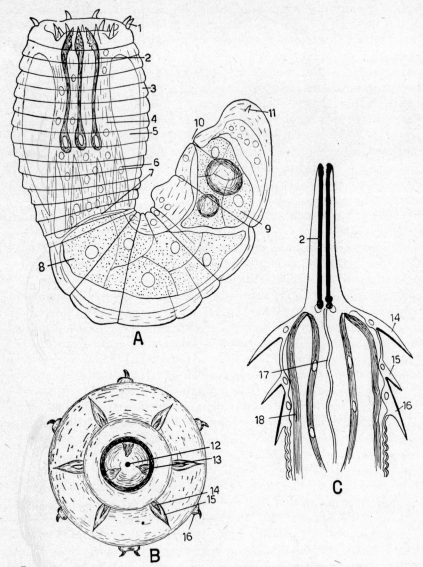

Fig. 207.—Gordioid larva. *A*. Larva of *Parachordodes*. *B. En face* view of *Gordius* larva, showing armature of presoma. (*A, B, after Mühldorf*, 1914.)   *C.* Anterior part of *Paragordius* larva, with proboscis protruded (*after Montgomery*, 1904).   1, spines; 2, stylets; 3, body wall; 4, proboscis; 5, pseudocoel; 6, retractor muscles; 7, septum; 8, gland; 9, intestine; 10, anus; 11, end spine; 12, opening of gland; 13, tips of stylets; 14, first circlet of spines; 15, second circlet of spines; 16, third circlet of spines; 17, gland duct; 18, muscle.

behind the septum, separates off as a solid mass, that seems to be some sort of gland (Fig. 207*A*) and opens by a long duct penetrating the septum and running along the center of the proboscis (Fig. 208). The remainder of the archenteron represents the intestine, blind anteriorly and opening to the exterior posteriorly by the blastopore. Muscles develop from the trunk mesenchyme and a cuticle differentiates on the surface of the embryo. According to Montgomery, the surface of the *Paragordius* larva is not ringed while that of *Gordius* and *Parachordodes*, according to Mühldorf, is completely ringed (Fig. 207*A*). May (1919) reports surface ringing in both *Paragordius* and *Gordius* larvae. In the presence of an armed evaginable proboscis and the division of the body into presoma and trunk, the gordioid larva is amazingly reminiscent of a priapulid or acanthocephalan. By some authors it is spoken of as an echinoderid larva, although resemblance to an echinoderid appears less striking to the author.

9. Later Development and Life Cycle.—The larva hatches in water and appears capable of only a brief free existence. It penetrates into almost any small aquatic animal but can develop further only in an appropriate host, which in gordioids is usually an insect, but sometimes a centipede or millipede. Grasshoppers, crickets, cockroaches, and beetles are the insects usually infested with juvenile gordioids. It is evident that the larva can attain only such hosts as frequent the edges of streams and other aquatic habitats. The manner of entry into the host has not been definitely observed but the equipment of the larva indicates penetration by boring through the body wall. However, Dorier (1925, 1930) states that the larvae of *Gordius aquaticus* may encyst in mucus secreted by the gland formed from the anterior part of intestine and in this condition may remain viable for weeks. Ingestion of such cysts was believed by this author to be a regular mode of infection with this worm. Thorne (1940) also considers it probable that crickets become infected with *Gordius robustus* by ingesting the larvae either while drinking or while feeding on aquatic plants. It is now certain that only one host is involved in the parasitic phase of the nematomorph life cycle.

Development in the host occupies several weeks to months and has been described by May for *Gordius* and *Paragordius*. The larva occupies the pseudocoel of the insect host and gradually grows into a juvenile worm without undergoing any definite metamorphosis. The larval cuticle and epidermis are retained and differentiate to the adult condition. The stylets and hooks of the proboscis and their accompanying epidermis and musculature degenerate and are lost at the molt. The brain is formed from a ring of epidermal cells situated just in front of the septum; this indicates that the larval presoma is represented by the adult calotte. The ventral nerve cord originates in the ventral epidermis as two longitudinal rows of nuclei.   The gland formed from the anterior end of the archenteron disintegrates and disappears.   The larval intestine develops directly into that of the adult and grows enormously; its terminal portion is lined with cuticle, at least in younger stages, and must be regarded as phylogenetically a proctodaeum.   The intestine remains blind anteriorly throughout life in most gordioids but in *Paragordius* the central strand of the larval proboscis persists, develops a lumen, and becomes a patent pharynx with an end bulb (Fig. 203*C*).   The gonads appear as two longitudinal strands of cells that later continue posteriorly and join the cloaca.

After reaching practically the adult condition, the juvenile worms leave the host and about this time molt, discarding such remnants of larval structures as do not develop into adult structures.   Emission from the host apparently occurs only when the latter is near water.   The worms then lead a free existence in or near water or in damp places until their death.

The early stages of *Nectonema* are unknown nor is it known whether or not a larval stage occurs similar to that of gordioids.   It was discovered by Perez in 1927 that *Nectonema*, like the gordioids, is parasitic in juvenile stages.   The young worms are found in hermit crabs and true crabs and appear to show little specificity as to hosts.   Feyel (1936) has described several growth stages of the young worms but these do not differ greatly from the adults in structure except that the natatory bristles appear only after the molt from the juvenile to the adult condition. Muscle cells and gonads were observed developing from the mesenchyme. The cuticularized tube representing the pharynx and surrounded by protoplasmic material bears internally a pair of hooks suggestive of the armature of the gordioid larva and the intestine is described as composed of syncytia and disappearing posteriorly as in the adult.   As in the gordioid larva, the body of the juvenile *Nectonema* is divided by a septum into a short anterior region containing the brain and a long trunk, not ringed.   This septum persists in the adult *Nectonema* but is wanting in adult gordioids in which the entire anterior end is filled with mesenchyme.

10. Ecology and Physiology.—The information available on these matters is decidedly meager.   The gordioids are found throughout the world in tropical and temperate zones in every sort of aquatic habitat, including alpine streams.   Many species have a wide distribution and it does not appear feasible at present to relate particular species to particular kinds of habitat.   It seems, however, that *Chordodes* and related genera are somewhat limited to tropical and subtropical regions.   As the adults do not feed they do not require any particular surroundings except that they be wet or moist and adequate in oxygen content.   Apparently the juvenile worms emerge from their hosts only when the latter are in or near water and hence must be able to sense the proximity of water.

Statements of various observers indicate that hosts tend to seek water when the juvenile worms are ready to emerge.

The activities of the adults are extremely limited. The males are much more active than the females and often swim about for hours or crawl on the bottom with serpentine undulations. Females show scarcely any activity, and seldom, if ever, swim. When gordians are placed in small dishes they tend to tangle themselves in knots, whence the name gordian, but this behavior probably has no significance in nature. The experiments of Müller (1927) indicate that males are able to sense females at some distance and can also discriminate between virgin and gravid females. However, males sometimes copulate with females that have been already fertilized.

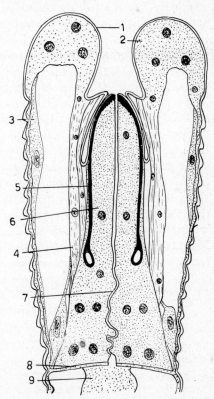

The gordioids take no food into the digestive tract at any stage of their life cycle and therefore must obtain their nutrition by absorption through the body surface. May (1919) notes that the worms lie in cavities in the host's viscera that they have produced by digesting the tissues around them. It therefore seems that the entire epidermis of the young gordioids must be capable of emitting digestive enzymes. The gordioids are devoid of any excretory mechanism unless the intestine acts as such as suggested by May.

Fig. 208.—Gordioid larva. Longitudinal section through the presoma of the larva of *Gordius* (*after Mühldorf*, 1914). 1, cuticle; 2, epidermis; 3, muscle layer; 4, retractor muscles; 5, stylets; 6, proboscis; 7, gland duct; 8, septum; 9, gland.

11. Relationships.—The Nematomorpha like the other classes of Aschelminthes show various similarities to other members of the phylum without being directly derivable from any of them. The general structure of the group is clearly of the pseudocoelomate type and the body cavity is demonstrated to be of blastocoelic nature. The cuticle with its homogeneous and fibrous layers presents some similarity to that of nematodes and the presence of epidermal chords is common to nematomorphs, kinorhynchs, and nematodes. The subepidermal musculature of the nectonematoids is identical with that of nematodes and that of gordioids is sufficiently similar. The occurrence of much mesenchyme in the pseudocoel with the formation of membranes simulating mesenteries is also seen in gastrotrichs, priapulids, and nematodes. The nervous system, taking the form of a circumenteric ring and ventral cord, is strikingly like that of kinorhynchs, priapulids, and nematodes, and the epidermal position of the ventral cord is also notable in priapulids and kinorhynchs. The utilization of the rear parts of the gonads as sex ducts accords with what is found in nematodes and priapulids. It is the gordioid larva, however, that furnishes the most convincing evidence of the aschelminth affinities of the Gordioidea; the division of its body into a presoma with armed circumoral region and a ringed trunk recalls strikingly the priapulids. One may further note that this larva molts as do juvenile kinorhynchs, priapulids, and nematodes. The life cycle of the nematomorphs resembles that of mermithid nematodes. The foregoing grounds appear to justify the inclusion of the Nematomorpha in the Aschelminthes. It seems that the Nectonematoidea are more nearly allied to the nematodes, whereas the Gordioidea are closer to the kinorhynchs and priapulids, especially the latter. Future evidence may indicate the desirability of making the Nectonematoidea an order of Nematoda but decision on this point must await settlement of the question whether or not *Nectonema* has an "echinoderid" larva in its cycle.

Bibliography

ROTIFERA

General

Ahlstrom, E. H. 1933. Quantitative study of the Rotatoria in Put-in-Bay, Ohio. Ohio Biol. Survey Bull. 30. **Beauchamp, P. de.** 1907. Morphologie et variations de l'appareil rotateur. Arch. Zool. Exp. Gén. 36. 1908. Sur l'interprétation de l'appareil rotateur dans les familles des Microcodonidés et Conochilidés. Bull. Soc. Zool. France 33. 1909. Recherches sur les rotifères: les formations tégumentaires et l'appareil digestif. Arch. Zool. Exp. Gén. 40. 1928. Coup d'oeil sur les recherches recentes relatives aux rotifères. Bull. Biol. France Belgique 62. 1932. Deux nouveaux cas de phorésie chez les rotifères. Arch. Zool. Exp. Gén. 74. **Bryce, D.** 1897. Fauna of Spitsbergen. II. Report on the Rotifera. Proc. Zool. Soc. London. 1929. Three cases of encystment among rotifers. Jour. Roy. Micro. Soc., ser. 3, 49. **Buchner, H.** 1936, 1941. Experimentelle Untersuchungen über den Generationswechsel der Rädertiere. I, II. Ztschr. Indukt. Abstamm. Vererbungslehre 72; Zool. Jahrb. Abt. Allg. Zool. 60. 1941 Freilanduntersuchungen über den Generationswechsel der Rädertiere. I. Zool. Jahrb. Abt. Allg. Zool. 60. **Budde, E.** 1925. Die parasitischen Rädertiere. Ztschr. Morphol. Ökol. Tiere 3. 1934. Neue Beobachtungen an parasitischen Rädertieren. Mikrokosmos, Stuttgart, 27. **Car, L.** 1899. Die embryonale Entwicklung von Asplanchna. Biol. Centralbl. 19. **Dieffenbach, H.,** and **R. Sachse.** 1911. Biologische Studien an pelagischen Rädertiere. Biologie litoraler Rädertiere. Internation. Rev. Ges. Hydrobiol. Biol. Suppl., ser. 3, 4. **Dutrochet, R. H. J.** 1812. Recherches sur les rotifères. Ann. Mus. Hist. Natur. Paris 19. **Gavaret, D.** 1859. Quelques experiences sur les rotifères. Ann. Sci. Natur., Zool., ser. 4, 11. **Harring, H. K.** 1913. Synopsis of the Rotatoria. Bull. U.S. Nation. Mus. No. 81. **Harring, H. K.,** and **F. J. Myers.** 1921. The rotifer fauna of Wisconsin I. 1924. II. Revision of the notommatid rotifers, exclusive of the Dicranophorinae. 1926. III. Revision of the genera Lecane and Monostyla. 1927. IV. The Dicranophorinae. Trans. Wisconsin Acad. Sci. Arts Lett. 20, 21, 22, 23. **Hartmann, O.** 1920. Studien über den Polymorphismus der Rotatorien. Arch. Hydrobiol. 12. **Heinis, F.** 1910. Systematik und Biologie der moosbewohnenden Rotatorien. Arch. Hydrobiol. Planktonk. 5. **Hofsten, N. von.** 1912. Marine-litorale Rotatorien der Skandinavischen Westküste. Zool. Bidrag 1. **Hudson, C. T.,** and **P. H. Gosse.** 1886–1889. *The Rotifera or Wheel-Animalcules.* 2 vols. **Issel, R.** 1900, 1901. Sulla fauna termale. Boll. Mus. Zool. Anat. Comp. Univ. Genova, Nos. 100, 108; Atti Acad. Sci. Torino 36. 1906. Sulla termobiose negli animali aquatica. Atti Soc. Ligustica Sci. Natur. Georg. Genova 17. **Jennings, H. S.** 1896 The early development of Asplanchna. Bull. Mus. Comp. Zool. Harvard University 30. 1900. Rotatoria of the U.S., especially the Great Lakes region. Bull. U.S. Comm. Fisheries for 1899, 19. 1906. *Behavior of the lower organisms.* 1918. The wheel-animalcules (Rotatoria). Chap. XVII in **H. B. Ward** and **G. C. Whipple** (eds.), *Fresh-water Biology.* **Koning, P. de.** 1929. Rädertieren van Meyendel. De Levende Natuur 34. **Kunike, G.** 1925. Nachweis und Verbreitung organischer Skeletsubstanzen bei Tieren. Ztschr. Vergl. Physiol. 2. **Lange, A.** 1913, 1914. Unsere gegenwärtige Kenntnis von den Fortpflanzungsverhältnissen der Rädertiere. Internat. Rev. Ges. Hydrobiol. 6. **Lauterborn, R.** 1898. Über die cyclische Fortpflanzung limnetischen Rotatorien. Biol. Centralbl. 18. **Luntz, A.** 1926, 1929. Untersuchungen über den Generationswechsel der Rotatorien. Biol. Centralbl. 46, 49. **Martini, E.** 1924. Die Zellconstanz und ihre Beziehungen zu anderen zoologischen Vorwürfen. Ztschr. Anat. Entw'gesch. 70. **Myers, F. J.** 1917. Rotatoria of Los Angeles. Proc. U.S. Nation. Mus. 52. 1936a. Brackish water and marine Rotatoria. Trans. Amer. Micro. Soc. 55. 1936b. Psammolittoral rotifers. Amer. Mus. Novitates, No. 830. **Nachtwey, R.** 1925. Keimbahn, Organogenese und Anatomie von Asplanchna. Ztschr. Wiss. Zool. 126. **Pai, S.** 1934. Regenerationsversuche an Rotatorien. Sci. Repts. Univ. Chekiang 1. **Pennak, R. W.** 1940. Ecology of the microscopic Metazoa inhabiting the sandy beaches of some Wisconsin lakes. Ecol. Monogr. 10. **Plate, L.** 1886. Untersuchungen einiger an den Kiemenblättern des Gammarus pulex levenden Ektoparasiten. Ztschr. Wiss. Zool. 43. **Rahm, P. G.** 1923. Beiträge zur Kenntnis der Moosfauna. Ztschr. Allg. Physiol. 20. **Remane, A.** 1929. Rotatoria. In **G. Grimpe** and **E. Wagler** (eds.), *Die Tierwelt der Nord- und Ostsee,* Lief. 16, Teil VIIe. 1929–1933. Rotatoria. In **H. G. Bronn** (ed.), *Klassen und Ordnungen des Tierreichs,* Band IV, Abt. II, Buch 1, Lief. 1–4. 1932. Nutzfilter und Strudelfilterapparate bei Rädertieren. Zool. Anz. 100. **Rousselet, C. F.** 1909. Geographical distribution of the Rotifera. Jour. Quekett Micro. Club, ser. 2, 10. **Shull, A. F.** 1923. Sex determination in rotifers. Eugenics, Genetics, and the Family 1. 1929. Determination of types of individuals in aphids, rotifers, and Cladocera. Biol. Rev. Cambridge 4. **Spemann, F. W.** 1924. Ueber Lebensdauer, Altern, und andere Fragen der Rotatorien-Biologie. Ztschr. Wiss. Zool. 123. **Tannreuther, G.** 1920. Development of Asplanchna. Jour. Morphol. 33. **Viaud, G.** 1938, 1940, 1943. Sur le phototropisme des rotifères. C. R. Soc. Biol. Paris 129; Bull. Biol. France Belgique 74, 77. **Weber, E. F.** 1898. Faune rotatorienne du Bassin de Léman. Rev. Suisse Zool. 5. **Wesenberg-Lund, C.** 1900. Von den Abhängigkeitsverhältnis zwischen dem Bau der Planktonorganismen und dem specifische Gewicht des Süsswassers. Biol. Centralbl. 20. 1923. The males of the Rotifera. Kong. Danske Vidensk. Selsk. Skrift. Naturvid. Math. Afdel. Raekke 8, 4. 1929. Rotatoria, Rotifera (Rädertierchen). In **W. Kükenthal** and **T. Krumbach** (eds.), *Handbuch der Zoologie*, Band II, Hälfte 1. 1930. Periodicity and sexual periods. Kong. Danske Vidensk. Selsk. Skrift. Naturvid. Math. Afdel. Raekke 9, 2. **Whitney, D. D.** 1906. Desiccation of rotifers. Amer. Natural. 42. **Wiszniewski, J.** 1934. Recherches ecologiques sur le psammon et spécialement sur les rotifères psammiques. Arch. Hydrobiol. Ichtyol. Suwalki 8. **Wulfert, K.** 1940. Rotatorien einiger Ostdeutscher Torfmoore. Arch. Hydrobiol. Planktonk. 36. **Zelinka, C.** 1886, 1888, 1891. Studien über Räderthiere. I-III Ztschr. Wiss. Zool. 44, 47, 63. 1907. Die Rotatorien der Plankton-Expedition. Ergebnisse der Plankton-Exped. II H. **Zschokke, F.** 1908. Die Resultate der zoologischen Erforschung hochalpinen Wasserbecken. Internat. Rev. Ges. Hydrobiol. 1.

Seisonacea

Claus, C. 1876. Organisation und systematische Stellung der Gattung Seison. Festschr. Zool. Bot. Gesell. Wien. 1880. Zur Kenntnis der Organisation von Seison. Zool. Anz. 3. **Grube, A.** 1859. Neue microskopische Thierform (Seison). Jahresber. Schlesischen Gesell. Vaterland. Kultur 37. **Illgen, H.** 1916. Biologie und Anatomie der parasitischen Rotatorien-Familie der Seisoniden. Zool. Anz. 47. **Plate, L.** 1887. Ectoparasitische Rotatorien des Golfes von Neapel. Mitt. Zool. Stat. Neapel 7.

Bdelloidea

Allen, Sally. 1933. Parasites and commensals of North Carolina crayfishes. Jour. Elisha Mitchell Scient. Soc. 49. **Bartos, E.** 1942. Der Bau des Plattenpanzers bei Mniobia incrassata. Die Zystenbildung bei Mniobia tetraodon. Zool. Anz. 138. **Beauchamp, P. de.** 1909. (Abrochtha). Bull. Soc. Zool. France 34. **Brakenhoff, H.** 1937. Zur Morphologie der Bdelloidea. Zool. Jahrb. Abt. Anat. 63. **Bryce, D.** 1892. On the matrotrachelous Callidinae. Jour. Quekett Micro. Club, ser. 2, 5. 1910. New classification of the bdelloid Rotifera. Jour. Quekett Micro. Club, ser. 2, 11. **Burger, A.** 1948. Studies on moss-dwelling bdelloids. Trans. Amer. Micro. Soc. 67. **Dobers, E.** 1915. Biologie der Bdelloidea. Internat. Rev. Ges. Hydrobiol., ser. 6, suppl. 7. **Giglioli, H.** 1863. On the genus Callidina. Quart. Jour. Micro. Sci. 3. **Hickernell, L. M.** 1917. Desiccation in Philodina. Biol. Bull. 32. **Jacobs, M. H.** 1909. The effects of desiccation on Philodina. Jour. Exp. Zool. 6. **Lankester, E. R.** 1868. Note on the Synaptae of Guernsey and a new parasitic rotifier. Quart. Jour. Micro. Sci. 8. **Marchaux, E.** 1898. Note sur un rotifère vivant dans la tube digestif de larves aquatiques d'insectes. C. R. Soc. Biol. Paris, ser. 10, 5. **Milne, E.** 1888. Rotifer as parasite or tube-dweller. Proc. Philos. Soc. Glasgow 20. **Murray, J.** 1905. New family and twelve new species of Bdelloida. Trans. Roy. Soc. Edinburgh 41. 1906. The Rotifera of the Scottish Lochs. Trans. Roy. Soc. Edinburgh 45. 1908. Arctic rotifers. Proc. Roy. Phys. Soc. Edinburgh 17. 1910. Antarctic Rotifera. British Antarctic Exped. 1907–1909. Repts. Scient. Invest., Biol. 1, Pt. 3. 1911. Rotifera collected by the Shackleton Antarctic Expedition 1909. Jour. Roy. Micro. Soc., ser. 2, 31. **Zelinka, C.** 1886. Symbiose und Anatomie von Rotatorien aus dem Genus Callidina. Ztschr. Wiss. Zool. 44. 1888. Der Raumparasitismus und die Anatomie von Discopus synaptae. Ztschr. Wiss. Zool. 47.

Monogononta

Ahlstrom, E. H. 1940. Revision of Brachionus and Platyias. Bull. Amer. Mus. Natur. Hist. 77. **Balbiani, M.** 1878. Observations sur le notommate de Werneck. Ann. Sci. Natur., Zool., ser. 6, 7. **Beauchamp, P. de.** 1904. Drilophaga. Bull. Soc. Zool. France 29. 1905. Remarques sur deux rotifères parasites. Bull. Soc. Zool. France 30. 1912. Contribution à l'étude des Atrochidés. Bull. Soc. Zool. France 37. 1932. Ascomorpha et des processus digestifs chez les rotifères. Bull. Soc. Zool. France 57. **Chu, J.** 1934. Reproduction, life-span, growth and senescence of Brachionus. Sci. Repts. Univ. Chekiang 1. **Claparède, E.** 1867. Sur le Balatro calvus. Ann. Sci. Natur., Zool., ser. 5, 8. **Cori, C.** 1925. Morphologie und Biologie von Apsilus vorax. Ztschr. Wiss. Zool. 125. **Daday, E.** 1893. Cypridicola parasitica. Termez Füzetek, Budapest 16. **Debray, F.** 1890. Zur Notommata werneckii. Bull. Scient. France Belgique 22. **Dehl, E.** 1934. Morphologie von Lindia. Ztschr. Wiss. Zool. 145. **Dixon-Nuttall, F. R.** 1896. Male of Stephanoceros. Jour. Roy. Micro. Soc., ser. 2, 16. **Dujardin, M. F.** 1838. Mémoire sur un ver parasite (Albertia). Ann. Sci. Natur., Zool., ser. 2, 10. **Edmondson, W. T.** 1940. Sessile Rotatoria of Wisconsin. Trans. Amer. Micro. Soc. 59. 1944, 1945. Ecological studies of sessile Rotatoria. Ecol. Monogr. 14, 15. **Ferris, Josephine.** 1932. Comparison of the life histories of mictic and amictic females in Hydatina. Biol. Bull. 63. **Finesinger, J.** 1926. Effect of certain chemical and physical agents on fecundity and length of life in Lecane. Jour. Exp. Zool. 44. **Gast, R.** 1900. Apsilus vorax. Ztschr. Wiss. Zool. 67. **Glasscott, L. S.** 1893. Some Rotifera of Ireland. Scient. Proc. Roy. Dublin Soc., n.s. 8. **Gosse, P. H.** 1852. Structure, functions, habits, and development of Melicerta ringens. Quart. Jour. Micro. Sci. 1. **Gruber, A.** 1882. Baukunst der Melicerta ringens. Zool. Anz. 5. **Hamburger, Clara.** 1907. Das Männchen von Lacinularia. Ztschr. Wiss. Zool. 86. **Hauer, J.** 1941. Pedalia. Internat. Rev. Ges. Hydrobiol. 41. **Hermes, G.** 1932. Die Männchen von Hydatina, Rhinops, und Asplanchna. Ztschr. Wiss. Zool. 141. **Hertel, E. W.** 1942. Studies on vigor in Hydatina. Physiol. Zool. 15. **Hirschfelder, G.** 1910. Histologie der Rädertiere (Eosphora). Ztschr. Wiss. Zool. 96. **Hlava, S.** 1904a. Die Exkretionsorgan der Rädertierfamilie Melicertidae und die Aufstellung eines neuem Genus Conochiloides. Zool. Anz. 27. 1904b. Albertia. Zool. Anz. 28. 1905. Die Anatomie von Conochiloides. Ztschr. Wiss. Zool. 80. 1908. Monographie der Familie Melicertidae. Arch. Naturwiss. Landesdurchforschung von Böhmen 13, No. 2. **Hodgkinson, Edith.** 1918. Experiments on Hydatina. Jour. Genetics 7. **Holloway, E.** 1945, 1946, 1947. Introduction to the study of the Rotifera. I. General. II, III. Habits and collecting methods. IV. Drawing rotifers. V. Four common littoral rotifers. VI. Four open water rotifers. VII. Keratella. VIII. Rhinoglena frontalis. IX. Proales daphnicola. X. Further common species. Microscope and Entomol. Monthly 5, 6. **Hudson, C. T.** 1872. On Pedalion mira. Quart. Jour. Micro. Sci. 12. **Hünerhoff, E.** 1931. Ueber ein bisher unbekanntes Larvenorgan und die Regeneration bei Apsilus vorax. Zool. Anz. 92. **Huxley, T. H.** 1853. Lacinularia socialis. Trans. Micro. Soc. London 1. **Issel, R.** 1904. Sui Rotiferi endoparassiti degli Enchitredi. Arch. Zool. Ital. 2. **Jennings, H. S.** 1898. Trochosphaera again. Science 8. 1903. Monograph of the Rattulidae. Bull. U.S. Comm. Fisheries for 1902, 22. **Jennings, H. S., and R. S. Lynch.** 1928. Age, mortality, fertility, and individual diversities in Proales sordida. I, II. Jour. Exp. Zool. 50, 51. **Joliet, M.** 1883. Monographie des Mélicértes. Arch. Zool. Exp. Gén., ser. 2, 1. **Jurczyk, Charlotte.** 1926. Regeneration bei Stephanoceros. Zool. Anz. 67. 1927. Morphologie, Biologie, und Regeneration von

Stephanoceros. Ztschr. Wiss. Zool. 129. **Kofoid, C. A.** 1896. Trochosphaera in the Illinois River. Science 4. **Kolisko, Agnes.** 1938a. Lebensgeschichte der Rädertiere auf Grund von Individualzuchten. Arch. Hydrobiol. 33. 1938b. Nahrungsaufnahme bei Anapus. Internat. Rev. Ges. Hydrobiol. 37. 1939. Über Conochilus und seine Koloniebildung. Internat. Rev. Ges. Hydrobiol. 39. **Krätschmar, H.** 1908. Polymorphismus von Anuraea aculeata. Internat. Rev. Ges. Hydrobiol. 1. **Lauterborn, R.** 1900, 1904. Der Formkreis von Anuraea cochlearis. I, II. Verhandl. Naturhist. Mediz. Versamml. Heidelberg 6, 7. 1908. Gallerthüllen bei loricaten Plankton-Rotatorien. Zool. Anz. 33. **Lehmensick, R.** 1926. Biologie, Anatomie und Eireifung der Rädertiere. (Euchlanis, Synchaeta, Asplanchna). Ztschr. Wiss. Zool. 128. **Leidy, J.** 1882. Rotifera without rotary organs (Acyclus). Proc. Acad. Natur. Sci. Philadelphia 34. **Leissling, R.** 1924. Das Männchen von Euchlanis. Zool. Anz. 59. **Levander, K. M.** 1894. Zur Kenntnis der Pedalion-Arten. Acta Soc. Flora Fauna Fennica 11. **Liebers, R.** 1937. Untersuchungen an Euchlanis und Proales. Ztschr. Wiss. Zool. 150. **Lite, J. C.,** and **D. D. Whitney.** 1925. The role of aeration in the hatching of the fertilized eggs of rotifers (Brachionus). Jour. Exp. Zool. 43. **Lynch, R. S.,** and **H. B. Smith.** 1931. Effects of modification of the culture medium on length of life and fecundity in Proales. Biol. Bull. 60. **Martini, E.** 1912. Hydatina senta. Ztschr. Wiss. Zool. 102. **Maupas, E.** 1891. Determination de la sexualité chez Hydatina. C. R. Acad. Sci. Paris 113. **Metschnikoff, E.** 1866. Apsilus. Ztschr. Wiss. Zool. 16. **Miller, Helen.** 1931. Alternation of generations in Lecane. Biol. Bull. 60. **Mitchell, C. W.** 1913. Sex determination in Asplanchna. Experimentally induced transitions in the morphological characters of Asplanchna. Jour. Exp. Zool. 15. **Mitchell, C. W.,** and **J. Powers.** 1914. Transmission through the resting egg of experimentally induced characters in Asplanchna. Jour. Exp. Zool. 16. **Montgomery, T. H.** 1903. Morphology of the Flosculariidae. Proc. Acad. Natur. Sci. Philadelphia 55. **Myers, F. J.** 1930. The rotifer fauna of Wisconsin. V. Euchlanis and Monommata. Trans. Wisconsin Acad. Sci. Arts Lett. 25. **Noyes, Bessie.** 1922. Life-history of Proales. Jour. Exp. Zool. 35. **Nussbaum, M.** 1896. Versuche, das Geschlecht an Hydatina willkürlich zu bestimmen. Sitzungsber. Niederrhein. Gesell. Natur-Heilk. Bonn for 1896, Hälfte 2. 1897. Die Entstehung des Geschlechts bei Hydatina. Arch. Mikro. Anat. 49. **Nuttall, F.,** and **R. Freeman.** 1903. Diaschiza, a monographic study. Jour. Roy. Micro. Soc., ser. 2, 23. **Pawlowski, L.** 1934, 1935. Drilophaga. Mem. Acad. Polon. Sci. Lett., Cl. Sci. Mat. Natur., ser. B, Sci. Natur. No. 6; Arch. Hydrobiol. Ichthyol. Suwalki 9. **Pénard, E.** 1905. Sur un rotifère du genre Proales. Arch. Sci. Phys. Natur. 4. 1909. Über ein bei Acanthocystis parasitisches Rotatorium. Mikrokosmos, Stuttgart, 2. **Peters, F.** 1931. Anatomie und Zellconstanz von Synchaeta. Ztschr. Wiss. Zool. 139. **Plate, L.** 1886. (Hertwigia volvocicola.) Jena. Ztschr. Naturwiss. 19. **Powers, J. H.** 1912. A case of polymorphism in Asplanchna. Amer. Natural. 46. **Punnett, R. C.** 1906. Sex-determination in Hydatina. Proc. Roy. Soc. London 78 B. **Remane, A.** 1929a. Proales gonothyraeae. Zool. Anz. 80. 1929b. Intrazelluläre Verdauung bei Rädertiere. Ztschr. Vergl. Physiol. 11. 1933. Pompholyx. Zool. Anz. 103. **Rothert, W.** 1896. Über die Gallen der Notommata werneckii auf Vaucheria. Jahrb. Wiss. Botanik 29. Zur Kenntnis der in Vaucherien-Arten parasitierenden Rotatorie Notommata werneckii. Zool. Jahrb. Abt. System. 9. **Rousselet, C. F.** 1892. On Conochilus unicornus. Jour. Quekett Micro. Club, ser. 2, 4. 1900. Note on Lacinularia. Jour. Quekett Micro. Club, ser. 2, 7. 1902. Synchaeta, a monographic study. Jour. Roy. Micro. Soc., ser. 2, 22. 1911. Rotifera (Ascomorpha volvocicola). Clare Island Survey. Proc. Roy. Irish Acad. 31, Pt. 3. **Schultze, M.**

1851. Beiträge zur Naturgeschichte der Turbellarien. (Albertia.) **Searle, J.** 1923. Short notes on the life-history of Volvox and its parasitic rotifer. Victorian Natural. 40. **Seehaus, W.** 1930. Testudinella. Ztschr. Wiss. Zool. 137. **Semper, C.** 1872. Zoologische Aphorismen. III. Trochosphaera. Ztschr. Wiss. Zool. 22. **Shull, A. F.** 1910–1912. Studies in the life cycle of Hydatina senta. I–III. Jour. Exp. Zool. 8, 10, 12. 1915. Periodicity in the production of males in Hydatina. Biol. Bull. 28. 1918a. Cell inconstancy in Hydatina. Jour. Morphol. 30. 1918b. Relative effectiveness of food, oxygen, and other substances in causing or preventing male production in Hydatina. Jour. Exp. Zool. 26. 1918c. Effect of environment upon inherited characters of Hydatina. Biol. Bull. 34. 1921. Chromosomes and the life cycle of Hydatina. Biol. Bull. 41. 1922. Relative nuclear volume and the life cycle of Hydatina. Jour. Exp. Zool. 35. **Shull, A. F., and S. Ladoff.** Factors affecting male production in Hydatina. Jour. Exp. Zool. 21. **Stevens, J.** 1912. Proales gigantea, a rotifer parasitic in the egg of the water snail. Jour. Quekett Micro. Club, ser. 2, 11. **Stoker, A. C.** 1884. Rotifer within an Acanthocystis. The Microscope 4, Jour. Roy. Micro. Soc., ser. 2, 4. **Stoszberg, K.** 1932. Euchlanis, Brachionus, und Rhinoglena. Ztschr. Wiss. Zool. 142. **Surface, F.** 1906. The formation of new colonies of Megalotrocha. Biol. Bull. 11. **Tannreuther, G.** 1919. Studies on Asplanchna, with special reference to the male. Biol. Bull. 37. **Tauson, A. O.** 1925, 1927. Wirkung des Mediums auf das Geschlecht des Rotators Asplanchna. Internat. Rev. Ges. Hydrobiol. 13, 14; Arch. Entw'mech. Org. 107, 109. **Thompson, P. G.** 1892. Notes on the parasitic tendency of rotifers of the genus Proales. Science Gossip, London, 28. **Thorpe, V.** 1891. The male of Trochosphaera. Jour. Roy. Micro. Soc. ser. 2, 11. 1893. Rotifera of China. Jour. Roy. Micro. Soc., ser. 2, 13. **Ubisch, L. von.** 1926. Bau, Funktion, Entwicklung, und Regeneration der Reuse von Stephanoceros. Ztschr. Wiss. Zool. 127. **Valkanov, A.** 1936. Trochosphaera. Trav. Soc. Bulgare Sci. Natur. Sofia, No. 17. **Vallentin, R.** 1890. Remarks on the anatomy of Stephanoceros. Ann. Mag. Natur. Hist., ser. 6, 5. **Van Cleave, H. J.** 1922. Determination of the degree of constancy in the nuclei of certain organs in Hydatina. Biol. Bull. 42. **Vejdovsky, F.** 1882. Drilophaga. Sitzungsber. Böhmischen Gesell. Wissensch. **Whitney, D. D.** 1907. Determination of sex in Hydatina. Jour. Exp. Zool. 5. 1909. Maturation stages of the parthenogenetic and sexual eggs of Hydatina. Jour. Exp. Zool. 6. 1912a. Strains in Hydatina. Biol. Bull. 22. 1912b. Reinvigoration produced by cross fertilization in Hydatina. Jour. Exp. Zool. 12. 1914. Influence of food in controlling sex in Hydatina. Jour. Exp. Zool. 17. 1915. Production of males and females controlled by food in Hydatina. Biol. Bull. 29. 1916. Transformation of Brachionus pala into Brachionus amphiceros by sodium silicate. Biol. Bull. 31. 1917. Relative influence of food and oxygen in controlling sex in rotifers. Jour. Exp. Zool. 24. **Wierzejski, A.** 1893. Atrochus. Ztschr. Wiss. Zool. 55. **Wulfert, K.** 1938. Cephalodella. Arch. Naturgesch. n. F. 7.

GASTROTRICHA

Beauchamp P., de. 1930. Le développement des Gastrotriches. Bull. Soc. Zool. France 54. 1934. Sur la morphologie et l'ethologie des Neogossea. Bull. Soc. Zool. France 58. **Blake, C. H.** 1933. Nomenclatorial notes on Gastrotricha. Science 77. **Brunson, R.** 1949. Life history and ecology of two gastrotrichs. Trans. Amer. Micro. Soc. 68. **Bryce, D.** 1904. Rotifera and Gastrotricha of North Dakota lakes. Jour. Quekett Micro. Club 15. **Bütschli, O.** 1876. Untersuchungen über die Gattung Chaetonotus. Ztschr. Wiss. Zool. 26. **Claparède, E.** 1867. Type d'un nouveau genre de Gastrotriches. Ann. Sci. Natur., Zool., ser. 5, 8.

Collin, A. 1912. Gastrotricha. Süsswasserfauna Deutschlands, Heft 14. **Cordero, E. H.** 1918. Notes sur les gastrotriches. Physis, Buenos Aires, 4. **Greuter, R.** 1918. Beiträge zur Systematik der Gastrotrichen in der Schweiz. Rev. Suisse Zool. 25. **Grünspan, T.** 1907. Beiträge zur Systematik der Gastrotrichen. Zool. Jahrb. Abt. System. 26. 1908. Die Süsswassergastrotrichen Europas. Ann. Biol. Lacustre 4. **Marcolongo, J.** 1912, 1914. Gastrotrichi del lago stagno craterico di Astroni. Annuario Mus. Zool. Univ. Napoli, nov. ser., suppl. 1, No. 3; Atti Reale Accad. Scienze Fis. Matem. Napoli, ser. 2, 15, No. 6. **Metschnikoff, E.** 1864. Über einige wenig bekannte niedere Thierformen. Ztschr. Wiss. Zool. 15. **Packard, C. E.** 1936. Observations on the Gastrotricha indigenous to New Hampshire. Trans. Amer. Micro. Soc. 55. **Remane, A.** 1924. Neue aberrante Gastrotrichen. I. Macrodasys. Zool. Anz. 61. 1925. II. Turbanella. Zool. Anz. 64. 1926. Morphologie und Verwandtschaftbeziehungen der aberranten Gastrotrichen. Ztschr. Morphol. Ökol. Tiere 5. 1927. Xenotrichula, ein chaetonotoides Gastrotrich mit männlichen Geschlechtsorganen. Zool. Anz. 71. Beiträge zur Systematik der Süsswassergastrotrichen. Zool. Jahrb. Abt. System. 53. Neue Gastrotricha Macrodasyoidea. Zool. Jahrb. Abt. System. 54. 1929. Gastrotricha. In **Kukenthal, W.** and **T. Krumbach** (eds.), *Handbuch der Zoologie*, Band II, Hälfte 1. 1932. Die Rotatorien, Gastrotrichen, Kinorhynchen und Archianneliden der Arktis. Fauna Arctica 6. 1936. Gastrotricha und Kinorhyncha. In **Bronn, H. G.** (ed.), *Klassen und Ordnungen des Tierreichs*, Band 4, Abt. 2, Buch 1, Teil 2. **Schultze, M.** 1853. Chaetonotus und Ichthydium und eine neue verwandte Gattung Turbanella. Arch. Anat. Physiol. **Spandl, H.** 1926. Die Süsswasser-Mikrofauna. Arch. Hydrobiol. 16. **Voigt, M.** 1901. Über einige bisher unbekannte Süsswasserorganismen. Zool. Anz. 24. 1902. Diagnosen bisher unbeschriebener Organismen aus Plöner Gewässern. Die Rotatorien und Gastrotrichen der Umgebung von Plön. Zool. Anz. 25. 1904. Die Rotatorien und Gastrotrichen der Umgebung von Plön. Forschungsber. Biol. Stat. Plön 11. 1909. Nachtrag zur Gastrotrichen-Fauna Plöns. Zool. Anz. 34. **Wagner, F.** 1893. Der Organismus der Gastrotrichen. Biol. Centralbl. 3. **Zelinka, C.** 1889. Die Gastrotrichen. Ztschr. Wiss. Zool. 49.

Kinorhyncha

Blake, C. H. 1930. Three new species of worms belonging to the order Echinodera. Biol. Survey Mt. Desert Is. Region, Pt. 4. **Bütschli, O.** 1876. Untersuchungen über die Gattung Chaetonotus. Ztschr. Wiss. Zool. 26. **Claparède, E.** 1863. Beobachtungen über Anatomie und Entwicklungsgeschichte wirbelloser Tiere. **Dujardin, F.** 1851. Sur un petit animal marin, l'echinodère. Ann. Sci. Natur., Zool., ser. 3, 15. **Greeff, R.** 1869. Untersuchungen über einige merkwürdige Formen des Arthropoden- und Wurm-Typus. Arch. Naturgesch. 35, Pt. 1. **Lang, K.** 1949. Echinoderida. Further Zool. Results Swedish Antarctic Exped. 1901–1903, vol. IV, No. 2. **Metschnikoff, E.** 1865. Über einige wenig bekannte Tierformen. Ztschr. Wiss. Zool. 15. **Nyholm, K. G.** 1947. Campyloderes. Studies in the Echinoderida. Arkiv Zool. 39A, Nos. 13, 14. **Reinhard, W.** 1887. Kinorhyncha. Ztschr. Wiss. Zool. 45. **Remane, A.** 1928. Kinorhyncha. In **G. Grimpe** and **E. Wagler** (eds.), *Die Tierwelt der Nord- und Ostsee*, Teil VII, D 2, Lief. 11. 1929. Kinorhyncha. In **W. Kükenthal** and **T. Krumbach** (eds.), *Handbuch der Zoologie*, Bd. II, Pt. 1. 1936. Gastrotricha und Kinorhyncha. In **H. G. Bronn** (ed.), *Klassen und Ordnungen des Tierreichs*, Bd. IV, Abt. II, Buch 1, Teil 2. **Schepotieff, A.** 1907. Die Echinoderiden. Ztschr. Wiss. Zool. 88. 1908. Zur Kenntnis der Echinoderiden. Zool. Anz. 32. **Schultze, M.** 1853. Über Chaetonotus und Ichthydium und eine neue verwandte Gattung Turbanella. Arch. Anat. Physiol.

Steiner, G. 1919. Zur Kenntnis der Kinorhyncha nebst Bemerkungen über ihr Verwandtschaftsverhältnis zu den Nematoden. Zool. Anz. 50. **Zelinka, C.** 1894. Über die Organisation von Echinoderes. Verhandl. Dtsch. Zool. Gesell. 4. 1907. Zur Kenntnis der Echinoderes. Zool. Anz. 32. 1908. Die Anatomie der Echinoderen. Zool. Anz. 33. 1928. Monographie der Echinodera.

PRIAPULIDA

Apel, W. 1885. Beiträge zur Anatomie und Histologie des Priapulus und Halicryptus. Ztschr. Wiss. Zool. 42. **Danielssen, D.,** and **J. Koren.** 1881. Gephyrea. Norwegian North-Atlantic Exped. 1876–1878. Zoology III, vol. 4. **Eggers, F.** 1925. Über die Entwicklung einiger Organe bei Priapuliden. Zool. Anz. Suppl. Bd. 1. **Ehlers, E.** 1862. Über die Gattung Priapulus. Über Halicryptus. Ztschr. Wiss. Zool. 11. **Fabricius, O.** 1780. Fauna Groenlandica. **Fischer, W.** 1922. Gephyreen der arktischen Meere. Wiss. Meeresuntersuch. Abt. Helgoland 13, Heft 2. 1922. Gephyreen. Wissensch. Ergebn. Dtsch. Tiefsee-Exped. 1898–1899. 1925. Priapulidae. In **G. Grimpe** and **E. Wagler** (eds.), *Die Tierwelt der Nord- und Ostsee,* Lief. 1, Teil VId. 1928. Die Sipunculiden, Priapuliden, und Echiuriden der Arktis. Fauna Arctica 5, Lief. 2. **Friedrich, H.,** and **H. Langeloh.** 1936. Untersuchungen zur Physiologie der Bewegung und des Hauptmuskelnschlauch bei Halicryptus und Priapulus. Biol. Centralbl. 56. **Hammarsten, O.** 1913. Beiträge zur Entwicklung von Halicryptus. Zool. Anz. 41. 1915. Zur Entwicklungsgeschichte von Halicryptus. Ztschr. Wiss. Zool. 112. **Hammarsten, O.,** and **J. Runnström.** 1918. Cytophysiologische Beobachtungen an den Hinterleibdrüsen und den Wanderzellen von Priapulus. Bergens Mus. Aarbok, Naturwid. Raekke 1917–1918, No. 13. **Horst, R.** 1882. Zur Anatomie und Histologie von Priapulus. Niederland. Arch. Zool., Suppl. Band 1. **Lang, K.** 1939. Über die Entwicklung von Priapulus. Kungl. Fysiogr. Sallskapet. Lund. Forh. 9, No. 7. 1948a. Contribution to the ecology of Priapulus. 1948b. On the morphology of the larva of Priapulus. Arkiv Zool. 41A, art. Nos. 5, 9. **Langeloh, H.** 1936. Sinnesphysiologische Untersuchungen an Priapuliden. Biol. Centralbl. 56. **Lüling, K.** 1940. Entwicklung des Urogenitalsystems der Priapuliden. Ztschr. Wiss. Zool. 153. **Moltschanov, L.** 1908. Morphologie und Physiologie der Priapuliden. Bull. Acad. Imper. Sci. St. Petersbourg, ser. 6, 2. **Müller, O. F.** 1806. Zoologia Danica IV. **Purasjoki, K.** 1944. Beiträge zur Kenntnis der Entwicklung und Ökologie der Halicryptus larva. Ann. Zool. Soc. Zool. Bot. Fennicae, Vanamo, 9, No. 6. **Quatrefages, M.** 1847. Mémoire sur l'echiure. Ann. Sci. Natur. Zool., ser. 3, 7. **Sato, H.** 1938. Echiuroidea, Sipunculoidea, and Priapuloidea obtained in northeast Honshon, Japan. Saito Ho-on Kai Museum, Research Bull. No. 12, Zool. No. 4. 1939. Studies on the Echiuroidea of Japan. Sci. Repts. Tohoku Imper. Univ., ser. 4, Biol. 14, No. 4. **Scharff, R.** 1885. The skin and nervous system of Priapulus and Halicryptus. Quart. Jour. Micro. Sci. 25. **Schauinsland, H.** 1886. Die Excretions- und Geschlechtsorgane der Priapuliden. Zool. Anz. 9. 1887. Zur Anatomie der Priapuliden. Zool. Anz. 10. **Siebold, C.** 1849. Beiträge zur Fauna Preussens. Neue Preuss. Provinzialblätter 7, Heft 3; reprinted in Ztschr. Wiss. Zool. 11. **Stephen, A. C.** 1941. The Echiuridae, Sipunculidae and Priapulidae. Discovery Repts. 21. **Theel, H.** 1906. Northern and Arctic invertebrates in the collection of the Swedish State Museum. II. Priapulids. K. Svenska Vetensk. Akad. Handl. 40, No. 4. 1911. Priapulids and sipunculids dredged by the Swedish Antarctic Expedition and the phenomenon of bipolarity. K. Svenska Vetensk. Akad. Handl. 47, No. 1. **Wesenberg-Lund, Elise.** 1929. Some remarks on the biology and anatomy of the genus Priapulus. Vidensk. Meddel. Dansk Naturhist. Foren. 88.

Willemoes-Suhm, R. 1871. Biologische Beobachtungen über niedere Meeresthiere. Ztschr. Wiss. Zool. 21.

NEMATODA

General

Ackert, J. E. 1942. Natural resistance to helminthic infections. Jour. Parasitol. 28. **Alicata, J.** 1935. Early developmental stages of nematodes occurring in swine. U.S. Dept. Agricult., Tech. Bull. 489. **Allgen, C.** 1921. Über die Natur und die Bedeutung der Fasersystem im Oesophagus einiger Nematoden. Zool. Anz. 53. 1926. Beiträge zur Kenntnis der freilebenden Nematoden Schwedens. Arkiv Zool. 18, art. 5. 1929. Über einige antarktische freilebende marine Nematoden. Zool. Anz. 84. Neue freilebende marine Nematoden von der Westküste Schwedens. Zool. Jahrb. Abt. System. 57. Über einige freilebende Moosnematoden. Nyt Mag. 67. Freilebende marine Nematoden aus den Umgebungen der staatlichen zoologischen Station Kristinberg. Capita Zoologica 2. 1933. Vorkommen und Häufigkeit freilebender mariner Nematoden. Zool. Anz. 104. Freilebende Nematoden aus dem Trondhjemsfjord. Capita Zoologica 4. 1934. Zur Kenntnis norwegischen Nematoden. I–III. Forh. Kongl. Norske Vidensk. Selsk. 7, Nos. 6, 12, 21. 1946. West American marine nematodes. Viddensk. Meddel. Dansk Naturhist. Foren. 110. **Bastian, H.** 1865. Monograph on the Anguillidae. Trans. Linn. Soc. London, Zool. 25. 1866. Anatomy and physiology of the nematodes, parasitic and free. Philos. Trans. Roy. Soc. London 156. **Baylis, H. A.** 1924. The systematic position of the Nematoda. Ann. Mag. Natur. Hist. ser. 9, 13. 1936, 1939. Nematoda. 2 vols. Fauna of British India. **Baylis, H. A.,** and **R. Daubney.** 1926. *A synopsis of the families and genera of nematodes.* **Becker, E.** 1933. Host specificity and specificity of animal parasites. Amer. Jour. Trop. Med. 13. **Belar, L.** 1924. Die Cytologie der Merospermie bei Rhabditis-Arten. Ztschr. Zellforsch. Mikro. Anat. 1. **Bilek, F.** 1909. Über die fibrillen Strukturen in den Muskel- und Darmzellen der Ascariden. Ztschr. Wiss. Zool. 93. **Bougis, P.** 1946. Analyse quantitative de la micro-faune d'une vase marine à Banyuls. C. R. Acad. Sci. Paris 222. **Boveri, T.** 1887. Differenzierung der Zellkern während der Furchung des Eis von Ascaris. Anat. Anz. .2. 1899. Die Entwicklung von Ascaris. Festschrift für Kupffer. **Bovien, P.** 1937. Some types of association between nematodes and insects. Vidensk. Meddel. Dansk Naturhist. Foren. 101. **Brakenhoff, H.** 1914. Nematodenfauna des nordwestdeutschen Flachlandes. Abhandl. Naturwiss. Verein Bremen 22. **Brand, T. v.** 1938. Nature of the metabolic activities of intestinal helminths in their natural habitat: aerobiosis or anaerobiosis? Biodynamica No 41. **Brand, T. v.,** and **W. Weise.** 1932. Untersuchungen über den Sauerstoffgehalt der Umwelt einiger Entoparasiten. Ztschr. Vergl. Physiol. 18. **Brandes, G.** 1899. Das Nervensystem der als Nemathelminthen zusammengefassten Wurmtypen. Ahbandl. Naturforsch. Gesell. Halle 21. **Brown, H. W.** 1927. A study of the regularity of egg-production in Ascaris, Necator, and Trichuris. Jour. Parasitol. 14 1931. Nematodes in the soil. Lingnan Sci. Jour. 8. **Bueding, E.** 1949. Metabolism of parasitic helminths. Physiol. Reviews 29. **Buerkel, E.** 1900. Biologische Studien über die Fauna der Kieler Föhrde. **Burkhalter, M.** 1928. Die Verbreitung der freilebenden Erdnematoden im Masif der Rochers de Naye. Rev. Suisse Zool. 35. **Busch, P. W.** 1905. Sur la localisation du glycogene chez quelques parasites intestinaux. Arch. Internat. Zool. 3. **Bütschli, O.** 1873. Beiträge zur Kenntniss der freilebenden Nematoden. Nova Acta Acad. Leopold. Carol. 36. 1874. Zur Kenntnis der freilebenden Nematoden. Abhandl. Senckenberg. Naturforsch. Gesell. 9. 1892. Über den feineren Bau der contractilen Substanz der Muskelzellen von

Ascaris. Festschrift für Leuckart. **Cameron, T. W.** 1931. Helminth parasites of poultry. Veterinary Jour. 87. 1932. The internal parasites of sheep. Veterinary Jour. 88. 1933. The internal parasites of pigs. The important helminth parasites of stock in the British Empire. Veterinary Jour. 89. **Cappe de Boullon, P.** 1911. Étude sur les fibers musculaires d'Ascaris. La Cellule 27. **Cassidy, G. W.** 1930. Nematodes associated with sugar cane in Hawaii. Hawaiian Plant Rec. 34. **Chance, M., and Dirnhuber, P.** 1949. The water-soluble vitamins of parasitic worms. Parasitology 39. **Chandler, A. C.** 1923. Speciation and host relationships of parasites. Parasitology 15. 1924. Artificial cultivation of free-living nematodes. Science 60. 1932. Susceptibility and resistance to helminthic infestations. Jour. Parasitol. 18. 1935. Parasites of fishes in Galveston Bay. Proc. U.S. Nation. Mus. 83. 1939. The nature and mechanism of immunity in various intestinal nematode infections. Amer. Jour. Trop. Med. 19. **Chitwood, B. G.** 1931. A comparative histological study of certain nematodes. Ztschr. Morphol. Ökol. Tiere 23. 1936a. Some marine nematodes from North Carolina. 1936b. Observations on the chemical nature of the cuticle of Ascaris. Proc. Helminthol. Soc. Washington 3. 1938. Further studies on nemic skeletoids. Proc. Helminthol. Soc. Washington 5. **Chitwood, B. G., and M. B. Chitwood.** 1933a. The characters of a protonematode. Jour. Parasitol. 20. 1933b. The histological anatomy of Cephalobellus. Ztschr. Zellforsch. Mikro. Anat. 19. 1934a. The histology of nemic esophagi. I. II. Ztschr. Zellforsch. Mikro. Anat. 22. 1934b. Somatic musculature in nematodes. Proc. Helminthol. Soc. Washington 1. 1937–. *An introduction to nematology* (incomplete in 1949). **Chitwood, B. G., and E. E. Wehr.** 1932. The value of head characters in nematode taxonomy and relationship. Jour. Parasitol. 19. 1934. The value of cephalic structures as characters in nematode classification with special reference to the Spiruroidea. Ztschr. Parasitenk. 7. **Clapham, Phyllis.** 1931. Tropisms of Dorylaimus and Rhabditis. Jour. Helminthol. 9. **Cobb, N. A.** 1913. New nematode genera found inhabiting fresh water and non-brackish soils. Jour. Washington Acad. Sciences 3. 1914a. Nematodes and their relationships. Yearbook U.S. Dept. Agricult. 1914b. North American free-living fresh-water nematodes. Trans. Amer. Micro. Soc. 33; Contribs. Sci. Nematology 2. 1914c. Antarctic marine free-living nematodes of the Shackleton Expedition. Contribs. Sci. Nematology 1. 1915. Mechanism of the spinneret of a free-living nematode. Jour. Parasitol. 2. 1917. Nema population of beach sand. Contribs. Sci. Nematology 5. 1918. Filter-bed nemas. Contribs. Sci. Nematology 7. 1921. Nematodes collected by the Canadian Arctic Expedition. Jour. Parasitol. 7. 1923a. Revival of desiccated nemas. Jour. Parasitol. 9. 1923b. Interesting features of nemas. Jour. Parasitol. 9. 1923c. Deirids of nemas. Jour. Parasitol. 9. 1929a. One hundred new nemas. Contribs. Sci. Nematology 9. 1929b. Survey of nemas in the upper 20 mm. of marine beach sand. Jour. Washington Acad. Sciences 19. 1930. Marine free-living nemas. Austral. Antarctic Exped., Scient. Repts., ser. C, 6, Pt. 7. 1931. Some recent aspects of nematology. Science 73. 1935a. Key to the genera of free-living nemas. Proc. Helminthol. Soc. Washington 2. 1935b. Contributions to the science of nematology, Nos. 1–26. **Coninck, L. de.** 1930. Bijdrage tot de kennis der vrijlevende Nematoden von Belgie. Natuurwetensch. Tijdschrift 12, No. 4. 1935. Connaissance des nématodes libres du Congo Belge I. Rev. Zool. Bot. Afrique 26. 1939. Les nématodes libres de la grotte de Han. Bull. Mus. Roy. Hist. Natur. Belgique 15, No. 20. 1940. Scientific results of P. van Oye's Expedition in Iceland. VIII. Les nématodes libres de sources chaudes. Biol. Jaarboek Konin. Natuurwet. Genootschap. Dodonaea 7, Afd. 1. 1942. De symmetrie-verhoudingen aan het vooreinde der (vrijlevende) nematoden. Natuurwet. Tijdschr. 24. **Coninck, L. de,** and **J. H. Schuurmans Stekhoven.** 1933. The free-living marine nemas of the Belgian coast. II. Mém. Mus. Hist. Natur. Belg. 58. **Cram, Eloise.** 1927. Bird parasites of the nematode suborders Strongylata, Ascaridata, and Spirurata. Bull. U.S. Nation. Mus. 140. **Danheim, Bertha.** 1925. Studies on the migratory habits of certain nematode larvae. Trans. Amer. Micro. Soc. 44. **Davey, D. G.** 1938. The respiration of nematodes of the alimentary tract. Jour. Exp. Biol. 15. **Dikmans, G.** 1933. Comparative study of the infective larvae of the common nematodes parasitic in the alimentary tract of sheep. Trans. Amer. Micro. Soc. 52. **Ditlevsen, H.** 1912, 1919. Danish free-living nematodes. Vidensk. Meddel. Naturhist. Foren. Copenhagen 63, 70. 1926. Free-living nematodes. Danish Ingulf Expedition 4. 1927. Free-living nematodes from Greenland. Meddel. Grönland 23, suppl. **Dougherty, E. C.,** and **H. G. Calhoun.** 1948. Possible significance of free-living nematodes in genetic research. Nature, London, 161. **Draschke, R.** 1882–1883. Revision der Nematoden-Sammlung. Verhandl. Zool. Bot. Gesell. Wien 32, 33. **Fallis, A. M.** 1938. Helminth parasites of lambs in Ontario. Trans. Roy. Canad. Inst. 22. **Fauré-Fremiet, E.** 1912. Maturation et fécondation chez l'Ascaris. Grasse et glycogene dans le développement de l'Ascaris. Bull. Soc. Zool. France 37. 1913. La formation de la membrane interne de l'oeuf d'Ascaris. C. R. Soc. Biol. Paris 74. **Filipjev, I. N.** 1912. Zur Kenntnis des Nervensystems bei den freilebenden Nematoden. Trav. Soc. Impér. Natural. St. Pétersbourg, Livr. 1, 43. 1918. Free-living nematodes in the vicinity of Sebastopol. I, II. Trav. Lab. Zool. Stat. Biol. Sebastopol 2, No. 4. 1934. The classification of the free-living nematodes. Smithson. Miscell. Collect. 89. **Filipjev, I. N.,** and **J. H. Schuurmans Stekhoven.** 1941. A manual of agricultural helminthology. **Foster, W.** 1912. The roundworms of domestic swine. Bur. Animal Industry, U.S. Dept. Agricult., No. 158. **Freeborn, S.,** and **M. Stewart.** 1937. The nematodes and certain other parasites of sheep. California Agricult. Exp. Sta. Bull. 603. **Fülleborn, F.** 1924. The wandering of certain nematode larvae in the body of their hosts. Jour. Parasitol. 11. 1931. Die Wanderung der Nematodenlarven im Körper des Wirtes. Naturwissenschaften 19. 1932. Haut und Helminthen. Handbuch Haut und Geschlechtskrankheiten 12. **Giovannola, A.** 1936. Energy and food reserves in the development of nematodes. Jour. Parasitol. 22. **Goldschmidt, R.** 1903. Dis Sinnesorgane von Ascaris. Zool. Jahrb. Abt. Anat. 18. 1905. Über die Cuticula von Ascaris. Zool. Anz. 28. 1906. Zur Histologie von Ascaris. Zool. Anz. 29. 1908–1910. Das Nervensystem von Ascaris. Ztschr. Wiss. Zool. 90, 92; Festschrift für Hertwig, vol. 2. **Greeff, R.** 1872. Über die frei im Wasser und in der Erde lebenden Nematoden. Sitzungsber. Verein Rheinland 27. **Hall, M. C.** 1921. Note on a neglected nematode structure. Proc. U.S. Nation. Mus. 59. 1924. Worm parasites of domestic animals. Parasites of swine. U.S. Bur. Animal Industry. Parasites and parasitic diseases of dogs. U.S. Dept. Agricult. Circular No. 338. 1929. Arthropods as intermediate hosts of helminths. Smithson. Miscell. Collect. 181. **Hamann, O.** 1892. Das System des Exkretionsorgans der Nematoden. Centralbl. Bakteriol. Parasitenk. 11. **Harwood, P. D.,** and **H. W. Brown.** 1934. In vitro consumption of oxygen by parasitic nematodes. Jour. Parasitol. 20. **Heinis, F.** 1920. Mikrofauna alpiner Polster- und Rosettenpflanzen. Festschrift f. Zschokke. 1928. Die Moosfauna des Krakatau. Treubia 10. **Hektoen, L.** 1926. Precipitin reactions of extracts of various animal parasites. Jour. Infect. Diseases 39. **Hesse, R.** 1892. Nervensystem von Ascaris. Ztschr. Wiss. Zool. 54. **Hetherington, D. C.** 1923. Comparative studies on certain features of nematodes. Illinois Biol. Monogr. 8. **Hinman, E. H.,** and **D. D. Baker.** 1936. Helminthological survey of 1315 dogs from New Orleans with special reference to age resistance. Jour. Trop. Med. Hyg. 39.

Hobson, A. D. 1948. The physiology and cultivation in artificial media of nematodes parasitic in the alimentary tract of animals. Parasitology 38. **Hoeppli, R.** 1925. Über das Vorderende der Ascariden. Ztschr. Zellforsch. Mikro. Anat. 2. 1926. Free-living nematodes from the thermal waters of Yellowstone Park. Trans. Amer. Micro. Soc. 45. 1927. Beziehungen zwischen dem biologischen Verhalten parasitischer Nematoden und histologischen Reaktionen des Wirbeltierkörpers. Beihefte Arch. Schiffs. Tropenhyg. 31. 1930. Parasitic nematodes and the lesions they cause. Nation. Med. Jour. China 16. **Hoeppli, R., and H. Chu.** 1932. Free-living nematodes from hot springs in China and Formosa. Hong Kong Naturalist, suppl. No. 1. **Hoeppli, R., F. Feng, and H. Chu.** 1938. Attempts to culture helminths of vertebrates in artificial media. Chinese Med. Jour., suppl. 2. **Hofmänner, B.** 1913. Nématodes libres du Lac Léman. Rev. Suisse Zool. 21. **Hofmänner, B., and R. Menzel.** 1915. Die freilebenden Nematoden der Schweiz. Rev. Suisse Zool. 23. **Honda, H.** 1925. Experimental and cytological studies on bisexual and hermaphroditic free-living nematodes. Jour. Morphol. 40. **Hsü, H.** 1939. Studies on the food and digestive system of certain parasites. I, II. Bull. Fan Memorial Inst. Biol., Zool. Ser. 8. **Hsü, H., and S. Y. Li.** 1940. Studies on the food, etc. VI. Chinese Med. Jour. 57. **Jacobs, L., and M. Jones.** 1939. Chemistry of the membranes of the pinworm egg. Proc. Helminthol. Soc. Washington 6. **Jägerskiöld, L.** 1894. Beiträge zur Kenntnis der Nematoden. Zool. Jahrb. Abt. Anat. 7. 1897. Über den Oesophagus der Nematoden. Bihang Svenska Vetensk. Akad. 23. 1901. Weitere Beiträge zur Kenntnis der Nematoden. Kong. Svenska Vetensk. Akad. Handl. 35, No. 2. **Kahl, W.** 1938–1939. Nematoden in Seefischen. I–III. Ztschr. Parasitenk. 10, 11. **Karve, J.** 1930. Some parasitic nematodes of frogs and toads. Ann. Trop. Med. Parasitol. 24. **Keilin, D.** 1926. The problem of the origin of nematodes. Parasitology 18. **Krakov, N. P.** 1892. Ueber verschiedenartige Chitin. Ztschr. Biol. 29. **Kreis, H. A.** 1927. Bedeutung der geographischen Verbreitung der freilebenden marinen und Süsswassernematoden. Verhandl. Schweiz. Naturforsch. Gesell. 108. 1929. Freilebende marine Nematoden von der Nordwestküste Frankreichs. Capita Zoologica 2. **Lapage, G.** 1937. Nematodes parasitic in animals. Methuen's Monogr. on biol. subjects. **La Rivers, I.** 1949. Entomic nematode literature from 1926 to 1946 exclusive of medical and veterinary. Wasmann Collector 7. **Linford, M.** 1937. The feeding of some hollow-stylet nematodes. Proc. Helminthol. Soc. Washington 4. **Linford, M., and J. Oliviera.** 1937. The feeding of hollow-spear nematodes on other nematodes. Science 85. **McBeth, C. W.** 1937. Observations on a predaceous nematode. Proc. Helminthol. Soc. Washington 4. **McGath, T. B.** 1928. The cuticula of nematodes. Science 67. **Man, J. G. de.** 1884. Die frei in der reinen Erde und in süsses Wasser lebenden Nematoden der niederländischen Fauna. 1886. Anatomische Untersuchungen an freilebende Nematoden. 1888. Sur quelques nématodes libres de la Mer du Nord. Mém. Soc. Zool. France 1. 1889. Nématodes libres de la Mer du Nord et de la Manche. Mém. Soc. Zool. France 2. 1890. Quatrième note sur les nématodes libres de la Mer du Nord et de la Manche. Mem. Soc. Zool. France 3. 1893. Cinquiéme note, etc. Mém. Soc. Zool. France 6. 1907. Nématodes libres habitant les cotes de la Zélande. Mém. Soc. Zool. France 20. 1922. Vrij levende Nematoden. Flora en Fauna der Zuiderzee. **Marcinowsky, Kati.** 1909. Parasitisch und semiparasitisch an Pflanzen lebende Nematoden. Arbeit. Biol. Anstalt Land. Forstwirtschaft 7. **Markov, G.** 1943. The dynamic of nutritive materials of parasitic worms in artificial media. Zool. Zhurnal 22. **Martini, E.** 1903. Über Furchung und Gastrulation bei Cucullanus. Ztschr. Wizz. Zool. 74. 1906–1909. Über Subcuticula und Seitenfelder einiger Nematoden. Ztschr. Wiss.

Zool. 81, 86, 91, 93, 98. 1907. Über Konstanz histologischer Elemente bei erwachsenen Nematoden. Sitzungsber. Naturforsch. Gesell. Rostock 61, Pt. 8. 1908. Die Konstanz histologischer Elemente bei Nematoden. Anat. Anz., Erganzungsheft to 32 (Verhandl. Anat. Gesell. 22). 1913. Über die Stellung der Nematoden im System. Verhandl. Dtsch. Zool. Gesell. 23. **Maupas, E.** 1900. Modes et formes de reproduction des nématodes. Arch. Zool. Exp. Gén., ser. 3, 8. **Menzel, R.** 1920a. Über die Nahrung der freilebenden Nematoden. Verhandl. Naturforsch. Gesell. Basel 31. 1920b. Über freilebende Nematoden aus der Arktis. Festschr. f. Zechokke, No. 17. 1923. Über den tierischen Inhalt der Kannen von Nepenthes. Treubia 3. 1925. Bewohner salzhaltiger Thermalgewässer. Treubia 6. 1930. Nematoden als Bewohner von Nepentheskannen. Verhandl. Schweiz. Naturforsch. Gesell. 111. **Merrill, J.,** and **A. Ford.** 1916. Life history and habits of two nematodes parasitic in insects. Jour. Agricult. Research 6. **Micoletzky, H.** 1914. Okologie ostalpiner Süsswasser nematoden. Internation. Rev. Ges. Hydrobiol. 6, Biol. Suppl. 6. 1921. Die freilebenden Erdnematoden. Arch. Naturgesch. 87A, Heft 8, 9. 1922. Freilebende Nematoden von der Sargassosee. Mitt. Zool. Staatsinst. Zool. Mus. Hamburg 39. 1925a. Die freilebenden Süsswasser- und Moornematoden Dänemarks. Kong. Danske Vidensk. Sels. Skrift., Naturwid. Math. Afd., ser. 8, 10. 1925b. Zur Kenntnis tropischer freilebende Nematoden. Zool. Anz. 64. **Morishita, K.** 1926. Studies on some nematodes of frogs and toads in Japan. Jour. Fac. Sci. Univ. Tokyo, sect. IV, Zool. 1. **Nassonov, N.** 1897. Sur les organs du système excréteur des Ascarides et des Oxyurides. Zool. Anz. 20. 1900. Zur Kenntnis der phagocytären Organe bei den parasitischen Nematoden. Arch. Mikro. Anat. 55. **Neveu-Lemaire, M.** 1933. Les arthropodes hôtes intermédiares des helminthes parasites de l'homme. Ann. Parasitol. Hum. Comp. 11. **Nigon, V.** 1943, 1946. La déterminisme du sexe chez un nématode hermaphrodite. C. R. Soc. Biol. Paris 137; Bull. Soc. Zool. France 71. 1947. Le déterminisme de sexe et la pseudogamie chez un nématode parthénogénetique. Bull. Biol. France Belg. 81. **Northrop, J. H.** 1926. Resistance of living organisms to digestion by pepsin and trypsin. Jour. Gen. Physiol. 9. **Oldham, J.** 1931. Helminth parasites of common rats. Jour. Helminthol. 9. **Oliver-Gonzalez, J.** 1946. Immunological relationships among polysaccharides from various infective organisms. Jour. Infect. Diseases 79. **Panikkar, N.,** and **N. Sproston.** 1941. Osmotic relations of some metazoan parasites. Parasitology 33. **Pax, F.,** and **A. Soos.** 1943. Die Nematoden der deutschen Schwefelquellen und Thermen. Arch. Hydrobiol. 40. **Peters, B.** 1930. A biological investigation of sewage. Some nematodes met with in a biological investigation of sewage. Jour. Helminthol. 8. **Potts, E.** 1910. Notes on free-living nematodes. Quart. Jour. Micro. Sci. 55. **Rahm, G.** 1921. Einwirkung sehr niederer Temperaturen auf die Moosfauna. Kon. Wetensch. Akad. Amsterdam, Proc. Sect. Sci. 23. 1922. Biologische und physiologische Beiträge zur Kenntnis der Moosfauna. Ztschr. Allg. Physiol. 20. 1926. Die Trockenstarre der Moostierwelt. Biol. Centralbl. 46. 1928. Wie überwintern die in Moos und Flechtenrasen der alpinen Region eingefrorenen Tiere? Rev. Suisse Zool. 35. 1937. Oekologische und biologische Bemerkungen zur anabiotischen Fauna Chinas. Peking Natur. Hist. Bull. 11. **Ransom, B. H.** 1911. Nematodes parasitic in the alimentary tract of cattle, sheep, and other ruminants. U.S. Dept. Agricult., Bull. Bur. Animal Industry 127. **Rauther, M.** 1907. Bau des Oesophagus und die Lokalisation der Nierenfunktion bei freilebenden Nematoden. Zool. Jahrb. Abt. Anat. 23. 1909. Morphologie und Verwandschaftsbeziehungen der Nematoden. Ergebn. Fortschr. Zool. 1. 1918. Mitteilungen zur Nematodenkunde. Zool. Jahrb. Abt. Anat. 40. 1930. Nematodes. In **W. Kükenthal** and **T. Krumbach** (eds.), *Handbuch der Zoologie*, Band II, Hälfte 1.

Reiber, R. 1941. Nematodes of Amphibia and Reptilia. Jour. Tennessee Acad. Sci. 16. **Retzius, G.** 1906. Zur Kenntnis der Hautschicht der Nematoden. Biol. Untersuchungen 13. **Rogers, W. P.** 1940a. Haematological studies on the gut contents of certain nematode parasites. Jour. Helminthol. 18. 1940b, 1941. Digestion in parasitic nematodes, I–III. Jour. Helminthol. 18, 19. 1948. Respiratory metabolism of parasitic nematodes. Parasitology 39. **Rogers, W. P.,** and **M. Lazarus.** 1949. The uptake of radio-active phosphorus from host tissues and fluids by nematode parasites. Glycolysis and related phosphorus metabolism in parasitic nematodes. Parasitology 39. **Roskin, G.** 1925. Die Muskelzelle von Ascaris. Ztschr. Zellforsch. Mikro. Anat. 2. **Sandground, J. H.** 1929. Relation of host-specificity of helminths to age resistance and acquired immunity. Parasitology 21. 1936. Longevity of various species of helminths. Jour. Parasitol. 22. **Schimkewitsch, W.** 1899. Über besondere Zellen in der Leibeshöhle der Nematoden. Biol. Centralbl. 19. **Schneider, A.** 1860. Ueber die Muskeln und Nerven der Nematoden. Arch. Anat. Physiol. 1866. *Monographie der Nematoden.* **Schneider, G.** 1927. Dritter Beitrag zur Kenntnis der Brackwassernematoden Finlands. Acta Soc. Fauna Flora Finlands 56, No. 10. **Schneider, W.** 1939. Freilebende und pflanzenparasitische Nematoden. In **F. Dahl** (ed.), Die Tierwelt Deutschlands und die angrenzenden Meeresteile, Teil 36. **Schönberg, Maria.** 1942. Die erste Furchungsstadien von Rhabditis. Arch. Entw'mech. Org. 142. 1943. Histologische Studien zu den Problemen der Zellkonstanz. Biol. Generalis 17. **Schulz, E.** 1931. Die Augen freilebender Nematoden. Zool. Anz. 95, 96. 1938. Beiträge zur Morphologie und Systematik freilebender marinen Nematoden. I. Kiel Meeresforsch. 3. **Schuurmans Stekhoven, J. H.** 1931. Das Problem der Ernährung und Verdauung bei den freilebenden und parasitären Nematoden. Zool. Anz. Suppl. 5 (Verhandl. Dtsch. Zool. Gesell. 34). 1933, 1935. Nematoda (Allgemeiner Teil). Nematoda Errantia. Nematoda parasitica. In **G. Grimpe** and **E. Wagler** (eds.), Die Tierwelt der Nord- und Ostsee, Teil Va, b, c. 1936. Nematoda. Flora en Fauna der Zuiderzee, Suppl. 1936– . Nematodes. In **H. G. Bronn** (ed.), *Klassen und Ordnungen des Tierreichs*, Band IV, Abt. 2, Buch 3. 1937. Interrelation between free-living and parasitic nematodes. Papers on Helminthology, 30 yr. Jubileum K. I. Skrjabin. 1942. The free-living nematodes of the Mediterranean. I–III. Zool. Jahrb. Abt. System. 76; Zool. Mededel. 23. 1943. Nématodes recueilles dans les grottes et des sources du Belgique. Bull. Mus. Hist. Natur. Belg. 19. **Schuurmans Stekhoven, J. H., W. Adam,** and **L. A. de Coninck.** 1931, 1933, 1935. The free-living marine nemas of the Belgian coast. I–III. Mém. Mus. Roy. Hist. Natur. Belg. 49, 58, 72. **Schuurmans Stekhoven, J. H., W. Adam,** and **A. Punt.** 1931, 1935. Oekologische Notizen über Zuiderzee Nematoden. I, II. Ztschr. Morphol. Ökol. Tiere 20, 29. **Schuurmans Stekhoven, J. H.,** and **L. H. de Coninck.** 1933. Morphologische Fragen zur Systematik der freilebenden Nematoden. Zool. Anz. Suppl. 6 (Verhandl. Dtsch. Zool. Gesell. 35). **Schuurmans Stekhoven, J. H.,** and **R. Tennissen.** 1938. Nématodes libres terrestres. Explor. Parc National Albert Mission de Witte 22. **Seck, P.** 1937. Zur Entwicklungsmechanik des Essigälchens. Arch. Entw'mech. Org. 137. **Shorb, D.** 1939. Differentiation of eggs of various nematodes parasitic in domestic ruminants. U.S. Dept. Agricult., Tech. Bull. 694. **Skrjabin, D.** 1941. On the phylogenetic interrelationships of nematodes of the subclass Phasmidia. Zool. Zhurnal 20. **Sprehn, C.** 1927. Nematoden in Säugetieren. Ztschr. Säugetierk. 2. **Stauffer, H.** 1924. Die Lokomotion der Nematoden. Zool. Jahrb. Abt. System. 49. **Stefanski, W.** 1917. Excretion chez les nématodes libres. Biol. Centralbl. 37. **Steiner, G.** 1916a. Freilebende Nematoden aus der Barentsee. Zool. Jahrb. Abt. System. 39. 1916b. Beiträge zur geographischen Verbreitung freilebender Nematoden. Zool. Anz. 46. 1917. Über das Verhalten der marinen freilebenden Nematoden zu denen des Süsswassers und des Landes. Biol. Centralbl. 37. 1920a. Freilebende Süsswasser-Nematoden aus peruanischen Hochgebirgeseen. Rev. Suisse Zool. 28. 1920b. Betrachtungen zur Frage der Verwandtschafts- verhältnissen der Rotatorien und Nematoden. Festschrift für Zschokke. 1921a. Beitrag zur Kenntnis mariner Nematoden. Zool. Jahrb. Abt. System. 44. 1921b. Untersuchungen über den allgemeinen Bauplan des Nematodenkörpers. Zool. Jahrb. Abt. Anat. 43. 1923. Intersexes in nematodes. Jour. Heredity 14. 1924. Some nemas from the alimentary tract of the Carolina tree frog. Jour. Parasitol. 11. 1940. Anabiosis in nematodes. Rept. Proc. III. Internation. Congr. Microbiology. **Steiner, G., and E. Buhrer.** 1933. Observations of interest on nematode diseases of plants. Plant Diseases Repts. 20. **Steiner, G., and R. Hoeppli.** 1926. Studies on the exoskeleton of some Japanese marine nemas. Arch. Schiffs. Tropenhyg. 30. **Stekhoven, see Schuurmans Stekhoven. Stephenson, W.** 1942. The effect of variations in osmotic pressure on a soil nematode. Resistance of a soil nematode to changes in osmotic pressure. Parasitology 34; Nature, London, 149. 1944. The effect of certain inorganic chloride solutions upon a soil nematode. Parasitology 35. 1945. The effects of acid on a soil nematode. Parasitology 36. **Taliaferro, W.** 1930. The immunology of parasitic infections. 1948. The inhibition of reproduc- tion of parasites by immune factors. Bacteriol. Reviews 12. **Tappeiner, —.** 1883. Die Gase des Verdauungsschlauches der Pflanzenfresser. Ztschr. Biol. 19. **Taylor, A. L.** 1935. A review of the fossil nematodes. Proc. Helminthol. Soc. Washington 2. **Taylor, E. L.** 1933. The longevity of parasitic worms. Veterinary Record 13. **Theiler, Gertrud.** 1923. The strongylids and other nematodes parasitic in the intestinal tract of South African equines. Union of South Africa, Rept. Director Veterinary Education and Research 9–10. **Threlkeld, W.** 1941. Notes on copula- tion of certain nematodes. Virginia Jour. Sci. 2. **Todd, A. C.** 1946. The nature of helminth infections in chickens in East Tennessee. Poultry Science 25. **Türk, F.** 1903. Über einige im Golfe von Neapel freilebende Nematoden. Mitt. Zool. Staz. Neapel 16. **Van Zwaluwenburg, R.** 1928. Interrelationships of insects and round- worms. Bull. Exp. Sta. Hawaiian Sugar Planters Assoc., Entomol. Series 20. **Wal- ton, A. C.** 1933–1948. Nematoda as parasites of Amphibia. I–IV. Jour. Parasitol. 20, 21, 23; Trans. Amer. Micro. Soc. 57. **Welch, P., and L. Wehrle.** 1918. Repro- duction in certain parthenogenetic and bisexual nematodes reared in artificial media. Trans. Amer. Micro. Soc. 37. **Wülker, G., and J. H. Schuurmans Stekhoven.** 1933. Nematoda (Allgemeiner Teil). In G. Grimpe and E. Wagler (eds.), Die Tierwelt der Nord- und Ostsee, Teil Va. **Yamaguti, S.** 1935. Studies on the helminth fauna of Japan. Pt. 9. Nematodes of fishes, I. Pt. 10. Amphibian nematodes. Pt. 11. Reptilian nematodes. Pt. 12. Avian nematodes, I. Pt. 13. Mammalian nematodes. Japan, Jour. Zool. 6. **Yorke, W., and P. Maplestone.** 1926. *The nematode parasites of vertebrates.* **Ziegler, H.** 1895. Untersuchungen über die ersten Entwick- lungsvorgänge der Nematoden. Ztschr. Wiss. Zool. 60. **Zur Strassen, O.** 1896. Embryonalentwicklung der Ascaris. Arch. Entw'mech. Org. 3.

Enoploidea

Allgen, C. 1929. Zur Kenntnis der Gattung Pelagonema. Zool. Anz. 83. 1936. Die Pelagonemen der Mittelmeeres. Festschrift f. Embrik Strand 1. **Chitwood, B. G.** 1936. Some marine nematodes of the superfamily Enoploidea. Trans. Amer. Micro. Soc. 55. **Chitwood, B. G., and M. B. Chitwood.** 1937. The esophagi of representatives of the Enoplida. Jour. Washington Acad. Sciences 27. **Cobb, N. A.** 1890. Anticoma. Proc. Linn. Soc. New South Wales, ser. 2, 5. 1917. The mononchs. Contribs. Science Nematology, No. 6. 1930. The demanian vessels of Oncholaimus. Jour. Washington Acad. Sciences 20. 1932. Metoncholaimus pristiurus. Jour. Washington Acad. Sciences 22. **Filipjev, I. N.** 1925. Les nématodes libres des mers septentrionales appartenant à la famille des Enoplidae. Arch. Naturg. 91A, Heft 6. 1928. Über die Zellmosaik in der Epidermis von Paroncholaimus. Zool. Anz. 61. **Filipjev, I. N.**, and **E. Michajlava.** 1924. Zahl der Entwicklungstadien bei Enoplus. Zool. Anz. 59. **Kreis, A.** 1934. Oncholaiminae. Capita Zoologica 4. **Schneider, G.** 1926. Zweite Beitrag zur Kenntnis der Brackwassernematoden Finlands. Acta Soc. Fauna Flora Fennica 56, No. 7. **Schuurmans Stekhoven, J. H.** 1933. Die Nahrung von Oncholaimus. Zool. Anz. 101. **Steiner, G.**, and **Florence Albin.** 1933. On the morphology of Deontostoma. Jour. Washington Acad. Sciences 23. **Steiner, G.**, and **H. Heinly.** 1922. Possibility of control of Heterodera by means of predatory nemas. Jour. Washington Acad. Sciences 12. **Stewart, F.** 1906. Anatomy of Oncholaimus. Quart. Jour. Micro. Sci. 50. **Thorne, G.** 1927. Life history, habits, and economic importance of some Mononchus. Jour. Agricult. Research. 34. **Zur Strassen, O.** 1894. Über das rohrenformige Organ von Oncholaimus. Ztschr. Wiss. Zool. 58.

Dorylaimoidea

Filipjev, I. 1931. Report on fresh-water nematodes of the Abyssinian fresh waters. Proc. Zool. Soc. London. **Issel, R.** 1906. Sulla termibiose negli animali acquatica. Atti Soc. Ligustica Sci. Natur. Geogr. 17. **Linstow, O. v.** 1901. Dorylaimus atratus. Boll. Mus. Zool. Anat. Comp. Genova, No. 109. **Thorne, G.** 1930. Predacious nemas of the genus Nygolaimus. Jour. Agricult. Research 41. 1935. Notes on free-living and plant-parasitic nematodes. II. Proc. Helminthol. Soc. Washington 2. 1939. A monograph of the superfamily Dorylaimoidea. Capita Zoologica 8. **Thorne, G.**, and **Helen Swanger.** 1936. A monograph of the genera Dorylaimus, Aporcelaimus, Dorylaimoides, and Pungentus. Capita Zoologica 6.

Mermithoidea

Baylis, H. A. 1933. Two new species of Mermis. Ann. Mag. Natur. Hist., ser. 10, 11. 1944. Observations on Mermis nigrescens and related species. Parasitology 36. 1947. The larval stages of Mermis nigrescens. Parasitology 38. **Caullery, M.**, and **M. Comas.** 1928. Le déterminisme du sexe chez Paramermis. C. R. Acad. Sci. Paris. 186. **Christie, J. R.** 1927. Males in Mermis. Jour. Helminthol. 14. 1929. Some observations on sex in the Mermithidae. Jour. Exp. Zool. 53. 1936. Life history of Agamermis. Jour. Agricult. Research 52. 1937. Mermis subnigrescens, a nematode parasite of grasshoppers. Jour. Agricult. Research 55. **Cobb, N. A.** 1919. Tetradonema. Jour. Parasitol. 5. 1926. The species of Mermis. Jour. Parasitol. 13. **Cobb, N. A., G. Steiner,** and **J. R. Christie.** 1923. Agamermis decaudata. Jour. Agricult. Research 23. 1927. When and how does sex arise? U.S. Dept. Agricult., Official Record 6. **Comas, Marguerite.** 1927. Sur la mode de pénétration de Paramermis dans la larvae Chironomus. C. R. Soc. Biol. Paris 96. **Crawley, W. C.**, and **H. A. Baylis.** 1921. Mermis parasitic on ants of the genus Lasius. Jour. Roy. Micro. Soc. **Goodey, T.** 1941. Morphology of Mermithonema. Jour. Helminthol. 19. **Gösswald, K.** 1929. Merminthogynen von Lasius. Zool. Anz. 84. 1930. Weiter Beiträge zur Verbreitung der Mermithiden bei Ameisen. Zool. Anz. 90. 1938. Über bisher unbekannte durch den Parasitismus der Mermithiden vermachte Formveränderungen bei Ameisen. Ztschr. Parasitenk. 10. **Hagmeier, A.** 1912. Beiträge zur Kenntnis der Mermithiden. Zool. Jahrb. Abt. System. 32. **Hungerford, H. B.** 1919. Biological notes on Tetradonema. Jour. Parasitol. 5. **Kaburaki, T.,** and **S. Imamura.** 1932. Mermithid-worm parasitic in leaf-hoppers. Proc. Imper. Acad. Japan 8. **Kaburaki, T.,** and **K. Iyatomi.** 1933. Notes on sex in Amphimermis Proc. Imper. Acad. Japan 9. **Keilin, D.,** and **V. Robinson.** 1933. Morphology and life history of Aproctonema entomophagum. Parasitology 25. **Kohn, F. G.** 1905. Einiges über Paramermis contorta. Arbeit. Zool. Inst. Univ. Wien 15. **Linstow, O. v.** 1892. Über Mermis nigrescens. Arch. Mikro. Anat. 40. **Meissner, G.** 1854. Beiträge zur Anatomie und Physiologie von Mermis albicans. Ztschr. Wiss. Zool. 5. **Müller, G. W.** 1931. Über Mermithiden. Ztschr. Morphol. Okol. Tiere 24. **Muspratt, J.** 1947. Laboratory culture of a nematode parasite of mosquito larvae. Jour. Entomol. Soc. Southern Africa 10. **Rauther, M.** 1906. Beiträge zur Kenntnis von Mermis albicans. Zool. Jahrb. Abt. Anat. 23. **Steiner, G.** 1917. Über die Verwandschaftsverhältnisse und die systematische Stellung der Mermithiden. Zool. Anz. 48. 1924. Beiträge zur Kenntnis der Mermithiden. Centralbl. Bakteriol. Parasitenk. Abt. 2, 62. 1933. Some morphological and physiological characters of the mermithids. Jour. Parasitol. 19. **Strickland, E.** 1911. Some parasites of Simulium larvae. Biol. Bull. 21. **Vandel, A.** 1930. La production d'intercastes chex la fourmi Pheidole sous l'action de parasites du genre Mermis. Bull. Biol. France Belg. 64. 1934. Le cycle évolutif d'Hexamermis parasite de la fourmi. Ann. Sci. Natur. Zool., ser. 10, 17. **Wheeler, W. M.** 1901. The parasitic origin of macro-ergates among ants. Amer. Natural. 35. 1928. Mermis parasitism and intercastes among ants. Jour. Exp. Zool. 50. 1937. *Mosaics and other anomalies among ants.* Harvard Univ. Press.

Chromadoroidea

Allgen, C. 1932. Die Desmodoren. Zool. Jahrb. Abt. System. 62. **Claparéde, R.** 1863. Beobachtungen über Anatomie und Entwicklungsgeschichte wirbellose Tiere. **Cobb, N. A.** 1913. Draconema. Jour. Washington Acad. Sciences 3. 1929. The ambulatory tubes and other features of Draconema. Jour. Washington Acad. Sci. 19. **Chitwood, B. G.,** and **M. B. Chitwood.** 1936. The esophagus of the Chromadorida. Jour. Washington Acad. Sci. 26. **Coninck, L. de.** 1942. Sur quelques espèces nouvelles de nématodes libres. Bull. Mus. Roy. Hist. Natur. Belg. 18, no. 22. **Irwin-Smith, Vera.** 1917. On the Chaetosomatidae. Proc. Linn. Soc. New South Wales 42. **Kreis, H.** 1938. Neue Nematoden aus der Südsee. Vidensk. Meddel. Dansk Naturhist. Foren 101. **Linstow, O. v.** 1901. Beobachtungen an Helminthen. Arch. Mikro. Anat. 58. **Metschnikoff, E.** 1867. Über Chaetosoma und Rhabdogaster. Ztschr. Wiss. Zool. 17. **Schepotieff, A.** 1908. Rhabdogaster. Die Chaetosomatidae. Zool. Jahrb. Abt. System. 26. **Steiner, G.** 1927. A new nemic family, Epsilonematidae. Jour. Parasitol. 14. 1931. Die Nematoden der deutschen Südpolar-Expedition. Dtsch. Südpolar-Exped. 20, Zoology 12.

Araeolaimoidea

Allgen, C. 1947. Die Nematoden-Familie Tripyloididae. Arkiv Zool. 39A, No. 15.

Monhysteroidea

Zur Strassen, O. 1904. Anthraconema. Zool. Jahrb. Suppl. 7.

Desmoscolecoidea

Chitwood, B. G. 1936. Some marine nematodes from North Carolina. Proc. Helminthol. Soc. Washington 3. **Cobb, N. A.** 1922. Greeffiella. Jour. Washington Acad. Sci. 12. **Kreis, H.** 1934. Neue Desmoscoleciden. Vidensk. Meddel.

Dansk Naturhist. Foren. 98. 1938. Neue Nematoden aus der Südsee. Vidensk. Meddel. Dansk Naturhist. Foren. 101. **Schepotieff, A.** 1907. Zur Systematik der Nematoideen. Zool. Anz. 31. 1908. Trichoderma. Zool. Jahrb. Abt. System. 26. **Stammer, H.** 1935. Desmoscolex aquaedulcis, der erste süsswasserwohnende Desmoscolecide. Zool. Anz. 109.

Rhabditoidea

Ackert, J., and **F. Wadley.** 1921. Observations on the distribution and life history of Cephalobium microbivorum. Trans. Amer. Micro. Soc. 40. **Atkinson, G.** 1889. Nematode root galls. Jour. Elisha Mitchell Scient. Soc. 6. **Aubertot, M.** 1923a. Sur la dissémination et la transport de nématodes du genre Rhabditis par les Diptères. C. R. Acad. Sci. Paris 176. 1923b. Sur la révivescence des larves du Rhabditis pellio. C. R. Soc. Biol. Paris 88. **Aurivillius, C.** 1883. Eine Anguillulide aus der Schneefauna Spitzbergens. K. Svenska Vetensk. Akad. Handl., Bihang 8, No. 11. **Baunacke, W.** 1922. Untersuchungen zur Biologie des Rübennematoden. Arbeit. Biol. Reichsanstalt Land. Forstwirtschaft 11, Heft 3. **Belehradek, J.,** and **V. Necasova.** 1929. Résistence du nématode Anguillula aceti vis-à-vis de quelques poisons protoplasmiques. Bull. Soc. Chim. Biol. 11. **Belehradek, J.,** and **F. Schwarz.** 1928. L'action toxique des acides de la série formique. Bull. Soc. Chim. Biol. 10. **Berliner, E.,** and **K. Busch.** 1914. Über die Züchtung der Rübennematoden auf Agar. Biol. Centralbl. 34. **Bovien, P.** 1932. On Scatonema wülkeri. Vidensk. Meddel. Dansk Naturhist. Foren 94. 1937. Some types of association between nematodes and insects. Vidensk. Meddel. Dansk Naturhist. Foren. 101. 1944. Proatractonema sciarae. Vidensk. Meddel. Dansk Naturhist. Foren. 108. **Boyd, A. E.** 1943. Observations on the biology of the potato-root eelworm. Ann. Applied Biol. 30. **Buhrer, Edna.** 1933. List of host plants of the root knot nematode. Jour. Parasitol. 20. **Byars, L.** 1914. Cultivation of Heterodera radicicola. Phytopathology 4. 1920. The nematode disease of wheat. U.S. Dept. Agricult. Bull. 842. **Carroll, J.** 1933. Study of Heterodera schachtii in the Irish Free State. Jour. Helminthol. 11, 13. **Chandler, A. C.** 1938. Diploscapter coronata as a facultative parasite of man with a general review of vertebrate parasitism by rhabditoid worms. Parasitology 30. **Chitwood, B. G.** 1930. Some physiological functions and morphological characters of Rhabditis. Jour. Morphol. 49. 1932. Synopsis of nematodes parasitic in Blattidae. Ztschr. Parasitenk. 5. 1933. On some nematodes of the superfamily Rhabditoidea. Jour. Washington Acad. Sci. 23. 1935. Nematodes parasitic in and associated with Crustacea. Proc. Helminthol. Soc. Washington 2. 1949. Revision of the genus Meloidogyne. Proc. Helminthol. Soc. Washington 16. **Chitwood, B. G.,** and **Edna Buhrer.** 1946. Life history of Heterodera rostochiensis under Long Island conditions. Phytopathology 36. 1946. Further studies of the life history of Heterodera rostochiensis. Proc. Helminthol. Soc. Washington 13. **Chitwood, B. G.,** and **M. B. Chitwood.** 1936. The esophagus of Rhabditis, Anguillulina, and Aphelenchus. Jour. Washington Acad. Sci. 26. **Christie, J. R.** 1936. Development of root-knot nematode galls. Phytopathology 26. **Christie, J. R.,** and **F. Albin.** 1944. Host-parasite relationships of the root-knot nematode. I. The question of races. Proc. Helminthol. Soc. Washington 11. **Christie, J. R.,** and **C. Arndt.** 1936. Feeding habits of Aphelenchoides and Aphelenchus. Phytopathology 26. **Christie, J. R.,** and **B. G. Chitwood.** 1931. Chondronema passali. Jour. Washington Acad. Sci. 21. **Christie, J. R.,** and **Grace Cobb.** 1941. Notes on the life history of Heterodera marioni. Proc. Helminthol. Soc. Washington 8. **Christie, J. R.,** and **L. Crossman.** 1936. Notes on Aphelenchoides fragariae. Proc. Helminthol. Soc. Washington 3. **Clapham, Phyllis.** 1930. Variations of Rhabditis succaris produced by different culture media. Jour.

Helminthol. 8. **Claus, C.** 1868. Beobachtungen über die Organisation und Fort-pflanzung von Leptodera. Schrift. Gesell. Beförd. Ges. Naturwiss. Marburg, Suppl. Heft 3. **Cobb, N. A.** 1893. Nematodes, mostly Australian and Fijian. Macleay Memorial Vol., Linn. Soc. New South Wales. 1915. Asymmetry of Bunonema. Contribs. Science Nematology No. 3. 1921. Howardula benigna. Contribs. Science Nematology No. 10. **Corder, Margaret.** 1933. Observations on the length of dormancy in certain nematodes infesting plants. Jour. Parasitol. 20. **Currie, G.** 1937. Galls on Eucalyptus trees. Proc. Linn. Soc. New South Wales 62. **Dotterweich, H.** 1938. Die Züchtung von Rhabditis teres. Zool. Anz. 122. **Dougherty, E., and H. Calhoun.** 1948. Experiences in culturing Rhabditis pellio and related soil nematodes. Proc. Helminthol. Soc. Washington 15. **Ellenby, C.** 1944. Influence of earthworms on larval emergence in the potato-root eelworm. Ann. Applied Biol. 31. **Franklin, M.** 1937. The survival of free larvae of Heterodera schachtii in soil. On the survival of Heterodera marioni infection out-of-doors in England. Jour. Helminthol. 15. 1938. Experiments with the cysts of Heterodera schachtii. Jour. Helminthol. 16. **Fuchs, G.** 1915. Die Naturgeschichte der Nematoden des Ips, des Hylobius. Zool. Jahrb. Abt. System. 38. 1929. Die Parasiten einiger Rüssel- und Borkenkäfer. Ztschr. Parasitenk. 2. 1930. Neue an Borken- und Rüsselkäfer gefundene Nematoden. Zool. Jahrb. Abt. System. 59. 1937, 1938. Neue parasitische und halbparasitsche Nematoden bei Borkenkäfern. I–IV. Zool. Jahrb. Abt. System. 70, 71. **Gadd, C., and C. Loos.** 1941. Observations on the life history of Anguillulina pratensis. Ann. Applied Biol. 28. 1943. Life history of Panagrolaimus. Spolia Zeylonica 23. **Glaser, R. W.** 1931. Cultivation of a nematode parasite of an insect. Science 73. 1932. Studies on Neoaplectana glaseri. New Jersey State Dept. Agricult., Bur. Plant Industry, Circ. No. 211. 1940a. Continued culture of a nematode parasitic in the Japanese beetle. Jour. Exp. Zool. 84. 1940b. Bacteria-free culture of a nematode parasite. Proc. Soc. Exp. Biol. Med. 43. **Glaser, R. W., E. McCoy, and H. Girth.** 1940. Biology and economic importance of a nematode parasitic in insects. Jour. Parasitol. 26. 1942. Biology and culture of Neoaplectana chresima. Jour. Parasitol. 28. **Godfrey, G. H.** 1929. Effect of some environmental factors on the root-knot nematode. Phytopathology 19. 1931. Some techniques used in the study of the root-knot nematode. Phytopathology 21. **Godfrey, G. H., and H. Hogan.** 1933. Influence of soil hydrogen-ion concentration on infection by Heterodera radicicola. Soil Science 35. **Godfrey, G. H., and H. Hoshino.** 1933. Certain environmental relations of the root-knot nematode. Phytopathology 23. **Godfrey, G. H., and J. Oliveira.** 1932. Development of the root-knot nematode. Phytopathology 22. **Goffart, H.** 1928. Zum Systematik und Biologie von Aphelenchus ritzemabosi. Zool. Anz. 76. 1929. Beobachtungen über Anguillulina pratensis. Ztschr. Parasitenk. 2. **Goodey, T.** 1922. The eel-worm in paper-hanger's paste. Ann. Mag. Natur. Hist. ser. 9, 10. 1923. Review of the plant-parasitic members of the genus Aphelenchus. Quiescence and reviviscence in nematodes. Jour. Helminthol. 1. 1925. On the nematode genus Aphelenchus. Jour. Helminthol. 6. 1927, 1930a, 1935. Cylindrogaster. Jour. Helminthol. 5, 8, 13. 1929. On some details of comparative anatomy in Aphelenchus, Tylenchus, and Heterodera. Jour. Helminthol. 7. 1930b. Presence of fats in the intestinal wall of nematodes. Jour. Helminthol. 8. 1930c. A remarkable new nematode parasitic in the frit-fly. Philos. Trans. Roy. Soc. London 218B. 1931a. Biological races in nematodes. Ann. Applied Biol. 18. 1931b. Further observations on a nematode parasite of the frit-fly. Jour. Helminthol. 9. 1932. Observations on the biology of the root gall nematode. Jour. Helminthol. 10. 1933. Anguillulina graminophila. Jour. Helminthol. 11. 1934a. Gall-formation due to Anguillulina graminis. Jour. Helminthol. 12. 1934b. Anguillulina cecidoplastes. Jour. Helminthol. 12. 1934c. Plant parasitic nematodes and the diseases they cause. 1936. Problems relating to plant-parasitic nematodes. Ann. Applied Biol. 23. 1939. Cylindrocorpus, nom. nov. for Cylindrogaster. Jour. Helminthol. 17. 1943a. Feeding of Anguillulina macrura. Jour. Helminthol. 21. 1943b. Systematic relationships of the vinegar eel and its congeners. Jour. Helminthol. 21. 1945. Note on the subfamily Turbatricinae and the genus Turbator. Jour. Helminthol. 21. 1947. On Anguillulina dipsaci. Jour. Helminthol. 22. **Guyénot, E.**, and **A. Zimmermann.** 1921. Elévages aseptiques d'Anguillula aceti. C. R. Soc. Biol. Paris 85. **Hastings, R.**, and **W. Newton.** 1934a. Effect of temperature on the larvae of Anguillulina dipsaci. Canad. Jour. Research 10. 1934b. Influence of a number of factors on the activation of dormant or quiescent bulb nematodes. Proc. Helminthol. Soc. Washington 1. **Henneberg, W.** 1900. Biologie des Essigaales. Zool. Centralbl. 7. **Hertwig, Paula.** 1922. Beobachtungen über die Fortpflanzungsweise und die systematische Einteilung der Regenwurmnematoden. Ztschr. Wiss. Zool. 119. **Hilgermann, R.**, and **R. Weissenberg.** 1918. Nematodenzüchtung auf Agarplatten. Centralbl. Bakteriol. Parasitenk. Abt. I. Orig. 80. **Hodson, W.** 1926. Biology of Tylenchus dipsaci. Ann. Applied Biol. 13. 1931. Further contribution to our knowledge of the biologic strains of nematodes. Ann. Applied Biol. 18. **Honda, H.** 1924. Resistance of Rhabditis to acids. Biol. Bull. 46. **Jägerskiöld, L.** 1905. Bunonema. Zool. Anz. 28. **Johnson, G.** 1913. On the nematodes of the common earthworm. Quart. Jour. Micro. Sci. 58. **Krüger, Eva.** 1913. Fortpflanzun und Keimzellenbildung von Rhabditis. Ztschr. Wiss. Zool. 105. **Leuckart, O.** 1885, 1886a. Sphaerularia bombi. Zool. Anz. 8; Biol. Centralbl. 6. 1886b. Ein Sphaerulariaartiger neuer Nematode. Zool. Anz. 9. Aproctonema gibbosum. Ber. Verhandl. Sächs. Gesell. Wissensch. Math. Phys. Kl. 38. 1887. Neue Beiträge zur Kenntnis des Baues und der Lebensgeschichte der Nematoden. Abhandl. Sachs. Gesell. Wissensch. 22. 1891. Über Rhabditis coarctata. Verhandl. Dtsch. Zool. Gesell. 1. **Linford, M. B.** 1937. Notes on the feeding of Ditylenchus dipsaci. Proc. Helminthol. Soc. Washington 4. 1939. Attractiveness of root and excised shoot tissues to certain nematodes. Proc. Helminthol. Soc. Washington 6. 1942. The transient feeding of root-knot nematode larvae. Phytopathology 32. **Ludwig, H.** 1938. Die Variabilität von Rhabditis teres unter veränderten Ernährungsbedingungen. Ztschr. Wiss. Zool. 151. **Luyet, B.**, and **M. Hartung.** 1941. Survival of Anguillula aceti after solidification in liquid air. Biodynamica 3. **McBeth, C.** 1937. Length of dormancy of certain plant-infesting nematodes. Proc. Helminthol. Soc. Washington 4. **McCoy, E.**, and **H. Girth.** 1938. The culture of Neoaplectana glaseri on veal pulp. Circular 285, New Jersey Dept. Agricult. **McCoy, E.**, and **R. Glaser.** 1936. Nematode culture for Japanese beetle control. Circular 265, New Jersey Dept. Agricult. **Man, J. G. de.** 1910. Beiträge zur Kenntnis der in dem weissen Schleimfluss der Eichen lebenden Anguilluliden. Zool. Jahrb. Abt. System. 29. 1914. Anguillula silusiae. Ann. Soc. Zool. Belgique 48. **Marcinowsky, Kati.** 1906. Zur Biologie von Cephalobus und Rhabditis. Arbeit. Biol. Reichanstalt Land Forstwirtsch. 5. **Menzel, R.** 1924. Verbreitung von Rhabditis Larven durch Dipteren. Zool. Anz. 58. **Merrill, J.**, and **A. Ford.** 1916. Life history and habits of two new nematodes parasitic on insects. Jour. Agricult. Research 6. **Metcalf, H.** 1902. Cultural studies of a nematode associated with plant decay. Trans. Amer. Micro. Soc. 24. **Micoletzky, H.**, and **R. Menzel.** 1929. Anguillula nepenthicola. Treubia 10. **Nagakura, K.** 1930. Ueber den Bau und die Lebensgeschichte der Heterodera radicola. Jap. Jour. Zool. 3. **Nebel, B.** 1926. Ein Beitrag zur Physiologie des Rübennematoden. Kühn-Arch.,

Halle, 12. **Neuhaus, C.** 1903. Die postembryonale Entwicklung von Rhabditis nigrovenosa. Jena. Ztschr. Naturwiss. 37. **Oldham, J.** 1937. Further observations on the occurrence and bionomics of Rhabditis coarctata. Papers Helminthol. 30 yr. Jubileum K. I. Skrjabin. **Otter, G.** 1933. Biology and life history of Rhabditis pellio. Parasitology 25. **Pai, S.** 1927. Lebenszyklus der Anguillula aceti. Zool. Anz. 74. 1928. Die Phasen des Lebenszyklus der Anguillula aceti. Ztschr. Wiss. Zool. 131. **Peters, B.** 1926. Heterodera schachtii and soil acidity. Jour. Helminthol. 4. 1927. On the anatomy of the vinegar eelworm. On the nomenclature of the vinegar eelworms. Jour. Helminthol. 5. 1928. On the bionomics of the vinegar eelworm. Jour. Helminthol. 6. **Raven, B.,** and **J. Schuurmans Stekhoven.** 1934. Zur Frage der Exkretion bei den Rhabditiden. Zool. Anz. 106. **Reiter, M.** 1928. Zur Systematik und Ökologie der zweigeschlechtlichen Rhabditiden. Arbeit. Zool. Instit. Univ. Innsbruck 3. **Rensch, B.** 1925. Zwei quantitative reizphysiologische Untersuchungensmethoden für Rübennematoden. Ztschr. Wiss. Zool. 123. **Smith, A.** 1929. Investigation on Heterodera schachtii. Ann. Applied Biol. 16. **Steiner, G.** 1919. Bemerkungen über die sogenannte Verpuppung der Rhabditis coarctata. Biol. Centralbl. 39. 1925. The problem of host-selection and host specialization of certain plant-infesting nemas. Phytopathology 15. 1926. Observations on the number of specimens of Tylenchus dipsaci a plant may harbor. Jour. Parasitol. 13. 1929a. On the gross morphology of Acrobeles. Ztschr. Morphol. Ökol. Tiere 15. 1929b. Neoaplectana glaseri. Jour Washington Acad. Sci. 19. 1933. The nematode Cylindrogaster longistoma. Jour. Parasitol. 20. 1935. Opuscula miscellanea nematologica II. Proc. Helminthol. Soc. Washington 2. 1936. Anguillulina askenasyi, a gall-forming nematode. Jour. Washington Acad. Sci. 26. **Steiner, G.,** and **F. Albin.** 1946. Resuscitation of Tylenchus polyhypnus. Jour. Washington Acad. Sci. 36. **Steiner, G.,** and **H. Heinly.** 1922. The possibility of control of plant-injurious nemas by predatory nemas. Jour. Washington Acad. Sci. 12. **Stephenson, W.** 1942. On the culturing of Rhabditis terrestris. Parasitology 34. **Stewart, F.** 1921. Anatomy and biology of the parasitic Aphelenchi. Parasitology 13. **Stoklasa, J.** 1933. La resistance de l'anguille de vinaigre aux différences de la pression osmatique. La survivie de l'anguillula de vinaigre dans un milieu à pH varié. Spisy Lekarske Fakulty Masarykovy University Brne 12. **Strubbel, A.** 1888. Untersuchungen über den Bau und die Entwicklung des Rübennematoden. Bibliotheca Zoologica 1, Heft 2. **Taniguchi, R.** 1933. Notes on the chemotactic response of Rhabditis filiformis. Proc. Imper. Acad. Japan 9. **Taylor, A.** 1936. Genera and species of the Criconematinae. Trans. Amer. Micro. Soc. 55. **Thorne, G.** 1925. The genus Acrobeles. Trans. Amer. Micro. Soc. 44. 1937. Revision of the nematode family Caphalobidae. Proc. Helminthol. Soc. Washington 4. 1949. On the classification of the Tylenchida, new order. Proc. Helminthol. Soc. Washington 16. **Thorne, G.,** and **L. Giddings.** 1922. Sugar-beet nematode in the western states. U.S. Dept. Agricult., Farmer's Bull. 1248. **Triffitt, M.** 1928. Morphology of Heterodera schachtii. Jour. Helminthol. 6. 1930. Observations on the life-cycle of Heterodera schachtii. On the bionomics of Heterodera schachtii on potatoes. Jour. Helminthol. 8. **Triffitt, M.,** and **J. Oldham.** 1927. Observations on the morphology and bionomics of Rhabditis coarctata. Jour. Helminthol. 5. **Tyler, Jocelyn.** 1933. Reproduction without males of the root-knot nematode. Hilgardia 7. 1938. Egg output of the root-knot nematode. Proc. Helminthol. Soc. Washington 5. 1944. The root-knot nematode. Univ. California College Agricult., Agricult. Exp. Sta. Berkeley, Circular 330. **Voss, W.** 1930. Älchenkrankheit der Chrysanthemen. Ztschr. Parasitenk. 2. **Wülker, G.** 1923. Über Fortpflanzung und Entwicklung von Allantonema und verwandten

Nematoden. Ergebn. Fortschr. Zool. 5. **Ziegler, H.** 1895. Untersuchungen über die ersten Entwicklungsvorgänge der Nematoden. Ztschr. Wiss. Zool. 60. **Zimmermann, A.** 1921. Recherches expérimentales sur l'elevage aseptique de l'anguillule du vinaigre. Rev. Suisse Zool. 28. **Zur Strassen, O.** 1892. Bradynema rigidum. Ztschr. Wiss. Zool. 54.

Rhabdiasoidea

Beach, T. 1935. Experimental propagation of Strongyloides in culture. Proc. Soc. Exp. Biol. Med. 32. 1936. Experimental studies on human and primate Strongyloides. Amer. Jour. Hygiene 23. **Chandler, A. C.** 1925. The species of Strongyloides. Parasitology 17. **Chitwood, B. G.** 1930. The excretory system of Rhabdias bufonis. Jour. Parasitol. 16. **Chitwood, B. G., and G. Graham.** 1940. Studies on Strongyloides VI. Jour. Parasitol. 26. **Chu, T.** 1936. Reptilian nematodes of the genus Rhabdias. Studies on the life history of Rhabdias fuscovenosa. Jour. Parasitol. 22. **Faust, E. C.** 1931. Infection experiments in monkeys with human, macaque and Ateles strains of Strongyloides. Proc. Soc. Exp. Biol. Med. 28. 1933, 1935. Experimental studies on human and primate Strongyloides. II, IV. Amer. Jour. Hygiene 18; Arch. Pathol. 19. **Faust, E. C., and A. De Groat.** 1940. Internal autoinfection in human strongyloidiasis. Amer. Jour. Trop. Med. 20. **Faust, E. C., and E. Kagy.** 1933. Experimental studies on human and primate Strongyloides. I. Amer. Jour. Trop. Med. 13. **Faust, E. C., J. Wells, C. Adams, and T. Beach.** 1934. Experimental studies, etc. III. Arch. Pathol. 18. **Fülleborn, F.** 1914. Untersuchungen über den Infektionsweg bei Strongyloides und Ancylostoma. Arch. Schiffs. Tropenhyg. 18, Beiheft 5. 1927. Über das Verhalten der Larven von Strongyloides im Körper des Wirtes. Arch. Schiffs. Tropenhyg. 31, Beiheft 2. 1928. Über den Infektionsweg bei Rhabdias bufonis. Centralbl. Bakteriol. Parasitenk. Abt. I, Orig. 109. **Goodey, T.** 1924. Anatomy and life history of Rhabdias fuscovenosa. Jour. Helminthol. 2. **Graham, G.** 1936–1940. Studies on Strongyloides. I–VIII. Amer. Jour. Hygiene 24, 27, 30; Jour. Parasitol. 24, 25, 26; Jour. Exp. Zool. 84. **Grassi, B.** 1878. L'Anguillula intestinale. Gaz. Med. Ital. Lomb. 48. **Griffiths, H.** 1940. Experimental studies on Strongyloides in the guinea-pig. Canad. Jour. Research 18. **Kreis, H.** 1932. Studies on the genus Strongyloides. Amer. Jour. Hygiene 16. **Lawler, H.** 1940. Passive transfer of immunity to Strongyloides ratti. Amer. Jour. Hygiene 31. 1941. Relation of vitamin A to immunity to Strongyloides infection. Amer. Jour. Hygiene 34. **Leichtenstern, O.** 1905. Studien über Strongyloides stercoralis. Arbeit. Kais. Gesundheitsamte 22. **Leuckart, R.** 1882. Über die Lebensgeschichte der sog. Anguillula stercoralis. Ber. Verhandl. Sächs. Gesell. Wissensch., Math. Phys. Kl. 34. **Lucker, J.** 1934. Development of Strongyloides ransomi. U.S. Dept. Agricult., Tech. Bull. 437. **Metschnikov, E.** 1865. Über die Entwicklung von Ascaris nigrovenosa. Arch. Anat. Physiol. **Nishigori, M.** 1928. The factors which influence the external development of Strongyloides stercoralis and on auto-infection with this parasite. Jour. Formosa Med. Soc. 277. **Sandground, J.** 1925. Speciation and specificity in Strongyloides. Jour. Parasitol. 12. 1926. Biological studies on the life cycle in Strongyloides. Amer. Jour. Hygiene 6. 1927. The acquisition of an active immunity in dogs and cats to infection with Strongyloides stercoralis. Jour. Parasitol. 13. 1928. Some studies in the susceptibility, resistance and acquired immunity to infection with Strongyloides stercoralis in dogs and cats. Amer. Jour. Hygiene 8. **Schuurmans Stekhoven, J. H.** 1928. Researches on nemas and their larvae. III. Strongyloides stercoralis. Ztschr. Parasitenk. 1. **Schwartz, B., and J. Alicata.** 1930. The species of Strongyloides parasitic in swine. Jour. Agricult. Research 40.

Seurat, L. 1920. Histoire naturelle des nematodes de la Barberie. **Sheldon, A.** 1937. Studies on active acquired resistance in the rat to infection with Strongyloides ratti. Amer. Jour. Hygiene 25. 1939. Specificity of artificially acquired immunity to Strongyloides ratti. Amer. Jour. Hygiene 29. **Travassos, L.** 1926. Entwicklung des Rhabdias fülleborni. Arch. Schiffs Trop. Hygien 30. **Van Durme, P.** 1902. Sur les embryons de Strongyloides et leur pénétration par le peau. Thompson Yates Lab. Rept. 4.

Oxyuroidea

Ackert, J. E. 1923. Habitat of Ascaridia. Jour. Parasitol. 10. 1931. Morphology and life history of Ascaridia. Parasitology 23. **Alicata, J.** 1939. Note on the life history of Subulura brumpti. Jour. Parasitol. 25. **Artigas, P.** 1926, 1928. Nematoides de invertebrades. I–VI. Boletim Biol. São Paulo, Fasc. 1, 2, 3, 4, 12. 1930. Nematoides dos generos Rhigonema, e Dudekemia. Mem. Inst. Oswaldo Cruz 24. **Baker, A.** 1935, 1936. Studies on Heterakis gallinae. Trans. Canad. Roy. Inst. 20, 21. **Basir, M.** 1942. Nematodes parasitic in Gryllotalpa. Records Indian Mus. 44. **Baylis, H. A.**, and **R. Daubney.** 1922. Report on the parasitic nematodes in the collection of the zoological survey of India. Mem. Indian Mus. 7; Records Indian Mus. 25. **Boulenger, C.** 1923. Nematode parasitic in a North American tortoise. Parasitology 15. **Bozeman, W.** 1942. Life history of Blatticola blattae. Trans. Kansas Acad. Sci. 45. **Bütschli, O.** 1871. Untersuchungen über die beiden Nematoden der Periplaneta. Ztschr. Wiss Zool. 21. **Chitwood, B. G.** 1930. A recharacterization of the genus Blatticola. Trans. Amer. Micro. Soc. 49. 1932. Synopsis of nematodes parasitic in the Blattidae. Ztschr. Parasitenk. 5. **Chitwood, B. G.**, and **J. Alicata.** 1932. Cephalic sensory organs of Ascaridia. Jour. Parasitol. 18. **Chitwood, B. G.**, and **M. B. Chitwood.** 1937. Snails as hosts and carriers of nematodes. Nautilus 50. **Chitwood, M. B.** 1935. Two new nematodes of the genus Heth. Proc. Helminthol. Soc. Washington 2. **Christenson, A.**, and **H. Creel.** 1942. Soil temperatures and soil moisture as factors in the seasonal incidence of certain animal parasites. Jour. Alabama Acad. Sci. 14. **Christie, J. R.** 1931. Some nemic parasites of coleopterous larvae. Jour. Agricult. Research 42. 1934. The nematode genera Histrignathus and Artigasia. Proc. Helminthol. Soc. Washington 1. **Christie, J. R.**, and **N. A. Cobb.** 1927. Rhigonema. Jour. Washington Acad. Sci. 17. **Clapham, Phyllis.** 1933. Life history of Heterakis gallinae. Jour. Helminthol. 11. **Cobb, N. A.** 1890. Oxyuris larvae hatched in the human stomach. Proc. Linn. Soc. New South Wales, ser. 2, 5. 1924. Amphids of the oxyurids. Jour. Parasitol. 11. **Conte, A.**, and **A. Bonnet.** 1903. Sur Angiostoma helicis. Ann. Soc. Linn. Lyon 50. **Cram, Eloise.** 1940. Studies on oxyiuriasis. 24. Comparative findings in the white and negro races. Proc. Helminthol. Soc. Washington 7. 1943. Studies on oxyuriasis. 28. Amer. Jour. Diseases Children 65. **Cram, Eloise,** and **M. Nolan.** 1939. Studies on oxyuriasis. 19. Examinations of children. U.S. Public Health Repts. 54. **Dikmans, D.** 1931. An interesting larval stage of Dermatoxys veligera. Trans. Amer. Micro. Soc. 50. **Dobrovolny, C.,** and **J. Ackert.** 1934. Life history of Leidynema appendiculata. Parasitology 26. **Dorman, H.** 1928. Studies on the life cycle of Heterakis papillosa. Trans. Amer. Micro. Soc. 47. **Drasche, R.** 1882–1883. Revision der in der Nematoden-Sammlung befindlichen Original-Exemplare Diesings und Molins. Verhandl. Zool. Bot. Gesell. Wien 32, 33. **Ehlers, H.** 1899. Zur Kenntnis der Anatomie und Biologie von Oxyuris curvula. Arch. Naturgesch. 65, Pt. 1. **Flögel, J.** 1869. Über die Lippen einiger Oxyurisarten. Ztschr. Wiss. Zool. 19. **Galeb, O.** 1878. Recherches sur les entozoaires des insectes. Arch. Zool. Exp. Gén., ser. 1, 7. **Gilson, G.** 1898.

Note sur un nématode nouveau des Iles Fiji. La Cellule 14. **Györy, A. v.** 1856. Über Pseudonymus. Sitzungsber. Math. Naturwiss. Cl., Akad. Wissensch. Wien 21. **Hall, M. C.** 1916. Nematode parasites of mammals of the orders Rodentia. Lagomorpha, and Hyracoidea. Proc. U.S. Nation. Mus. 50. **Hall, M. C., and E. Cram.** 1939. Studies on oxyuriasis XVII. Vol. Jub. Prof. Sadao Yoshida II. **Harwood, P. D.** 1930. New species of Oxysomatum with remarks on the genera Oxysomatum and Aplectana. Jour. Parasitol. 17. **Holl, F.** 1928. Two new nematode parasites. Jour. Elisha Mitchell Scient. Soc. 43. **Ihle, J., and G. van Oordt.** 1921. On the larval development of Oxyuris equi. Akad. Wetensch. Amsterdam, Proc. Sect. Sci. 23. **Jacobs, L., and M. Jones.** 1939. Chemistry of the membranes of the pinworm egg. Proc. Helminthol. Soc. Washington 6. **Jerke, M.** 1901. Zur Kenntnis der Oxyuren des Pferdes. Jena. Ztschr. Naturwiss. 35. **Jones, M., and L. Jacobs.** 1941. Survival of eggs of Enterobius vermicularis under known conditions of temperature and humidity. Amer. Jour. Hygiene 33, Sect. D. **Kreis, H.** 1932. Trionchonema rusticum, parasitie nematode from the land snail. Trans. Amer. Micro. Soc. 51. **Lane, C.** 1914. Suckered roundworms from India and Ceylon. Indian Jour. Med. Research 2. **Leidy, J.** 1849. New genera and species of Entozoa. Proc. Acad. Natur. Sci. Philadelphia 4. **Lentze, F.** 1935. Zur Biologie des Oxyuris vermicularis. Centralbl. Bakteriol. Parasitenk. Abt. I, Orig. 135. **Linstow, O. v.** 1884. Helminthologisches. Arch. Naturgesch. 50. 1899. Nematoden aus der Berliner Zoologischen Sammlung. Mitt. Zool. Mus. Berlin 1. **Maplestone, P.** 1930. Nematode parasites of pigs in Bengal. Records Indian Mus. 32. **Martini, E.** 1916. Die Anatomie von Oxyuris curvula. Ztschr. Wiss. Zool. 116. 1926. Zur Anatomie des Vorderendes von Oxyuris robusta. Arch. Schiffs. Tropenhyg. 30. **Miranda, C.** 1924. Alguns nematodeos do genero Aplectana. Mem. Inst. Oswaldo Cruz 17. **Nolan, M., and M. Jones.** 1942. Notes on the survival of eggs of Enterobius vermicularis exposed to household fumigants. Proc. Helminthol. Soc. Washington 9. **Nolan, M., and L. Reardon.** 1936. Distribution of the ova of Enterobius vermicularis in household dust. Jour. Parasitol. 25. **Railliet, A.** 1917. L'oxyurose des équidés. Recueil Méd. Vétérin. 93. **Railliet, A., and A. Henry.** 1912. Quelques nématodes parasites des reptiles. Bull. Soc. Pathol. Exotique 5. 1916. Sur les oxyuridés. C. R. Soc. Biol. Paris 79. **Ransom, B. H.** 1907. Probstmayria vivipara, a nematode of horses. Trans. Amer. Micro. Soc. 27. **Reardon, Lucy.** 1938. The number of eggs produced by the pinworm. U.S. Public Health Service, Public Health Repts. No. 24. **Roberts, F.** 1937. Studies on the biology and control of Ascaridia galli. Queensland Dept. Agricult. Stock, Animal Health Sta., Bull. No. 2. **Sanchez, A.** 1947. Nematodes parásitos intestinales de los artrópodos en España. Revista Iberica Parasitol. 7. **Schueffner, W.** 1947. Experimentelle Infektionen mit Staubeeiern von Enterobius. Centralbl. Bakteriol. Parasitenk. Abt. I, Orig. 152. **Schwartz, B.** 1923. Life history of the horse oxyurid. Philipp. Jour. Sci. 23. **Seurat, L.** 1912. Sur les oxyures de Uromastix. C. R. Soc. Biol. Paris 73. 1915a. Sur deux nouveaux oxyures du Maroc. Bull. Soc. Hist. Natur. Afrique du Nord, ser. 2, 7. 1915b. Sur l'existence en Algérie du Dermatoxys veligera. C. R. Soc. Biol. Paris 78. 1916. Sur les oxyures des mammifères. C. R. Soc. Biol. Paris 79. 1917. Sur les oxyures des sauriens du Nord-Africain. Arch. Zool. Exp. Gén. 56. **Skrjabin, K.** 1916. Parasitic nematodes collected in British East Africa. Scient. Results Zool. Exped. British East Africa and Uganda, 1, No. 4. **Steiner, G.** 1924. Some nemas from the alimentary tract of the Carolina tree frog. Jour. Parasitol. 11. **Thapar, G. S.** 1925. Studies on the oxyuroid parasites of reptiles. Jour. Helminthol. 3. **Tiner, J.** 1948. Syphacia eutamii with a key to the genus. Jour. Parasitol. 34. **Todd, A.** 1944. Two new nematodes from the aquatic beetle Hydrous. Jour. Parasitol. 30. **Travassos, L.** 1922. Contribution to the knowledge of the Brazilian helminthological fauna. Mem. Inst. Oswaldo Cruz 14. 1925. Quelques nématodes du Gryllotalpa. C. R. Soc. Biol. Paris 93. 1929. Contribucas preliminar a systematica dos nematodeos dos arthropodos. Mem. Inst. Oswaldo Cruz, suppl. No. 5. **Uribe, C.** 1922. Observations on the development of Heterakis papillosa in the chicken. Jour. Parasitol. 8. **Valkanov, A.** 1936. Über die Anatomie und Cytologie der Nematode Binema. Trav. Soc. Bulgare Sci. Natur., No. 17. **Vogel, R.** 1925. Zur Kenntnis der Fortpflanzung von Oxyuris obvelata. Zool. Jahrb. Abt. Allg. Zool. 42. **Walton, A. C.** 1940. The nematode genus Raillietnema. Jour. Washington Acad. Sci. 30. 1941a. Distribution of the genus Thelandros. Proc. Helminthol. Soc. Washington 8. 1941b. The finer structure of Aplectana. Proc. Helminthol. Soc. Washington 8. 1941c. Notes on some helminths from California Amphibia. Trans. Amer. Micro. Soc. 60. 1942. Some oxyurids from a Galapagos tortoise. Proc. Helminthol. Soc. Washington 9. **Wetzel, R.** 1930. The fourth stage larva of Oxyuris equi. On the biology of the fourth stage larva of Oxyuris equi. Jour. Parasitol. 17. 1931. On the biology of the fourth stage larva of Dermatoxys veligera. Jour. Parasitol. 18. **Wilkie, J.** 1930. Some parasitic nematodes from Japanese Amphibia. Ann. Mag. Natur. Hist., ser. 10, 6. **Yorke, W.,** and **T. Southwell.** 1920. Crossocephalus zebrae. Ann. Trop. Med. Parasitol. 14. **Zawadowsky, M.,** and **L. Schalimov.** 1929a. Is auto-invasion possible of Enterobius vermicularis? Trans. Lab. Exp. Biol. Zoopark Moscow 5. 1929b. Die Eier von Oxyuris vermicularis. Ztschr. Parasitenk. 2.

Ascaroidea

Abderhalden, E. 1911. Über den Gehalt von Eingeweidewürmern an peptolytischen Fermenten. Ztschr. Phyiol. Chem. 74. **Abderhalden, E.,** and **R. Heise.** 1909. Über das Vorkommen peptolytischen Fermente bei den Wirbellosen. Ztschr. Physiol. Chem. 62. **Ackert, J. E.** 1930. Vitamin requirements of intestinal nematodes. Anat. Record 47. **Ackert, J.,** and **T. Beach.** 1933. Resistance of chickens to Ascaridia affected by dietary supplements. Trans. Amer. Micro. Soc. 52. **Ackert, J.** and **G. Cauthen.** 1931. Viability of the eggs of Ascaridia exposed to natural climatic factors. Jour. Parasitol. 18. **Ackert, J., S. Edgar,** and **L. Frick.** 1929. Goblet cells and age resistance of animals to parasitism. Trans. Amer. Micro. Soc. 58. **Ackert, J., L. Eisenbrandt, J. Wilmuth, B. Glading,** and **I. Pratt.** 1935. Comparative resistance of five breeds of chickens to Ascaridia. Jour. Agricult. Research 50. **Ackert, J., M. Fisher,** and **J. Zimmerman.** 1927. Resistance to parasitism affected by vitamin A. Jour. Parasitol. 13. **Ackert, J., H. Graham, L. Nolf,** and **X. Porter.** 1931. Quantitative studies on the administration of variable numbers of nematode eggs to chickens. Trans. Amer. Micro. Soc. 50. **Ackert, J., M. McIlvaine,** and **J. Crawford.** 1931. Resistance of chickens to parasitism affected by vitamin A. Amer. Jour. Hygiene 13. **Ackert, J., D. Porter,** and **T. Beach.** 1932, 1935. Age resistance of chickens to Ascaridia. Jour. Parasitol. 19, 21. **Ackert, J., I. Pratt,** and **A. Freeman.** 1936. Resistant and susceptible groups of white leghorn chickens to Ascaridia. Anat. Record 67. **Ackert, J.,** and **L. Spindler.** 1929. Vitamin D and resistance of chickens to parasitism. Amer. Jour. Hygiene 9. **Ackert, J., A. Todd,** and **W. Tanner.** 1938. Growing larval Ascaridia in vitro. Trans. Amer. Micro. Soc. 57. **Ackert, J., J. Whitlock,** and **A. Freeman.** 1940. The food of Ascaridia. Jour. Parasitol. 26. **Ackert, J.,** and **J. Wilmoth.** 1934. Resistant and susceptible strains of white minorca chickens to Ascaridia. Jour. Parasitol. 20. **Adam, W.** 1932. Über die Stoffwechselprozesse von Ascaris. Ztschr. Vergl.

Physiol. 16. **Alicata, J.** 1934. Period required for Ascaris eggs to reach infectivity. Proc. Helminthol. Soc. Washington 1. **Archer, V.,** and **C. Peterson.** 1930. Roentgen diagnosis of ascariasis. Jour. Amer. Med. Assoc. 95. **Baldwin, E.** 1943. An in vitro method for the chemotherapeutic investigation of anthelminthic potency. Parasitology 35. **Baldwin, E.,** and **V. Moyle.** 1947. An isolated nerve-muscle preparation from Ascaris. Jour. Exp. Biol. 23. **Baylis, H.** 1916. Some ascarids in the British Museum. Parasitology 8. 1920, 1923. On the classification of the Ascaridae. I–III. Parasitology 12, 15. 1924. Toxascaris leonina as a parasite of the domestic cat. Jour. Parasitol. 10. **Beams, H.,** and **R. King.** 1936. Survival of Ascaris eggs after centrifuging. Science 84. 1940. Some effects of ultra-centrifuging the eggs of Ascaris. Jour. Roy. Micro. Soc., ser. 3, 60. **Brand, T. v.** 1934. Die Stoffwechsel von Ascaris bei Oxybiose und Anoxybiose. Ztschr. Vergl. Physiol. 21. 1936. Observations upon the glycogen relationships in Ascaris. Jour. Parasitol. 22. 1937. The anaerobic glycogen consumption in Ascaris females and males. The aerobic synthesis of glycogen in Ascaris. Jour. Parasitol. 23. 1941. Aerobic fat metabolism of Ascaris. Proc. Soc. Exp. Biol. Med. 46. **Brand, T. v.,** and **M. Winkeljohn.** 1945. Observations on the ether extract of Ascaris males and Eustrongylides larvae. Proc. Helminthol. Soc. Washington 12. **Brown, H.** 1928a. A quantitative study of the influence of oxygen and temperature on the development of Ascaris eggs. Jour. Parasitol. 14. 1928b. Further studies on the longevity of the eggs of Ascaris. Jour. Parasitol. 15. **Brown, H.,** and **W. Cort.** 1927. Egg production of Ascaris. Jour. Parasitol. 14. **Brunner, M.** 1928. Immunological studies in human parasitic infections. I. Jour. Immunology 15. **Buckley, J.** 1931. Observations on human resistance to infection with pig Ascaris. Jour. Helminthol. 9. **Caldwell, F.,** and **E. Caldwell.** 1926. Are Ascaris lumbricoides and Ascaris suilla identical? Jour. Parasitol. 13. **Campbell, D.** 1936. Antigenic polysaccharide fraction of Ascaris. Jour. Infect. Diseases 59. **Canning, G.** 1929. Precipitin reactions with various tissues of Ascaris and related helminths. Amer. Jour. Hygiene 9. **Chitwood, B. G.** 1938. Notes on the physiology of Ascaris. Proc. Helminthol. Soc. Washington 5. **Chitwood, B. G.,** and **C. Hill.** 1931. The esophageal glands of Ascaris. Jour. Parasitol. 18; Ztschr. Zellforsch. Mikro. Anat. 14. **Christenson, R., H. Earle, R. Butler,** and **H. Creel.** 1942. Studies on the eggs of Ascaridia galli and Heterakis gallinae. Trans. Amer. Micro. Soc. 61. **Clapham, Phyllis.** 1933. On the prophylactic action of vitamin A in helminthiasis. Jour. Helminthol. 11. 1934. Ascariasis and vitamin A deficiency in pigs. Effect of dietary deficiency on infestations of chickens with Heterakis. Jour. Helminthol. 12. **Clavera, J.,** and **A. Mallol.** 1945. La composicion quimica de los Ascaris del hombre y del cerdo. Revista Iberica Parasitol., Tom. Extraord. **Cobb, N. A.** 1929. Amphids of the mackerel nema. Jour. Parasitol. 15. **Cort, W.** 1931. Recent investigations on the epidemiology of human ascariasis. Jour. Parasitol. 17. **Coventry, Frances.** Cutaneous and precipitin tests with Ascaris extracts. Jour. Preventive Med. 3. **Coventry, Frances,** and **W. Taliaferro.** 1928. Cutaneous tests with proteins of Ascaris, hookworm, and Trichuris. Jour. Preventive Med. 2. **Cram, Eloise.** 1924. Influence of low temperature and disinfectants on the eggs of Ascaris. Jour. Agricult. Research 27. 1925. Egg-producing capacity of Ascaris. Jour. Agricult. Research 30. **Danheim, Bertha.** 1923. Migratory habits of certain nematode larvae. Anat. Record 26. **Davenport, H.** 1945, 1949. Haemoglobins of Ascaris. Nature, London, 155; Proc. Roy. Soc. London 136B. **Duval, M.,** and **A. Courtois.** 1928. Milieu intérieur de l'Ascaris du cheval. C. R. Soc. Biol. Paris 99. **Eisenbrandt, L.,** and **J. Ackert.** 1940. Resistance of chickens to Ascaridia following immunization. Amer. Jour. Hygiene 32, sect. D. **Fauré-Fremiet, E.** 1913. La cellule intestinale et le liquide cavitaire de l'Ascaris. C. R. Soc. Biol. Paris 74. **Fenwick, D.** 1938. Oxygen consumption of newly hatched larvae of Ascaris. Proc. Zool. Soc. London 108A. 1939a. Experiments on the extracorporal hatching of Ascaris eggs. Jour. Helminthol. 17. 1939b. Studies on the saline requirements of Ascaris larvae. Jour. Helminthol. 17. **Fischer, A.** 1924. Über den Kohlehydratstoffwechsel von Ascaris. Biochem. Ztschr. 144. **Flury, F.** 1912. Zur Chemie und Toxikologie der Ascariden. Arch. Exp. Pathol. Pharmakol. 67. **Freitas, J., and H. Lent.** 1946. Infestaceo de apaiaris Astronotus pelo nematodeo Goezia. Revista Brasil. Biol. 6. **Fülleborn, F.** 1922. Über den Infektionsweg bei Ascaris. Klin. Wochenschr. 1. **Gallego Berenguer, J.** 1947. Revision de las familia Atractidae. Revista Iberica Parasitol. 7. **Galli-Valerio, B.** 1915. Notes de parasitologie. Centralbl. Bakteriol. Parasitenk. 75. **Glaue, H.** 1910. Beiträge zu einer Monographie der Ascaris felis und Ascaris canis. Ztschr. Wiss. Zool. 95. **Goodey, T.** 1926. On the Ascaris from sheep. Jour. Helminthol. 4. **Goodey, T., and T. Cameron.** 1923. Morphology and life cycle of Ascaris columnaris. Jour. Helminthol. 6. **Gothie, S.** 1942. Développement de l'oeuf d'Ascaris en anaérobie et en aérobie. C. R. Soc. Biol. Paris 136. **Graham, G., J. Ackert, and R. Jones.** 1932. Acquired resistance of chicken to Ascaridia. Amer. Jour. Hygiene 15. **Hall, M.** 1917. The longevity of adult Ascaris outside the body of the host. Jour. Amer. Med. Assoc. 65. **Harnisch, O.** 1933. Untersuchungen zur Kennzeichnung des Sauerstoffverbrauches von Ascaris. Ztschr. Vergl. Physiol. 19. 1935. Daten zur Beurteilung des Sauerstoffverbrauchs von Ascaris. Ztschr. Vergl. Physiol. 22. 1937. Zellfreiarbeitendes Oxydans im Gaswechsel von Ascaris. Ztschr. Vergl. Physiol. 24. **Hartman, E.** 1923. Viability of the eggs of Ascaridia. Anat. Record 26. **Herrick, C.** 1926. Resistance of chickens to Ascaridia. Amer. Jour. Hygiene 6. **Herrick, C., and M. Thede.** 1945. Cytochrome oxidase of the pig Ascaris. Jour. Parasitol. 31, suppl. **Hill, G., and J. Smyth.** 1944. Localization of vitamin C in Belascaris. Nature, London, 153. **Hirsch, G., and L. Bretschneider.** 1937a. Die Arbeitsräume in den Darmzellen von Ascaris. Fujii Jub. Vol. 1. 1937b. Der intraplasmatische Stoffwechsel in den Darmzellen von Ascaris. Protoplasma 29. **Hoffmann, R.** 1934. Untersuchungen über die Wärmeentwicklung von Ascaris bei Futterung mit Glukose, Fruktose, and Galaktose. Ztschr. Biol. 95. **Hsue, H.** 1929. On the esophagus of Ascaris. Ztschr. Zellforsch. Mikro. Anat. 9. **Huff, G.** 1936. Experimental studies of factors influencing the development of eggs of pig ascarids. Jour. Parasitol. 22. **Huff, G., and E. Boell.** 1936. Effect of ultra-centrifuging on oxygen consumption of the eggs of Ascaris. Proc. Soc. Exp. Biol. Med. 34. **Hurlaux, R.** 1942. La cytologie des cellules "phagocytaires" de l'Ascaris. Bull. Soc. Zool. France 67. **Kahl, W.** 1936. Beitrag zur Kenntnis des Nematoden Contracaecum. Ztschr. Parasitenk. 8. **Keilin, D.** 1925. On cytochrome, a respiratory pigment. Proc. Roy. Soc. London 98B. **Kemnitz, G. v.** 1912. Die Morphologie des Stoffwechsels bei Ascaris. Arch. Zellforsch. Mikro. Anat. 7. **Kerr, K.** 1938. Cellular response in acquired resistance in guinea pigs to an infection with pig Ascaris. Amer. Jour. Hygiene 27. **Kobert, R.** 1903. Über einige Enzyme wirbelloser Thiere. Arch. Ges. Physiol. 99. **Kosmin, Natalie.** 1928. Die Entwicklungsgeschwindigkeit der Eier von Ascaris bei verschiedenem Sauerstoffpartialdruck. Ztschr. Vergl. Physiol. 8. **Krüger, F.** 1936. Untersuchungen zur Kenntnis des aeroben und anaeroben Stoffwechsels des Ascaris suilla. Zool. Jahrb. Abt. Allg. Zool. 57. 1937. Bestimmungen über den aeroben und anaeroben Stoffumsatz beim Schweinespulwurm. Ztschr. Vergl. Physiol. 24. 1940. Die Beziehung des Sauerstoffverbrauches zur Körperoberflächen beim Schweinespulwurm. Ztschr. Wiss. Zool. 152. **Krummacher, O.** 1919. Untersuchungen über die Wärmeentwicklung der Spulwürmer. Ztschr. Biol. 69. **Laser, H.** 1944. The oxidative metabolism of Ascaris suis. Biochem. Jour. 38. **Lebour, Marie.** 1917. Parasites of Sagitta. Jour. Marine Biol. Assoc. 11. **Li, H.** 1933a. The feeding of dog Ascaris. Lignan Sci. Jour. 12, suppl. 1933b. Feeding experiments on representatives of Ascaroidea and Oxyuroidea. Chinese Med. Jour. 47. **Lièvre, H.** 1934. Apropos de l'hematophagie des Ascaris. C. R. Soc. Biol. Paris 116. **Linstow, O. v.** 1901. Helminthen von dem Ufern des Nuassa-Sees. Jena. Ztschr. Naturwiss. 35. **Long, J., and F. Fenger.** 1917. On the normal reaction of the intestinal tract. Jour. Amer. Chem. Soc. 39. **McRae, Anne.** 1935a. The extra-corporal hatching of Ascaris eggs. Jour. Parasitol. 21. 1935b. A study of the moisture requirements of the chicken Ascaridia. Jour. Parasitol. 21. **Marcet, W.** 1865. Chemical examination of the fluid from the peritoneal cavity of the nematode Entozoa. Proc. Roy. Soc. London 14. **Markowski, S.** 1937. Entwicklungsgeschichte und Biologie des Nematoden Contracaecum. Bull. Internation. Acad. Polonaise Sci. Lettr., Cl. Sci. Math. Natur., ser. B, Sci. Natur. **Martin, A.** 1913. Recherches sur les conditions du développement embryonnaire des nematodes parasites. Ann. Sci. Natur. Zool., ser. 9, 18. **Martin, H.** 1922. The common intestinal roundworm of swine. Univ. Nebraska Agricult. Exp. Sta. Circ. 17. 1926. Studies on Ascaris lumbricoides. Univ. Nebraska Agricult. Exp. Sta. Research Bull. 37. **Morris, R.** 1911. Viability of parasitic ova in 2% formalin. Bull. Johns Hopkins Hospital 22. **Mueller, J.** 1927. The excretory system of Anisakis simplex. Ztschr. Zellforsch. Mikro. Anat. 5. 1929. Microscopical anatomy and physiology of Ascaris. Ztschr. Zellforsch. Mikro. Anat. 8. 1930. The mechanics of copulation in Ascaris. Trans. Amer. Micro. Soc. 49. **Müller, H.** 1903. Beitrag zur Embryonalentwicklung der Ascaris. Zoologica, Stuttgart, 17, Heft 41. **Musov, O.** 1930. Die Genitalröhren von Ascaris. Ztschr. Wiss. Zool. 137. **Oesterlin, M.** 1937. Die von oxybiotisch gehaltenen Ascariden ausgeschiedenen Fettsäuren. Ztschr. Vergl. Physiol. 25. **Ogata, S.** 1925. The destruction of Ascaris eggs. Ann. Trop. Med. Parasitol. 19. **Oliver-Gonzalez, J.** 1943. Antigenic analysis of the isolated tissues and body fluids of Ascaris. Jour. Infect. Diseases 72. **Otto, G.** 1928. Observations on the development of ova of Ascaris in various concentrations of atmospheric moisture. Jour. Parasitol. 15. 1929. Moisture requirements of the eggs of the horse, dog, human, and pig ascarids. Amer. Jour. Hygiene 10. **Otto, G., and W. Cort.** 1934. Distribution and epidemiology of human ascariasis in the United States. Amer. Jour. Hygiene 19. **Owen, M.** 1928. Survival of the ova of Toxacara canis under natural soil conditions. Jour. Parasitol. 15. **Pannikar, N., and N. Sproston.** 1941. Osmotic relations of some metazoan parasites. Parasitology 33. **Payne, F., J. Ackert, and E. Hartman.** 1925. The question of human and pig Ascaris. Amer. Jour. Hygiene 5. **Pease, D., and D. Marsland.** 1939. Cleavage of Ascaris eggs under exceptionally high pressure. Jour. Cell. Comp. Physiol. 14. **Pick, F.** 1947. Le mécanisme de l'éclosion des oeufs d'Ascaris in vitro. Acta Tropica 4. **Pitts, T.** 1948. Experimental hatching of the eggs of Ascaris. Proc. Soc. Exp. Biol. Med. 69. **Punt, A.** 1941. Recherches sur quelques nématodes parasites de poissons. Mem. Mus. Roy. Hist. Natur. Belgique, No. 98. **Raffensperger, H.** 1921. Viability of Ascaris ova exposed to weather conditions. Veterinary Medicine 22. **Ransom, B., and E. Cram.** 1921. The course of migration of Ascaris larvae. Amer. Jour. Trop. Med. 1. **Ransom, B., and W. Foster.** 1917. Life history of Ascaris lumbricoides. Jour. Agricult. Research 11. 1919. Recent discoveries concerning the life-history of Ascaris. Jour. Parasitol. 5. 1920. Observations on the life-history of Ascaris. U.S. Dept. Agricult. Bull. No. 817. **Reid, W.** 1944. Effects of host starvation on worm elimination and glycogen depletion with Ascaridia. Jour. Parasitol. 30, suppl. 1945a. Comparison between in vitro and in vivo glycogen utilization in Ascaridia.

Jour. Parasitol. 31. 1945b. Relationship between glycogen depletion in Ascaridia and elimination of the parasite by the host. Amer. Jour. Hygiene 41. **Ro, M.** 1939. Anaerobic glycogen consumption in Ascaris. Acta Japon. Med. Trop. 1. **Roberts, F.** 1934. The large roundworm of pigs. Dept. Agricult. Queensland, Animal Health Sta., Bull. No. 1. 1936. Studies on the biology and control of Ascaridia galli. Dept. Agricult. Queensland, Animal Health Sta., Bull. No. 2. 1937. Studies on the life history and economic importance of Heterakis gallinae. Austral. Jour. Exp. Biol. Med. Sci. 15. **Rogers, W.** 1945. Studies on the nature and properties of the perienteric fluid of Ascaris. Parasitology 36. 1947. Histological distribution of alkaline phosphatase in helminth parasites. Nature, London, 159. **Sarles, M.** 1933. Resistance of the cat to Ascaris infection. Jour. Parasitol. 20. **Sarles, M., and N. Stoll.** 1935. Resistance of the cat to superimposed infection with Toxocara cati. Jour. Parasitol. 21. **Schimmelpfennig, C.** 1903. Über Ascaris megalocephala. Beiträge zur Biologie und physiologischen Chemie derselben. Arch. Wiss. Prakt. Tierheilk. 29. **Schopfer, W.** 1924. La perméabilité et l'osmose chez les parasites intestinaux. Verhandl. Schweiz. Naturforsch. Gesell. 105. 1925. Recherches sur la concentration moleculaire des sucs de parasites. Parasitology 17. 1926. Recherches physico-chimiques sur les liquides de parasites. Parasitology 18. 1927. Recherches physico-chimiques sur le milieu intérieur de quelques parasites. Rev. Suisse Zool. 39. **Schulte, E.** 1916. Versuche über Stoffwechselvorgänge bei Ascaris. Arch. Ges. Physiol. 166. **Schultz, F., and M. Becker.** 1933. Über Ascarylalcohol. Biochem. Ztschr. 265. **Schwartz, B.** 1922. Life cycle of Ascaris vitulorum. Philipp. Jour. Sci. 20. 1925. Two new larval nematodes belonging to Porrocaecum from Insectivora. Proc. U.S. Nation. Mus. 67. **Skrjabin, K., and V. Karokhin.** 1945. On the rearrangement of nematodes of the order Ascaridata. C. R. Acad. Sci. U.S.S.R. 48. **Slater, W.** 1925. Nature of metabolic processes in Ascaris. Biochem. Jour. 19. **Smorodinzev, I., and K. Bebeschin.** 1926. La teneur en glocogéne des ascarides. C. R. Acad. Sci. U.S.S.R. 11. 1936. Die chemische Zusammensetzung der Ascaris. Jour. Biochem. Tokyo 23. **Smyth, J., W. Bingley, and G. Hill.** 1945. Distribution of vitamin C in Toxocara canis. Jour. Exp. Biol. 21. **Spindler, L.** 1929. Isolation of Ascaris eggs from soil. Amer. Jour. Hygiene 10. **Stewart, F.** 1916. Life history of Ascaris lumbricoides. Brit. Med. Jour. 2. 1918. On the development of Ascaris in the mouse. Parasitology 10. **Taylor, E.** 1924. On the ascarids of the dog and cat. Ann. Trop. Med. Parasitol. 18. **Thomas, L.** 1937a. On the life cycle of Contracaecum. Jour. Parasitol. 23. 1937b. Life cycle of Rhaphidascaris. Jour. Parasitol. 23. **Thornton, H.** 1924. The relationship between the ascarids of man, pig, and chimpanzee. Parasitology 8. **Thwaite, J.** 1927. On a collection of nematodes from Ceylon. Ann. Trop. Med. Parasitol. 21. **Toryu, Y.** 1933. Glycogen content of Ascaris. Sci. Repts. Tohoku Imper. Univ., ser. 4, Biol., 8. 1934. The respiratory exchange in the Ascaris. Sci. Repts. Tohoku Imper. Univ., ser. 4, Biol., 9. 1935. Survival and glycogen content of Ascaris in the presence and absence of oxygen. Sci. Repts. Tohoku Imper. Univ., ser. 4, Biol., 10. 1936. Products from glycogen during anaerobic and aerobic existence of Ascaris. Survival and respiratory exchange of Ascaris intercepted from light in presence and absence of oxygen. Sci. Repts. Tohoku Imper. Univ., ser. 4, Biol., 10, 11. **Voltzenlogel, S.** 1902. Untersuchungen über den anatomischen und histologischen Bau des Hinterendes von Ascaris. Zool. Jahrb. Abt. Anat. 16. **Waechter, J.** 1934. Über die Natur der beim Stoffwechsel der Spulwürmer ausgeschiedenen Fettsäuren. Ztschr. Biol. 95. **Walton, A. C.** 1937. The nematode parasites of Amphibia. III. Studies on life histories. Jour. Parasitol. 23. **Weinland, E.** 1901a. Über den Glykogengehalt einiger parasitischer Würmer. Ztschr. Biol. 41. 1901b.

Über Kohlehydratzersetzung ohne Sauerstoffaufnahme bei Ascaris. Ztschr. Biol. 42. 1904. Ueber die von Ascaris ausgeschiedenen Fettsäure. Über die Zersetzung Stickstoffhaltiger Substanz bei Ascaris. Ztschr. Biol. 45. **Wharton, L.** 1915. The development of the eggs of Ascaris. The eggs of Ascaris lumbricoides. Philipp. Jour. Sci. 10B. **Wigdor, M.** 1918. Some studies on the resistance of ova of Toxascaris. New Orleans Med. Surgery Jour. 71. **Winfield, G.** 1933. Quantitative experimental studies on the rat Heterakis. Amer. Jour. Hygiene 17. **Wright, W.** 1935a. Observations on the life history of Toxascaris leonina. Proc. Helminthol. Soc. Washington 2. 1935b. Relation of vitamin A deficiency to ascariasis in the dog. Jour. Parasitol. 21. 1936. Observations on the life history of Toxocara canis and Toxascaris leonina. Bull. George Washington Univ. for 1934–1936. **Wülker, G.** 1929. Der Wirtwechsel der parasitischen Nematoden von Meeresfischen. Zool. Anz. suppl. 4 (Verhandl. Dtsch. Zool. Gesell. 33). **Yoshida, S.** 1919. On the migrating course of ascarid larvae in the body of the host. Jour. Parasitol. 6. 1920. The resistance of Ascaris eggs. Jour. Parasitol. 6. **Yoshimura, S.** 1930. Beiträge zur Chemie der Askaris. Jour. Biochem. Tokyo 12. **Zawadowsky, M.** 1927. Aussere Entwicklungsbedingungen des Eier von Ascaris. Arch. Entw'mech. Org. 109. 1929. The nature of the egg-shells of various species of Ascaris. Trans. Lab. Exp. Biol. Zoopark Moscow 4. **Zawadowsky, M.,** and **A. Orlov.** 1927. Is there any possibility of auto-invasion during ascariasis? Trans. Lab. Exp. Biol. Zoopark Moscow 3. **Zawadowsky, M.,** and **K. Sidorov.** 1927. The influence of temperature on the development of Ascaris eggs. Trans. Lab. Exp. Biol. Zoopark Moscow 3. 1928. Die Abhängigkeit der Entwicklung der Eier von Ascaris von der Temperatur. Arch. Entw'mech. Org. 113. **Zimmerman, N., L. Vincent.,** and **J. Ackert.** 1926. Vitamin B as a factor in the resistance of chickens to Ascaridia. Jour. Parasitol. 12.

Strongyloidea

Ackert, J. 1923. Observations on conditions under which hookworm eggs and larvae develop. Amer. Jour. Hygiene 3. 1924. Notes on the longevity and infectivity of hookworm larvae. Amer. Jour. Hygiene 4. **Ackert, J.,** and **F. Payne.** 1922. The domestic pig and hookworm dissemination. Amer. Jour. Hygiene 2. 1923. Studies on the occurrence, distribution and morphology of species of Necator. Amer. Jour. Hygiene 3. **Africa, C.** 1931. Studies on the host relations of Nippostrongylus muris. Jour. Parasitol. 18. **Alicata, J.** 1934. Life history of Metastrongylus salmi. Proc. Helminthol. Soc. Washington 1. **Anantaraman, M.** 1942. Life-history of Oesophagostomum radiatum. Indian Jour. Veterinary Sci. 12. **Andrews, J.** 1934. Egg production by Nematodirus and Chabertia. Proc. Helminthol. Soc. Washington 1. 1935. Morphology of the anterior ends of the infective larvae of some nematodes parasitic in sheep. Proc. Helminthol. Soc. Washington 2. 1937. Location of Cooperia curticei in sheep. Proc. Helminthol. Soc. Washington 4. 1939. Life history of Cooperia curticei and development of resistance in sheep. Jour. Agricult. Research 58. **Andrews, J.,** and **J. Maldonado.** 1941. Life history of Oesophagostomum radiatum. Univ. Puerto Rico Agricult. Exp. Sta. Research Bull. 2. **Augustine, D.** 1922. Investigations on the control of hookworm disease. VIII. Experiments on the migration of hookworm larvae in soils. IX. On the position of the infective hookworm larvae in soils. X. Experiments on the length of life of infective hookworm larvae in soils. Amer. Jour. Hygiene 2. 1923. XXII. Further observations on the migrations and the position of infective hookworm larvae in soils. XXIII. Experiments on the factors determining the length of life of infective hookworm larvae. Amer. Jour. Hygiene 3. 1926. Studies and observations on soil infestation with hookworm in southern Alabama. Amer. Jour. Hygiene 6, suppl.

1. **Augustine, D., and W. Smilie.** 1926. The relation of types of soils of Alabama to the distribution of hookworm disease. Amer. Jour. Hygiene 6, suppl. 1. **Baker, D.** 1939. Survival of worm parasite infection on New York State pastures. Cornell Veterinarian 29. **Baylis, H., and R. Daubney.** 1925. A revision of the lung worms of the Cetacea. Parasitology 17. **Bhalero, G.** 1945. Life cycle of the lung worm Varestrongylus. Current Science 14. **Boulenger, C.** 1915. The life history of Nematodirus filicollis. Parasitology 8. 1916. Sclerostome parasites of the horse. Parasitology 8. 1920. Sclerostomes of the donkey in Zanzibar and East Africa. Parasitology 12. 1921. Strongylid parasites of horses in the Punjab. Parasitology 13. **Bozevitch, J.** 1930. Viability and migration of Haemonchus contortus larvae under various conditions of weather and soil. Jour. Parasitol. 17. **Brand, T. v., and G. Otto.** 1938. Some aspects of the carbohydrate metabolism of Ancylostoma caninum. Amer. Jour. Hygiene 27. **Buckley, J.** 1934. On Syngamus ierei from domestic cats. Jour. Helminthol. 12. 1939. Observations on the vertical migrations of infective larvae of certain bursate nematodes. Jour. Helminthol. 18. **Cameron, T.** 1923a. Morphology of Ollulanus tricuspis. Jour. Helminthol. 1. 1923b. Biology of the infective larva of Monodontus trigonocephalus. Anatomy of Monodontus trigonocephalus. Jour. Helminthol. 1. 1924. On Gaigeria pachycelis. Jour. Helminthol. 2. 1926a. Morphology of the free-living larvae of Chabertia ovina. Jour. Helminthol. 4. 1926b. Life history of the lungworm, Synthetocaulus. Jour. Helminthol. 4. 1926c. Morphology of the adults and the free-living larvae of Dictyocaulus arnfieldi. Jour. Helminthol. 4. 1927a. Parasitic development of Monodontus trigonocephalus. Jour. Helminthol. 5. 1927b. Life history of Ollulanus tricuspis. Jour. Helminthol. 5. 1927c. Life-history of Aelurostrongylus abstrusus. Jour. Helminthol. 5. 1927d. Studies on the nematode family Protostrongylidae. Jour. Helminthol. 5. 1928. On the habitat of Aelurostrongylus abstrusus. Jour. Helminthol. 6. 1933. The bursate lungworms of domesticated animals. Publ. by Imper. Bur. Agricultural. Parasitol., England. **Chandler, A. C.** 1926–1928. Prevalence and epidemiology of hookworm and other helminthic infections in India. 12 pts. Indian Jour. Med. Research 14, 15. 1932a. A new species of Longistriata. Jour. Parasitol. 19. 1932b. Experiments on the resistance of rats to superinfection with Nippostrongylus. Amer. Jour. Hygiene 16. 1935. The local nature of immunity of white rats to Nippostrongylus. Correlation between degree of resistance of white rats to Nippostrongylus and interval between infections. Amer. Jour. Hygiene 22. 1936a. Renewal of growth and egg production in Nippostrongylus after transfer from immune to non-immune rats. Amer. Jour. Hygiene 23. 1936b. Interrelations between parenteral and intestinal immunity in rats infected with Nippostrongylus. Amer. Jour. Hygiene 24. 1937. Experiments on the role of the skin in parenteral immunity and further experiments on passive immunization in Nippostrongylus infections in rats. Amer. Jour. Hygiene 26. 1938. Further experiments on passive immunity of rats to Nippostrongylus infections. Amer. Jour. Hygiene 28. **Chapin, E.** 1925. Review of the nematode genera Syngamus and Cyathostoma. Jour. Agricult. Research. 30. **Clapham, Phyllis.** 1934. Experimental studies on the transmission of gapeworm by earthworms. Proc. Roy. Soc. London 115B. 1938. Are there host strains within the species Syngamus trachea? Jour. Helminthol. 16. 1939. On flies as intermediate hosts of Syngamus trachea. Larval migration of Syngamus trachea. Three new intermediary vectors for Syngamus trachea. Jour. Helminthol. 17. **Cort, W., et al.** 1922–1925. Investigations on the control of hookworm disease. I–XXXIV. Amer. Jour. Hygiene 1–5. **Cort, W., and G. Otto.** 1940. Immunity in hookworm disease. Rev. Gasterenterol. 7. **Court, R.** 1945. Les Trichostrongylus. Bull. Soc. Hist. Natur. Afrique du Nord 36.

Cram, Eloise, and **E. Cuvillier.** 1933. Observations on Trichostrongylus infestations in domestic and game birds in the U.S.A. Jour. Parasitol. 20. **Crofton, H.** 1947. The second ecdysis of Trichostrongylus retortaeformis. Parasitology 38. 1948, 1949. Ecology of immature phases of trichostrongyle nematodes. I–III. Parasitology 39. **Cuvillier, Eugenia.** 1937. Ornithostrongylus quadriradiatus. U.S. Dept. Agricult. Tech. Bull. 569. **Daubney, R.** 1923. The kidney worm of swine. Jour. Comp. Pathol. Therap. 36. **Davenport, H.** 1949. The haemoglobins of Nippostrongylus and Strongylus. Proc. Roy. Soc. London 136B. **Davey, D.** 1938. Studies on the physiology of the nematodes of the alimentary canal of sheep. Parasitology 30. **Delaune, E.,** and **R. Mayhew.** 1941. Studies on bovine gastrointestinal parasites. Trans. Amer. Micro. Soc. 60. **Dikmans, G.** 1931. Two new lungworms from North American ruminants. Proc. U.S. Nation. Mus. 79. 1935. Two nematodes of the genus Longistriata in rodents. Jour. Washington Acad. Sci. 25. **Dikmans, G.,** and **J. Andrews.** 1933a. Comparative morphological study of the infective larvae of the common nematodes parasitic in the alimentary tract of sheep. Trans. Amer. Micro. Soc. 52. 1933b. Note on the time of survival of Haemonchus, Ostertagia, and Nematodirus on pastures. Jour. Parasitol. 20. **Dinaburg, A.** 1944. Development and survival under outdoor conditions of eggs and larvae of Haemonchus contortus. Jour. Agricult. Research 69. **Doll, E.,** and **F. Hull.** 1948. Survival of sheep nematode larvae on pasture during summer. Veterinary Medicine 43. **Donaldson, A.,** and **G. Otto.** 1946. Effects of protein-deficient diets on immunity to nematode infection. Amer. Jour. Hygiene 44. **Doubrow, S.,** and **J. Rousset.** 1930. Étude cytologique du contenu intestinal de l'Ancylostoma duodenale. C. R. Soc. Biol. Paris 103. **Dougherty, E.** 1943. Notes on the lungworms of porpoises. The genus Filaroides. Proc. Helminthol. Soc. Washington 10. 1944a. The lungworms of the Odontoceti. Parasitology 36. 1944b. The genus Metastrongylus. Proc. Helminthol. Soc. Washington 11. 1945. Review of the genus Crenosoma. Proc. Helminthol. Soc. Washington 12. 1946. A brief survey of the genus Dictyocaulus. The genus Aelurostrongylus. Proc. Helminthol. Soc. Washington 13. 1947. New species of Parafilaroides from sea-lions with a list of the lungworms of the Pinnipedia. Proc. Helminthol. Soc. Washington 14. 1949. A list of the trichostrongylid lungworms. The phylogeny of the family Metastrongylidae. Parasitology 39. **Dougherty, E.,** and **F. Goble.** 1946. The genus Protostrongylus. Jour. Parasitol. 32. **Drobble, J.** 1922. The kidney worm of hogs in New South Wales. Jour. Comp. Pathol. Therap. 35, 36. **Enigk, K.** 1934. Die Widerstandsfähigkeit der Strongyliden ausserhalb des Wirtstieres. Arch. Wiss. Prakt. Tierheilk. 67. 1938. Zur Physiologie und Wirt-Parasitenverhältnis von Graphidium strigosum. Ztschr. Parasitenk. 10. **Fallis, A.** 1938. Helminth parasites of lambs in Ontario. Trans. Roy. Canad. Inst. 22, Pt. 1. **Faust, E.,** and **C. Tang.** 1934. Syngamus from the middle ear of the cat in Foochow. China Jour. Parasitol. 26. **Feng, L.** 1931. Tissue lesions produced by helminths. Arch. Schiffs. Tropenhyg. 35. **Foster, A.** 1935. Immunity of dogs to Ancylostoma caninum. Amer. Jour. Hygiene 22. 1936. Quantitative study of nematodes from equines in Panama. Jour. Parasitol. 22. **Foster, A.,** and **W. Cort.** 1931. Effect of diet on hookworm infestation in dogs. Science 73; Jour. Parasitol. 18. 1932, 1935. Effect of a deficient diet on susceptibility of dogs and cats to hookworms. Relation of diet to susceptibility of dogs to Ancylostomum. Further studies on the effect of a generally deficient diet upon resistance of dogs to hookworm. Amer. Jour. Hygiene 16, 21. **Foster, A.,** and **S. Cross.** 1934. Direct development of hookworms after oral infection. Amer. Jour. Trop. Med. 14. **Fraser, A.,** and **D. Robertson.** 1933. Nutritional condition of sheep and susceptibility to stomach worm. Nature, London, 131. **Fülleborn, F.** 1924.

Über Taxis bei Strongyloides und Ankylostoma-larven. Arch. Schiffs. Tropenhyg. 28. 1926. Über das Verhalten der Hookwurmlarven bei der Infektion per os. Arch. Schiffs. Tropenhyg. 30. **Gedoelst, L.** 1923. Le genre Metastrongylus. Bull. Soc. Pathol. Exot. 16. **Gerichter, C.** 1948. Observations on the life history of lung nematodes using snails as intermediate hosts. Amer. Jour. Veterinary Research 9. 1949. Nematodes parasitic in the lungs of Felidae in Palestine. Parasitology 39. **Glaser, R.,** and **N. Stoll.** 1938. Sterile culture of the free-living stages of Haemonchus contortus. Parasitology 30; Science 87. **Goble, F.,** and **E. Chaetum.** 1944. Lungworms of North American Leporidae. Jour. Parasitol. 30. **Goodey, T.** 1922. Observations on ensheathed larvae of some parasitic nematodes. Ann. Applied Biol. 9. 1924a. Oesophagostomes of goats, sheep, and cattle. Jour. Helminthol. 2. 1924b. The anatomy of Oesophagostomum dentatum. Jour. Helminthol. 2. 1926. Some stages in the development of Oesophagostomum dentatum. Jour. Helminthol. 4. **Graham, G.** 1933. Reaction of laboratory rats to graded numbers of Nippostrongylus larvae. Jour. Parasitol. 20. 1934. Resistance studies with Nippostrongylus muris in laboratory rats. Amer. Jour. Hygiene 20. **Graham, G.,** and **D. Porter.** 1934. Strains of Nippostrongylus muris and their behavior in various strains of rats. Jour. Parasitol. 20. **Graybill, H.** 1924. A new Trichostrongylus from the rabbit. Proc. U.S. Nation. Mus. 66. **Gregory, P., R. Miller,** and **M. Stewart.** 1940. An analysis of environmental and genetic factors influencing stomach worm infestation in sheep. Jour. Genetics 39. **Griffiths, H.** 1937. Some observations on the overwintering of certain helminth parasites of sheep in Canada. Canad. Jour. Research 15, sect. D. **Hall, M. C.** 1922. Lungworms of domestic animals. Cornell Veterinarian 12. 1923. Hookworms of swine. Jour. Parasitol. 9. 1936. Parasites and parasitic diseases of sheep. U.S. Dept. Agricult., Farmer's Bull. 1330 (revised, 1946). **Hawkins, P.,** and **C. Cole.** 1945. Studies of sheep parasites. I. Immunity to gastrointestinal nematodes. Jour. Parasitol. 31. **Herrick, C.** 1928. Quantitative study of infections with Ancylostoma in dogs. Amer. Jour. Hygiene 8. **Hesse, A.** 1923. Free-living stages of Bunostomum trigonocephalum. Jour. Helminthol. 1. **Heydon, G.** 1927. Conditions affecting hookworm ova and larvae. Effect of light and drying on infective hookworm larvae. Med. Jour. Australia 14, IIB. **Hill, Rolla.** 1926. Estimation of the number of hookworms harbored. Amer. Jour. Hygiene 6, suppl. 2. **Hirst, L.** 1924. Observations on the viability of hookworm larvae. Ceylon Jour. Sci., sect. D. **Hobmaier, A.,** and **M. Hobmaier.** 1929a. Die Entwicklung der Larve des Lungenwurms Metastrongylus elongatus. München. Tierärztl. Wochenschr. 80. 1929b. Über die Entwicklung des Lungenwurmes Synthetocaulus capillarius. München. Tierärztl. Wochenschr. 80. 1930a. Limax und Succinea, zwei neue Zwischen-Wirte von Müllerius capillaris. München. Tierärztl. Wochenschr. 81. 1930b. Life history of Protostrongylus rufescens. Proc. Soc. Exp. Biol. Med. 28. 1934. The route of intestation and the site of localization of lungworms in mollusks. Science 80. **Hobmaier, M.** 1934. Lungenwurmlarven in Mollusken. Ztschr. Parasitenk. 6. 1935. Intermediate hosts of Aelurostrongylus abstrusus of the cat. Proc. Soc. Exp. Biol. Med. 32. 1937. Auxiliary hosts in the life cycle of Aelurostrongylus abstrusus. Papers Helminthol. 30 Yr. Jubileum K. I. Skrjabin. **Hüber, S.** 1928. Beiträge zur Kenntnis der Strongyliden der Schaf- und Ziegenlungen. Centralbl. Bakteriol. Parasitenk. Abt. I, Orig. 105. **Ihle, J.** 1922. Adult strongylids inhabiting the large intestine of the horse. Rept. of the Commission appointed to inquire into the Sclerostomiasis in Holland. Zool. Pt., vol. I. **Ihle, J.,** and **G. van Oordt.** 1923. On some strongylid larvae in the horse. Ann. Trop. Med. Parasitol. 17. 1924. Development of the larva of the fourth stage of Strongylus vulgaris. Akad. Wetensch.

Amsterdam, Proc. Sect. Sci. 27. **Kates, K.** 1943. Overwinter survival on pasture of preparasitic stages of some nematodes parasitic in sheep. Proc. Helminthol. Soc. Washington 10. **Kauzal, G.** 1933. Observations on the bionomics of Dictyocaulus filaria. Austral. Veterinary Jour. 9. **Keller, A., W. Leathers, and P. Deusen.** 1940. The results of recent studies of hookworm in eight southern states. Amer. Jour. Trop. Med. 20. **Keller, A., W. Leathers,** and **J. Knox.** 1937. Present status of hookworm infestation in North Carolina. Amer. Jour. Hygiene 26. **Khalil, M.** 1922a. Revision of the nematode parasites of elephants. Proc. Zool. Soc. London. 1922b. Thermotropism in ankylostoma larvae. Proc. Roy. Soc. Med., Sect. Trop. Diseases Parasitol. 15. **Korke, V.** 1925. Observations on the life history of hookworms in nature. Indian Jour. Med. Research 13. **Kotlan, A.** 1948. Studies on the life history of Oesophagostomum of the domestic pig. Acta Veterinaria Hungarica 1. **Lane, C.** 1914. Bursate nematodes from the Indian elephant. Indian Jour. Medical Research 2. 1916. The genus Ancylostoma in India and Ceylon. Indian Jour. Med. Research 4. 1917. Bunostomum and the Ancylostomidae. Indian Jour. Med. Research 4. 1930. Behavior of infective hookworm larvae. Ann. Trop. Med. Parasitol. 24. 1932. *Hookworm infection.* 1933. The taxies of infective hookworm larvae. Ann. Trop. Med. Parasitol. 27. **Lapage, G.** 1933. Cultivation of parasitic nematodes. Nature, London, 131. 1935. The second ecdysis of the infective larvae of certain Trichostrongylidae in solutions. The behavior of sterilised exsheathed infective trichostrongylid larvae in sterile media. Jour. Helminthol. 13. **Laurans, R.** 1946. Notes sur la résistance des larves de strongylines et trichostrongylines du mouton a quelques agents de destruction. Bull. Soc. Pathol. Exotique 39. **Lawrence, J.** 1948. Cultivation of the free-living stages of the hookworm. Austral. Jour. Exp. Biol. Med. Sci. 26. **Leathers, W., A. Keller,** and **W. McPhail.** 1939. Status of the hookworm in Florida. Amer. Jour. Hyg. 29, sect. D. **Leathers, W., A. Keller,** and **B. Wyman.** 1936. Investigation of hookworm in South Carolina. Amer. Jour. Hygiene 23. **Lewis, E.** 1928. Observations on the morphology of Syngamus. Jour. Helminthol. 6. **Lie, K.** 1947. Trichostrongylus infections in man and domestic animals in Java. Jour. Parasitol. 33. **Looss, A.** 1898. Zur Lebensgeschichte des Ankylostoma duodenale. Centralbl. Bakteriol. Parasitenk. Abt. I, Orig. 24. 1901. The Sclerostomidae of horses and donkeys in Egypt. Rec. Egypt. Govt. School Med. 1. 1905a. Die Wanderung der Ancylostoma und Strongyloides-Larven von den Haut nach dem Darm. C. R. 6 Internation. Congress Zool. 1905b. Das Genus Trichostrongylus. Centralbl. Bakteriol. Parasitenk., Abt. I, Orig. 39. 1905c. The anatomy and life history of Agchylostoma duodenale. Pt. I. The anatomy of the adult worm. 1911. Pt. II. The development in the free state. Rec. Egypt. Govt. School. Med. 3, 4. **Lucker, J.** 1934. Morphology and development of preparasitic larvae of Poteriostomum. Jour. Washington Acad. Sci. 24. 1935. Survival of horse strongyle eggs under anaerobic conditions. Proc. Helminthol. Soc. Washington 2. 1936a. Comparative morphology and development of infective larvae of some horse strongyles. Proc. Helminthol. Soc. Washington 3. 1936b. Preparasitic molts in Nippostrongylus muris. Parasitology 28. 1936c. Extent of vertical migration of horse strongyle larvae in soils of different types. Jour. Agricult. Research 52. 1938a. Description and differentiation of infective larvae of horse strongyles. Proc. Helminthol. Soc. Washington 5. 1938b. Vertical migration, distribution, and survival of infective horse strongyle larvae. Jour. Agricult. Research 57. 1941. Survival of infective horse strongyle larvae. Proc. Helminthol. Soc. Washington 8. **McCoy, O.** 1929. The suitability of various bacteria as food for hookworm larvae. Amer. Jour. Hygiene 10. 1930. The influence of temperature, hydrogen ion concentration, and oxygen tension on the develop-

ment of eggs and larvae of Ancylostoma caninum.   Amer. Jour. Hygiene 11.   1931a.
Immunity reactions of the dog against hookworm.   Amer. Jour. Hygiene 14.   1931b.
The egg production of two physiological strains of dog hookworm.   Amer. Jour.
Hygiene 14.   **Martin, C., and I. Ross.**   1934.   A minimal computation of the amount
of blood removed daily by Haemonchus contortus.   Jour. Helminthol. 12.   **Maupas,**
E., and L. Seurat.   1913.   La mue et l'enkystement chez les strongyles du tube
digestif.   C. R. Soc. Biol. Paris 74.   **Mayhew, R.**   1940.   Immunity to hookworm
and nodular worm infection in calves.   Immunity to the stomach worm.   Jour.
Parasitol. 26.   1942.   Preliminary note on the length of life of Haemonchus contortus
in the calf.   Proc. Helminthol. Soc. Washington 9.   1944.   Attempts to develop an
active immunity to Haemonchus contortus.   Proc. Helminthol. Soc. Washington 11.
1946.   Infection experiments with Bunostomum in calves.   Proc. Soc. Exp. Biol.
Med. 63.   1948.   Life cycle of Bunostomum phlebotomum in the calf.   Amer. Jour.
Veterinary Research 9.   **Mhoskar, K.**   1924.   Hookworm infection in the soil.
Indian Jour. Med. Research 11.   **Mönnig, H.**   1926.   The life-histories of Trichostrongylus of sheep in South Africa.   Union of South Africa, Director Veterinary
Education and Research, Repts. 11–12.   1930.   Studies on the bionomics of the free-
living stages of Trichostrongylus and other parasitic nematodes.   Union of South
Africa, Director Veterinary Services and Animal Industry, Rept. 16.   **Morgan, D.**
1928.   On the infective larva of Ostertagia.   Jour. Helminthol. 6.   1929.   On the
morphology and biology of a larval stage of Muellerius capillaris.   Jour. Helminthol.
7.   **Nagaty, H.**   1932.   The genus Trichostrongylus.   Ann. Trop. Med. Parasitol.
26.   **Nicoll, W.**   1917.   Observations on the influence of salt and other agents in
modifying the larval development of the hookworm.   Parasitology 9.   **Nishi, M.**
1933.   Experimental observations on the blood-sucking activities of Ancylostomidae.
Jour. Med. Assoc. Formosa 32.   **Ober-Blöbaum, W.**   1932.   Untersuchungen über
die Einwirkungen physiologischen Einflüsse auf die Larven von Pferdestrongyliden.
Tierärtzl. Rundschau 38.   **Olivier, L.**   1944.   Acquired resistance in chickens,
turkeys, and ring-necked pheasants to Syngamus trachea.   Jour. Parasitol. 30.
Ortlepp, R.   1923a.   Life history of Syngamus trachea.   Jour. Helminthol. 1.   1923b.
Observations on Kalicephalus, Diaphanocephalus and Occipitodontus.   Jour. Helminthol. 1.   1925.   Observations on the life history of Triodontophorus.   Jour.
Helminthol. 3.   1937.   Morphology and life history of Gaigeria pachyscelis.   Onder-
stepoort Jour. Veterinary Sci. and Animal Industry 8.   **Otto, G.**   1940.   A serum
antibody in dogs actively immunized against the hookworm.   Amer. Jour. Hygiene
31, sect. D.   1941.   Further observations on the immunity induced in dogs by
repeated infections with hookworm.   Amer. Jour. Hygiene 32, sect. D.   1948.
Immunity against canine hookworm.   Veterinary Medicine 43.   **Otto, G., and K.**
Kerr.   1939.   Immunization of dogs against hookworm.   Amer. Jour. Hygiene 29,
sect. D.   **Otto, G., and J. Landsberg.**   1940.   Dietary deficiencies and iron salts in
hookworm infections.   Amer. Jour. Hygiene 31, sect. D.   **Parnell, I.**   1934.   Studies
on the bionomics and control of the bursate nematodes of horses and sheep.   Canad.
Jour. Research 10.   **Pavlov, P.**   1935.   Recherches sur le cycle évolutif de Metastrongylus et Dictyocaulus.   Ann. Parasitol. Hum. Comp. 13.   1937.   Recherches
expérimentales sur le cycle évolutif de Synthetocaulus.   Ann. Parasitol. Hum. Comp.
15.   **Payne, Florence.**   1922.   Vertical migration of infective hookworm larvae in
the soil.   Amer. Jour. Hygiene 2.   1923a.   Field experiments on vertical migration
of hookworm larvae.   Studies on factors involved in migration of hookworm larvae.
Amer. Jour. Hygiene 3.   1923b.   The relations of physiological age of hookworm
larvae to their ability to infect the host.   Amer. Jour. Hygiene 3.   **Petrov, A.**   1942.
Life cycle of Crenosoma.   C. R. Acad. Sci. U.S.S.R. 30.   **Porter, D.**   1935.   Effect

of a milk diet on resistance of rats to Nippostrongylus. Amer. Jour. Hygiene 22. 1936. The ingestion of the inflammatory exudate by swine lungworms. Jour. Parasitol. 22. 1942. Survival of preparasitic stages of the cattle lungworm on pastures. Proc. Helminthol. Soc. Washington 9. **Porter, D.,** and **G. Cauthen.** 1942. Experiments on the life history of Dictyocaulus viviparus. Amer. Jour. Veterinary Research 3. **Ransom, B. H.** 1906. The life history of Haemonchus contortus. U.S. Dept. Agricult., Bur. Animal Industry, Circ. 93. 1921. The turkey an important factor in the spread of gapeworm. U.S. Dept. Agricult. Bull. 939. **Rickard, E.,** and **J. Kerr.** 1926. The incidence and intensity of hookworm infection in the various soil provinces of Tennessee. Jour. Preventive Med. 1. **Rogers, W.** 1939. Physiological ageing of Ancylostoma larvae. Jour. Helminthol. 17. 1940a. Effects of environmental conditions on the accessibility of third stage trichostrongyle larvae to grazing animals. Parasitology 32. 1940b. The occurrence of zinc and other metals in the intestines of Strongylus. Jour. Helminthol. 18. **Ross, I.** 1931. Host specificity of Haemonchus contortus of sheep and cattle. Austral. Jour. Exp. Biol. Med. Sci. 8. **Ross, I.,** and **G. Kauzal.** 1932. Life cycle of Stephanurus dentatus. Austral. Council Sci. and Industrial Research, Bull. 58. **Ryzhikov, K.** 1941. Limnaea as a reservoir host of Syngamus trachea. C. R. Acad. Sci. U.S.S.R. 31. **Sandground, J.** 1931. Life history of Ternidens diminutus. Ann. Trop. Med. Parasitol. 25. **Saquenet, A.** 1945. Les nématodes parasites du genre Ostertagia. Bull. Soc. Hist. Natur. Afrique du Nord 36. **Sarles, M.** 1928a. Age resistance of the cat to infections with hookworm. Jour. Parasitol. 15. 1928b. Length of life of the dog hookworm. Jour. Parasitol. 15. 1929a. Effect of age and size of infestation on the egg production of the dog hookworm. Amer. Jour. Hygiene 10. 1929b. Length of life and rate of loss of the dog hookworm. Amer. Jour. Hygiene 10. 1929c. Reaction and susceptibility of dogs of different ages to cutaneous infection with the dog hookworm. Amer. Jour. Hygiene 10. 1929d. Quantitative studies on the dog and cat hookworm, with special emphasis on age resistance. Amer. Jour. Hygiene 10. 1932. Development of an acquired resistance in rabbits by repeated infection with Trichostrongylus calcaratus. Jour. Parasitol. 19. 1939. Protective and curative action of immune serum against Nippostrongylus muris. Jour. Infect. Diseases 65. 1943. Overwinter loss of Haemonchus contortus larvae from a sheep pasture. Proc. Helminthol. Soc. Washington 10. **Sarles, K.,** and **W. Taliaferro.** 1936. Local points of defence and passive transfer of acquired immunity to Nippostrongylus muris. Jour. Infect. Diseases 59. **Schuurmans Stekhoven, J.** 1927. The nemas Anchylostoma and Necator. Akad. Wetensch. Amsterdam, Proc. Sect. Sci. 30. **Schwartz, B.** 1925. Preparasitic stages in the life history of the cattle hookworm. Jour. Agricult. Research 29. 1931. Nodular worm infestation of domestic swine. Veterinary Med. 26. **Schwartz, B.,** and **J. Alicata.** 1930. Two new species of nodular worms in the intestine of domestic swine. Jour. Agricult. Research 40. 1934a. Life history of lungworms parasitic in swine. U.S. Dept. Agricult., Tech. Bull. 456. 1934b. Development of Nippostrongylus muris in rats. Jour. Washington Acad. Sci. 24. 1935. Life history of Longistriata musculi. Jour. Washington Acad. Sci. 25. **Schwartz, B., J. Alicata,** and **J. Lucker.** 1931. Resistance of rats to superinfections with Nippostrongylus. Jour. Washington Acad. Sci. 21. **Schwartz, B.,** and **D. Porter.** 1938. Localization of swine lungworm larvae in the earthworm. Livro Jub. Prof. Lauro Travassos. **Schwartz, B.,** and **E. Price.** 1929. Life history of the swine kidney worm. Science 70. 1931. Infection of pigs through the skin with larvae of the swine kidney worm. Jour. Amer. Veterinar. Med. Assoc. 81. 1932. Infection of pigs and other animals with kidney worms. Jour. Amer. Veterin. Med. Assoc. 81. **Scott, J.** 1928. Experimental study of the development of Ancylostoma caninum in normal and abnormal hosts. Amer. Jour. Hygiene 8. 1929a. Strain of the dog hookworm especially adapted to the cat. Jour. Parasitol. 15; Science 69. 1929b. Host induced variation in the growth curve of the dog hookworm. Amer. Jour. Hygiene 10. 1930. Biology of hookworms in their hosts. Quart. Rev. Biol. 5. **Seghetti, L.** 1948. Effect of environment on the survival of free-living stages of Trichostrongylus and other nematode parasites of range sheep. Amer. Jour. Veterinary Research 9. **Shope, R.** 1939. An intermediate host for the swine influenza virus. Science 89. 1941. The swine lungworm as a reservoir and intermediate host for swine influenza virus. Jour. Exp. Med. 74. **Shorb, D.** 1942. Survival of sheep nematodes on pastures. Jour. Agricult. Research 65. 1944. Factors influencing embryonation and survival of eggs of Haemonchus contortus. Jour. Agricult. Research 69. **Skrjabin, K.** 1942. Phylogenetic evolution of the family Pseudaliidae. C. R. Acad. Sci. U.S.S.R. 37. **Smillie, W.**, and **D. Augustine.** 1925. Intensity of hookworm infestation in Alabama. Its relationship to residence, occupation, age, sex, and race. Jour. Amer. Med. Assoc. 85. **Soper, F.** 1927. The relative egg-laying function of Necator and Ancylostoma. Amer. Jour. Hygiene 7. **Spindler, L.** 1931. Viability of larvae and eggs of Stephanurus dentatus. Jour. Parasitol. 18. 1933. Development of the nodular worm in the pig. Jour. Agricult. Research 46. 1934. Field and laboratory studies on the behavior of the larvae of the swine kidney worm. U.S. Dept. Agricult., Tech. Bull. 405. 1936a. Effects of various physical factors on the survival of eggs and infective larvae of the swine nodular worm. Jour. Parasitol. 22. 1936b. Resistance of rats to superinfection with Nippostrongylus. Amer. Jour. Hygiene 23. 1938. Persistence of swine lungworm larvae in earthworms. Proc. Helminthol. Soc. Washington 5. **Sprent, J.** 1946a. Studies on the life history of Bunostomum phlebotomum. Some observations on the bionomics of Bunostomum phlebotomum. Parasitology 37. 1946b. Immunological phenomena in the calf following experimental infection with Bunostomum phlebotomum. Jour. Exp. Pathol. Therap. 56. **Stewart, M.**, and **J. Douglas.** 1938. Studies on the bionomics of Trichostrongylus axei. Parasitology 30. **Stewart, M., R. Miller,** and **J. Douglas.** 1937. Resistance of sheep of different breeds to infestation by Ostertagia circumcincta. Jour. Agricult. Research 55. **Stiles, C. W.** 1902. A new species of hookworm parasitic in man. Amer. Medicine 3. 1921. The hookworm thermometer. Jour. Parasitol. 7. **Stoll, N. R.** 1923a. Hookworm cultures with humus, sand, loam, and clay. Amer. Jour. Hygiene 3, suppl. 2. 1923b. Relation between the number of eggs found in human feces and the number of hookworms. Amer. Jour. Hygiene 3. 1929. Studies with Haemonchus contortus I. Acquired resistance of hosts. Amer. Jour. Hygiene 10. 1940. In vitro conditions favoring ecdysis at the end of the first parasitic stage of Haemonchus contortus. Growth 4. **Svensson, Ruth.** 1925. Observations on the development and longevity of hookworm larvae in different temperature conditions. China Med. Jour. 39. **Svensson, Ruth,** and **J. Kessel.** 1926. Morphological differences between Necator and Ancylostoma larvae. Jour. Parasitol. 13. **Swales, W.** 1940. Notes on the effect of winter upon the free-living stages of nematode parasites of sheep. Canad. Jour. Comp. Med. 4. **Taliaferro, W.**, and **M. Sarles.** 1939. The cellular reactions in the skin, lungs, and intestine of normal and immune rats after infection with Nippostrongylus. Jour. Infect. Diseases 64. 1942. The histopathology of the skin, lungs and intestine of rats during passive immunity to Nippostrongylus. Jour. Infect. Diseases 71. **Taylor, E.** 1928. Syngamus trachea from the starling transferred to the chicken. Ann. Trop. Med. Parasitol. 22. 1934. Field experiments on the immunity of lambs to parasitic gastritis caused by trichostrongylid nematodes. Jour. Helminthol. 12. 1935. Syngamus trachea. The longevity of the infective larvae in the earthworm. Slugs and snails as intermediate hosts. Jour. Comp. Pathol. 48. **Taylor, Louise.** 1899. Our present knowledge of the kidney worm of swine. U.S. Bur. Animal Industry, Ann. Rept. 16. **Tetley, J.** 1935. Ecological studies on Nematodirus species in sheep in New Zealand. Jour. Helminthol. 13. 1941. The egg-laying function of a nematode as shown by a study of Nematodirus eggs. Jour. Parasitol. 27. **Thapar, G.** 1921. On Kiluluma. Jour. Helminthol. 2. **Theiler, H.** 1923. The strongylids of South African equines. Thesis, Univ. Neuchâtel. **Threlkeld, W.** 1934. Life history of Ostertagia circumcincta. Virginia Agricult. Exp. Sta. Tech. Bull. 52. 1946. Life history of Ostertagia ostertagi. Virginia Agricult. Exp. Sta. Tech. Bull. 100. **Threlkeld, W., and M. Henderson.** 1942. Notes on the musculature of the male genitalia of Haemonchus contortus. Jour. Parasitol. 28. **Thwaite, J.** 1928. Parasitic life history of Strongylus equinus. Ann. Trop. Med. Parasitol. 22. **Travassos, L.** 1914. Über die brasilianischen Arten des Genus Tetrameres. Mem. Inst. Oswaldo Cruz 6. 1921. Essai monographique sur le famille des Trichostrongylidae. Mem. Inst. Oswaldo Cruz 13. 1937. Revisao da familia Trichostrongylidae. Monogr. Inst. Oswaldo Cruz. **Veglia, F.** 1915. Anatomy and life history of Haemonchus contortus. Union of South Africa, Director Veterin. Research, Rept. 3/4. 1924. Life-history of Oesophagostomum columbianum. Union of South Africa, Director Veterinary Education and Research, Rept. 9/10. 1928. Oesophagostomes in sheep. Union of South Africa, Director Veterinary Education and Research, Rept. 13/14. **Wakeshima, T.** 1933. Experimental studies on the tropisms of the mature larvae of Ancylostomidae. I–IV. Jour. Med. Assoc. Formosa 32, Nos. 8–11. **Watt, J.** 1944. The influence of vitamin B_1 and B_2 upon the resistance of rats to infection with Nippostrongylus. Amer. Jour. Hygiene 39. **Wehr, E.** 1937. Development of Syngamus trachea. Trans. Amer. Micro. Soc. 56. **Wells, H.** 1931. Observations on the blood-sucking activities of the hookworm. Jour. Parasitol. 17. **Wetzel, R.** 1931. On the feeding habits of Chabertia ovina. North. Amer. Veterinarian 12. 1937. Zur Entwicklung des Filaroides. Sitzungsber. Gesell. Naturforsch. Freunde Berlin. 1938. Untersuchungen über die Entwicklung der Pferdestrongyliden. Sitzungsber. Gesell. Naturforsch. Freunde Berlin. 1945. Überwintern ansteckfähigen Larven des grossen Lungenwurms und der Magenwurm der Schafe auf der Weide? Tierärztl. Ztschr. **Wetzel, R., and K. Enigk.** 1938a. Zur Biologie von Dictyocaulus arnfieldi. Arch. Wiss. Prakt. Tierheilk. 73. 1938b. Wandern die Larven der Palisadenwürmer der Pferde durch die Lungen? Arch. Wiss. Prakt. Tierheilk. 73. **Whitlock, J., R. Link, and E. Leasure.** 1939. Influence of hydrogen ion concentration upon the longevity of Strongylus vulgaris in vitro. Amer. Jour. Hygiene 30, sect. D. **Williams, D.** 1942. Studies on the biology of the larva of Muellerius capillaris in molluscs. Jour. Animal Ecol. 11. **Yokogawa, S.** 1920. A new nematode from the rat. Jour. Parasitol. 7. 1922. Development of Heligmosomum muris. Parasitology 14. **Yorke, W., and J. Macfie.** 1918–1920. Strongylidae in horses. I–XI. Ann. Trop. Med. Parasitol. 11–14. **Zawadowsky, M.** 1929. Resistance of larvae of Trichostrongylidae and Ostertagia to desiccation and chemical agencies. Biology of the Trichostrongylidae. The eggs of Nematodirus and the properties of their shell. Trans. Lab. Exp. Biol. Zoopark Moscow 5.

Spiruroidea

Africa, C., P. Refuerzo, and E. Garcia. 1936. Observations on the life cycle of Gnathostoma spinigerum. Further observations on the life cycle of Gnathostoma spingerum. Philipp. Jour. Sci. 59, 61. **Alicata, J.** 1935. Early developmental stages of nematodes occurring in swine. U.S. Dept. Agricult., Tech. Bull. 489. 1937. Larval development of Physaloptera turgida in the cockroach. Papers Helminthol. 30 Yr. Jubileum K. I. Skrjabin. 1938. Life history of the gizzard-worm and its mode of transmission to chickens. Livro Jub. Prof. Lauro Travassos. **Bacigalupo, J.** 1933. Anisolabris nouvel hote intermediaire du Gongylonema. C. R. Soc. Biol. Paris 113. 1934. El ciclo evolutivo del Gongylonema. Actas Trabajos 5 Congreso Nacional de Medicina III. **Barreto, A.** 1922. Revision of the family Cucullanidae. Mem. Inst. Oswaldo Cruz 14. **Basir, M.** 1948. On a Physaloptera larva from an insect. Canad. Jour. Research 26, sect. D. **Baylis, H. A.** 1923. Report on a collection of parasitic nematodes. III. Camallanidae. Parasitology 15. 1933. Nematode genus Proleptus. Ann. Mag. Natur. Hist., ser. 10, 12. 1934. The nematode genera Cystidicola, Metabronema, and Cystidicoloides. Oxyspirura parvovum a synonym of O. mansoni. Ann. Mag. Natur. Hist., ser. 10, 14. **Baylis, H. A., A. Sheather,** and **W. Andrews.** 1926. Further experiments with the Gongylonema of cattle. Jour. Trop. Med. 29. **Boughton, R.** 1937. Endoparasitic infestations in grouse. Minnesota Tech. Bull. 121. **Chabaud, A.** 1949. Contribution à l'étude du cycle évolutif du genre Metathelazia. Ann. Parasitol. Hum. Comp. 24. **Chandler, A. C.** 1925. Contribution to the life history of a gnathostome. Parasitology 17. **Cobbold, T.** 1883. On Simondsia paradoxa. Trans. Linn. Soc. London, Zool., ser. 2, 2. **Cram, Eloise.** 1927. Bird parasites of the nematode suborders Strongylata, Ascaridata, and Spirurata. Bull. U.S. Nation. Mus. 140. 1928. Observations on the life history of Physocephalus sexalatus. Jour. Parasitol. 15. 1929. Life history of Tetrameres. Jour. Parasitol. 15. 1930. The isopod Porcellio scaber as intermediate host of Dispharynx spiralis. Jour. Parasitol. 16. 1931. Developmental stages of some nematodes of the Spiruroidea parasitic in poultry and game birds. U.S. Dept. Agricult., Tech. Bull. 227. 1933a. Observations on the life history of Tetrameres pattersoni. Jour. Parasitol. 20. 1933b. Observations on the life history of Seurocyrnea colini. Jour. Parasitol. 20. 1934. Recent record of the gizzard worm, Acuaria anthuris, with observations on its life history. Proc. Helminthol. Soc. Washington 1. 1935. New avian and insect hosts for Gongylonema ingluvicola. Proc. Helminthol. Soc. Washington 2. 1937a. A species of Orthoptera serving as intermediate host of Tetrameres americana. Proc. Helminthol. Soc. Washington 4. 1937b. A review of the genus Oxyspirura. Papers Helminthol. 30 Yr. Jubileum K. I. Skrjabin. **Cuvillier, Eugenia.** 1934. Life history of Cheilospirura hamulosa. Proc. Helminthol. Soc. Washington 1. **Diesing, K.** 1839. Neue Gattungen von Binnenwürmer. Ann. Wien. Mus. Naturgesch. 2. **Dollfus, R.,** and **C. Desportes.** 1945. Sur le genre Rictularia. Ann. Parasitol. Hum. Comp. 20. **Faust, E. C.** 1927a. Thelazia infections in China. Jour. Parasitol. 13. 1927b. Migration route of Spirocerca sanguinolenta. Proc. Soc. Exp. Biol. Med. 25. 1928a. The life cycle of Spirocerca sanguinolenta. Science 68. 1928b. Studies on Thelazia callipaeda. Jour. Parasitol. 15. 1929. The egg and first stage larva of Spirocerca sanguinolenta. Trans. Amer. Micro. Soc. 48. **Fielding, J.** 1926–1928. Eye worm of poultry. Austral. Jour. Exp. Biol. Med. Sci. 3, 4, 5. **Foster, A.,** and **C. Johnson.** 1938. Protospiruriasis. Jour. Parasitol. 24. **Gendre, E.** 1912. Sur quelques espèces de Dispharages. Actes Soc. Linn. Bordeaux 66, Proc. Verb. 1921. Notes d'helminthologie africaine. Actes Soc. Linn. Bordeaux 73, Proc. Verb. **Goble, F.,** and **H. Kutz.** 1945. The genus Dispharynx. Jour. Parasitol. 31. **Gustafson, P.** 1942. A peculiar larval development of Rhabdochona. Jour. Parasitol. 28. **Hall, M. C.** 1929. Arthropods as intermediate hosts of helminths. Smithson, Miscell. Collections 81, No. 15. **Hamann, O.** 1893. Der Zwischenwert von Filaria uncinata. Centralbl. Bakteriol. Parasitenk. 14. **Hedrick, L.** 1935a. Taxonomy of the genus

Spiroxys. Jour. Parasitol. 21. 1935b. Life history and morphology of Spiroxys contortus. Trans. Amer. Micro. Soc. 54. **Herman, C.** 1944. Eye worm infection in deer in California. California Fish a. Game 30. **Hill, G.** 1918. Life history of Habronema muscae, H. microstoma, and H. megastoma. Proc. Roy. Soc. Victoria 31. **Hill, W.** 1940. The genus Physaloptera. Wasmann Collector 4. **Hobmaier, M.** 1941. Extra-mammalian base of Physaloptera maxillaris. Jour. Parasitol. 27. **Hoeppli, R.** 1929. Histologische Beiträge zur Biologie der Helminthen. Arch. Pathol. Anat. Physiol. 271. **Hoeppli, R., and L. Feng.** 1931. On the action of esophageal glands of parasitic nematodes. Nation. Med. Jour. China 17. **Howard, H.** 1927. Thelaziasis of the eye and its adnexa in man. Amer. Jour. Ophthalmol. 10. **Hsue, H.** 1933a. On Thelazia callipaeda infection in man and dog. Arch. Schiffs. Tropenhyg. 37. 1933b. Oesophageal glands of some species of Spiruroidea and Filarioidea. Ztschr. Parasitenk. 6. **Hu, C., and R. Hoeppli.** 1936. The migration route of Spirocerca sanguinolenta. Chinese Med. Jour., suppl. 1. **Johnston, T., and M. Bancroft.** 1920. The life history of Habronema in relation to Musca domestica and native flies in Queensland. Proc. Roy. Soc. Queensland 32. **Johnston, T., and P. Manson.** 1942. Remarks on some parasitic nematodes. Records S. Austral. Mus. 7. **Kofoid, C., O. Williams, and N. Veale.** 1937. Thelazia californiensis, with a review of the Thelazias of domestic animals. Univ. California Publ. Zool. 41. **Krastin, N., and V. Tvashkin.** 1946. Biology of nematodes of the genus Thelazia. C. R. Acad. Sci. U.S.S.R. 52. **Leiper, R.** 1917. Thelaziasis in man. Brit. Jour. Ophthalmol. 1. **Leuckart, R.** 1876. Die menschlichen Parasiten, vol. II. **Li, H.** 1935. Taxonomy and early development of Procamallanus. Jour. Parasitol. 21. **Linstow, O. v.** 1892. Beobachtungen an Helminthen-larven. Arch. Mikro. Anat. 39. 1894. Helminthologische Studien. Jena. Ztschr. Naturwiss. 28. 1898. Nemathelminthen. R. Semon's Forschungsreise in Australien und dem Malayischen Archipel, vol. V, Lief. 4. 1899. Nematoden aus der Berliner zoologischen Sammlung. Mitt. Zool. Sammlung Mus. Naturhist. Berlin 1. **Lloyd, J.** 1920. Structure and life-history of the common nematode of the dogfish. Proc. Zool. Soc. London. 1928. Life-history of the common nematode of the dogfish. Ann. Mag. Natur. Hist., ser. 10, 1. **McClure, H.** 1949. The eyeworm in Nebraska pheasants. Jour. Wildlife Management 13. **Magath, T.** Camallanus americanus. Trans. Amer. Micro. Soc. 38. **Moniez, R.** 1889. Recherches sur le genre Hedruris. Rev. Biol. Nord France 1. **Moorthy, V.** 1938a. Observations on the life history of Camallanus sweeti. Jour. Parasitol. 24. 1938b. Spinitectus corti. Jour. Parasitol. 24. **Morgan, B.** 1941. A summary of the Physalopterinae of North America. Additional notes on North American Physalopterinae. Proc. Helminthol. Soc. Washington 8. 1942. The nematode genus Skrjabinoptera. Lloydia 5. 1943a. The Physalopterinae of Aves. Trans. Amer. Micro. Soc. 62. 1943b. The Physaloptera of reptiles. Le Natural. Canadien 70. 1944. Physaloptera of Carnivora. Trans. Wisconsin Acad. Sci. Arts Lett. 36. 1945a. The Physaloptera of carnivores. Trans. Wisconsin Acad. Sci. Arts Lett. 36. 1945b. The nematode genus Abbreviata. Amer. Midland Natural. 34. 1946. Host-parasite relationships and geographical distribution of the Physalopterinae. Trans. Wisconsin Acad. Sci. Arts Lett. 38. **Mueller, J.** 1925. Some new features of nematode morphology in Proleptus. Jour. Parasitol. 12. **Ortlepp, R.** 1922. The nematode genus Physaloptera. Proc. Zool. Soc. London. **Pereira, C., M. Vianna Dias, and P. de Azevedo.** 1936. Biology do nematode Procamallanus. Arquivos Inst. Biol. São Paulo, Brasil, 7. **Piana, G.** 1896. Osservazioni sul Dispharagus nasutus. Atti. Soc. Ital. Sci. Natur. Milano 26. 1897. Ricerche sulla morfologia della Simondsia paradoxa. Atti. Soc. Ital. Sci. Natur. Milano 37. **Prommas, C., and**

S. Daengsvang. 1933. Preliminary report of the life cycle of Gnathostoma spinigerum. Jour. Parasitol. 19. 1936. Further report of a study of the life cycle of Gnathostoma spinigerum. Jour. Parasitol. 22. 1937. Feeding experiments on cats with Gnathostoma spinigerum larvae. Jour. Parasitol. 23. **Ransom, B. H.** 1904a. Manson's eye worm of chickens. U.S. Dept. Agricult., Bur. Animal Industry, Bull. 60. 1904b. Gongylonema ingluvicola. U.S. Dept. Agricult. Bur. Animal Industry, Circ. 64. 1913. Life history of Habronema muscae. U.S. Dept. Agricult., Bur. Animal Industry, Bull. 163. **Ransom, B. H.,** and **M. Hall.** 1915. Life history of Gongylonema scutatum. Jour. Parasitol. 2. **Ransom, B. H.,** and—**Raffensperger.** 1921. Development of Arduenna strongylina in the guinea pig. Jour. Parasitol. 7. **Refuerzo, P.,** and **E. Garcia.** 1938. Crustacean intermediate hosts of Gnathostomum spinigerum. Philipp. Jour. Animal Industry 5. **Romanova, N.** 1947. Study of the development cycle of Echinuria. C. R. Acad. Sci. U.S.S.R. 55. **Rouboud, E.,** and **J. Descazeaux.** 1921. Contributions a l'histoire de la mouche domestique comme agent vecteur des habronèmoses des equidés. Cycle évolutif et parasitisme de l'Habronema megastoma. Bull. Soc. Pathol. Exotique 14. 1922. Evolution de l'Habronema muscae chez la mouche domestique et de l'H. microstomum chez le stomoxe. Bull. Soc. Pathol. Exotique 15. **Rust, —.** 1905. Entenerkrankung durch Tropidocerca fissispina. Veröffentlichungen aus den Jahres-Veterinär-Berichten der beamteten Tierärtze Preussens 6, Pt. 2. **Sanders, D.** 1928. Manson's eyeworm of poultry. Florida Agricult. Sta. Bull. 206. **Schuurmans Stekhoven, J.** 1932. Zur Ernährungs Biologie von Proleptus. Ztschr. Parasitenk. 4. **Seurat, L.** 1911. Sur l'hbaitat et les migrations du Spirura talpae. C. R. Soc. Biol. Paris 71. 1912. Sur le cycle évolutif du Spiroptère du chien. C. R. Acad. Sci. Paris 154. 1913a. Sur l'évolution du Spirura gastrophila. C. R. Soc. Biol. Paris 74. 1913b. Sur l'évolution du Physocephalus sexalatus. C. R. Soc. Biol. Paris 75. 1914. Sur un nouveaux parasite de la Perdrix. C. R. Soc. Biol. Paris 76. 1915. Nématodes parasites. Expéd. Rothschild, Hautert et Hilgert dans le Sud Algérien. Novitates Zoologicae 22, No. 1. 1916a. Dispharynges d'Algerie. C. R. Soc. Biol. Paris 79. 1916b. Sur un nouveau dispharage des Palmipèdes. C. R. Soc. Biol. Paris 79. 1916c. Sur la quatrième mue d'un dispharage du flammant. C. R. Soc. Biol. Paris 79. 1916d. Contribution a l'étude des formes larvaires des nématodes parasites hétéroxènes. Bull. Scient. France Belg. 49. 1916e. Sur la morphologie et la phylogènie des Acuariidae. C. R. Acad. Sci. Paris 162. 1918. Sur le dispharage de l'echasse. Bull. Soc. Hist. Natur. Afrique du Nord 9. 1919a. Sur la résistance vitale des nématodes parasites. C. R. Soc. Biol. Paris 82. 1919b. Contribution nouvelles a l'étude des formes larvaires des nématodes parasites hétéroxénes. Bull. Biol. France. Belg. 52. 1919c. Sur la morphologie du Proleptus. Bull. Mus. Hist. Natur. Paris 3. **Skinker, Mary.** 1931. Three new parasitic nematode worms. Proc. U.S. Nation. Mus. 79. **Skrjabin, K. I.** 1915. Nematodes des oiseaux du Turkestan russe. Ann. Mus. Zool. Acad. Imper. Sci. Petrograd 20. 1917. Sur quelques nématodes des oiseux de la Russie. Parasitology 9. 1941. On the rearrangement and taxonomy of nematodes of the families Acuariidae and Ancyracanthidae. C. R. Acad. Sci. U.S.S.R. 30. 1946. A new revision of the taxonomy of the nematodes Spirurata parasitizing in fishes. C. R. Acad. Sci. U.S.S.R. 54. **Skvortsov, A.** 1937. Biology of Habronema megastoma. Papers Helmint. 30 yr. Jub. K. I. Skrjabin. **Sobolov, A.** The trend of evolution of the nematodes of the family Acuariidae. C. R. Acad. Sci. U.S.S.R. 39. **Stefanski, W.** 1934. Sur la développement et les caractères specifiques de Spirura rytipleurites. Ann. Parasitol. Hum. Comp. 12. **Swales, W.** 1936. Tetrameres crami, a nematode parasite of ducks. Canad. Jour. Research 14, sect. D. **Theiler, A.** 1918. A new nematode in fowls having a termite as intermediate host. Union of South Africa, Dept. Agricult. Director Veterinary Research, Repts. 5/6. **Tiner, J.** 1948a. Rictularia from the kangaroo rat. Jour. Parasitol. 34. 1948b. Observations on the Rictularia of North America. Trans. Amer. Micro. Soc. 67. **Törnquist, N.** 1931. Die Nematoden-familien Cucullanidae und Camallanidae. Göteborgs K. Vetensk. Vitterhets Handl., ser. 5, 32. **Torres, C.** 1925. L'haematropisme des larves mûres d'Habronema muscae. C. R. Soc. Biol. Paris 93. **Van Cleave, H. J.,** and **J. Mueller.** 1934. Parasites of Oneida Lake fishes. Pt. III. Roosevelt Wild Life Annals 3, Nos. 3/4. **White, F.,** and **R. Cable.** 1942. Morphology of Cystidicola. Amer. Midland Natural. 28. **Williams, O.** 1929. A critical analysis of the specific characters of the genus Acuaria. Univ. California Publ. Zool. 33. **Yoshida, S.** 1934. Contribution to the study of Gnathostoma spinigerum. Trans. 9 Congr. Far Eastern Assoc. Trop. Med., Pt. 1; Jap Jour. Zool. 6.

Dracunculoidea

Brackett, S. 1938. Description and life history of the nematode Dracunculus ophidensis. Jour. Parasitol. 24. **Chandler, A. C.** 1942. The helminths of raccoons in east Texas. Jour. Parasitol. 28. **Chitwood, B. G.** 1933. Does the guinea-worm occur in North America? Jour. Amer. Med. Assoc. 100. **Dikmans, G.** 1948. Another case of Dracunculus infestation in the United States. Proc. Helminthol. Soc. Washington 15. **Furuyama, T.** 1934. On the morphology and life history of Philometra. Keijo Jour. Medicine 5. **Moorthy, V.** 1937. A redescription of Dracunculus medinensis. Jour. Parasitol. 23. 1938. Observations on the development of Dracunculus medinensis larvae in Cyclops. Amer. Jour. Hygiene 27. **Moorthy, V.,** and **W. Sweet.** 1936. Note on the experimental infection of dogs with dracantiasis. Indian Med. Gazette 71. **Thomas, L.** 1929. Philometra nodulosa, with notes on its life history. Jour. Parasitol. 15.

Filarioidea

Abe, S. 1937. Development of Wuchereria bancrofti in the body of the mosquito. Biological behavior of the mature larvae of Wuchereria bancrofti. Jour. Med. Assoc. Formosa 36. **Augustine, D., M. Field,** and **C. Drinker.** 1936. Observations on living microfilariae immitis in the capillary circulation of bats. Trans. Roy. Soc. Trop. Med. Hygiene 30. **Baylis, H. A.** 1936. On the nomenclature and synonymy of the nematode Setaria labiato-papillosa. Ann. Trop. Med. Parasitol. 30. **Bell, S.,** and **H. Brown.** 1945. Studies on the microfilarial periodicity of Litomosoides carinii. Amer. Jour. Trop. Med. 25. **Bertram, D.** 1947. The period required by Litomosoides to reach the infective stage. Ann. Trop. Med. Parasitol. 41. **Bertram, D., K. Unsworth,** and **R. Gordon.** 1946. The biology and maintenance of Liponyssus. Ann. Trop. Med. Parasitol. 40. **Blacklock, D.** 1926. The development of Onchocerca volvulus in Simulium. Ann. Trop. Med. Parasitol. 20. **Boulenger, C.** 1920. On some filariid parasites of cattle and other ruminants. Parasitology 12. **Bozicevich, J.,** *et al.* 1947. Intradermal and complement fixation reactions in persons infected with Onchocerca. Amer. Jour. Trop. Med. 55. **Breinl, A.** 1921. Preliminary note on the development of the larvae of Dirofilaria immitis in dog fleas. Ann. Trop. Med. Parasitol. 14. **Brumpt, E.** 1919. Une nouvelle filaire pathogène parasite de l'homme. Bull. Soc. Pathol. Exotique 12. **Bubberman, C.,** and **F. Kraneveld.** 1934. Stephanofilariosis. Nederl. Indische Bladen Diergeneesk. 46. **Buckley, J.** 1934. On the development in Culicoides of Mansonella ozzardi. Jour. Helminthol. 12. 1938. On Culicoides as a vector of Onchocerca. Jour. Helminthol. 16. **Canavan, W.** 1929. Nematode parasites of vertebrates in the

Philadelphia Zoological Garden. Parasitology 21. **Causey, O.** 1939. Mosquitoes as intermediate hosts of frog filaria. Amer. Jour. Hygiene 29. **Chandler, A. C.** 1929. Some new genera and species of Filarioidea. Proc. U.S. Nation. Mus. 75. 1931. New genera and species of nematode worms. Proc. U.S. Nation. Mus. 78. **Chitwood, B. G.** 1934. Stephanofilaria from the skin of cattle in the United States. North Amer. Veterinarian 15. **Connal, A.,** and **S. Connal.** 1922. Development of Loa loa in Chrysops. Trans. Roy. Soc. Trop. Med. Hygiene 16. **Coutelen, F.** 1928. Culture in vitro d'embryons de filaires. Bull. Soc. Pathol. Exotique 21. 1929. Essai de culture in vitro de microfilaires de Bancroft. Ann. Parasitol. Hum. Comp. 7. **Cowper, S.** 1945. Some observations on Foleyella. Ann. Trop. Med. Parasitol. 39. **Cross, J.,** and **J. Scott.** 1947. Developmental anatomy of the fourth stage larvae and adults of Litomosoides carinii. Trans. Amer. Micro. Soc. 66. **Dikmans, G.** 1934. Observations on stephanofilariasis in cattle. Proc. Helminthol. Soc. Washington 1; North Amer. Veterinarian 15. **Fülleborn, F.** 1912a. Beiträge zur Biologie der Filarien. Centralbl. Bakteriol. Parasitenk. Abt. I, Orig. 66. 1912b. Zur Morphologie der Dirofilaria immitis. Centralbl. Bakteriol. Parasitenk. Abt. I, Orig. 65. 1913. Beiträge zur Morphologie und Differential diagnose der Microfilarien. Arch. Schiffs. Tropenhyg. 10, Beiheft 1. **Galliard, H.** 1941. Recherches sur le mécanisme de la transmission de filaires par les culicidés. Ann. Parasitol. Hum. Comp. 18. 1947. La filariose au chien a Dirofilaria immitis. Périodicité. Ann. Parasitol. Hum. Comp. 22. **Grassi, G.,** and **S. Calandruccio.** 1890. Entwicklungscyklus einer Filaria des Hundes. Centralbl. Bakteriol. Parasitenk. 7. **Highby, P.** 1943a. Dipetalonema arbuta from the porcupine. Mosquito vectors and larval development of Dipetalonema arbuta. Jour. Parasitol. 29. 1943b. Vectors, transmission, development and incidence of Dirofilaria scapiceps from the snowshoe hare. Jour. Parasitol. 29. **Hinman, E., E. Faust,** and **M. DeBakey.** 1934. Filarial periodicity in Dirofilaria immitis. Proc. Soc. Exp. Biol. Med. 31. **Hsu, H.** 1938. Food of Diplotriaena. Bull. Fan Memorial Inst. Biol., Zool. Ser. 8. **Hu, S.** 1931. Studies on host-parasite relationships of Dirofilaria immitis and its culicine intermediate hosts. Amer. Jour. Hygiene 14. **Ihle J.,** and **M. Ihle-Landenberg.** 1933. Stephanofilaria. Nederl. Indische Bladen Diergeneesk. 45. **Joyeaux, C.,** and **J. Sautet.** 1937. Contribution à l'étude de la culture des microfilaires. C. R. Soc. Biol. Paris 126. **Kershaw, W.** 1948. Observations on Litomosoides carinii. Ann. Trop. Med. Parasitol. 42. **Kotcher, E.** 1941. Studies on the development of frog filariae. Amer. Jour. Hygiene 34, sect. D. **Kraneveld, F.** 1935. Stephanofilariasis. Nederl. Indische Bladen Diergeneesk. 47. **Leiper, R. T.** 1913a. Observations on certain helminths of man. Trans. Soc. Trop. Med. Hygiene 6. 1913b. Metamorphosis of Filaria loa. Jour. Trop. Med. 16. **Looss, A.** 1904. Zur Kenntnis des Baues der Filaria loa. Zool. Jahrb. Abt. System. 20. **Manson, P.** 1878. On the development of Filaria sanguinis hominis and on the mosquito considered as a nurse. Jour. Linn. Soc. London, Zool. 14. **Manson-Bahr, O.** 1925. On the longevity of Loa loa. Arch. Schiffs. Tropenhyg., Beiheft 29. **Maplestone, P.** 1929. A re-description of Wuchereria bancrofti with special reference to the tail of the male. Indian Jour. Med. Research 16. **Maplestone, P.,** and **S. Rao.** 1939. The tail of the male Wuchereria bancrofti. Records Indian Mus. 41. **Menon, K.,** and **P. Iyer.** 1936. The viability of the infective forms of the larvae of Wuchereria bancrofti. Indian Jour. Med. Research 23. **Menon, T.,** and **B. Ramamurti.** 1940. Preservation in vitro of microfilaria Bancrofti. Indian Jour. Med. Research 28. 1941. Behavior of infective larvae of Wuchereria bancrofti. Indian Jour. Med. Research 29. **Nagano, K.** 1923. Beitrag zur Kultur der Mikrofilarien ausserhalb des Wirtskörpers. Arch. Schiffs. Tropenhyg. 27. **Noe, G.** 1901. Sur ciclo evolutivo della Filaria bancrofti e della Filaria immitis. Ricerche Lab. Anat. Roma 8. 1903. Studi su ciclo evolutivo della Filaria labiatopapillosa. Atti Accad. Lincei, Rend. Cl. Sci. Fis. Mat. Natur., ser. 5, 12, sem. 2. 1907. La Filaria Grassii e la Filaria recondita. Atti Accad. Lincei, Rend. Cl. Sci. Fis. Mat. Natur., ser. 5, 16, sem. 2. 1908. Il ciclo evolutivo della Filaria grassii. Atti Accad. Lincei, Rend. Cl. Sc. Fis. Mat. Natur., ser. 5, 17, sem. 1. **Oliver-Gonzalez, J.,** and **Z. Bercovitz.** 1944. Precipitin reactions with antigen prepared from microfilariae of Wuchereria bancrofti. Amer. Jour. Trop. Med. 24. **Pratt, I.,** and **W. Newton.** 1946. The migration of infective larvae of Wuchereria bancrofti within the mosquito host. Jour. Parasitol. 32. **Railliet, A.** 1893. *Traite de zoologie médicale et agricole.* **Railliet, A., A. Henry,** and **M. Langeron.** 1912. Le genre Acanthocehilonema. Bull. Soc. Pathol. Exotique 5. **Rao, M.** 1923. Observations on the morphology and life cycle of Filaria recondita. Agricult. Research Inst. Pusa, Bull. 144. 1933. The duration of life of the embryos of Wuchereria bancrofti. Indian Med. Gazette 68. **Savani, G.** 1933. Distribuzione della microfilaria dei cani. Arch. Ital. Sci. Med. Colon. 14. **Scott, J.** 1946. Observations on the rate of growth and maturity of Litomosoides carinii. Jour. Parasitol. 32. **Sharp, N.** 1928. Filaria perstans, its development in Culicoides. Trans. Roy. Soc. Trop. Med. Hygiene 21. **Skrjabin, K. I.,** and **N. Shikhobalova.** 1936. Contribution au remaniement de la classification des nématodes de l'ordre Filariata. Ann. Parasitol. Hum. Comp. 14. 1945a. A new arrangement of the taxonomy of the nematodes belonging tô the family Filariidae. C. R. Acad. Sci. U.S.S.R. 47. 1945b. The taxonomic position of the genera Acanthocheilonema and Molinema. C. R. Acad. Sci. U.S.S.R. 47. **Strong, R., J. Hissette, J. Sandground,** and **J. Bequaert.** 1938. Onchocercosis in Africa and Central America. Amer. Jour. Trop. Med. 18, suppl. **Strong, R., J. Sandground, J. Bequaert,** and **M. Ochoa.** 1934. Onchocercosis, with special reference to the Central American form of the disease. Contribs. Dept. Trop. Med., Inst. Trop. Biol. Med., Harvard University, No. 6. **Summers, W.** 1940. Fleas as acceptable intermediate hosts of Dirofilaria immitis. Proc. Soc. Exp. Biol. Med. 43. **Taliaferro, W.,** and **W. Hoffman.** 1930. Skin reactions to Dirofilaria immitis in persons infected with Wuchereria bancrofti. Jour. Preventive Med. 4. **Underwood, P.,** and **P. Harwood.** 1939. Survival and location of the microfilariae of Dirofilaria immitis in the dog. Jour. Parasitol. 25. **Vogel, H.** 1927. Beiträge zur Anatomie der Gattungen Dirofilaria und Loa. Centralbl. Bakteriol. Parasitenk., Abt. I, Orig. 102. 1928a. Zur Anatomie von Filaria bancrofti und Loa loa. Arch. Schiffs. Tropenhyg. 32. 1928b. Zur Anatomie der Microfilaria perstans. Arch. Schiffs. Tropenhyg. 32. **Walton, A.** 1929. Studies on some nematodes of North American frogs. Jour. Parasitol. 15. **Warren, V.** 1947. Serological relationships between antigenextracts of four nematodes. Amer. Jour. Hygiene 45. **Wehr, E.** 1935. A revised classification of the nematode superfamily Filarioidea. Proc. Helminthol. Soc. Washington 2. **Wehr, E.,** and **O. Causey.** 1939. Two new nematodes from Rana. Amer. Jour. Hygiene 30, sect. D. **Weinman, D.,** and **J. McAllister.** 1947. Observations on the storage of helminths. Amer. Jour. Hygiene 45. **Wellman, C.,** and **F. Johns.** 1912. Artificial culture of filarial embryos. Jour. Amer. Med. Assoc. 59. **Welman, F.** 1907. Some bodies found in ticks. Brit. Med. Jour. No. 2429. **Wharton, D.** 1947. Further evaluation of the skin test for filariasis in man. Jour. Infect. Diseases 80. **Williams, R.** 1948. Studies on the life cycle of Litomosoides carinii. Jour. Parasitol. 34. **Williams, R.,** and **H. Brown.** 1946. The transmission of Litomosoides carinii by the tropical rat mite. Science 103. **Witenberg, G.,** and **C. Gerichter.** 1944. Morphology and life history of Foleyella. Jour. Parasitol. 30. **Yokogawa, S.** 1939. Studies on the mode of transmission of Wuchereria bancrofti.

Trans. Roy. Soc. Trop. Med. Hygeine 32. **Zarrow, M.,** and **H. Rifkin.** 1946. Observations on the specificity and clinical use of Dirofilaria immitis antigen in the diagnosis of human filariasis. Amer. Jour. Med. Sci. 211.

Trichuroidea

Allen, W., and **E. Wehr.** 1942. Earthworms as possible intermediate hosts of Capillaria caudinflata. Proc. Helminthol. Soc. Washington 9. **Bachman, G.,** and **J. Gonzalez.** 1936. Immunization in rats against Trichinella. Proc. Soc. Exp. Biol. Med. 35. **Baylis, H. A.** 1931. Structure and relationships of Capillaria hepatica. Parasitology 23. **Brown, H.** 1927. Studies on the rate of development and viability of the eggs of Trichuris trichiura under field conditions. Jour. Parasitol. 14. **Chitwood, B. G.** 1930. The structure of the esophagus in the Trichuroidea. Jour. Parasitol. 17. 1935. The nature of the cell body of Trichuris and stichosome of Agamermis. Jour. Parasitol. 21. **Chitwood, B. G.,** and **M. B. Chitwood.** 1937. The histology of nemic esophagi. VIII. **Christenson, R.** 1935. Studies on the morphology of Capillaria aerophila. Trans. Amer. Micro. Soc. 54. 1938. Life history and epidemiological studies on Capillaria aerophila. Livro Jub. Prof. Lauro Travassos. **Christoffersen, N.** 1914. Trichocephalus im Darmkanal des Menschen. Beiträge Pathol. Anat. Allg. Pathol. 57. **Cort, W. W.,** and **N. Stoll.** 1931. Studies on Trichuris trichiurá in China. Amer. Jour. Hygiene 14. **Cram, Eloise.** 1936. Species of Capillaria parasitic in the upper digestive tract of birds. U.S. Dept. Agricult., Tech. Bull. 516. **Culbertson, J.** 1942. Active immunity in mice against Trichinella. Passive transfer of immunity to Trichinella in the rat. Jour. Parasitol. 28. 1943. Natural transfer of immunity against Trichinella from mother rats to their offspring. Jour. Parasitol. 29. **Culbertson, J.,** and **S. Kaplan.** 1938. Passive immunity in experimental trichiniasis. Parasitology 30. **Davaine, C.** 1858. Recherches sur le développement et la propagation du trichocephale de l'homme. C. R. Acad. Sci. Paris 46. 1863. Nouvelles recherches sur la développement et la propagation du trichocephale de l'homme. Mém. Soc. Biol. Paris, ser. 3, 4. **Deo, P.** 1946. On the life history of Trichuris ovis. Proc. 33 Indian Sci. Congr., Pt. III. **Dinnik, Y.,** and **N. Dinnik.** 1937. The structure of the shell and resistance of the eggs of Trichocephalus trichiuris. Papers Helminthol. 30 Yr. Jubileum K. I. Skrjabin. **Ducas, R.** 1921. L'immunite dan la trichinose. Thesis, Paris. **Evans, C.** 1938. Trichinosis in Cleveland. Jour. Infect. Diseases 63. **Flury, F.** 1913. Beiträge zur Chemie und Toxikologie der Trichinen. Arch. Exp. Pathol. Pharmakol. 73. **Frisch, A., C. Whims,** and **J. Oppenheim.** 1937. Intradermal reactions in trichinosis. Complement fixation and precipitin tests in trichinosis. Immunologic reactions in trichinosis with purified antigens. Amer. Jour. Clin. Pathol. 17. **Fülleborn, F.** 1923. Über den Mundstachel der Trichotrachelidenlarven und Bemerkungen über die jüngsten Stadien von Trichocephalus trichiuris. Arch. Schiffs. Tropenhyg. 27. 1924. Über den Infektionsweg bei Hepaticola hepatica. Arch. Schiffs. Tropenhyg. 28. **Gould, S.** 1940. Incidence of trichinosis in the Detroit area. Amer. Jour. Clin. Pathol. 1943. Immunologic reactions in subclinical trichinosis. Amer. Jour. Hygiene 37. 1945. *Trichinosis.* **Gursch, O.** 1948. Effects of digestion and refrigeration on the ability of Trichinella to infect rats. Jour. Parasitol. 34. 1949. Intestinal phase of Trichinella. Jour. Parasitol. 35. **Hall, M. C.** 1938. Studies on trichinosis. III. U.S. Public Health Repts. 53. **Hall, M. C.,** and **B. Collins.** 1937. Studies on trichinosis. I, II. U.S. Public Health Repts. 52. **Heinze, K.** 1933. Die Gattung Capillaria als Fischparasit. Ztschr. Parasitenk. 5. **Heller, M.** 1933. Entwickelt sich die Trichinella in der Darmlichtung ihres Wirt? Ztschr. Parasitenk. 5. **Hoeppli, R.** 1933. On histolytic changes and extra-intestinal diges-

tion in parasitic infections. Lignan Science Jour. 12. **Hood, M.,** and **S. Olson.**
1939. Trichinosis in the Chicago area. Amer. Jour. Hygiene 29. **Janicki, C.,** and
K. Rasin. 1930. Bemerkungen über Cystoopsis acipenseri. Ztschr. Wiss. Zool. 136.
Kaufman, R. 1940. Trichiniasis. Ann. Internal Med. 13. **Kerr, K.,** *et al.* 1941.
The incidence of human infection with trichinae. U.S. Public Health Repts. 56.
Larsh, J., and **J. Hendricks.** 1949. The probable explanation of the difference in
localization of adult Trichinella in young and old rats. Jour. Parasitol. 35. **Levin, A.**
1940. Culturing Trichinella in vitro. Jour. Parasitol. 26, suppl. **Levin, A.,** and
T. Evans. 1942. The use of Roentgen radiation in locating an origin of host resistance to Trichinella infections. Jour. Parasitol. 28. **Li, H.** 1933. On the mouth
spear of Trichocephalus trichurus. Chinese Med. Jour. 47. **Linstow, O. v.** 1874.
Beobachtungen an Trichodes crassicauda. Arch. Naturgesch. 40, Pt. 1. **Lucker, J.**
1933. Failure of repeated injections of Trichina extracts to immunize rats to trichinosis. Jour. Parasitol. 19. **Luttermoser, G.** 1938. An experimental study of
Capillaria hepatica in the rat. Factors influencing the development and viability of
the eggs of Capillaria hepatica. Amer. Jour. Hygiene 27. **McCoy, O.** 1931.
Immunity of rats to infection with Trichinella. Amer. Jour. Hygiene 14. 1933.
Artificial immunization of rats against trichiniasis. Jour. Parasitol. 20. 1934a.
The effect of vitamin A deficiency on the resistance of rats to infection with Trichinella. Amer. Jour. Hygiene 20. 1934b. Development of adult trichinae in chick
and rat embryos. Jour. Parasitol. 20. 1936. The development of trichinae in
abnormal environments. Jour. Parasitol. 22. 1940. Rapid loss of Trichinella
larvae fed to immune rats. Amer. Jour. Hygiene 32, sect. D. 1942. The incubation period of trichinosis. Amer. Jour. Trop. Med. 22. **Madsen, H.** 1945. The
species of Capillaria parasitic in the digestive tract of Danish gallinaceous and anatine
game birds. Danish Review of Game Biol. 1. **Mauss, Evelyn.** 1940a. Transmission of immunity to Trichinella from infected animals to their offspring. Amer.
Jour. Hygiene 32, sect. D. 1940b. The in vitro effect of immune serum upon
Trichinella larvae. Amer. Jour. Hygiene 32, sect. D. **Melcher, L.,** and **D. Campbell.**
1942. A serologically active polysaccharide from Trichinella. Science 96. **Miller,
M.** 1939a. The egg-count index of Trichocephalus vulpis. Proc. Soc. Exp. Biol.
Med. 42. 1939b. Studies on the embryonation and hatching of eggs of Tricho-
cephalus vulpis. Proc. Soc. Exp. Biol. Med. 42. 1941. Quantitative studies on
Trichocephalus vulpis infections in dogs. Amer. Jour. Hygiene 33, sect. D. 1947.
Studies on the life history of Trichocephalus vulpis. Canad. Jour. Research 25.
Morehouse, N. 1944. Life cycle of Capillaria caudinflata. Iowa State College
Jour. Sci. 18. **Müller, G.** 1929. Die Ernährung einiger Trichuroiden. Ztschr.
Morphol. Ökol. Tiere 15. **Nolf, L.** 1932. Experimental studies on the develop-
ment and viability of the ova of the human trichuris. Amer. Jour. Hygiene 16.
Nolf, L., and **H. Zamian.** 1941. The effect of host age on the number of Trichinella
recovered from rats. Jour. Parasitol. 27, suppl. **Onorato, A.** 1932. The effects of
temperature and humidity on the ova of Trichuris vulpis. Amer. Jour. Hygiene 16.
Otto, G., and **E. Abrams.** 1938. Quantitative studies on the effect of heat on
trichina larvae. Amer. Jour. Hygiene 29, sect. D. **Petrov, A.,** and **A. Borovkova.**
1942. Cycle of development of Capillaria plica, a nematode of the bladder of dog and
fox. C. R. Acad. Sci. U.S.S.R. 35. **Ransom, B. H.** 1914. The effect of cold upon
the larvae of Trichinella. Science 39. **Ransom, B. N.,** and **B. Schwartz.** 1919.
Effects of heat on trichinae. Jour. Agricult. Research 17. **Read, C.** 1949. Studies
on North American helminths of the genus Capillaria. I–III. Jour. Parasitol. 35.
Roth, H. 1938, 1939. Experimental studies on the course of Trichina infection in
guinea pigs. Amer. Jour. Hygiene 28. 1945. Serodiagnosis of trichinosis in micro-

scopical testing with living larvae. Nature, London, 155. 1949. Trichinosis in arctic animals. Nature, London, 163. **Sawitz, W.** 1938. Prevalence of trichinosis in the United States. U.S. Public Health Repts. 53. **Schwartz, B.** 1926. Specific identity of whipworms from swine. Jour. Agricult. Research 33. **Shorb, D.** 1931. Experimental infestation of white rats with Hepaticola hepatica. Jour. Parasitol. 17. **Skarbilovich, T.** Biological cycle of Capillaria mucronata. C. R. Acad. Sci. U.S.S.R. 48. **Smith, Vivian.** 1946. Reaction of rat serum to eggs of Trichosomoides crassicauda. Jour. Parasitol. 32. **Spindler, L.** 1929a. Temperature and moisture requirements in the development of the eggs of the dog Trichuris. Jour. Parasitol. 16. 1929b. Relation of moisture to the distribution of human trichuris. Amer. Jour. Hygiene 10. **Spindler, L., and S. Cross.** 1939. Intracutaneous tests for the detection of trichina infections. Proc. Helminthol. Soc. Washington 6. **Spindler, L., S. Cross., and J. Avery.** 1941. Results of intracutaneous tests for the detection of trichina infections in swine. Proc. Helminthol. Soc. Washington 8. **Sprehn, C.** 1927. Einige Bemerkungen über die Trichocephalen der Wiederkäuer. Zool. Anz. 70. **Stannard, J., O. McCoy, and W. Latchford.** 1938. Studies on the metabolism of Trichinella larvae. Amer. Jour. Hygiene 27. **Thomas, L.** 1924. Studies on the life history of Trichosomoides crassicauda. Jour. Parasitol. 10. **Todd, A.** 1946. On the genus Capillaria in Tennessee chickens. Trans. Amer. Micro. Soc. 65. **Van Someren, V.** 1937. The excystment of Trichinella larvae in artificial gastric juice. Jour. Helminthol. 15. 1939. On the presence of a buccal stylet in adult Trichinella and the mode of feeding of the adults. Jour. Helminthol. 17. **Vogel, H.** 1930. Über die Organotropie von Hepaticola hepatica. Ztschr. Parasitenk. 2. **Wehr, E.** 1936. Earthworms as transmitters of Capillaria annulata. North Amer. Veterinarian 17. 1939. Studies on the development of the pigeon capillarid. U.S. Dept. Agricult., Tech. Bull. 679. **Wehr, E., and R. Allen.** 1945. Additional studies on the life cycle of Capillaria caudinflata. Proc. Helminthol. Soc. Washington 12. **Weller, T.** 1943. Development of the larvae of Trichinella in roller tube tissue cultures. Amer. Jour. Pathol. 19. **Wright, W., K. Kerr, and L. Jacobs.** 1943. Summary of the findings of Trichinella in samplings of the population of the United States. U.S. Public Health Repts. 58. **Yokogawa, S.** 1920. The migratory course of Trichosomoides in the body of the final host. Jour. Parasitol. 7. **Zamian, H.** 1940. Effect of host vitamin E deficiency on Trichinella infections. Jour. Parasitol. 26, suppl. **Zucchero, P.** 1942. Notes on the life cycle of Capillaria annulata. Proc. West Virginia Acad. Sci. 15.

Dioctophymoidea

Bezdek, H. 1942. Studies on Soboliphyme. Trans. Amer. Micro. Soc. 61. **Brand, T. v.** 1937. Haemoglobin in a larval nematode. Jour. Parasitol. 23. 1938. Physiological observations on a larval Eustrongylides. Jour. Parasitol. 24. 1941. Physiological observations on a larval Eustrongylides. II. The aerobic respiration. Biol. Bull. 82. 1943. IV. Influence of temperature, pH, and inorganic ions upon the oxygen consumption. Biol. Bull. 84. 1944. VI. Transmission to various cold-blooded intermediate hosts. Proc. Helminthol. Soc. Washington 11. 1945. VIII. Influence of respiratory poisons upon the aerobic gaseous metabolism. Jour. Parasitol. 31. 1947. XI. Influence of oxygen tension on the aerobic and post-anaerobic oxygen consumption. Biol. Bull. 92. **Brand, T. v., and W. Simpson.** 1942. III. Culture attempts in vitro under sterile conditions. Proc. Soc. Exp. Biol. Med. 49. 1944. VII. Studies upon survival and metabolism in sterile surroundings. Jour. Parasitol. 30. 1945. IX. Influence of oxygen lack upon survival and glycogen consumption. Proc. Soc. Exp. Biol. Med. 60. **Brown, H., A. Sheldon, and W. Taylor.**

1940. Occurrence of Dioctophyme renale in dogs of North Carolina. Jour. Parasitol. 26, suppl. **Chapin, E.** 1926. Eustrongylides ignotus in the United States. Jour. Parasitol. 13. **Ciurea, J.** 1921. Sur la source d'infestation par l'Eustrongyle géant. C. R. Soc. Biol. Paris 85. 1924. Die Eustrongylides-Larven bei Donaufischen. Ztschr. Fleisch. Milchhyg. 34. **Cullinan, R.** 1945. The larvae of Eustrongylides ignotus in Fundulus. Jour. Parasitol. 31. **Gray, H.** 1933. Dioctophyme in the kidney of a dog. Veterinary Record 13. **Jägerskiöld, L.** 1909. Zur Kenntnis der Nematoden-Gattungen Eustrongylides, und Hystrichis. Nova Acta Soc. Sci. Upsaliensis, ser. 4, 2. **Law, R.,** and **A. Kennedy.** 1932. Dioctophyme renalis of mink. North Amer. Veterinarian 13. **Petrov, A.** 1930. Zur Charakteristik des Nematoden Soboliphyme. Zool. Anz. 86. **Price, E.** 1930. Occurrence of Soboliphyme in North America. Jour. Parasitol. 17. **Railliet, A.** 1893. *Traité de zoologie médicale et agricole.* **Woodhead, A.** 1941. The life cycle of Dioctophyme renale. Jour. Parasitol. 27, suppl. 1945. The life history cycle of Dioctophyme renale. Jour. Parasitol. 31, suppl.

NEMATOMORPHA

Baylis, H. 1943. Notes on the distribution of hairworms in the British Isles. Proc. Zool. Soc. London 113B. **Berthold, A.** 1843. Über den Bau des Wasserkalbes. Abhandl. König. Gesell. Wissensch. Göttingen 1. **Bock, S.** 1913. Zur Kenntnis von Nectonema und dessen systematischer Stellung. Zool. Bidrag 2. **Bürger, O.** 1891. Zur Kenntnis von Nectonema. Zool. Jahrb. Abt. Anat. 4. **Camerano, L.** 1888. Ricerche intorno alla anatomia ed istologia dei Gordei. Boll. Mus. Zool. Anat. Comp. Univ. Torino 3, No. 38. 1897. Monografia dei Gordei. Mem. R. Accad. Sci. Torino, ser. 2, 47. 1915. Revisio dei Gordei. Mem. R. Accad. Sci. Torino, ser. 2, 66. **Carvalho, J.** 1942. Studies on some Gordiacea of North and South America. Jour. Parasitol. 28. **Charvet, P.** 1834. Observations sur deux espèces du genre dragonneau. Nouvelles Ann. Mus. Hist. Natur. Paris 3. **Dorier, A.** 1925. Sur la faculté d'enkystement dans l'eau de la larve du Gordius. C. R. Acad. Sci. Paris 181. 1929. Sur les Gordiacés des Myriapodes. C. R. Acad. Sci. Paris 188. 1930. Recherches biologiques et systématiques sur les Gordiacés. Trav. Lab. Hydrobiol. Piscicult. Univ. Grenoble. 1935. Sur le passage à la vie latente des larves de Gordiacés. C. R. Acad. Sci. Paris 200. **Dufour, L.** 1828. Notice sur la filaria forficulae espèce de ver trouvée dans l'abdomen du perce-orielle. Ann. Sci. Natur., Zool., ser. 1, 13. **Dujardin, F.** 1842. Mémoire sur la structure anatomique des Gordius. Ann. Sci. Natur., Zool., ser. 2, 18. **Fewkes, J.** 1883. On the development of certain worm larvae. Bull. Mus. Comp. Zool. Harvard Univ. 11. **Feyel, Thérèse.** 1936. Recherches histologiques sur Nectonema. Arch. Anat. Micro. 32. **Grenacher, H.** 1868. Zur Anatomie der Gattung Gordius. Ztschr. Wiss. Zool. 18. **Grube, E.** 1849. Über die Entwicklung von Gordius aquaticus. Arch. Naturg. 15, Pt. 1. **Heider, K.** 1920. Ueber die Stellung der Gordiiden. Sitzungsber. Preuss. Akad. Wiss. Berlin. **Heinze, K.** 1934. Zur Systematik der Gordiiden. Zool. Anz. 106. 1935. Über das Genus Parachordodes und die Chordodidae. Ztschr. Parastienk. 7. 1937. Die Saitenwürmer Deutschland. Ztschr. Parasitenk. 9. 1941. Saitenwürmer oder Gordioidea. Die Tierwelt Deutschlands, Teil 39. **Janda, J.** 1893. Beiträge zur Kenntnis der Gordiiden. Zool. Jahrb. Abt. System 7. **May, H.** 1919. Contributions to the life histories of Gordius and Paragordius. Illinois Biol. Monogr. 5. **Meissner, G.** 1856. Beiträge zur Anatomie und Physiologie der Gordiaceen. Ztschr. Wiss. Zool. 7. **Meyer, N.** 1913. Zur Entwicklung von Gordius aquaticus. Ztschr. Wiss. Zool. 105. **Montgomery, T.** 1898. The Gordiacea of certain American collections. I, II. Bull. Mus. Comp. Zool.

Harvard Univ. 32; Proc. California Acad. Sci., ser. 3, 1. 1903. The adult organisation of Paragordius varius. Zool. Jahrb. Abt. Anat. 18. 1904. Development and structure of the larva of Paragordius. Proc. Acad. Natur. Sci. Philadelphia 56. **Mühldorf, A.** 1914. Beiträge zur Entwicklungsgeschichte der Gordius larve. Ztschr. Wiss. Zool. 111. **Müller, G.** 1927. Über Gordiaceen. Ztschr. Morphol. Ökol. Tiere 7. 1929. Die systematische Stellung der Gordiaceen. Zool. Anz. 84. **Nierstrasz, H.** 1907. Die Nematomorpha der Siboga Expedition. Siboga Exped. Monogr. 20. **Pérez, C.** 1927. Sur le parasitisme protélien du Nectonema. Sur le cycle évolutif du Nectonema. C. R. Acad. Sci. Paris 185; C. R. 10 Congr. Internation. Zool. 1938. Non-spécificité du parasitisme du Nectonema. Bull. Soc. Zool. France 59, 60. **Pintner, T.** 1899. Nectonema agile in der Bai von Neapel. Anz. Akad. Wiss. Wien 36. **Rauther, M.** 1905. Beiträge zur Kenntnis der Morphologie und der phylogenetischen Beziehungen der Gordiiden. Jena. Ztschr. Naturwiss. 40. 1914. Zur Kenntnis und Beurteilung von Nectonema. Zool. Anz. 43. 1930. Nematomorpha, Saitenwürmer. In **W. Kükenthal,** and **T. Krumbach** (eds.), *Handbuch der Zoologie,* Band II, Hälfte 1. **Römer, F.** 1896. Beitrag zur Systematik der Gordiiden. Abhandl. Senckenberg. Naturforsch. Gesell. 23. **Schepotieff, A.** 1908. Über die feineren Bau der Gordiuslarven. Ztschr. Wiss. Zool. 89. **Siebold, C.** 1838. Helminthologische Beiträge 4. Arch. Naturg. 4, Pt. 1. 1843. Bericht über die Leistungen im Gebiete der Helminthologie während des Jahres 1842. Arch. Naturg. 9, Pt. 2. **Steiner, G.** 1932. Die arktischen Mermithiden, Gordioiden und Nectonematoiden. Fauna Arctica 6. **Thorne, G.** 1940. The hairworm, Gordius robustus as a parasite of the mormon cricket. Jour. Washington Acad. Sci. 30. **Vejdovsky, F.** 1886. Zur Morphologie der Gordiiden. Ztschr. Wiss. Zool. 43. 1888. Studien über Gordiiden. Ztschr. Wiss. Zool. 46. 1894. Organogenie der Gordiiden. Ztschr. Wiss. Zool. 57. **Villot, A.** 1874. Monographie des Dragonneaux. Arch. Zool. Exp. Gén. 3. 1881. Nouvelles recherches sur l'organization et le développement des Gordiens. Ann. Sci. Natur., Zool., ser. 6, 11. 1887. Sur l'anatomie des Gordius. Ann. Sci. Natur., Zool., ser. 7, 2. **Ward, H. B.** 1892. On Nectonema agile. Bull. Mus. Comp. Zool. Harvard Univ. 23.

CHAPTER XIV

THE PSEUDOCOELOMATE BILATERIA—PHYLUM ENTOPROCTA

I. HISTORICAL

A member of this phylum—a colony of *Pedicellina* growing on a coralline alga—was recognizably described and figured by Pallas in 1774 and *Pedicellinas* were later noticed by Sars (1835), who created the generic name, Gervais (1837), Hassall (1841), and Van Beneden (1845). The fresh-water entoproct, *Urnatella gracilis*, was named by Leidy in 1851 from the stalks and this author later found and described complete colonies (1854, 1883). Another genus, *Loxosoma*, was described by Keferstein in 1863. These authors realized that they were dealing with related forms which they assigned to the Bryozoa although well aware of their decided differences from typical bryozoans. In recognition of these differences, Nitsche in 1870 proposed to divide the Bryozoa into two groups, Entoprocta, to include the genera *Pedicellina*, *Urnatella*, and *Loxosoma*, and Ectoprocta for the other known bryozoans. These terms refer to the salient difference between the two groups, namely, that in the Entoprocta the anus lies inside the circlet of tentacles whereas it is outside the tentacles in the Ectoprocta. This division at once achieved acceptance and further knowledge of the entoprocts only served to widen the gap between them and the ectoprocts. Hatschek in 1877 studied the embryology of *Pedicellina*, noted the resemblance of the protonephridia to those of rotifers, and understood that the entoprocts represent a much lower grade of organization than do the ectoprocts. In his textbook of zoology published in 1888, Hatschek raised the Entoprocta to the rank of phylum. This view was not generally accepted and the entoprocts continued to be listed as Byrozoa in zoological texts until very recently. In 1921, A. H. Clark recognized the noncoelomate nature of the entoprocts and also gave them phylum status, proposing a new name for the group, Calyssozoa. Cori in the *Handbuch der Zoologie* agreed on the necessity of separating the entoprocts altogether from the ectoprocts and invented still another name for the group, Kamptozoa. The author opposes the invention of new names when names covering the same animals already exist and hence adopts Entoprocta after Nitsche (1870) as the just name of the phylum. Cori has given a satisfactory account of the group, both in the *Handbuch der Zoologie* and in Bronn's *Klassen und Ordnungen des Tierreichs*.

II. CHARACTERS OF THE PHYLUM

1. Definition.—The Entoprocta are solitary or colonial stalked sessile pseudocoelomates with a distal circlet of ciliated tentacles, with flame-bulb protonephridia, and with a looped digestive tract of which both mouth and anus open inside the tentacular circlet.

2. General Characters.—The Entoprocta are without exception sessile organisms and therefore the body is divided into a rounded or oval mass, termed the *calyx*, that contains all the viscera, and a slender stalk that bears the calyx and is attached basally to some object or to another

521

animal (Figs. 209 to 211).   On the free edge of the calyx is borne a circlet
of tentacles ciliated on their inner faces.   The surface of the calyx
bordered by the tentacles is regarded as ventral and hence the convex
surface from which the stalk extends is dorsal.   Mouth and anus open
on the free surface of the calyx inside the tentacles at opposite ends of the
sagittal axis and the digestive tract is therefore strongly curved into a
U-shape (Fig. 210C).   The central part of the nervous system consists of
a ganglionic mass located in the concavity of the digestive tract.   There
is a pair of protonephridia, each provided with a single flame bulb.   The
majority of the Entoprocta are dioecious but a few species are hermaphroditic.   The two gonads lie in the pseudocoel to either side of the terminal
part of the intestine and open by a common gonopore shortly anterior to
the anus.   The yolky eggs develop in a brood chamber formed of the
calyx surface around the gonopore into a trochophore type of larva that
after being set free attaches and undergoes a process of metamorphosis
into the adult condition.   Extensive reproduction by asexual processes
is characteristic of the phylum.   The Entoprocta are solitary or colonial,
free-living or epizoic.   They are marine with the exception of the genus
Urnatella found in fresh water, and are widely distributed, although usually occurring only in small numbers.   There are about 60 known species
which are not classifiable into categories higher than family.

III. MORPHOLOGY AND PHYSIOLOGY

1. External Characters.—The Entoprocta are small, almost microscopic animals, below 5 mm. in length, growing singly or in colonies
attached to objects or to other animals and having the general appearance of hydroid polyps, from which they are easily distinguished by the
ciliation of the tentacles.   Cursory examination shows that the main
features of the entoproct are the *crown of tentacles*, the body mass or
calyx, the *stalk*, and the *basal attachments* of the stalk.

As the calyx is somewhat flattened laterally, the tentacular crown is
oval or elliptical in outline (Fig. 223).   The number of tentacles ranges
from 8 to 30 in different species and is somewhat variable within the same
species.   The tentacles are usually of the same length throughout the
crown but in some loxosomatids, there are four longer tentacles at the
oral end of the crown (Fig. 222B).   The tentacles are evenly spaced
except that there is a wider gap at the oral and anal ends and this confers
a bilateral symmetry upon the tentacular crown (Fig. 223).   The tentacles are simple protrusions of the body wall and in both sexual and
asexual development appear from the oral end analward so that the
youngest tentacles occur on each side of the anal end of the crown.   The
tentacles are usually held in an incurved attitude but can be moved
individually and the entire crown can be bent inward simultaneously,

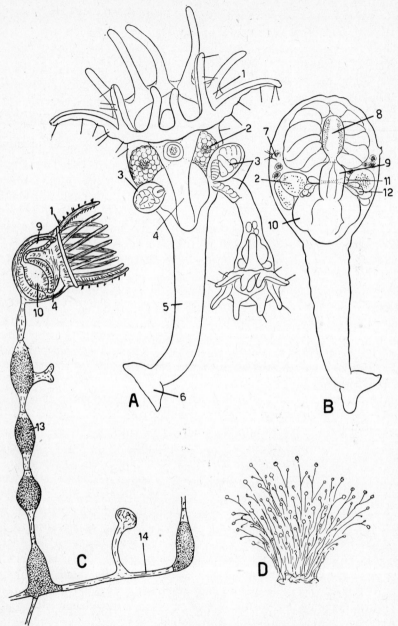

Fig. 209.—Types of Entoprocta. *A. Loxosoma* with buds, expanded. *B. Loxosoma* contracted. (*A, B, after Atkins,* 1932.) *C. Arthropodaria* (*after Nasonov,* 1926). *D.* Colony of *Barentsia,* from life, California. 1, tentacular crown; 2, ovaries; 3, buds; 4, esophagus; 5, stalk; 6, attachment disk; 7, lateral sense organ; 8, anal cone; 9, intestine; 10, stomach; 11, ganglion; 12, esosinophilous glands of gonoduct; 13, stalk joints; 14, stolon.

this being in fact a characteristic response of the entoproct to food bodies or to any kind of disturbance (Fig. 209*B*). The tentacles are ciliated on their inner surfaces and this ciliation is related to a ciliated *vestibular groove* that runs along the inner side of the tentacular bases, starting on either side at the bases of the most anal tentacles and proceeding to the mouth, into the corners of which it opens (Fig. 223). Outwardly the tentacular bases are connected by a *tentacular membrane* (Fig. 223) that forms the edge of the calyx.

The body mass or calyx is slightly compressed laterally and is oriented either at right angles to the stalk or obliquely to it. Its free flattened or concave surface is shown by the embryonic development to be ventral and hence the convex attached surface is dorsal. Mouth and anus open on the ventral surface at opposite ends of the sagittal axis, inside the tentacles (Fig. 210*C*). When the calyx is placed obliquely on the stalk, the downward tilt is toward the mouth and the anus may attain still greater elevation by being mounted on an *anal cone* (Fig. 217*B*). Posterior to the mouth in the sagittal axis is located the nephridiopore and, posterior to that, the gonopore (Fig. 217*B*). The concavity between mouth and anus is termed *vestibule* (also atrium) and the part of this that lies between gonopore and anus serves as a brood chamber for the developing eggs. The outer or dorsal surface of the calyx is usually smooth but is beset with spines in some species and in the genera *Chitaspis* and *Loxosomatoides* presents an area of thickened cuticle forming a dorsal shield (Figs. 210*A*, 211*C*).

The entoproct stalk is developmentally an outgrowth or elongation of the calyx and remains in full continuity with it throughout life in *Loxosoma* but in other entoprocts is partially constricted from the calyx by an incomplete septum formed by the infolding of the body wall (Fig. 215). The stalk offers much variation throughout the group and in fact its characters provide a main basis for generic distinctions. The stalk may be smooth or spiny. It may take the form of a simple cylinder as in *Loxosoma* and *Pedicellina* (Fig. 212*A*) or may be constricted at regular intervals so as to present a string-of-beads appearance as in *Urnatella* and *Arthropodaria* (Fig. 209*C*). In several genera the stalk base shows a pronounced muscular enlargement and similar enlargements may occur along the stalk and near the calyx as in *Barentsia* and *Gonypodaria* (Fig. 210*B*). These muscular swellings, acting like sockets, permit the odd flicking, bowing movements characteristic of such entoprocts and are also related to asexual reproduction.

The stalk base in the solitary Loxosomatidae simply forms an attachment disk supplied during youth or throughout life by a pedal gland furnishing an adhesive secretion. In *Urnatella* there is a basal plate from which two or three stalks arise to form a small colony (Fig. 212*B*). In

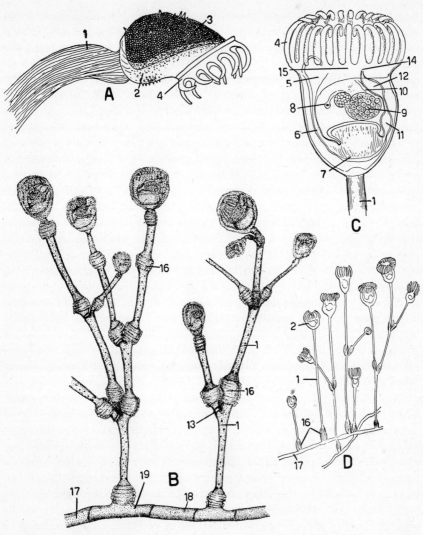

FIG. 210.—Types of Entoprocta (continued). *A. Loxosomatoides (after Annandale,*
1908). *B. Gonypodaria (after Robertson,* 1900). *C.* Calyx of *Barentsia.* *D.* Portion of
Barentsia colony. (*C, D, from life,* California.) 1, stalk; 2, calyx; 3, cuticular shield;
4, tentacular crown; 5, mouth; 6, esophagus; 7, stomach; 8, protonephridium; 9, gonad;
10, gonoduct; 11, intestine; 12, rectum; 13, septum; 14, anus; 15, vestibule; 16, muscular
sockets; 17, stolon; 18, sterile segment of stolon; 19, segment bearing polyps.

other genera the stalk base puts out slender stolons that run over and
adhere to a substratum and may branch and anastomose, giving rise to
numerous stalks and so resulting in the formation of a considerable
colony (Fig. 209*D*).   These stolons are usually subdivided by septa at
short intervals and typically interseptal stalk-bearing lengths of stolon

alternate with *sterile* sections devoid of a stalk (Fig. 210*B*). Colonies may be further complicated and enlarged by branching at the muscular swellings or bead-like thickenings of the stalk mentioned above (Fig. 210*B*, *D*).

2. Body Wall.—The structure of the body wall is typically pseudo-coelomate and is practically the same throughout stalk, stolons, calyx, and tentacles. The body surface is clothed with a cuticle except on the tentacles and vestibule. The cuticle varies in thickness in different regions and is particularly thick on the stolons where it may be layered. The cuticular thickening of the dorsal surface of the calyx in *Chitaspis* and *Loxosomatoides* forms a shell-shaped shield that may be ornamented with spines or polygonal markings (Figs. 210*A*, 211*C*). Cuticular spines occur in some species but some of these appear to be of the nature of adhesive tubes. Such contain a large epidermal cell that is accompanied basally by gland cells and opens at the tip of the spine from which secretion may exude (Fig. 213*F*). The septum between calyx and stalk and the septa along the stolons consist of inturned cuticle plus the underlying epidermis.

The cuticle is everywhere underlain by a cellular epidermis, consisting of a single layer of mostly cuboidal cells. The tentacles are simply epidermal tubes enclosing loose mesenchyme (Fig. 212*D*). The epidermis is taller on the inner surface of the tentacles and along the vestibular groove, in which locations it is also heavily ciliated. Numerous large gland cells occur in the epidermis of the calyx in loxosomatids (Harmer, 1885; Atkins, 1932) and were also found in *Barentsia* by Ehlers (1890). They are of two sorts—a granular opaque type and a transparent type filled with vacuoles (Fig. 212*F*). Ehlers (1890) has described clusters of enlarged epidermal cells, apparently glandular, in the stalk of *Barentsia* and *Pedicellinopsis* (Fig. 213*D*); he suggested that these clusters are fore-runners of the adhesive spines accompanied by gland cells mentioned above. In *Loxocalyx* the attachment disk of the stalk is supplied throughout life by a large multicellular pedal gland that may open directly on the disk or by way of a long groove formed of conspicuous epithelial cells (Fig. 213*B*). In other loxosomatids a pedal gland is present only in juveniles, deteriorating later, and indications of it also appear during the metamorphosis of other entoprocts.

To the inner side of the epidermis occurs the body-wall musculature in the form of longitudinal fibers. This musculature is sparsely present in the calyx whence the slight motility of this region. Muscle strands are present along the inner wall of the tentacles (Fig. 212*D*) and enable these to be curved inward toward the vestibule. A band of muscle fibers courses within the tentacular membrane forming a sphincter that contracts this membrane over the tentacular crown when the latter is curled

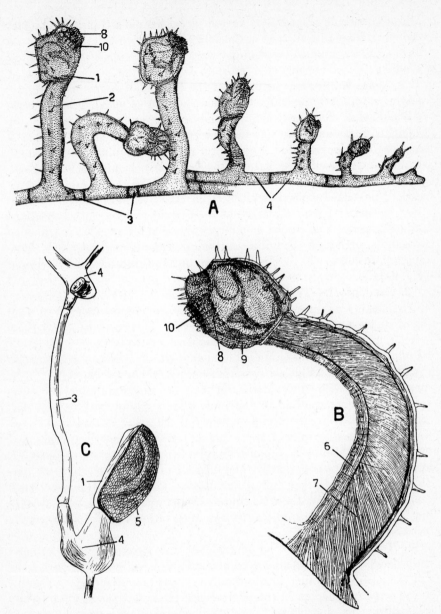

Fig. 211.—Types of Entoprocta (continued). *A.* Colony of *Mysoma.* *B. Myosoma,* enlarged. (*A, B, after Robertson,* 1900.) *C. Chitaspis (after Annandale,* 1916). 1, calyx; 2, stalk; 3, sterile segments of stolon; 4, polyp-bearing segments of stolon; 5, cuticular shield; 6, longitudinal muscles of stalk; 7, diagonal muscles of stalk; 8, contracted tentacles; 9, vestibular depressor; 10, sphincter of the tentacular crown.

into the vestibule (Fig. 223). In the calyx there is a transverse bundle extending from side to side ventral to the digestive tract and a set of fibers originating on the septum between calyx and stalk and extending to either side of the digestive tract to insert on the ventral surface of calyx, hence acting as a depressor of the vestibule (Fig. 211*B*). In the simpler entoprocts the stalk contains a sheath of subepidermal longitudinal muscle fibers, permitting bending in various directions, but in genera with pronounced muscular swellings, these swellings contain a thick layer of longitudinal fibers whereas the intervening areas of stalk are devoid of musculature. Hence the stalks of such entoprocts can bend only at the swellings in a jerky fashion suggestive of an automaton. The genus *Myosoma* described by Robertson (1900) is more muscular than other entoprocts; the sphincter of the tentacular membrane is broader and the vestibular depressor is more strongly developed and is continuous with the longitudinal fibers that course along one side of the stalk. The muscle stratum of the remainder of the stalk runs in a diagonal direction (Fig. 211*B*).

3. **Pseudocoel.**—The pseudocoel occupies the interior of tentacles, stalks, and stolons and the space in the calyx between body wall and digestive tract. It is everywhere filled with a gelatinous material containing mesenchyme cells. The pseudocoel of the tentacles of *Pedicellina* is filled with large rounded cells (Fig. 213*A*) that probably confer rigidity upon the tentacles; free amoeboid cells are also present. The mesenchyme of the calyx consists of stellate wandering amoeboid cells (Fig. 215) and of somewhat fixed cells with long processes attached to the viscera and body wall. The pseudocoel of the calyx is separated from that of the stalk (except in *Loxosoma*) not only by the septum already mentioned but also by a plug of cells (Fig. 215) blocking the central hole in the septum; but presumably there is passage of materials through this plug. The septa along the stolons are similarly constructed. The pseudocoel of stalk and stolons contains some wandering amoeboid cells but is mostly filled with long, fusiform, more or less rigid cells known as *tube* cells.

4. **Nervous System.**—The central nervous system consists of one main ganglionic mass located ventral to the stomach between the latter and the vestibular wall. It apparently represents a subenteric ganglion as the cerebral ganglion in connection with the apical plate of the larva is lost during metamorphosis. The ganglion is of rectangular to bilobular shape and consists peripherally of ganglion cells, centrally of fibers. The details of the nervous system are known chiefly for *Loxosoma* (Harmer, 1885) and *Pedicellina* (Cori, 1929). From the ventral surface of the ganglion three pairs of nerves proceed to supply the crown of tentacles. Their branches each terminate in a large ganglion cell or group of cells

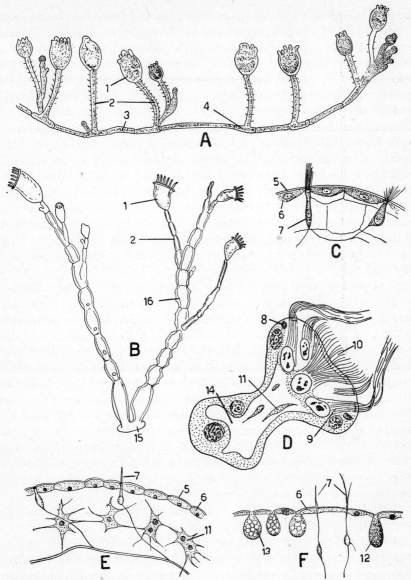

Fig. 212.—Entroproct types (concluded), epidermis. *A.* Colony of *Pedicellina* (*after Ehlers*, 1890). *B.* Colony of *Urnatella* (*after Cori*, 1936). *C.* Tentacular epidermis of *Pedicellina* with sensory nerve cells (*after Retzius*, 1905). *D.* Section through a tentacle of *Loxosoma* (*after Atkins*, 1932). *E.* Tentacle of *Loxosoma* with sensory nerve cells and mesenchyme cells. *F.* Epidermis of calyx wall of *Loxosoma* with sensory nerve cells and gland cells. (*E, F,* after Harmer, 1885.) 1, calyx; 2, stalk; 3, sterile segment of stolon; 4, polyp-bearing segment of stolon; 5, cuticle; 6, epidermis; 7, sensory nerve cell; 8, tentacular muscles; 9, lateral cilia; 10, frontal cilia; 11, mesenchyme; 12, granular type of gland cells; 13, vacuolated type of gland cell; 14, pseudocoel; 15, attachment disk; 16, stem joints.

situated in the tentacular membrane between the tentacle bases (Fig. 214*A*); from each such ganglion nerves are given off into the adjacent tentacle. From the dorsal surface of the subenteric ganglion spring a pair of nerves to the calyx wall, a pair to the stalk, and a small pair to the adjacent gonads. Little further is known about the peripheral nervous system except that, by staining with methylene blue, Hilton (1923) demonstrated the presence of a nerve net in the stalk, stolons, and muscular swellings of *Barentsia* (Fig. 214*B*).

5. Sense Organs.—Sensory nerve cells of the usual tactile type, consisting of one or more bristles proceeding from a nerve cell situated beneath the epidermis and piercing the latter, are abundant on the outer surface of the tentacles and along the calyx margin in *Loxosoma* (Harmer, 1885, Fig. 212*E*, *F*) and *Pedicellina* (Fig. 212*C*, Retzius, 1905) and presumably occur in other entoprocts. Similar receptors were observed by Hilton (1923) at the junction of calyx and stalk in *Barentsia* (Fig. 213*G*) under methylene blue staining, and this author also reported sensory pits (Fig. 213*H*) on stalks and stolons of this genus. In loxosomatids either throughout life or in larval stages only, there occurs on the sides of the calyx near its oral end a pair of sense organs bearing a remarkable resemblance to the antennae of rotifers. Each consists of a tuft of bristles underlain by a ganglion cell, from which a nerve proceeds to a ganglionic mass connected in turn with the subenteric ganglion (Fig. 214*A*). This pair of sense organs has not been found in other adult entoprocts but is undoubtedly represented by the preoral organ of the entoproct larva. What are clearly the same structures were seen by Nickerson (1901) on the calyx of *Loxosoma davenporti* and termed by him flask organs. Other pairs of projections superficially similar to but histologically different from the preoral organs were found by Assheton (1912) on the calyx of *Loxosoma loxalina*. It is not clear whether these are of nervous or glandular nature and they have not been recorded for other species of loxosomatids.

6. Digestive System.—The U-shaped digestive tract (Fig. 215) occupies the greater part of the interior of the calyx and is bilaterally symmetrical with respect to the sagittal plane of the latter. The mouth, situated at what is thereby the anterior end of the ventral surface of the calyx, is a transversely elongated ciliated aperture located just within the tentacles. The vestibular groove enters either angle of the mouth opening (Fig. 223). There is usually but little if any indication of an upper lip but a lower (i.e., posterior) lip is often present. The mouth leads into a funnel-shaped buccal cavity that narrows into the tubular esophagus. This opens into the enlarged sacciform stomach, the most conspicuous organ of the entoproct, occupying most or part of the curve of the U. From the stomach the narrowed intestine proceeds ventrally and is usu-

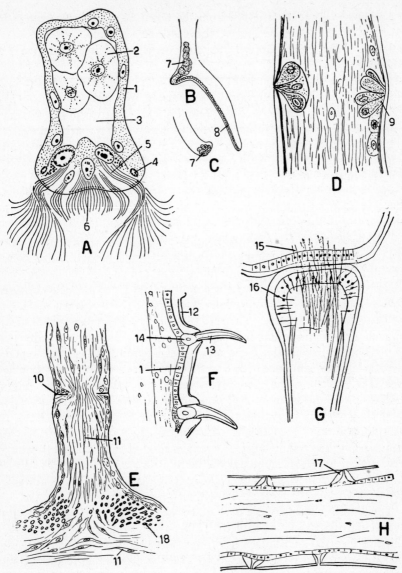

Fig. 213.—Epidermal structures, stalk, nervous system. *A.* Section through the tentacle of *Pedicellina*. *B.* Foot gland of young *Loxocalyx*. *C.* Foot gland of adult of *B*, greatly reduced. (*A–C, after Atkins*, 1932.) *D.* Gland-cell clusters of the stalk of *Barentsia*. *E.* Longitudinal section of the stalk of *Barentsia*, including part of muscular socket. (*D, E, after Ehlers*, 1890.) *F.* Adhesive spines of *Myosoma*. *G.* Nerve fibers and sense cells at junction of calyx and stalk of *Barentsia*. *H.* Sensory pits along the stalk of *Barentsia*. (*F–H, after Hilton*, 1923.) 1, epidermis; 2, large mesenchyme cells in pseudocoel of tentacle; 3, pseudocoel; 4, muscle fibers; 5, lateral cilia; 6, frontal cilia; 7, foot gland; 8, its duct in the form of a groove; 9, gland-cell cluster; 10, septum; 11, tube cells; 12, cuticle; 13, adhesive spine; 14, cell of same; 15, nerve fibers; 16, sensory nerve cells; 17, sensory pits; 18, muscle thickening.

ally separated by a constriction from the terminal rectum, that opens by the anus at the posterior end of the vestibular surface, well inside the tentacles. The anus is often mounted on a projecting eminence, the anal cone.

The digestive tract consists throughout of a one-layered epithelium of varying height and histological appearance in different regions and ciliated almost everywhere (Figs. 215, 216*A*). An exceedingly detailed account of the histology of the entoproct digestive tract, based on *Pedicellina cernua*, has been furnished by Becker (1937). The buccal cavity and esophagus are lined by a ciliated epithelium, cuboidal on the outer wall, columnar on the wall toward the ganglion. The cells of these regions contain fat and protein spherules and hence serve in food storage. The stomach presents several histologically different areas. Near its beginning there is to either side a strip of epithelium with especially long cilia that act to rotate and waft along the food strands. The floor (usually called roof) of the stomach consists of tall columnar cells ciliated only around their margins and filled with brown or olive inclusions. Because of its color, this area is generally called liver, although it is not proved to have any of the functions of a liver. The inclusions appear to be of an excretory nature. The roof ("floor") of the anterior part of the stomach is a low ciliated cuboidal epithelium except for a small nonciliated area. The posterior part of the roof forms a glandular area that sends a lateral wing forward along either wall of the anterior part of the stomach sides (Fig. 216*A*). The glandular area of the stomach is a columnar ciliated epithelium composed of two kinds of cells—dark granular cells containing enzymatic granules, and paler cells that appear to be of an absorptive nature (Fig. 214*C*). At the passage into the intestine, the stomach floor has a short area of strongly ciliated cells. The intestine is composed of a ciliated cuboidal epithelium decreasing in height toward the rectum in which a taller epithelium is met with, which, however, flattens out when the rectum is filled with feces.

The digestive tract lacks a muscular coat but there is a limited amount of musculature associated with it. Thus fibers originating on the calyx wall and inserted on the lower lip act to expand the mouth opening. The esophagus can be constricted by fibers that encircle it and extend from its posterior surface (Fig. 215) to the calyx wall and expanded by other fibers from this surface to the lateral calyx walls. Sphincter fibers occur at the junction of intestine and rectum and around the anus.

7. **Nephridial System.**—The Entoprocta are provided with a single pair of flame bulbs in each calyx, situated ventral to the stomach between the esophagus and the subenteric ganglion (Fig. 217*B*). The intracellular canal from each bulb forms a channel through a few enlarged cells often provided with amoeboid extensions and apparently functioning

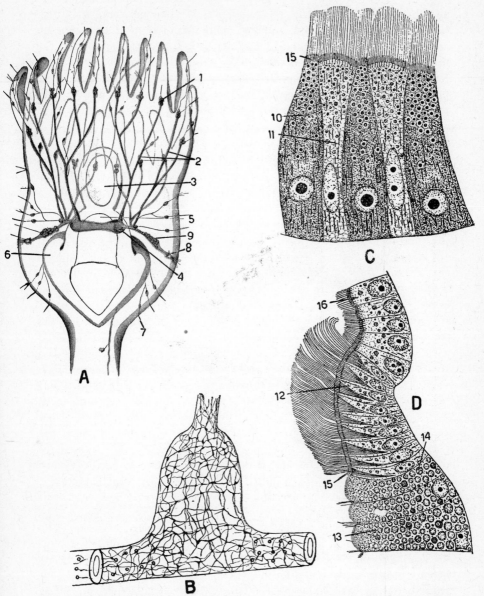

Fig. 214.—Nervous system, digestive system. *A.* Nervous system of *Loxosoma* (*after Harmer*, 1885). *B.* Nerve net at the muscular socket of *Barentsia* (*after Hilton*, 1923). *C.* Stomach epithelium of the glandular tract, *Pedicellina*. *D.* Transition from esophagus to stomach floor, *Pedicellina*. (*C, D*, after *Becker*, 1937.) 1, ganglia at tentacle bases; 2, nerves to tentacles; 3, rectum; 4, subenteric ganglion; 5, intestine; 6, stomach; 7, sensory nerve cells; 8, lateral sense organ; 9, ganglion of same; 10, gland cells of stomach epithelium; 11, absorptive cells; 12, region of long cilia at entrance to stomach; 13, cells of stomach floor; 14, inclusions; 15, rod border; 16, esophagus.

as athrocytes (Fig. 216*B*).   The two ducts then converge and unite before opening by a single nephridiopore situated in the median line shortly posterior to the mouth; Harmer (1885) was of the opinion that in *Loxosoma* the ducts open separately.   In addition to this typical system, Davenport (1893) reported flame bulbs in the stalk and lateral portions of the calyx in *Urnatella* but the relation of these, if any, to the main pair of flame bulbs was not ascertained.

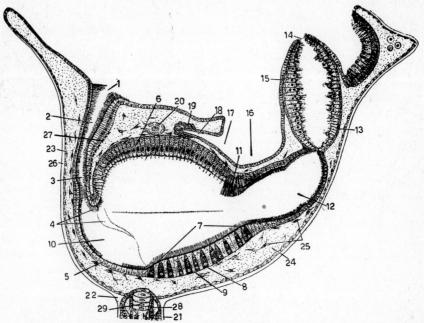

Fig. 215.—Median sagittal section of *Pedicellina*, showing histology of the digestive tract (*after Becker*, 1937).   1, mouth; 2, buccal tube; 3, esophagus; 4, long cilia at stomach entrance; 5, area without cilia; 6, stomach floor or so-called liver; 7, glandular area of stomach roof; 8, gland cells; 9, absorptive cells; 10, stomach; 11, area of long cilia at entrance to the intestine; 12, intestine; 13, rectum; 14, anus; 15, anal cone; 16, brood chamber; 17, gonopore; 18, gonoduct; 19, gland cells of gonoduct; 20, ganglion; 21, stalk; 22, septum; 23, body wall epidermis; 24, pseudocoel; 25, mesenchyme; 26, cuticle; 27, muscles of esophagus; 28, muscles of stalk; 29, cell plug at septum.

8. Reproductive System.—The available information indicates that some entoprocts are hermaphroditic and others dioecious; but it is suspected that at least some apparently dioecious species may be actually protandric hermaphrodites.   Marcus (1939) found only unisexual colonies of *Barentsia discreta*, *gracilis*, and *laxa*, and *Loxosomatoides evelinae* although Ehlers (1890) recorded calyces of both sexes in the same colony of *B. discreta* (= *Ascopodaria macropus*).   Apparently all the Loxosomatidae are dioecious.   Many species of *Pedicellina* are also dioecious but the very common *P. cernua* is seemingly sometimes hermaphroditic, sometimes dioecious. The gonads are a single pair of sacciform bodies located ventral to the liver region of the stomach, either anterior or posterior to the ganglion (Fig. 216). In hermaphroditic species, there is a pair of testes posterior to the pair of ovaries. From each gonad a short duct proceeds medially and unites with its fellow (Fig. 217*A*) to open on the ventral surface of the calyx by a common gonopore; in hermaphrodites the sperm duct unites with the oviduct of that side prior to the formation of the common duct. The gonoducts are beset with eosinophilous unicellular glands or else have an area of glandular epithelium (Fig. 217*A*, *B*). In males the common sperm duct may present an enlargement, the seminal vesicle, for the storage of ripe sperm. The sperm are of the usual flagellate type (Fig. 218*H*). The common gonopore is medially located behind the nephridiopore at the base of a pronounced elevation so that the calyx surface between this elevation and the anal cone forms a considerable depression, the *genital recess*, which in females and hermaphrodites acts as a brood chamber (Fig. 217*B*) for the developing eggs (see later).

9. Systematic Account.—The Entoprocta are classifiable into three families—Loxosomatidae, Pedicellinidae, and Urnatellidae. The first family comprises solitary forms, with the stalk attached by a simple adhesive disk. All members of this family are epizoic, adhering to the surface of sponges, gorgonians, sipunculoids, ectoprocts, polychaetes, ascidians, and other animals. The author saw at Bermuda a sponge completely covered with a loxosomatid. There are two genera, both with a number of species, *Loxosoma* (Fig. 209*A*, *B*) in which the pedal gland by whose secretion the stalk becomes attached is present during larval stages only and *Loxocalyx* with the pedal gland persistent throughout life.

The Pedicellinidae are colonial, creeping over objects by basal stolons from which new stalks with calyces arise at intervals. In *Pedicellina* (Fig. 212*A*) with many species the stalk is of approximately the same diameter and muscularity throughout, lacking special muscular enlargements. *Myosoma* differs in the much more muscular stalk and calyx (Fig. 211*A*, *B*). *Chitaspis* (Fig. 211*C*) and *Loxosomatoides* (Fig. 210*A*) are characterized by the dorsal shield formed by the thickening of the cuticle along the dorsal surface from the stalk attachment to the anal side of the tentacular crown. In *Pedicellinopsis*, the base of the slender but heavily cuticularized nonmuscular stalk is set in a thick muscular socket. *Barentsia* (includes *Ascopodaria*) also has a basal muscular socket but muscular thickenings also usually occur along the stalk (Fig. 210*C*, *D*) where they may give rise to branches and the cuticle is not especially thickened. *Gonypodaria* (Fig. 210*B*) differs from *Barentsia* chiefly in a muscular thickening directly beneath the calyx. In *Arthro*-

podaria (Fig. 209*C*) the stalk is muscularly thickened at regular short intervals so as to present a beaded appearance and a branch may be given off at every such thickening.

The Urnatellidae comprise the single genus *Urnatella* (Figs. 212*B*, 217*C*) in which a small colony is formed by a few stalks arising from a basal plate. Here the stalks also are beaded but this is caused by cuticular constrictions. *Urnatella* also differs from other entoprocts in that rectum, gonoduct, and nephridioduct open into a common pocket of the vestibule. For years there was considered to be but one species, *U. gracilis*, found sparingly in rivers in Pennsylvania, Ohio, and Illinois, but in 1946 Seshaiya reported a species *U. indica*, from India. *U. gracilis* appears to be dioecious but *U. indica* is hermaphroditic.

10. Asexual Reproduction and Regeneration.—All entoprocts proliferate extensively by asexual budding. In the Loxosomatidae buds arise on the sides of the calyx near its oral end in a pair of bilaterally symmetrical areas (Fig. 209*A*). Buds may appear simultaneously on the two sides or alternately; in some species only a pair of buds is present at any one time whereas in others each budding zone may bear two or three or even more buds in different stages of development simultaneously. When completed, loxosomatid buds constrict from the parent and attach elsewhere by aid of the secretion of the pedal gland. In the Pedicellinidae buds are produced only by the stolons and stalks, never by the calyces, and as the buds remain attached colony formation results. As the stolons creep along the substratum they give off buds at right angles to their surface behind the advancing tip (Figs. 211*A*, 212*A*). As already mentioned stretches of budless stolon usually alternate with stretches bearing a bud and are separated from them by cuticular septa (Fig. 211*A*). Stalks also bud at muscular thickenings or bead-like swellings (Fig. 210*B*, *D*) in those genera that possess such structures. *Urnatella* buds from the more distal beads or joints of the stalk; some of the buds grow a length of stalk from the joints of which secondary buds proliferate so that there is a considerable accumulation of calyces at the distal end of the *Urnatella* colony (Fig. 217*C*).

The manner of development of the buds has been carefully described by Seeliger (1889, 1890). The bud begins as an epidermal proliferation which cuts off into the interior as an epithelial vesicle (Fig. 217*D*, *E*). This shortly constricts into two vesicles of which the outer one becomes the free surface of the calyx and the tentacular crown and proliferates the ganglion from its inner wall and the inner vesicle develops into the digestive tract (Fig. 217*F*). The muscles, gonads, and other mesodermal structures arise from the parental mesenchyme included in the bud. A constriction then separates the outgrowth into calyx and stalk (Fig. 217*G*). So far as known, this description applies to budding in all ento-

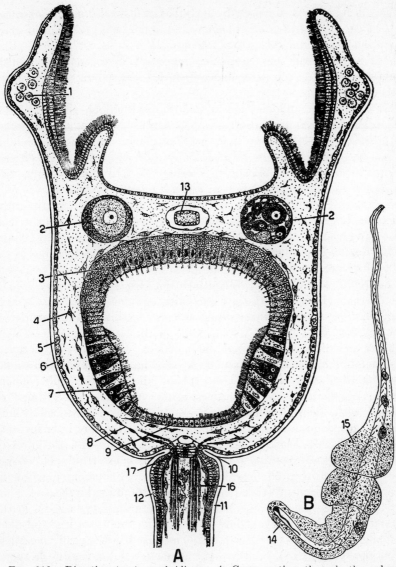

FIG. 216.—Digestive tract, nephridium. *A.* Cross section through the calyx of *Pedicellina* (*after Becker*, 1937). *B.* Nephridium of *Loxosoma* (*after Harmer*, 1885). 1, round mesenchyme cells in tentacle; 2, ovary; 3, stomach floor or liver; 4, mesenchyme cells in pseudocoel; 5, epidermis of calyx; 6, cuticle; 7, glandular tract of stomach; 8, muscle cells; 9, nonciliated tract; 10, septum; 11, stalk; 12, epidermis of stalk; 13, subenteric ganglion; 14, flame bulb; 15, athrocytes; 16, muscles of stalk; 17, cell plug in septum.

procts although derived chiefly from studies on *Pedicellina* and *Loxosoma*. In the Loxosomatidae another conspicuous epidermal invagination gives rise to the pedal gland, persistent throughout life in *Loxocalyx* (Fig. 213*B*, *C*). It is thus seen that in asexual reproduction the entire organism originates from the ectoderm and mesoderm without any participation of the entoderm.

As is usual in animals that reproduce by budding, the entoprocts possess good powers of regeneration. Under adverse conditions colonies shed their calyces but the stalks and stolons remain alive for considerable periods and regenerate new calyces upon return of favorable conditions. In experiments on *Arthropodaria*, Nasonov (1926) found that removed portions of the tentacular crown including the tentacular membrane were readily regenerated in a few days but excision of the entire margin of the calyx resulted in the death of the latter. Any joint of the stalk of this genus can regenerate a calyx and stolons and so give rise to a new colony.

11. Sexual Reproduction and Development.—The chief studies of the embryology are those of Vogt (1876), Barrois (1877), and Harmer (1885) for *Loxosoma*, and Barrois (1877), Hatschek (1877), Lebedinsky (1905), and Marcus (1939) for *Pedicellina*. The account of Marcus is here followed. The small but rather yolky eggs are fertilized in the ovaries or gonoduct and during their passage through the latter become covered with the secretion of its eosinophilous glands. This secretion forms a loose membrane over the eggs and embryos (Fig. 218*D*) and is drawn out into a stalk of attachment. These stalks adhere to the embryophore (Fig. 217*B*), which is the name given to the vestibular wall anterior to the anal cone. During brooding of the embryos this wall becomes thickened and pocketed and filled with food inclusions that are later ingested by the embryos. As new eggs issue from the gonopore, the already attached embryos are pushed forward so that there is a regular succession of stages in the brood chamber (Fig. 217*B*). Development proceeds in the brood chamber to the production of free-swimming larvae.

The cleavage pattern is of the spiral determinate type in its broad features. The third cleavage lacks the usual inequality so that the eight blastomeres are of about the same size, arranged in the usual two alternating tiers (Fig. 218*A*). Inequalities arise later and at the 16-cell stage, the upper and lower tiers (Fig. 218*B*) are slightly larger than the two middle tiers, a condition also not usual in typical spiral cleavage. There are produced five quartets of micromeres and one of macromeres but the latter are not actually larger than many of the micromeres. At the 56-cell stage (Fig. 218*C*), there are present 24 descendents of the first quartet, of which eight transversely elongated cells become a ciliated girdle and hence apparently represent trochoblasts, 16 cells of the second quartet, and four cells of each of the remaining four quartets. The first three

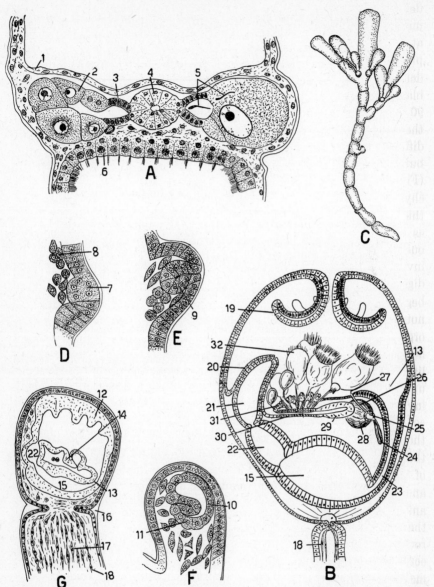

Fig. 217.—Reproductive system, budding. *A*. Transverse section of calyx of *Pedicellina*. *B*. Sagittal section of calyx of *Pedicellina*, with embryos in the brood chamber. (*A*, *B*, *after Marcus*, 1939.) *C*. *Urnatella* budding (*after Davenport*, 1893). *D–G*. Four stages in development of a bud of *Pedicellina* (*after Seeliger*, 1889). 1, epidermis of calyx floor; 2, ovary; 3, oviduct; 4, common oviduct with wall of gland cells; 5, sperm; 6, stomach floor (liver); 7, epidermal thickening; 8, mesenchyme; 9, thickening invaginated; 10, invaginated vesicle constricting in two; 11, future digestive tract; 12, primordia of tentacles; 13, mouth; 14, ganglion; 15, stomach; 16, septum; 17, tube cells; 18, muscle cells; 19, contracted tentacles; 20, anal cone; 21, rectum; 22, intestine; 23, esophagus; 24, flame bulb; 25, union of the two flame bulbs; 26, nephridioduct; 27, nephridiopore; 28, ovary; 29, glandular part of oviduct; 30, distal part of oviduct; 31, vestibular epidermis acting as embryophore; 32, embryos in various stages of development.

quartets are ectodermal, the other three entodermal. As is usual in spiral cleavage, the cell 4*d* is the mesentoblast cell that early passes into the interior and proliferates loose mesenchyme without the formation of definite mesoderm bands. The mesenchyme so formed is thus an ento-mesoderm. Both Harmer and Hatschek described two conspicuous cells at the vegetal pole of the embryo that they considered to be teloblasts producing mesoderm bands but according to Marcus these cells are ecto-dermal and participate in the stomodaeum. A coeloblastula with a small blastocoel is formed at a stage of about 67 cells (Fig. 218*D*) and at about 90 cells a typical gastrula arises by embolic gastrulation (Fig. 218*E*). In the meantime certain ectodermal cells at the apical pole have begun to differentiate to form an apical plate (Fig. 218*E*). The blastopore closes but very close to its anterior margin a stomodaeal invagination begins (Fig. 218*F*) and from this cells are given off into the blastocoel as mesen-chyme that joins the previously formed entomesodermal mesenchyme; this mesenchyme originating from the stomodaeum is regarded by Marcus as representing the ectomesoderm. The stomodaeum joins the previ-ously invaginated archenteron and this in turn unites with a proctodaeal invagination initiated on the posterior side of the embryo (Fig. 218*G*); the digestive tube is thus completed and has the shape of a loop from the beginning (Fig. 219*A*). On the anterior face of the embryo there is noticeable an area of taller ectoderm, the primordium of the preoral organ (Fig. 218*G*), a sensory organ very characteristic of the entoproct larva. The apical plate and the preoral organ then invaginate to form little sacs provided with a tuft of long cilia (Fig. 219*A*). Each is underlain by a thick ganglionic mass formed from the same ectodermal invagination and these two ganglionic masses are connected by a nervous commissure. The presumption is that the apical ganglion represents the brain and the preoral organ is an ancestral reminiscence. Meantime there has occurred a deep invagination of the oral or ventral surface of the embryo to form an extensive depression situated between mouth and anus (Fig. 219*A*, *B*). This depression is termed vestibule or atrium and corresponds to the vestibular concavity of the ventral surface of the future calyx. Apparently the subenteric ganglion arises from its roof (Fig. 219*A*). According to Marcus the protonephridia are of ectodermal origin. The embryo, having already ruptured its enclosing membrane, develops a girdle of cilia on the cells indicated above as trochoblasts (Fig. 218*C*), escapes from the maternal brood chamber, and swims about as a free larva.

The larva of *Pedicellina* (Fig. 219*A*, *B*) is designated throughout the literature as a modified trochophore but appears to the author to bear no great resemblance to a trochophore either superficially or as to structural details. At the summit of the dorsal surface or somewhat displaced

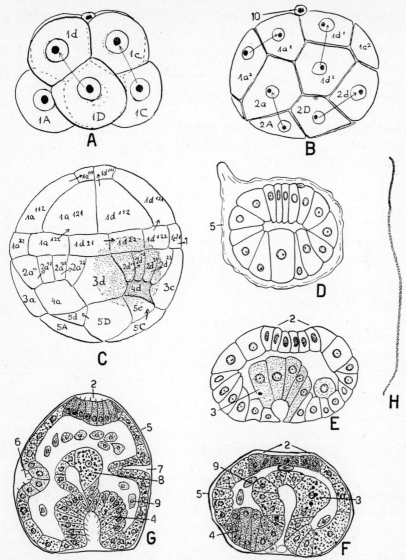

Fig. 218.—Embryology. *A.* 8-cell stage, side view. *B.* 16-cell stage, side view. *C.* 56-cell stage, side view. *D.* Section through the blastula. *E.* Early gastrula, 130 cells. *F.* Later gastrula, beginning of stomodaeum. *G.* Formation of proctodaeum. *H.* Sperm. (*All after Marcus,* 1939.) 1, circle of trochoblasts; 2, apical organ; 3, entoderm; 4, stomodaeum; 5, membrane around embryo; 6, preoral organ forming; 7, proctodaeal invagination; 8, primordium of stomach-intestine (entoderm); 9, mesenchyme; 10, polar body.

anteriorly is found the apical organ consisting of a ciliary tuft borne by an epidermal sac underlain by a large ganglionic mass.   This structure undoubtedly corresponds to the apical organ of the typical trochophore but of course a similar organ is common among the larvae of various lower invertebrates.   On the anterior surface of the *Pedicellina* larva is borne the preoral organ, very similar in structure to the apical organ and like it underlain by a ganglionic mass.   This structure has no counterpart in the typical trochophore.   The fact that the commissure connecting the apical and preoral organs is double indicates an original paired condition of the preoral organ (see further below, with regard to the *Loxosoma* larva).   The ciliary girdle which encircles the equator of the trochophore borders the ventral surface of the entoproct larva.   The digestive tube in the trochophore is L-shaped with the anus opposite the apical plate whereas in the entoproct larva the digestive tract is bent into a U and the anus is at the posterior edge of the ventral surface.   The vestibular invagination between mouth and anus is also wanting in the trochophore. Its roof is supplied by three paired clusters of gland cells.   The entoproct larva lacks mesodermal bands present in the trochophore and its protonephridia are of the flame-bulb type whereas those of the trochophore are solenocytic.   The entoproct larva is very mobile and changeable. The apical and preoral organs can be protruded and retracted, the ciliary girdle can be expanded or contracted, and the areas bearing the mouth and the anus can be conspicuously exserted (Fig. 219*B*) or so far withdrawn that they seem to open into the vestibular depression (Fig. 219*A*).

The only other colonial entoproct of which the larva is known is *Barentsia*.   The detailed structure of the *Barentsia* larva has been figured by Cori (1936) and several habit sketches have been furnished by Rogick (1948).   There is a close similarity between the larvae of *Pedicellina* and *Barentsia*.

On the other hand, the larva of *Loxosoma* differs markedly from that of the colonial entoprocts and bears almost no resemblance to a trochophore, suggesting rather a rotifer.   As *Loxosoma* is the most primitive genus of the Entoprocta, the characters of its larva merit special attention. This larva has been depicted by Vogt (1876), Barrois (1877), and Atkins (1932).   The larva (Figs. 219*C*, 220*A*, *B*) is of oval flattened shape with an arched dorsal surface, which bears the apical organ anteriorly placed. There are two large and conspicuous preoral organs situated symmetrically at the anterior end of the larva.   Near each of them is a red or brownish eye of the structure of which all that is known is that it includes a pigment mass and a lens-like body.   The oval ventral surface is bordered by the ciliary girdle to the inner side of which a deep groove represents the future vestibular groove.   The mouth opens at the anterior end of the ventral surface just inside the ciliary girdle and behind the mouth is a

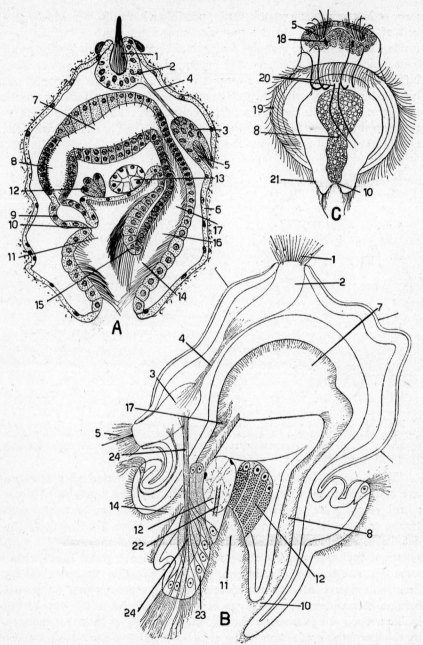

Fig. 219.—Entoproct larvae. *A.* Nearly mature larva of *Pedicellina* (*after Marcus,* 1939). *B.* Free-swimming larva of *Pedicellina* (*after Czwiklitzer,* 1909). *C.* Free-swimming larva of *Loxosoma,* ventral view (*after Atkins,* 1932). 1, apical organ; 2, apical ganglion; 3, ganglion of preoral organ; 4, commissure between the two ganglia; 5, preoral organ; 6, definitive epidermis with debris adhering; 7, stomach; 8, intestine; 9, rectum; 10, anus; 11, vestibular concavity; 12, vestibular gland; 13, subenteric ganglion; 14, mouth; 15, lower lip with ciliary tuft; 16, buccal tube; 17, esophagus; 18, eyes; 19, ciliary girdle; 20, bristles behind mouth; 21, bifurcated posterior end; 22, nephridium; 23, sensory area behind mouth; 24, nerve tract to same.

more or less prominent protuberance, possibly a lower lip, provided with a tuft of stiff bristles. At the posterior end of the ventral surface, just inside the ciliated rim, is found a prominent projection bearing the anus. This eminence may protrude well beyond the ciliary girdle and is often bifurcated into a pair of lobes topped with bristles. This eminence and bifurcation are somewhat suggestive of the rotifer foot. Between mouth and anus occurs the usual vestibular concavity. The interior contains the looped digestive tract and the ganglionic masses associated with the apical and preoral organs plus the usual mesenchyme.

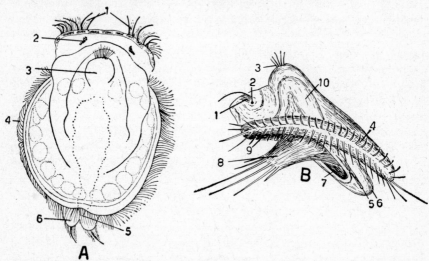

Fig. 220.—Larvae of *Loxosoma*. A. Dorsal view (*after Atkins*, 1932). B. Side view (*after Barrois*, 1877). 1, preoral organs; 2, eyes; 3, apical organ; 4, ciliary girdle; 5, anus; 6, posterior end; 7, vestibular concavity; 8, projection behind mouth (lower lip); 9, location of mouth; 10, stomach.

The entoproct larva swims or creeps for a short period, then attaches to a suitable surface by the ciliary rim, and undergoes a process of metamorphosis (Fig. 221). The ciliary rim loses its cilia and gradually contracts, eventually fusing to a one-layered epithelium that becomes the definitive attachment disk. This epithelium thickens and fills with granules, thus representing a more or less developed pedal gland whose secretion assists the attachment. In loxosomatids the pedal gland becomes evident in late embryonic stages as a conspicuous epidermal invagination which develops into a large gland persistent throughout life in *Loxocalyx*. In *Pedicellina* the pedal gland appears to be represented by the glandular epithelium of the attachment disk of the metamorphosing larva and is lost later. By the closure of the ciliary rim the vestibular concavity into which open the mouth and anus becomes completely cut off from the exterior. Mesenchyme accumulates between the vestibule and the attachment disk and this region rapidly elongates to form the definitive stalk. The apical and preoral sense organs and their ganglia degenerate except in some loxosomatids where the preoral organs presumably persist as the pair of sense organs on the sides of the calyx. In the interior of the young entoproct the vestibular cavity and its attached digestive tract undergo a rotation of 180 degrees so that the vestibular cavity comes to lie opposite the stalk. Tentacles then form as outgrowths of the vestibular margin and the covering epidermis thins and disappears. Thus the originally ventral surface of the larva comes to face upward opposite to the stalk in the adult and the vestibular concavity becomes the free surface of the adult calyx. All the larval parts persist as adult structures except the apical organ and its ganglion, the preoral organ and its ganglion (except in some loxosomatids where they are retained as shown in Fig. 214A), and the ciliary girdle. The subenteric ganglion presumably arises in the same manner as in bud formation. The buccal tube and esophagus come from the stomodaeum, the rectum from the proctodaeum, and the entodermal archenteron differentiates into the stomach and intestine. Budding may begin very early in loxosomatids, even while the embryo is still attached in the maternal brood chamber. In the colonial entoprocts, each larva becomes a single adult and this produces a colony by budding from stalks and stolons.

12. Ecology and Physiology.—As already noted the Entoprocta are all marine with the exception of the fresh-water genus *Urnatella*, so far found only in the eastern United States and in India. The distribution of the marine Entoprocta is imperfectly known because of a lack of intensive collecting and information about them comes chiefly from the vicinity of marine stations. The genera *Loxosoma*, *Loxocalyx*, *Pedicellina*, and *Barentsia* appear to be widely distributed. They are common along European coasts and also have been taken along African, Asiatic, and American shores as well as in the Indo-Malay region. Species of these genera have been recorded from the Atlantic Coast of the United States by Osburn (1910, 1944) and Rogick (1948) and species of *Barentsia* and *Pedicellina* from the California Coast by Robertson (1900). Marcus (1937–1939) has recorded from the coast of Brazil one species each of *Loxocalyx* and *Loxosomatoides*, two species of *Pedicellina*, and three of *Barentsia*. Entoprocta reported by Johnston and Angel (1940) from a number of widely separated localities in the antarctic and subantarctic were mostly species of *Barentsia* and members of this genus have also been taken in several localities in the arctic. Entoprocta collected by the Siboga expedition in the Indo-Malay region comprised one species of *Loxocalyx*, 12 of *Loxosoma*, one of *Pedicellina*, and four of *Barentsia* (Harmer, 1915). Whereas members of these four genera appear to have a wide distribution, other genera seem highly restricted.

Thus *Myosoma* is known by one species, *spinosa*, found only on the coast of California (Robertson, 1900). *Chitaspis athleticus* from the Gulf of Siam (Annandale, 1916) is the only record for this genus. *Arthropodaria* is represented by *A. kovalevskii* in the Black Sea and *A. benedeni* on the Belgian Coast. The marine Entoprocta in general are limited to coastal waters, including brackish bays. The Loxosomatidae are always found attached to other animals whereas the Pedicellinidae may grow on inert objects but more commonly are found fastened to algae, worm tubes, mollusk shells, and hydroid and ectoproct colonies.

Little is known of the relations of the Entoprocta to environmental conditions except that under certain circumstances the calyces degenerate or fall off and new calyces are regenerated under favorable conditions. In the Black Sea, *Arthropodaria kovalevskii* is found without calyces from October to April, not so much as a result of winter temperatures as from the influx of fresh water into the Black Sea during this period, with a consequent great reduction of salinity (Nasonov, 1926). Rogick (1948) noted degeneration of the calyces in *Barentsia laxa* when kept in the laboratory for a few days but did not analyze the factors involved. At the onset of winter or under other unfavorable circumstances the calyces of *Urnatella gracilis* die and disappear but the stalks remain alive and regenerate new calyces in spring or at the return of suitable conditions (Leidy, 1883).

As is usual in sessile animals, the movements of the Entoprocta are rather limited. Apparently the solitary Loxosomatidae are capable of considerable activity. Thus *Loxosoma saltans*, which inhabits the tubes of polychaete annelids, is described by Assheton (1912) as "extremely active, moving over the body of the worm or along the lining of the tube in a manner fascinating and unique by a series of gymnastic efforts, which combine the agility of the kangaroo and the deliberation of a geometer caterpillar." In this species there are four especially long tentacles at the oral end of the tentacular crown and these are provided with stiff bristles on the outer side of the tips. The creature moves by bending over and attaching the tips of these four tentacles to the substratum; it then suddenly bends these four tentacles outward, whisks the stalk forward with great rapidity, and attaches the foot disk to a new location. This action is in the form of a jump with the animal completely free from contact (Fig. 222*B*). Probably other loxosomatids provided with four extra-long tentacles move in the same way. The colonial entoprocts are incapable of detaching themselves from the substratum but can execute movements in correlation with the arrangement of their musculature. However, very little exact information is available except the account of Hilton (1923) for *Barentsia*, one of the genera in which the stalk musculature is limited to certain swellings (Fig. 210*D*). In *Barentsia* the

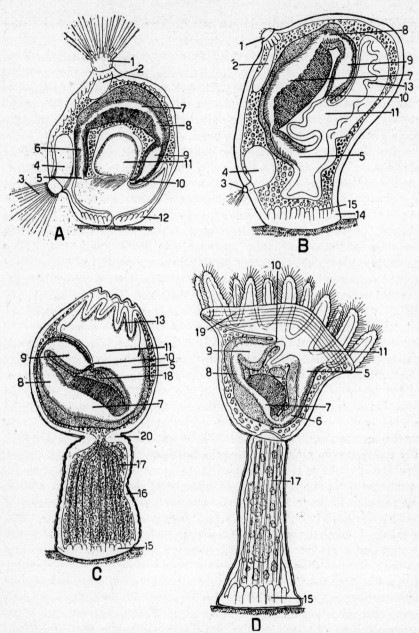

Fig. 221.—Metamorphosis of *Pedicellina*. *A*. Larva shortly after attaching. *B*. Stalk forming, rotation beginning. *C*. Stalk well developed, rotation complete, tentacles indicated. *D*. Primary polyp practically completed. (*All after Cori*, 1936.) 1, apical organ; 2, apical ganglion; 3, preoral organ; 4, preoral ganglion; 5, mouth; 6, esophagus; 7, stomach; 8, intestine; 9, rectum; 10, anus; 11, vestibular concavity; 12, epithelium of stalk base; 13, primordia of tentacles; 14, adhesive disk; 15, pedal gland of adhesive disk; 16, stalk; 17, muscle fibers; 18, subenteric ganglion; 19, tentacular sphincter; 20, septum.

infolding of the tentacular crown results from a jar or rather strong tactile stimuli; changes of light or temperature or exposure to chemicals are not effective. The polyps bend or rotate at the muscular swellings, either spontaneously or in response to tactile stimuli, jarring, or water currents. The parts most sensitive to tactile stimuli are the junction of calyx and stalk, the general surface of the stalk, and the surface of the stolons. Sufficiently strong stimulation of the stolons is transmitted for some distance as shown by the response of adjacent polyps.

The Entoprocta are ciliary feeders as might be surmised from their structure. The tentacular crown and the vestibular groove constitute the food-catching apparatus, the operation of which has been thoroughly studied by Atkins (1932) for the loxosomatids. When engaged in feeding, the tentacular crown is well expanded (Fig. 222*A*) and is turned in different directions by movements of the calyx. As already noted the tentacles are ciliated on their inner surfaces only. The ciliation (Fig. 212*D*) is made up of long lateral cilia and shorter medial or frontal cilia. By the energetic beating of the long lateral cilia water is drawn between the tentacles into the space bounded by them and passes out above (Fig. 223). Particles in suspension in the water current are diverted by the lateral cilia onto the short frontal cilia which maintain a current down the inner face of the tentacle into the vestibular groove. In this a current passes from the anal to the oral end, thus conveying food particles into the mouth. Any disturbance of the animal while feeding or the presence of too many or too large particles in the water current will cause the cessation of beat of the lateral cilia and the closure of the tentacular crown by the incurving of the tentacles and the contraction of the tentacular membrane over them. Tentacles may also bend in individually as a result of particles striking the tactile hairs on their outer surface. Organisms too large to be captured in the usual manner may be trapped in the vestibular space by the sudden bunching of the tentacles and then swallowed. To undesirable particles or an overly thick suspension of particles or food in the water, various degrees of rejection occur. The esophageal sphincter may close so that particles pass out of the mouth corners and so get into the outgoing current; or the lateral cilia may cease to beat, thus slowing down the incoming current, and by interlacing across the interstices between the partially contracted tentacles may act as a strainer; or there may be a convulsive contraction of the tentacular crown and the whole animal. It appears that the lateral cilia are under nervous control of the animal since if the animal is narcotized they beat continuously whereas the frontal cilia beat at all times without intermission. According to the figure given by Cori (1936) the ciliary currents of *Pedicellina* are similar to those of the loxosomatids.

The food of the entoprocts consists of diatoms, desmids, protozoans, and similar small organisms and particles. After ingestion food is swallowed by esophageal contractions. In the stomach, the food particles become entangled in mucous strands which gradually consolidate into clumps as they pass toward the intestine. These strands and clumps are kept in constant rotation by the cilia lining the digestive tract. From

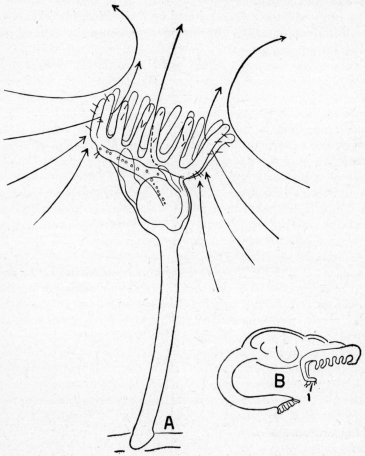

Fig. 222.—Ecology. *A. Loxosoma* expanded and feeding, showing the water currents (*after Atkins*, 1932). *B. Loxosoma saltans* "on the jump" (*after Assheton*, 1912). 1, especially long oral tentacles.

time to time the sphincter between intestine and rectum opens and allows clumps to pass into the rectum from which by the opening of the anal sphincter feces are ejected into the outgoing water current. Becker (1937) surmises that the state of distension of the stomach with food controls the relaxation of the intestinal and anal sphincters as they open more frequently in connection with rapid feeding. By adding powdered carmine, carbon, or egg white, or plankton to the water, Cori (1936) determined that the stomach of *Pedicellina* would fill with food in 5 minutes; the complete passage through the digestive tract required only an hour. Becker (1937) made similar observations but found that, when only a little food is available to the animal, the food clumps might delay for hours in the rectum.

The study of Becker (1937), based on *Pedicellina*, furnishes the only available information about digestion in the Entoprocta. The esophagus

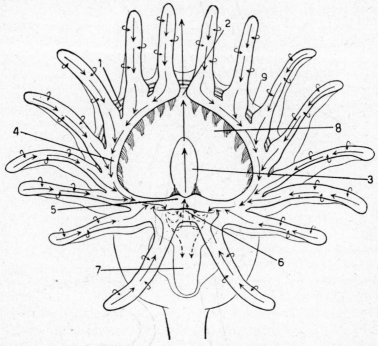

Fig. 223.—Ecology. Tentacular crown of *Loxosoma* during feeding, showing the water currents (*after Atkins*, 1932). 1, tentacular sphincter; 2, anal end of tentacular crown; 3, anal cone; 4, vestibular grove; 5, upper lip; 6, lower lip; 7, esophagus; 8, vestibular concavity; 9, tentacular membrane.

apparently has no digestive function but may serve for food storage as its cells contain numerous fat and protein spheres. In the stomach the dark cells of the glandular area furnish the digestive enzymes whereas the pale cells appear to be of an absorptive nature. Digestion is said to be entirely extracellular, occurring in the stomach lumen in a slightly acid medium (Cori, 1936). The so-called liver region of the stomach floor is considered by Becker to have an excretory function; the brown inclusions are excreta containing uric acid and guanin and are ejected into the stomach lumen. During starvation these inclusions are markedly diminished by extrusion into the stomach but are soon built up again on the resumption of feeding. According to Cori, carmine particles in the food are taken up by the liver region but are soon again ejected. The intestine acts mainly in the absorption and storage of food; its proximal half next the stomach is filled with fat and protein spheres but these diminish distally, toward the rectum. The rectum appears to absorb fluid from the fecal masses, rendering them more solid, and may also possibly absorb products of digestion.

Food is therefore stored as fat, protein, and glycogen particles in various parts of the digestive epithelium—the esophagus, the proximal part of the stomach, and the proximal part of the intestine. Food supplies appear to be transported by the mesenchyme cells for according to Becker those of the calyx and stalk contain considerable quantities of fat and protein and those of the stalk fine glycogen granules in addition. The ripe eggs are also richly provided with protein, fat, and glycogen stores which nourish the developing embryo. Later the epithelium of the brood chamber becomes filled with the same kinds of food reserves and its cells then break loose and are ingested by the embryos.

IV. PHYLOGENETIC CONSIDERATIONS

In the opinion of the author, the union of the Entoprocta and the Ectoprocta into a phylum Bryozoa cannot be maintained although supported as recently as 1939 by so informed a student of the Bryozoa as Marcus. The insuperable difficulty in the way of this union is the pseudocoelomate nature of the body cavity of the Entoprocta whereas the Ectoprocta are typical coelomate animals. The Entoprocta are thus of a much lower grade of structure than are the Ectoprocta and cannot be united with them in the same phylum. It may be questioned whether there is in fact any affinity between the two groups. As principal anatomical similarities may be mentioned the possession by both groups of a crown of ciliated tentacles and a looped digestive tract. However, the occurrence of tentacular structures on the distal end is common in sessile animals as a food-catching device. There is no fundamental resemblance between the tentacular provision of the Entoprocta and Ectoprocta for in the former the tentacles are simple outgrowths of the body margin in the form of a circle that embraces both mouth and anus, whereas in the latter they are borne on a variously shaped ridge, the lophophore, that embraces the mouth but not the anus, and are completely withdrawable into the interior. A looped digestive tract bringing the anus near the mouth is also a frequent feature of sessile animals, serving presumably to prevent the feces from accumulating around the animal. As regards other anatomical features the two groups are quite dissimilar.

The occurrence of spiral determinate cleavage in the Entoprocta does not necessarily ally them with the coelomate Protostomia because the same kind of cleavage is met with in polyclad flatworms.   In fact, cleavage in the latter group more nearly follows the annelid-molluscan pattern than does the entoproct cleavage.   In the account of the embryology of *Pedicellina*, several discrepancies from the typical spiral pattern were pointed out, as, the size equality of the early blastomeres, the large size of the blastomeres apical to the trochoblasts (Fig. 218*C*), the lateness and aberrant mode of formation of the mesectoderm, and the lack of definite mesoderm bands.   Differences between the entoproct larva, especially that of *Loxosoma*, and a typical trochophore were also noted, such as the presence in the former of preoral organs and the vestibular depression, the differences in the shape and relations of the digestive tract, the displacement of the ciliary girdle from its equatorial position in the trochophore ventrally to border the ventral surface of the entoproct larva, and the mounting of the anus of the latter on a bifurcated projection suggesting the rotifer foot.   Whereas, then, the entoproct larva departs considerably from the typical trochophore, it must be admitted that it markedly resembles the ectoproct larva.   The larval similarities of the two groups seem to the author the best ground for postulating relationship.   But in their further development the two larvae diverge altogether and it must always be borne in mind that pelagic larvae present certain similarities, anyway.

It seems most consistent with all the facts to seek for the affinities of the Entoprocta among the pseudocoelomate groups.   Among these the Rotifera at once suggest themselves as the most likely candidate.   The resemblance between a loxosomatid and a collothecacean rotifer is certainly considerable and cannot be dismissed as merely superficial.   There is the same trumpet-shaped body with the free surface bordered by ciliated or bristle-bearing projections that are simple extensions of the body wall.   The stalk in both is a postembryonic outgrowth provided, at least evanescently, with pedal glands.   In both the mouth lies within the crown of tentaculate projections, and in both the digestive tract makes a decided curve.   In the rotifers this curvature of the digestive tract begins among the sessile forms and gets more and more pronounced with greater assumption of the sessile life.   Although even in the most evolved of the collothecacean rotifers the anus still remains outside the coronal projections, it is clearly getting nearer and nearer to the mouth.   However, no great importance can be placed on this point because, as noted above, a looped digestive tract is a common feature of sessile animals.   The parts of the digestive tract are similar in the two groups and it may be noted that the mastax, of which no trace occurs in the Entoprocta, is in process of degeneration among the collothecacean rotifers.   Both groups have protonephridia of the flame-bulb type. A pair of eyes is present in both loxosomatid and collothecacean juveniles. The ciliary rim of the ventral surface of the entoproct larva is probably a remnant of an originally completely ciliated ventral surface and, as discussed under Rotifera, the rotifer corona, represented in the Collothecacea by the anterior projecting arms, also derives from a large ventral ciliated area. But the most striking rotifer feature of the entoproct larva and the loxosomatid adult is the pair of preoral organs. The similarity of these to the antennae of rotifers was first pointed out by Salensky in 1877 and has been admitted by various investigators since. There appears no way of accounting for these organs except by granting their homology with the lateral antennae of rotifers. In the collothecacean rotifers they have migrated to an anterior position similar to that which they occupy in the loxosomatid adult. The author therefore inclines to the view, already expressed in various articles in the literature of the Entoprocta, that the nearest affinities of the latter lie with the rotifers.

The account of the Entoprocta concludes the discussion of the non-coelomate invertebrates. The remaining volumes of the series will deal with the coelomate invertebrates, beginning with those groups having an enterocoelous mode of formation of the coelom.

Bibliography

Annandale, N. 1908. The fauna of brackish ponds at Port Canning, Lower Bengal. Pt. VII. Description of a new genus of Entoprocta. Records Indian Mus. 2. 1916. Zoological results of a tour of the Far East. Polyzoa Entoprocta and Ctenostomata. Mem. Asiatic Soc. Bengal 6. **Assheton, R.** 1912. Loxosoma loxalina and Loxosoma saltans. Quart. Jour. Micro. Sci. 58. **Atkins, D.** 1932. The Loxosomatidae of the Plymouth area. The ciliary feeding mechanism of the entoproct Polyzoa. Quart. Jour. Micro. Sci. 75. **Barrois, J.** 1877. Mémoire sur l'embryologie des Bryozoaires. Trav. Sta. Zool. Wimereux 1. 1886. Mémoire sur la métamorphose de quelques Bryozoaires. Ann. Sci. Natur., Zool., ser. 7, 1. 1925. Études complémentaires sur la métamorphose des Bryozoaires. Ann. Sci. Natur., Zool., ser. 10, 8. **Becker, G.** 1937. Untersuchungen über den Darm und die Verdauung von Kamptozoa. Ztschr. Morphol. Ökol. Tiere 33. **Clark, A. H.** 1921. A new classification of animals. Bull. Inst. Océanogr. Monaco, No. 400. **Cori, C.** 1929. Kamptozoa. In **W. Kükenthal** and **T. Krumbach** (eds.), *Handbuch der Zoologie*, Band II, Hälfte 1. 1930. Kamptozoa. In **G. Grimpe** and **E. Wagler** (eds.), *Die Tierwelt der Nord- und Ostee*, Teil IVa (Lief. 19). 1936. Kamptozoa. In **H. G. Bronn** (ed.), *Klassen und Ordnungen des Tierreichs*, Band IV, Abt. II, Buch 4. **Czwiklitzer, R.** 1909. Die Anatomie der Larve von Pedicellina echinata. Arbeit. Zool. Inst. Univ. Wien 17. **Davenport, C.** 1893. On Urnatella gracilis. Bull. Mus. Comp. Zool. Harvard Univ. 24. 1904. Report on the fresh-water Bryozoa of the United States. Proc. U.S. Nation. Mus. 27. **Ehlers, E.** 1890. Zur Kenntnis der Pedicellinen. Abhandl. König. Gesell. Wiss. Göttingen 36. **Gervais, M.** 1837. Recherches sur les polypes d'eau douce. Ann. Sci. Natur., Zool., ser. 2, 7. **Harmer, S.** 1885. On the structure and development of Loxosoma. Quart. Jour. Micro.

Sci. 25. 1887. On the life history of Pedicellina. Quart. Jour. Micro. Sci. 27. 1915. The Polyzoa of the Siboga Expedition. Siboga Exped. Monogr. 28a. **Hassall, A.** 1841. Supplement to a catalogue of Irish zoophytes. Ann. Mag. Natur. Hist., ser. 1, 7. **Hatschek, B.** 1877. Embryonalentwicklung und Knospung der Pedicellina echinata. Ztschr. Wiss. Zool. 29. **Hilton, W.** 1923. A study of the movements of entoproctan Bryozoans. Trans. Amer. Micro. Soc. 42. **Johnston, T., and L. Angel.** 1940. Endoprocta. Repts. British, Australian, New Zealand Antarctic Exped., ser. B, vol. IV, Pt. 7. **Keferstein, W.** 1863. Untersuchungen über niedere Seetiere. VIII. Ztschr. Wiss. Zool. 12. **Kowalevsky, A.** 1866. Beiträge zur Anatomie und Entwicklungsgeschichte des Loxosoma. Mem. Acad. Impér. Sci. St. Petersburg, ser. 7, 10, No. 2. **Lebedinsky, J.** 1905. Die Embryonalentwicklung der Pedicellina echinata. Biol. Centralbl. 25. **Leidy, J.** 1854. On Urnatella gracilis. Proc. Acad. Natur. Sci. Philadelphia 7. 1883. Urnatella gracilis. Jour. Acad. Natur. Sci. Philadelphia 9. **Marcus, E.** 1937, 1939. Bryozoarios marinhos brasileiros. I–III. Zoologia, Univ. São Paulo, Nos. 1, 2, 3. **Nasonov, N.** 1926. Arthropodaria kovalevskii und die Regeneration ihrer Organe. Trav. Lab. Zool. Sta. Biol. Sebastipol, ser. 2, No. 5. **Nickerson, W.** 1899. Notes on Loxosoma. Science 9. 1901. On Loxosoma davenporti. Jour. Morphol. 17. **Nitsche, H.** 1870. Beiträge zur Kenntnis der Bryozoen. Ztschr. Wiss. Zool. 20. **Osburn, R.** 1910. The Bryozoa of the Woods Hole region. Bull. U.S. Bur. Fisheries 30. 1944. A survey of the Bryozoa of Chesapeake Bay. Chesapeake Biol. Lab., Solomons Is., Publ. 63. **Retzius, G.** 1905. Das sensible Nervensystem der Bryozoen. Biologische Untersuchungen, neue Folge 12. **Ritchie, J.** 1911. On a entoproctan Polyzoon. Trans. Roy. Soc. Edinburgh 47. **Robertson, Alice.** 1900. Studies on Pacific coast Entoprocta. Proc. California Acad. Sci., ser. 3, Zool. 2. **Rogick, Mary.** 1948. Studies on marine Bryozoa. II. Barentsia laxa. Biol. Bull. 94. **Salensky, M.** 1877. Études sur les Bryozoaires entoproctes. Ann. Sci. Natur., Zool., ser. 6, 5. **Sars, M.** 1835. Beskrivelser og Jagttagelse over nye. **Seeliger, O.** 1889. Die ungeschlechtliche Vermehrung der endoprokten Bryozoen. Ztschr. Wiss. Zool. 49. 1890. Bemerkungen zur Knospenentwicklung der Bryozoen. Ztschr. Wiss Zool. 50. 1906. Über die Larven und Verwandtschaftsbeziehungen der Bryozoen. Ztschr. Wiss. Zool. 84. **Seshaiya, R.** 1946. Urnatella indica. Proc. 33 Indian Sci. Congress, Pt. III. **Stiasny, G.** 1904. Beitrag zur Kenntnis der Exkretionsapparates der Entoprocta. Arbeit. Zool. Inst. Univ. Wien 15. **Uljanin, B.** 1869. Zur Anatomie und Entwicklungsgeschichte der Pedicellina. Bull. Soc. Impér. Natural. Moscou 42. **Van Beneden, P.** 1845. Histoire naturelle du genre Pedicellina. Mém. Acad. Roy. Sci. Lett. Bruxelles 19. **Vogt, C.** 1876. Sur le loxosomes des Phascolosomes. Arch. Zool. Exp. Gén. 5. **Waters, A.** 1904. Bryozoa. Exped. Antarctique Belge, Zool.

INDEX

Pages bearing illustrations are given in boldface when not included in text references